THE THEORY OF SPACE, TIME AND GRAVITATION

THE THEORY OF

SPACE, TIME AND GRAVITATION

2nd Revised Edition

by

V. FOCK

UNIVERSITY OF LENINGRAD
ACADEMY OF SCIENCES OF THE U.S.S.R.

Translated from the Russian by

N. KEMMER

TAIT INSTITUTE OF MATHEMATICAL PHYSICS
UNIVERSITY OF EDINBURGH

A Pergamon Press Book

THE MACMILLAN COMPANY
NEW YORK
1964

THE MACMILLAN COMPANY
60 Fifth Avenue
New York 11, N.Y.

This book is distributed by
THE MACMILLAN COMPANY
pursuant to a special arrangement with
PERGAMON PRESS LIMITED
Oxford, England

Library of Congress Catalog Card Number 58–12666

A translation of the revised Russian edition
Теория пространства, времени и тяготения
Fizmatgiz, Moscow, 1961

Made in Great Britain
and Printed by Compton Printing Works (London) Ltd.

CONTENTS

TRANSLATOR'S PREFACE

STUDENTS of what is usually termed " General Relativity " will need no reminder of the importance of Academician V. Fock's work on their subject. Up to now very little of this work has been available in English and it is a privilege to help to make it accessible to the English-speaking world. I am myself no specialist in this field and when asked to undertake the translation I approached the project with quite a measure of doubt.

However, even the first cursory reading of Professor Fock's book convinced me that the task would be not too difficult and both rewarding and pleasurable. So it proved to be.

Professor Fock's clear and precise style of exposition made my task an easy one. I found that I could translate almost literally, in striking contrast to some of my experience of Russian scientific writing. The only sections of the translation, and there were not many, in which the Russian original is not followed almost line by line, are those in which Professor Fock himself provided an amended text, which, incidentally, he did in English so near perfect as to require practically no correction.

There are a number of reasons why my task was rewarding. The earlier parts of the book give an exposition of so-called " Special " Relativity the merits of which I am more competent to judge than that of the later chapters. I found that I was transmitting a presentation of the greatest possible clarity and completeness with many an original turn to it, even in a field so often presented before. In subsequent chapters I naturally found more that was new and by the time I got to Professor Fock's principal personal contributions to Relativity I found myself being guided through a most stimulating new field of thought with even the most lengthy and detailed calculation presented in a manner that never obscured the main argument. Where Professor Fock's views are in disagreement with the opinions of others he states his case well—and his opponents have a formidable case to answer.

The pleasure of my task lay, of course, partly in its scientific interest to which I have just referred, but, in addition, the work has brought me into a most happy contact with a great figure in theoretical physics and it gives me much satisfaction to testify to the ease of collaboration with Professor Fock and to the establishment of what I feel to be a strong personal bond. May it be a token of the greater bond of friendship between the scientists and between the peoples of our two countries.

N. KEMMER

September 1958

TRANSLATOR'S PREFACE TO SECOND EDITION

It has been a further pleasure to help in producing this second English edition of Professor Fock's book. I acknowledge with gratitude the substantial help given to me by Professor Fock himself in providing a complete record of all changes made in the original Russian text. But for this aid the work of translation would have been a much more lengthy one.

N. KEMMER

September 1962

PREFACE

THE aim of this book is threefold. Firstly, we intended to give a text-book on Relativity Theory and on Einstein's Theory of Gravitation. Secondly, we wanted to give an exposition of our own researches on these subjects. Thirdly, our aim was to develop a new, non-local, point of view on the theory and to correct a widespread misinterpretation of the Einsteinian Gravitation Theory as some kind of general relativity.

The Russian edition of this book* was published in 1955. In the present English edition only very few changes are made : some mathematical proofs are altered (Sections 8 and 31) and some reasonings are made more precise (Sections 61 and 93).

It is hoped that the publication of the present edition, by making the book accessible to English-speaking readers, will contribute to a wider discussion of the author's ideas on Gravitation Theory.

In conclusion the author wishes to express his thanks to Professor N. Kemmer for his excellent translation.

August 1958   V. FOCK

Physical Institute of the
Leningrad University,
U.S.S.R.

PREFACE TO SECOND EDITION

IT IS a pleasure to me that my book has received sufficient attention to make it necessary to publish a second edition soon after the first. This edition follows closely the second Russian edition published in 1961.

The second edition differs from the first by some additions and reformulations. The question of the uniqueness of the mass tensor is treated in more detail (Section 31*) and is illustrated by two examples (Appendices B and C). The notion of conformal space is introduced and used as a basis for the treatment of Einsteinian statics (Sections 56 and 57). Greatest care has been applied to the formulation of the basic ideas of the theory and to the elucidation of those points on which the author's views differ from the traditional (Einsteinian) ones. Thus, in order to discuss the general aspects of the relativity principle Section 49* has been added.

The author's views on the theory are explicitly formulated in different parts of the book and are implicit in the reasoning throughout the whole text. Their general trend is to lay stress on the Absolute rather than on the Relative. The basic ideas of Einstein's Theory of Gravitation are considered to be: (a) the introduction of a space-time manifold with an indefinite metric, (b) the hypothesis that the space-time metric is not rigid but can be influenced by physical processes and (c) the idea of the unity of metric and gravitation. On the other

---

* В. А. Фок, Теория пространства, времени и тяготения, Государственное издательство технико-теоретической литературы, Москва, 1955

hand, the principles of relativity and of equivalence are of limited application and, notwithstanding their heuristic value, they are not unrestrictedly part of Einstein's Theory of Gravitation as expressed by the gravitational equations.

The author expresses once more his thanks to Professor Kemmer for his excellent translation and considers his efforts as a token of friendship.

Leningrad, *June* 1962   V. A. FOCK

INTRODUCTION†

FROM the geometrical point of view the theory of space and time naturally divides into the theory of uniform, Galilean, space and the theory of non-uniform, Riemannian and Einsteinian, space.‡

Galilean space is of maximal uniformity. This means that in it:

(a) All points in space and instants in time are equivalent.
(b) All directions are equivalent, and
(c) All inertial systems, moving uniformly and in a straight line relative to one another, are equivalent (Galilean principle of relativity).

The uniformity of space and time manifests itself in the existence of a group of transformations which leave invariant the four-dimensional distance or interval between two points. The expression for this interval plays an important part in the theory of space and time because its form is directly related to the form taken by the basic laws of physics, viz. the law of motion of a free mass-point and the law of propagation in free space of the front of a light wave.

The indications (a), (b) and (c) of the uniformity of Galilean space are related to the following transformations:

(a) To the equivalence of all points and instants corresponds the transformation of displacing the origins of the spatial coordinates and of time; the transformation involves four parameters, namely, the three space coordinates and the time coordinate of the origin.
(b) To the equivalence of all directions corresponds the transformation of rotating the spatial coordinate axes; this involves three parameters, the three angles of rotation.
(c) To the equivalence of inertial frames corresponds a change from one frame of reference to another moving uniformly in a straight line with respect to the first; this transformation involves three parameters, the three components of relative velocity.

The most general transformation involves ten parameters. This is the Lorentz transformation.

It is well known that in a space of n dimensions the group of transformations which leave invariant the expression for the squared distance between infinitely near points, can contain at most $\frac{1}{2}n(n+1)$ parameters. If there is a group involving all $\frac{1}{2}n(n+1)$ parameters then the space is of maximal uniformity; it may be a space of constant curvature, or, if the curvature vanishes, a Euclidean or pseudo-Euclidean space.

---

† In this introduction we frequently use terms and concepts which will be defined precisely only in the subsequent text. This is somewhat inconsistent but, unfortunately, unavoidable, for it is our aim to give in this introduction an outline of our attitude to the theory discussed in this book. Since, however, we hope that the intending reader has some prior knowledge of the subject we feel no great inconvenience will be caused by this manner of presentation. If a reader does not fully understand what is said, he will be well advised to return to the introduction after reading the book.

‡ We shall often use the word " space " short for " space and time ".

In the case of space-time the number of dimensions is four and therefore the greatest possible number of parameters is ten. This is also the number of parameters in the Lorentz transformation, so that Galilean space, to which the transformation relates, is indeed of maximal uniformity.

It is customary to call the theory based on the Lorentz transformations the Special Theory of Relativity. More precisely, the subject of that theory is the formulation of physical laws in accordance with the properties of Galilean space. The creator of the theory of relativity was Albert Einstein (1879–1955). Poincaré and Lorentz should be considered his predecessors. In this book Chapters I–IV are devoted to the theory of Galilean space.

Universal gravitation does not fit into the framework of uniform Galilean space. The deepest reason for this fact was given by Einstein. It is that not only the inertial mass, but also the gravitational mass of a body depends on its energy.

It proved possible to base a theory of universal gravitation on the idea of abandoning the uniformity of space as a whole† and attributing to space only a certain kind of uniformity in the infinitesimal. Mathematically, this meant abandoning Euclidean, or rather pseudo-Euclidean, geometry in favour of the geometry of Riemann. The modern theory of gravitation was also created by Einstein.

According to gravitational theory there still exists in the infinitely small a uniformity like the one expressed by Lorentz transformations. That this is so is connected with the fact that in the vicinity of a given point of space the gravitational field can be imitated by a field of acceleration (the so-called Principle of Equivalence). The physical basis of this is the law already known to Galileo that in the absence of a resistive medium all bodies fall equally fast, or, more accurately, with equal acceleration. The law of Galileo can be stated in generalized form as the law of the equality of inertial and gravitational mass. It should be stressed that this fundamental law is of a general character whereas the principle of equivalence is strictly local. The law of the equality of inertial and gravitational mass applies to the extent to which it is possible to define inertial and gravitational properties of mass as attributes of a particular body, independently of the positions and motions of other bodies. (Such independence exists in Newton's theory of gravitation, but does not necessarily hold in generalizations of that theory).

The law of equality of inertial and gravitational mass is the simple physical basis on which a theory of gravitation can be constructed; of course, the very process of constructing a theory involves introducing new generalizations. As a result of this the equality law may acquire the status of an approximate law, but this does not detract from its fundamental character. As a basis for con-

† We use terms such as " space as a whole ", " conditions at infinity ", etc., not literally, but in the mathematical sense accepted in field theory. By " space as a whole " we mean a region so large that at its boundaries the field due to the systems we are considering is negligibly small. " Conditions at infinity " refer to the boundaries of this region. The actual dimensions of the region can differ according to the nature of the particular problem: for an atom or a molecule a distance of the order of a micron can be considered infinitely great, for the solar system, a light year, for the galactic system, a thousand million light years. We never use " space as a whole " to denote the Universe. A consideration of the Universe seems to us impossible for gnosiological reasons.

structing a more general theory, the law of equality of inertial and gravitational mass has the following advantage over the principle of equivalence: in the first place it is not confined to local considerations, in the second it avoids dealing with frames of reference in accelerated motion—the precise definition of which is not easy to make.

In order to construct a theory of gravitation or to apply it to physical problems it is, however, insufficient to study space and time only locally, i.e. in infinitely small regions of space and periods of time. One way or another one must also characterize the properties of space as a whole. If one does not do this, it is quite impossible to state any problem uniquely. This is particularly clear in view of the fact that the equations of the gravitational, or any other field, are partial differential equations, the solutions of which are unique only when initial, boundary or other equivalent conditions are given. The field equations and the boundary conditions are inextricably connected and the latter can in no way be considered less important than the former. But, in problems relating to the whole of space, the boundary conditions refer to distant regions and their formulation requires knowledge of the properties of space as a whole.

One should note that Einstein did not fully appreciate the inadequacy of a local description and the importance of boundary conditions. This is why it is necessary to change substantially Einstein's statement of the basic problems of gravitational theory; this has been done in the author's research and in this book.

The simplest and at the same time the most important case is when one can assume space to be uniform at infinity in the sense of the Lorentz transformation. In this case the non-uniformities arising from material bodies will have local character. Masses and their gravitational fields will be, so to speak, embedded in unlimited Galilean space. This case is particularly important because the existence of integrals of motion is connected with the uniformity of space at infinity. Only if space at infinity allows the full Lorentz transformation with ten parameters do there exist the ten integrals of motion, including the energy integral.

Chapters V, VI and VII of this book are almost solely devoted to the case of a space uniform at infinity.

The assumption is also possible that space-time as a whole is not completely, but only partially, uniform; viz., that as before an arbitrary shift of the origin of space coordinates and an arbitrary rotation of axes are permissible, giving six parameters, but that four parameters of the Lorentz transformation, i.e. the three components of relative velocity and the origin of time reckoning, are fixed in terms of the first six. Such a space-time was first considered by Friedmann and because the spatial part of it obeys Lobachevsky's geometry, it may be called the space of Friedmann–Lobachevsky. In contrast to Galilean space, this space allows a well-defined gravitational field to exist when the mean density of ponderable matter is different from zero. For this reason, one can surmise that when in cosmology one considers enormous regions, thousands of millions of light years in extension and approximately uniformly filled with galaxies, the space of Friedmann–Lobachevsky will be a better approximation to reality than Galilean space. The theory of local non-uniformities in

3

Friedmann–Lobachevsky space has hitherto not been developed, and we devote only Sections 94–95 of this book to this space. Other assumptions concerning the properties of space as a whole are also possible, but we shall not discuss them.

For the question of whether preferred systems of coordinates exist, the properties of space as a whole are also of primary importance.

In Galilean space the familiar cartesian coordinates together with time, are preferred. This set of variables is called the set of Galilean coordinates. The privileged position of these coordinates arises from the fact that in terms of them the Lorentz transformations, which express the uniformity of space, prove to be linear.

In the case of a space uniform only at infinity it also proves possible to introduce a preferred system of coordinates, which is well defined up to a Lorentz transformation: they are the harmonic coordinates. This fact, first proved in the author's work, has great importance in matters of principle. Only with its support can one show in particular that Einstein's gravitional theory retains for the heliocentric Copernican system a preferred position compared to the geocentric Ptolomaic one. A more detailed exposition of this is given in Sections 92–93. All concrete problems in gravitational theory discussed in this book are solved in harmonic coordinates. This ensures that the solutions are unique.

It is probable that in Friedmann–Lobachevsky space there also exist some preferred systems of coordinates. However, this question has not been investigated; even the theory of local non-uniformity in this space has not as yet been formulated.

On the question of the existence of privileged systems of coordinates Einstein, the founder of gravitational theory, maintained a point of view opposite to ours, denying their existence in all cases. This is connected with his afore-mentioned preference for the local method of discussing properties of space (which method is the basis of Riemannian geometry), and his underestimation of the importance of considering space as a whole. Undoubtedly the philo-sophical attitude of Einstein, influenced throughout his life by the ideas of Mach, played its part in this.

An important place in the theory of space and time is taken up by the question of different coordinate systems and the change in the appearance of equations on going from one such system to another.

Great importance is usually attached to the covariance of equations. By this is meant the following: We consider a transformation of the coordinates accompanied by a transformation of dependent variables, or functions, according to some specified rule, for instance, the tensor rule. We examine the appearance of the equations satisfied by the original and the transformed functions. If, as a result of the transformation, the new functions of the new variables satisfy equations of the same appearance as the old functions of the old variables, the equations are called covariant. Covariance permits one to write down equations without presupposing any particular coordinate system. In addition, the requirement of covariance of equations has great heuristic value because it limits the variety of possible forms of equations and thereby makes it easier to choose correct ones. However, one should stress that the equations can so be limited only under the necessary condition that the number of functions introduced is also limited; if one permits the introduction of an arbitrary number of new auxiliary functions, practically any equation can be given covariant form.

Thus, covariance of equations in itself is in no way the expression of any kind of physical law. For instance, in the mechanics of systems of mass-points Lagrange's equations of the second kind are covariant with respect to arbitrary transformations of the coordinates, although they do not express any new physical law compared to, for instance, Lagrange's equations of the first kind, which are stated in cartesian coordinates and are not covariant.

In the case of Lagrange's equations covariance is achieved by introducing as new auxiliary functions the coefficients of the Lagrangian considered as an expression quadratic, but not necessarily homogeneous in the velocities.

In Riemannian geometry the new functions at our disposal are the coefficients $g_{\mu\nu}$ of the quadratic form for the squared infinitesimal distance. The law according to which these functions transform in passing to a new coordinate system follows from their definition as coefficients of a quadratic form, together with the condition that this form is an invariant; in the following we shall always assume that a transformation of the coordinates is accompanied by a transformation of the $g_{\mu\nu}$ according to this law. The set of quantities $g_{\mu\nu}$ is called the metric tensor.

Having introduced the metric tensor, one can form expressions that are covariant with respect to any coordinate transformation. If we consider only those metric tensors which are obtainable from a particular one (e.g. from the Galilean tensor) by coordinate transformation, this will give us nothing new except the fact that our equations are covariant. But if we extend the discussion to metric tensors of a more general form, tensors which cannot be transformed into one another by coordinate transformations, the generalization so obtained is an essential one. In this case the metric tensor will express not only properties of the coordinate system but also properties of space, and these latter can be related to the phenomenon of gravitation. It is Einstein's idea that the description of the gravitational field demands the introduction of no functions other than the metric tensor itself. This idea of the unity of metric and gravitation is the very basis of Einstein's theory of gravitation. It leads almost uniquely to the equations of the gravitational field found by Einstein.

Having clarified the concept of covariance as applied to Riemannian geometry, let us now consider it together with the previously discussed concept of the uniformity of space. As was shown above, the property of uniformity in Galilean space manifests itself in the existence of transformations that leave unchanged the expression for the four-dimensional distance between two points. More precisely, these transformations leave unchanged the coefficients of this expression, i.e. the quantities $g_{\mu\nu}$. If the $g_{\mu\nu}$ are functions of the coordinates we mean by this that the mathematical form of these functions is unchanged: the dependence of the new $g_{\mu\nu}$ on the new coordinates has the same mathematical form as that of the old $g_{\mu\nu}$ on the old coordinates. In the general case of Riemannian geometry there are no transformations that leave the $g_{\mu\nu}$ unchanged because Riemannian space is not uniform. In Riemannian geometry one deals with transformations of coordinates *accompanied by transformations of the* $g_{\mu\nu}$ and neither such a combined transformation nor covariance with respect to it, has any relation to the uniformity or non-uniformity of space.†

These statements can be illustrated by a simple example.

Let us consider the surface of a sphere. This surface can be transformed into itself by means of rotations by any angle around any axis passing through the centre. Such a transformation involves three parameters, but since the surface of the sphere is two-dimensional it follows from the remarks at the beginning of this introduction that it will be of maximum uniformity. On the surface of a sphere there are no preferred points or preferred directions.

Let us now consider a more general non-spherical surface of revolution. It also can be transformed into itself by rotation about an axis, but now the direction of the axis is fixed and only the angle of rotation remains arbitrary, so that the allowed transformations involve only a single parameter. Certain points on the surface will be singled out (the poles through which the axis passes) and so will certain directions (meridians and latitude circles). Finally, if we consider a surface of general form, there will be no transformations taking it into itself. Thus the sphere, a surface of a very particular form, possesses the greatest degree of uniformity (3 parameters), a surface of revolution has partial uniformity (1 parameter), while a surface of general form possesses no uniformity whatsoever.

We see that the generality of the form of the surface is a concept antagonistic to the concept of uniformity. This conclusion remains valid for the geometry of the 4-dimensional space-time manifold : the generality of its geometry is antagonistic to its uniformity.

We shall now clarify the meaning given to the concept of relativity in the theory of space and time and will show that it is extremely closely related to the concept of uniformity.

When speaking of the relativity of a frame of reference or simply of relativity, one usually means that there exist identical physical processes in different frames of reference (for more detail see Sections 6 and 49*). According to the generalized Galilean principle of relativity identical processes are possible in all inertial frames of reference related by Lorentz transformations. On the other hand, Lorentz transformations characterize the uniformity of Galilean space-time. Thus the principle of relativity is directly related to uniformity. This also shows that the nomenclature introduced in Einstein's first papers, by which the theory of uniform Galilean space is named " Theory of Relativity " can to some extent be justified.‡

In the following we shall see that relativity in the sense defined above is related to uniformity in all those cases in which the space-time metric can be considered fixed. This can be done not only in the theory of Galilean space, where the metric is given once and for all, but also in the theory of Riemann and Einstein space, provided only the processes under discussion have no practical influence on the metric. In these cases relativity is uniquely related to uniformity : in uniform Galilean space it exists, in non-uniform Riemannian space it is absent. If, however, the discussion is to include processes which themselves essentially influence the metric (displacement of heavy masses) it will be shown

---

† These ideas were expressed by E. Cartan [1].

‡ The name *Chronogeometry* suggested by A. D. Fokker [1a] would be more appropriate.

6

at the end of the book (Section 93) that relativity can to a certain extent be retained, even in inhomogeneous space, albeit only in those cases in which the non-uniformity produced by heavy masses may be treated as a local perturbation in infinite Galilean space.

The preservation of a certain degree of relativity, even in non-uniform space, is due to the fact that in going over to a new frame of reference the previous gravitational field is replaced by a new one, which has the same form in the new frame as the old in the old frame. Thus, if a laboratory on the Earth is turned upside down, the processes in it will be disturbed (there is no relativity) but if the reversal is accompanied by a parallel transport of the laboratory to the antipodes, the course of all processes in it will be the same as in the beginning (relativity is maintained).

Thus, even in non-uniform space the still existing relativity is indirectly connected with uniformity, namely with the uniformity at infinity if one discusses relativity " in the large", and with local uniformity in a geodesic coordinate system if one is discussing relativity " in the infinitely small ". We have seen, however, that uniformity stands in an antagonistic relation to the degree of generality of the geometry; this is why relativity either does not exist at all in a non-uniform space with Riemannian geometry, or else it does exist, but does not go beyond the relativity of Galilean space. But there can be no question of a generalization of the concept of relativity in going over to non-uniform space.

However, when Einstein created his theory of gravitation, he put forward the term " general relativity " which confused everything. This term was adopted in the sense of " general covariance ", i.e. in the sense of the covariance of equations with respect to arbitrary transformations of coordinates accompanied by transformations of the $g_{\nu\mu}$. But we have seen that this kind of covariance has nothing to do with the uniformity of space, while in one way or another relativity is connected with uniformity. This means that " general relativity " has nothing to do with " relativity as such ". At the same time the latter received the name " special " relativity, which purports to indicate that it is a special case of " general " relativity.

To show what misunderstandings resulted we shall consider some examples.

As will be shown in Chapter IV, the theory of uniform Galilean space can be formulated not only in a way covariant with respect to Lorentz transformations, but also in a generally covariant manner. In the language of " general " and " special " relativity it would be extremely difficult to express this simple idea, and we shall not attempt to do so, for we would have to say that " special " relativity includes " general " relativity or something of that kind.

Remembering that even in Newtonian mechanics one deals with the generally covariant Lagrange equations of the second kind, one would also have to say that Newtonian mechanics contain in itself " general " relativity.

It has become a convention, since Einstein, to use the term " general " relativity or " the general principle of relativity " in the sense of " theory of gravitation ". Einstein's fundamental paper on the theory of gravitation (1916) is already entitled " Foundations of the General Theory of Relativity ". This confuses the issue still further because the words " general " and " relativity " are not used with their proper meaning. In the theory of gravitation, space is

7

assumed non-uniform whereas relativity relates to uniformity so that it appears that in the general theory of relativity there is no relativity.

Enough has been said to make clear that the use of the terms " general relativity ", " general theory of relativity " or " general principle of relativity " should not be admitted. This usage is inconvenient because it not only leads to misunderstanding, but also reflects an incorrect understanding of the theory itself. However paradoxical this may seem, Einstein, himself the author of the theory, showed such a lack of understanding when he named his theory and when in his discussions he stressed the word " general relativity ", not seeing that in the new theory he had created, the notion of relativity was not among the concepts subjected to generalization.

In the present book we do not use the term " general relativity ". Following established practice, we call the theory of Galilean space the Theory of Relativity, but without the adjective " special ". We call the theory of Einstein space the Theory of Gravitation, not the " general theory of relativity ", because the latter name is nonsensical

*   *   *   *

The philosophical side of our views on the theory of space, time and gravitation was formed under the influence of the philosophy of dialectical materialism, in particular under the influence of Lenin's " Materialism and Empiriocriticism", The teachings of dialectical materialism helped us to approach critically Einstein's point of view concerning the theory created by him and to think it out anew. It helped us also to understand correctly, and to interpret, the new results we ourselves obtained. We wish to state this here, although this book does not explicitly touch philosophical questions.

CHAPTER I

THE THEORY OF RELATIVITY

1. Coordinates of Space and Time

Space and time are primary concepts. In the philosophical sense they are the forms of existence of matter. This can be understood as meaning that the concepts of space and time are obtained by appropriate abstractions from the concept of spatio-temporal relations between material processes. The simplest notion relating to space and time is a point in space considered at a particular instant in time. To " mark " a point in space one must place there a material body of sufficiently small dimensions. The position of this body can only be fixed relative to other material bodies since there does not exist any cartographic grid inherent in space and independent of material bodies. When a frame of reference, or " base ", is chosen, i.e. a system of material bodies relative to which the position of the given point body is measured, that position can be fixed in terms of three coordinates relating to a particular instant in time, reckoned according to a clock at the base. Generally speaking coordinates are auxiliary quantities characterizing the disposition of bodies relative to the frame. They allow one to calculate according to the laws of Euclidean geometry the relative positions of the bodies, in particular their distances apart and the angles between the directions of lines joining them. Usually one takes the coordinates to be rectilinear and orthogonal because such coordinates are simplest to relate to lengths and distances, but any other (curvilinear) coordinates are admissible, for instance, two angles defining the direction towards a point-body and the distance to it.

One should stress that both the coordinates themselves and the distances, angles, etc., calculated from them in describing the relative positions of bodies have a definite meaning only when a particular base is postulated. In the same way instants in time to which the coordinates and the distances refer, and likewise time differences, become well-defined only when a definite spatial base and a definite time-measure in that base are assumed, i.e. a definite frame of reference.

In this way the variables x, y, z and t, the space and time coordinates with which we shall deal in the following, are related to a base.

2. The Position of a Body in Space at a given Instant, in a Fixed Reference Frame

Let us first disregard time and consider the usual methods for determining the situation of objects in space. The logical foundation of these methods is, in principle, the hypothesis that Euclidean geometry is applicable to real physical space together with two further assumptions, viz. that rigid bodies exist and that light travels in straight lines. In fact, to find the position of a distant object one has to use a rigid graduated rule to map out a definite base in the sense of ordinary triangulation, and a light ray to take bearings on the object at different points of the base. Assuming that the light rays are straight lines the laws of Euclidean geometry then allow one to calculate the distance to the object and all other data characterizing its position. The rectilinear nature of light rays *in vacuo* is a basic postulate. In the atmosphere light rays are only approximately straight and corrections for refraction, etc., must be made. The validity of the laws of Euclidean geometry in the real physical world should be taken as an experimental fact, not as an *a priori* assumption. Indeed, although these laws can be verified with an enormous degree of accuracy, Einstein's theory of Universal Gravitation is based on the consideration of small departures from them.

Thus the properties of light and the properties of rigid bodies play a basic part in establishing the geometry of real physical space.

However, one must note that in this connection the concept of a rigid body is, to some extent, auxiliary. Absolutely rigid bodies do not exist; one can take actual physical bodies to be rigid and to possess invariable geometric dimensions only as an approximation and only in certain conditions, namely at constant temperature, in the absence of elastic vibrations, etc. The invariability of a standard of length can be checked with greatest accuracy by comparing it with the wave length of some definite spectral line. Thus the notion of length ultimately depends on the properties of atoms or molecules radiating the spectral line and on the properties of light.

Another method for determining the disposition of objects in space, which is in principle different from triangulation, is radiogeodesy or radar. Basically this method consists of emitting radio signals from a certain point and reflecting them from the object to be observed so that they return to the point of origin. The time elapsing during the passage of the signal there and back is noted and also, of course, the direction. Knowing the speed of propagation of a radio signal—it is in fact equal to the speed of light—one obtains the distance to the object as the product of the speed and half the time taken by the signal.

As a matter of principle this method is important because it reduces the measurement of length to a measurement of time intervals and does not make use of the properties of absolutely rigid bodies. The essential assumption is that the speed of light is constant. Here this speed plays the part of a conversion factor from time to length. Its numerical value must be determined by other experiments and these do have to use a standard of length.

In principle, a time measurement can be performed with the aid of any periodic process. At present the clocks of greatest precision rely on the proper vibrations of a quartz crystal or of an ammonia molecule. In practice astronomical time measurements are used which rely on applying Newton's laws of motion to the rotation of the earth, with due observance of all deviations from uniform rotation that the theory predicts, such as nutation, etc.

Such methods of time measurement make it possible to regulate a clock at the base.

When measuring the position of moving bodies from a fixed base the question arises: to what instant, by the clock at base, does the measured value of distance or any other spatial coordinate refer? We accept the following definition: If the light signal (or the signal from the radar station) is sent off at a time t_1 and returns at t_2, then the value of the coordinates x, y, z of the object and also the distance $r = c(t_2 - t_1)/2$, refer to the instant $t = (t_1 + t_2)/2$. This definition is in accord with the natural assumption that the speeds of light to and fro are equal.

We have shown that, starting from a definite base and equipped with graduated rules, clocks and other necessary apparatus, we can measure out the position of bodies in space with reference to the base and refer the resulting values of coordinates, such as the cartesian ones x, y and z, to a definite instant t, which also refers to a clock at base. In the following we shall call this kind of base a reference frame. We shall still use the word "base" in those cases when it is desirable to stress the fact already pointed out at the beginning of Section 1, namely, that a reference frame is not some kind of coordinate grid in space together with some "universal time", but is connected with rules and clocks located at a definite place and moving in a definite way.

3. The Law of Propagation of an Electromagnetic Wave Front

The laws of propagation of light in empty space are thoroughly understood. They find their expression in the well-known equations of Maxwell

$$\text{curl } \mathbf{H} - \frac{1}{c} \frac{\partial \mathbf{E}}{\partial t} = 0, \qquad \text{div } \mathbf{E} = 0$$

$$\text{curl } \mathbf{E} + \frac{1}{c} \frac{\partial \mathbf{H}}{\partial t} = 0, \qquad \text{div } \mathbf{H} = 0$$

$$(3.01)$$

where $\mathbf{E}$ and $\mathbf{H}$ are the vectors of electric and magnetic field intensity. However, we are not interested in the general case of light propagation, but only in the propagation of a signal advancing with maximum speed, i.e. the propagation of a wave front. Ahead of the front of the wave all components of the field vanish. Behind it some of them are different from zero. Therefore, some of the field components must be discontinuous at the front.

On the other hand, given the field on some surface moving in space, the derivatives of the field on the surface are, in general, determined by Maxwell's equations. Hence the value of the field at an infinitely near surface is also determined and discontinuities of the field are impossible. The only case when this is not so is when the form and motion of the given surface satisfies certain special conditions subject to which the value of the derivatives is not determined by the values of the field components themselves. Such a surface is called a characteristic surface or, briefly, a characteristic. Thus, discontinuities of the field can occur only on a characteristic, but since there must certainly be discontinuities at a wave front, such a front is clearly a characteristic.

Let us determine the equation of a characteristic for the system of Maxwell's equations.

Let the value of the field be given for those points and instants whose coordinates are related by the equation

$$t = \frac{1}{c} f(x, y, z) \tag{3.02}$$

In particular, if $f \equiv 0$ this amounts to stating *initial conditions*. Equation (3.02) may be looked upon as the equation of a certain hypersurface in the four-dimensional space-time manifold. When $(\operatorname{grad} f)^2 > 1$ the same equation can be considered as the equation of an ordinary surface moving through space (see also Section 35). Assume that on the hypersurface (3.02) the values of a certain function u are given

$$u\left(x, y, z, \frac{f}{c}\right) = u_0(x, y, z) \tag{3.03}$$

The following combinations of derivatives with respect to space and time coordinates will thereby also be given

$$\frac{\partial u}{\partial x_i} + \frac{1}{c}\frac{\partial u}{\partial t} \cdot \frac{\partial f}{\partial x_i} = \frac{\partial u_0}{\partial x_i} \qquad (i = 1, 2, 3) \tag{3.04}$$

Here we have used x_1, x_2, x_3 for brevity instead of x, y, z. If, in addition, the derivative $\partial u/\partial t$ were given, the values of all the derivatives of u at the surface would be known.

Let us take as the function u one of the components of electromagnetic field, for instance E_x, and denote by $E_x^0 = E_x^0(x, y, z)$ the value of this component on the hypersurface. We shall use the same notation (superfix 0) for the other components. If the field is given on the hypersurface, the whole set of quantities $\mathbf{E}^0$ and $\mathbf{H}^0$ can be considered as known functions of x, y and z. As in (3.04) we shall have for instance

$$\frac{\partial E_x}{\partial z} + \frac{1}{c}\frac{\partial E_x}{\partial t} \cdot \frac{\partial f}{\partial z} = \frac{\partial E_x^0}{\partial z}, \text{ etc.} \tag{3.05}$$

whence
$$\operatorname{div} \mathbf{E} + \frac{1}{c}\left(\operatorname{grad} f \cdot \frac{\partial \mathbf{E}}{\partial t}\right) = \operatorname{Div} \mathbf{E}^0 \tag{3.06}$$

$$\operatorname{curl} \mathbf{E} + \frac{1}{c}\left[\operatorname{grad} f \times \frac{\partial \mathbf{E}}{\partial t}\right] = \operatorname{Curl} \mathbf{E}^0 \tag{3.07}$$

and also
$$\operatorname{div} \mathbf{H} + \frac{1}{c}\left(\operatorname{grad} f \cdot \frac{\partial \mathbf{H}}{\partial t}\right) = \operatorname{Div} \mathbf{H}^0 \tag{3.08}$$

$$\operatorname{curl} \mathbf{H} + \frac{1}{c}\left[\operatorname{grad} f \times \frac{\partial \mathbf{H}}{\partial t}\right] = \operatorname{Curl} \mathbf{H}^0 \tag{3.09}$$

In the last equations we have denoted the operators div and curl when applied to $\mathbf{E}^0$ and $\mathbf{H}^0$ by Div and Curl.

The values of the six functions $\mathbf{E}^0$ and $\mathbf{H}^0$ are not independent: they must satisfy two relations which we shall now give.

Taking the scalar product of equations (3.07) and (3.09) with $\operatorname{grad} f$ and using Maxwell equations (3.01) we get

$$(\operatorname{grad} f \cdot \operatorname{Curl} \mathbf{E}^0) = -\frac{1}{c}\left(\operatorname{grad} f \cdot \frac{\partial \mathbf{H}}{\partial t}\right) \tag{3.10}$$

$$(\operatorname{grad} f \cdot \operatorname{Curl} \mathbf{H}^0) = \frac{1}{c}\left(\operatorname{grad} f \cdot \frac{\partial \mathbf{E}}{\partial t}\right) \tag{3.11}$$

Now the first terms on the left-hand sides of both equations (3.08) and (3.06) vanish by virtue of Maxwell's equations and the second terms are the same as the right-hand sides of (3.10) and (3.11). We have, therefore,

$$\operatorname{Div} \mathbf{H}^0 + (\operatorname{grad} f \cdot \operatorname{Curl} \mathbf{E}^0) = 0 \tag{3.12}$$

$$\mathrm{Div}\,\mathbf{E}^0 - (\mathrm{grad}\,f\cdot\mathrm{Curl}\,\mathbf{H}^0) = 0 \tag{3.13}$$

These are the conditions which the given functions $\mathbf{E}^0$ and $\mathbf{H}^0$ must satisfy. In the case that $f = \mathrm{const.}$, we have to choose initial values in the ordinary way and then the conditions amount to the obvious requirement that div $\mathbf{E}$ and div $\mathbf{H}$ must both vanish at the initial instant.

Using Maxwell's equations we can write (3.07) and (3.09) in the form

$$\frac{\partial\mathbf{E}}{\partial t} + \left[\mathrm{grad}\,f \times \frac{\partial\mathbf{H}}{\partial t}\right] = c\,\mathrm{Curl}\,\mathbf{H}^0 \tag{3.14}$$

$$-\frac{\partial\mathbf{H}}{\partial t} + \left[\mathrm{grad}\,f \times \frac{\partial\mathbf{E}}{\partial t}\right] = c\,\mathrm{Curl}\,\mathbf{E}^0 \tag{3.15}$$

Multiplying these equations vectorially by grad f and using the relations just deduced, we transform them into :

$$\{1 - (\mathrm{grad}\,f)^2\}\frac{\partial\mathbf{E}}{\partial t} = \dot{\mathbf{E}}^0 - (\mathrm{grad}\,f\cdot\dot{\mathbf{E}}^0)\,\mathrm{grad}\,f - [\mathrm{grad}\,f \times \dot{\mathbf{H}}^0] \tag{3.16}$$

$$\{1 - (\mathrm{grad}\,f)^2\}\frac{\partial\mathbf{H}}{\partial t} = \dot{\mathbf{H}}^0 - (\mathrm{grad}\,f\cdot\dot{\mathbf{H}}^0)\,\mathrm{grad}\,f + [\mathrm{grad}\,f \times \dot{\mathbf{E}}^0] \tag{3.17}$$

Here we have written for brevity

$$\dot{\mathbf{E}}^0 = c\,\mathrm{Curl}\,\mathbf{H}^0\,; \qquad \dot{\mathbf{H}}^0 = -\,c\,\mathrm{Curl}\,\mathbf{E}^0 \tag{3.18}$$

The functions on the right-hand side of (3.16) and (3.17) are all known. These equations can be solved for the time derivatives if their coefficient, i.e. the quantity $1 - (\mathrm{grad}\,f)^2$, is not zero. In that case equations analogous to (3.05) lead to finite values of all the other first derivatives of the field, so that the field itself will be continuous on the surface (3.02). If there is to be a discontinuity there, the coefficient of the time derivatives must thus necessarily be zero, giving the condition

$$(\mathrm{grad}\,f)^2 = 1 \tag{3.19}$$

A surface satisfying this equation will be a characteristic. If we write the equation of a surface without solving for time, but instead in the form

$$\omega(x, y, z, t) = 0 \tag{3.20}$$

the equation (3.19) for the characteristic takes on the form

$$\frac{1}{c^2}\left(\frac{\partial\omega}{\partial t}\right)^2 - (\mathrm{grad}\,\omega)^2 = 0 \tag{3.21}$$

Therefore the propagation of an electromagnetic wave front satisfies this equation (3.21).

Particular functions satisfying the equation (3.19) or (3.21) are

$$t = \frac{1}{c}(\alpha x + \beta y + \gamma z) \qquad (\alpha^2 + \beta^2 + \gamma^2 = 1) \tag{3.22}$$

$$t = t_0 + \frac{1}{c}\sqrt{[(x - x_0)^2 + (y - y_0)^2 + (z - z_0)^2]} \tag{3.23}$$

The former gives a plane wave front, the latter a spherical one.

4. Equations for Rays

The equation describing the propagation of a wave front can be written in the form

$$\frac{\partial \omega}{\partial t} + c\sqrt{(\omega_x^2 + \omega_y^2 + \omega_z^2)} = 0 \tag{4.01}$$

(for definiteness we have chosen the plus sign before the square root). The form of this equation is the same as that of the Hamilton–Jacobi equation in mechanics with ω playing the part of the action function S and the derivatives ω_x, ω_y and ω_z, the part of the " momenta ", p_x, p_y and p_z. Corresponding to the Hamiltonian we have here the expression

$$H = c\sqrt{(\omega_x^2 + \omega_y^2 + \omega_z^2)} \tag{4.02}$$

To the trajectories of mechanics there correspond light rays. The equations for them are analogous to Hamilton's equations. They can be written as

$$\frac{dx}{dt} = \frac{\partial H}{\partial \omega_x} = c \frac{\omega_x}{\sqrt{(\omega_x^2 + \omega_y^2 + \omega_z^2)}}, \text{ etc.} \tag{4.03}$$

$$\frac{d\omega_x}{dt} = -\frac{\partial H}{\partial x} = 0, \qquad \text{etc.} \tag{4.04}$$

Equation (4.04) shows that the quantities ω_x, ω_y and ω_z are constant along a ray, though they can, of course, vary from one ray to another. Therefore the rays will be straight :

$$x - x_0 = c \frac{\omega_x}{\sqrt{(\omega_x^2 + \omega_y^2 + \omega_z^2)}} (t - t_0), \text{ etc.} \tag{4.05}$$

If the sign of ω, and hence of ω_x, ω_y and ω_z is changed, the direction of the ray is reversed ; the sign must be chosen according to the given sense of direction of the ray.

Any wave surface can be considered as formed of points moving along the rays with the speed of light according to (4.05).

We thus have the possibility of constructing a wave surface at time t when its form at time t_0 is known. Let the equation of the wave surface at time t_0 have the form

$$\omega^0(x_0, y_0, z_0) = 0 \tag{4.06}$$

where x_0, y_0 and z_0 are coordinates varying over this surface. Knowing the equation of the surface we can calculate the quantities

$$\alpha(x_0, y_0, z_0) = \left(\frac{\omega_x^0}{\sqrt{(\omega_x^{0^2} + \omega_y^{0^2} + \omega_z^{0^2})}} \right)_0, \text{ etc.} \tag{4.07}$$

Here the sign of the right-hand sides is determined by the given direction of wave propagation. The equation of the ray passing through the point (x_0, y_0, z_0) of the initial wave surface is

$$\begin{aligned} x - x_0 &= c\alpha(t - t_0) \\ y - y_0 &= c\beta(t - t_0) \qquad (\alpha^2 + \beta^2 + \gamma^2 = 1) \\ z - z_0 &= c\gamma(t - t_0) \end{aligned} \tag{4.08}$$

The quantities x, y and z give the positions of the point to which the point (x_0, y_0, z_0) moves at time t. Allowing x_0, y_0 and z_0 to take on all values which satisfy $\omega^0 = 0$, we obtain from (4.08) all points which at time t lie on the wave surface.

If we solve (4.08) for x_0, y_0 and z_0 and insert the functions

$$x_0 = x_0(x, y, z, t - t_0), \text{ etc.} \tag{4.09}$$

into the wave surface equation $\omega^0 = 0$, we get the relation

$$\omega(x, y, z, t - t_0) = 0 \tag{4.10}$$

which is the explicit form of the equation of the wave surface at time t. At $t = t_0$, obviously, $x_0 = x$, $y_0 = y$, $z_0 = z$ and equation (4.10) reduces to (4.06), which is the equation of the initially given wave surface.

From the ray equation (4.05) there follows the relation

$$c^2(t - t_0)^2 - [(x - x_0)^2 + (y - y_0)^2 + (z - z_0)^2] = 0 \tag{4.11}$$

which connects the coordinates of the initial and final points on each ray. It is the equation of a sphere centred at the point x_0, y_0, z_0 and of a radius $R = c(t - t_0)$ that increases linearly with time. Just as equation (3.21), from which we started, this equation expresses the fact that the velocity of light propagation is constant.

For points infinitesimally separated relation (4.11) takes on the form

$$c^2 dt^2 - (dx^2 + dy^2 + dz^2) = 0 \tag{4.12}$$

In this form the equation follows directly from Hamilton's equation (4.03).

A more general treatment of the problem of integrating the wave front equation is given in Appendix F.

5. Inertial Frames of Reference

In Section 2 we explained what is meant by a frame of reference and showed that it is essentially a certain base equipped with graduated rules and clocks ; it can be roughly represented as a kind of radar station. The important thing is that the base consists of certain material bodies that have some definite position in space and some definite motion.

To describe any phenomenon, in particular propagation of light or motion of material bodies, requires a definite frame of reference or base. For example, the motion of the planets is normally described in the heliocentric system. The origin of this system, i.e. the position of the imaginary base, is the mass-centre of the solar system and the three axes are chosen to point to three fixed stars, by which choice the orientation of the base is fixed.

In general, the mathematical form of the laws of nature will be different in different frames. Thus, for instance, the motion of bodies relative to the Earth may be described either in a frame with axes pointing to three fixed stars or in one rigidly fixed to the Earth and in the latter case one has to introduce Coriolis forces into the equations of motion.

There exist frames of reference in which the equations of motion have a particularly simple form ; in a certain sense these are the most " natural " frames of reference. They are the *inertial* frames in which the motion of a body is uniform and rectilinear, provided no forces act on it. (Here the question arises how to tell that no forces are acting on the given body ; we shall take it that this is the case if all bodies capable of exerting forces are sufficiently distant.) The heliocentric frame is an inertial one to a very good approximation. In an inertial frame we shall almost always use cartesian coordinates, because in terms of them it is particularly simple to formulate both the laws of Euclidean geometry and the laws of mechanics, in particular, the aforementioned law of the rectilinear uniform motion 'of a body not subject to forces. Of course, the very concept of an inertial frame permits one to go over to other, especially curvilinear, coordinates and if the equations of the transformation do not involve time explicitly one can take it that both the initial and the transformed coordinates refer to the same inertial frame.

In pre-relativistic physics the notion of an inertial system was related only to the laws of mechanics. Newton's first law of motion is, in fact, nothing but a definition of an inertial frame.

However, we have seen that the laws of light propagation play a fundamental part in the definition of the basic concepts relating to space and time. Therefore it proves more correct to relate the notion of an inertial frame not only to the laws of mechanics but also to those of light propagation.

The usual form of Maxwell's equations refers to some inertial frame. It is obvious and has always been assumed, even before Relativity, that at least one reference frame exists that is inertial with respect to mechanics and in which at the same time Maxwell's equations are true. The law of propagation of an electromagnetic wave front in the form

$$\frac{1}{c^2}\left(\frac{\partial \omega}{\partial t}\right)^2 - \left[\left(\frac{\partial \omega}{\partial x}\right)^2 + \left(\frac{\partial \omega}{\partial y}\right)^2 + \left(\frac{\partial \omega}{\partial z}\right)^2\right] = 0 \qquad (5.01)$$

also refers to this inertial frame. A frame for which (5.01) is valid may be called inertial in the electromagnetic sense. A frame that is inertial both in the mechanical and in the electromagnetic senses will be simply called inertial.

Thus, by the definition we have adopted, an inertial frame is characterized by the following two properties:

1. In an inertial frame a body moves uniformly and in a straight line, provided no forces act on it. (The inertial property in the usual mechanical sense.)

2. In an inertial frame the equation of propagation of an electromagnetic wave front has the form (5.01). (The inertial property for the field.)

We have spoken only of the propagation of an *electromagnetic* wave, thereby apparently giving this field preference over other fields. However, the preference is only apparent. The maximum speed of propagation of all fields must actually be the same, so that equation (5.01) is of universal validity. This question will be discussed in detail in the following section.

6. The Basic Postulates of the Theory of Relativity

The fundamental postulate of the theory of relativity, also called the Principle of Relativity, asserts that phenomena occurring in a closed system are independent of any non-accelerated motion of the system as a whole.

We shall attempt to make the content of this postulate more precise.†

Assume a closed system of material bodies and a variety of mechanical, electromagnetic or any other processes taking place within the system. We shall describe the state of the system, including the electromagnetic and other fields involved, with reference to some definite frame, or base in the sense of Section 2. Consider two frames. Let the first be inertial and let the second move uniformly in a straight line with respect to the first. We define the initial state of the system in relation to the first frame, using the word " initial " in the sense of

† See L. I. Mandelstam [6].

" relating to the initial instant according to a clock of the frame ". We then imagine a copy of our system which has the same initial state with respect to the second frame as the original system had with respect to the first, with " initial " now, of course, defined with respect to the other frame. We shall compare the subsequent course of events in the original system, described in the first frame, with the course of events in the copy, as described in the second frame.

The Principle of Relativity asserts that the two sequences of events will be exactly the same (at least insofar as they are determined at all). If a process in the original system can be described in terms of certain functions of the space and time coordinates of the first frame, *the same functions* of the space and time coordinates of the second frame will describe a process occurring in the copy.

One can say more descriptively, if less precisely, that *the uniform rectilinear motion of a material system as a whole has no influence on the course of any processes occurring within it.*

Many natural laws governing the course of various physical processes can be stated in terms of differential equations, the form of which does not depend on the initial state of the system concerned. The initial conditions enter as supplementary equations. This is so, for example, for the equations of motion in mechanics, and also for the equations of the electromagnetic field and the associated equation for the propagation of an electromagnetic wave front. It follows then from the Principle of Relativity that the mathematical form of such laws must be the same in the initially chosen frame and in any other which moves uniformly and in a straight line with respect to it. Remembering our definition of an inertial frame (in the mechanical sense and for fields) we are led to the following important conclusion : *If an inertial frame is given, any other frame that moves uniformly and rectilinearly with respect to it is itself inertial.* This postulate will serve us as the basis from which to derive the formulae linking the space and time coordinates in two frames moving without acceleration with respect to one another.

The Principle of Relativity is confirmed by the whole of our experience of the natural world. In the domain of mechanics the principle has long been known ; it is the Galilean relativity principle. Einstein's achievement was to extend it to all phenomena (though in the first place to electromagnetism) and to derive from it certain consequences regarding the interrelation of space and time.

The Theory of Relativity can be built up on two postulates, namely, the Principle of Relativity and another principle that states that the velocity of light is independent of the velocity of its source. We have accepted the latter principle from the first, for we have based our development on the law of propagation of an electromagnetic wave front and the second principle is an immediate consequence of this law.

It is appropriate to give here a generalized interpretation of the law of wave front propagation and to formulate the following general postulate :

There exists a maximum speed for the propagation of any kind of action. This is numerically equal to the speed of light in free space.

This principle is very significant because the transmission of signals with greatest possible speed plays a fundamental part in the definition of concepts concerning space and time. The very notion of a definite frame of reference for describing events in space and time depends on the existence of such signals. In Section 2 we have considered methods of determining the positions of bodies in space that were based on the use of light, or other electromagnetic, signals. In principle, however, signals could be transmitted not only by electromagnetic waves but by waves of some other nature. One could, for instance, imagine signalling with particles having the limiting speed and with the matter-waves that correspond to them in quantum mechanics. Also conceivable, though unattainable in practice, would be to use gravitational waves, the existence of which follows from Einstein's theory of Gravitation (see Section 90). It is not excluded that other fields capable of transmitting signals might be discovered. Therefore the question arises : is the notion of a reference frame sufficiently general, if its definition is based on the use of electromagnetic signals only ? For if more rapid means of signalling existed, or even instantaneous transmission, the concept of a reference frame defined in terms of light propagation could not aptly reflect the properties of space and time but would, at best, give one possible form of description.

The principle formulated above, by asserting the existence of a general upper limit for all kinds of action and signal, endows the speed of light with a universal significance, independent of the particular properties of the agency of transmission and reflecting a certain objective property of space-time.

This principle has a logical connection with the Principle of Relativity. For if there was no single limiting velocity but instead different agents, e.g. light and gravitation, propagated *in vacuo* with different speeds, then the Principle of Relativity would necessarily be violated as regards at least one of the agents.

The principle of the universal limiting velocity can be made mathematically precise as follows :

For any kind of wave advancing with limiting velocity and capable of transmitting signals the equation of front propagation is the same as the equation for the front of a light wave.

Thus the equation

$$\frac{1}{c^2}\left(\frac{\partial \omega}{\partial t}\right)^2 - (\text{grad } \omega)^2 = 0 \tag{6.01}$$

acquires a general character ; it is more general than Maxwell's equations from which we derived it. As a consequence of the principle of the existence of a universal limiting velocity one can assert the following : the differential equations describing any field that is capable of transmitting signals must be of such a kind that the equation of their characteristics is the same as the equation for the characteristics of light waves.[†]

We shall see in Chapters V–VII that the presence of a gravitational field somewhat alters the appearance of the equation of the characteristics from the form (6.01), but in this case one and the same equation still governs the propa-

[†] The work of A. D. Aleksandrov [2, 3] contains a formulation of the basic postulates of the theory of relativity as a theory of the " absolute " properties of space and time, which is close to ours. The ideas of A. D. Fokker [1a] and the name Chronogeometry proposed by him for this theory also underline the "absolute" side of spatio-temporal relations.

gation of all kinds of wave fronts travelling with limiting velocity, including electromagnetic and gravitational ones.

In the preceding section we have taken equation (6.01) together with the fact of the uniform rectilinear motion of a body not subject to forces, as the basis for defining inertial reference frames.

The principle just formulated asserting the universality of the equation shows that such a definition of inertial systems is appropriate.

7. The Galileo Transformations and the Need to Generalize Them

Let one and the same phenomenon be described in two inertial frames of reference. The question arises of passing from the first frame to the second in the description of some phenomenon. For a rough illustration we can imagine two radar stations, one on the Earth, the other on an aeroplane or on a Sputnik; the problem is to convert from the data recorded at the first station to those found at the second.

For such a conversion one must know first of all the relation between the space and time coordinates x, y, z and t in the first frame and the corresponding x', y', z' and t' in the second. In pre-relativity physics one accepted as self-evident the existence of a universal time t, the same for all frames; on that view one had to put $t' = t$ or $t' = t - t_0$, if a change of time-origin was admitted.

Considering two events occurring at times t and τ, the old point of view required the time elapsed between them to be the same in all reference frames so that

$$t - \tau = t' - \tau' \tag{7.01}$$

Further, it was considered to be evident that the length of a rigid rod, measured in the two frames, would have the same value. (Instead of the length of a rigid rod one could equally well consider the distance between the "simultaneous" positions of two points which need not necessarily be rigidly connected.) Denoting the spatial coordinates of the two ends of the rod (or the two points) by (x, y, z) and (ξ, η, ζ) in the one frame and by (x', y', z') and (ξ', η', ζ') in the other the old theory required

$$(x - \xi)^2 + (y - \eta)^2 + (z - \zeta)^2 = (x' - \xi')^2 + (y' - \eta')^2 + (z' - \zeta')^2 \tag{7.02}$$

Equations (7.01) and (7.02) determine uniquely the general form of the transformation connecting x, y, z and t with x', y', z' and t'. It consists of a change in origin of spatial coordinates and of time, of a rotation of the spatial axes and of a transformation such as

$$\begin{aligned}
x' &= x - V_x t \\
y' &= y - V_y t \\
z' &= z - V_z t \\
t' &= t
\end{aligned} \tag{7.03}$$

where V_x, V_y and V_z are constants whose physical meaning is easy to see: they give the velocity with which the primed frame moves relatively to the unprimed one; more exactly they are the components of this velocity in the unprimed frame.

The transformation (7.03) is called a Galileo transformation.

Thus, pre-relativistic physics asserted that, given an inertial frame (x, y, z), space and time coordinates in any other frame moving uniformly and rectilinearly relative to the former are connected with x, y, z and t by a Galileo transformation, apart from a rotation and a displacement of origin.

Galileo transformations satisfy the Principle of Relativity as far as the laws of (Newtonian) mechanics are concerned, but not in relation to the propagation of light. Indeed the wave front equation changes its appearance when subjected to a Galileo transformation. If Galileo transformations were valid—and the Principle of Relativity in its generalized form therefore not—there would exist only one inertial system in the sense of our definition and the changed form of the wave front equation in any other frame would allow one to detect even uniform rectilinear motion relative to the single inertial system—the " immobile ether "—and to determine the velocity of this motion. The fact that numerous accurate experiments devised to discover such motion relative to the " ether " all had negative results leaves no room whatever to doubt that the form of the law of wave front propagation is the same in all non-accelerated frames. Therefore the Principle of Relativity is certainly also applicable to electromagnetic phenomena.

It follows also that the Galileo transformation is in general wrong and should be replaced by another.

The general postulates formulated in the preceding sections provide all that is required to derive a transformation of space and time coordinates to supersede the Galileo transformation.

The problem can be stated as follows. Let a reference frame be given which is inertial by our definition, i.e. in both the mechanical and the electromagnetic senses (see Section 5). We denote the space and time coordinates in it by x, y, z and t. Let another frame (x', y', z', t') be given which is also inertial. The connection between (x', y', z', t') and (x, y, z, t) is to be found.

The problem of finding a transformation between two inertial frames is purely mathematical; it can be solved without any further physical assumptions, other than the definition of an inertial frame given in Section 5.

We shall obtain the solution in two stages: first we shall prove that the required transformation is linear and then we shall determine its coefficients.

From the linearity of the transformation it follows that the motion of the new inertial frame relative to the old is uniform and rectilinear. This conclusion is essentially merely another formulation of the principle of relativity, according to which any frame of reference moving uniformly in a straight line with respect to some given inertial frame is itself inertial. Thus the principle of relativity is already contained in the premises of the theorem to be proven.

8. Proof of the Linearity of the Transformation Linking Two Inertial Frames

It follows from the first condition characterizing inertial frames (the mechanical condition), that the property of a motion to be uniform and rectilinear must be preserved in going from one inertial frame to another. This means that the equations

$$x = x_0 + v_x(t - t_0); \qquad y = y_0 + v_y(t - t_0); \qquad z = z_0 + v_z(t - t_0) \quad (8.01)$$

must lead to transformed equations

$$x' = x'_0 + v'_x(t' - t'_0); \qquad y' = y'_0 + v'_y(t' - t'_0); \qquad z' = z'_0 + v'_z(t' - t'_0) \tag{8.02}$$

The second condition for inertial frames demands that from the equation

$$\frac{1}{c^2}\left(\frac{\partial\omega}{\partial t}\right)^2 - \left[\left(\frac{\partial\omega}{\partial x}\right)^2 + \left(\frac{\partial\omega}{\partial y}\right)^2 + \left(\frac{\partial\omega}{\partial z}\right)^2\right] = 0 \tag{8.03}$$

in the unprimed frame there should follow, in the primed frame:

$$\frac{1}{c^2}\left(\frac{\partial\omega}{\partial t'}\right)^2 - \left[\left(\frac{\partial\omega}{\partial x'}\right)^2 + \left(\frac{\partial\omega}{\partial y'}\right)^2 + \left(\frac{\partial\omega}{\partial z'}\right)^2\right] = 0 \tag{8.04}$$

Now, we can write this second condition in a form analogous to the first; consequences of (8.03) are the ray equations (4.08) which express the fact that light propagates in straight lines and with constant speed. This must be true in both the unprimed and the primed frames. Therefore, the point of intersection of a light ray with the wave surface must satisfy equations

$$x = x_0 + v_x(t - t_0); \qquad y = y_0 + v_y(t - t_0); \qquad z = z_0 + v_z(t - t_0) \tag{8.05}$$

where

$$v_x^2 + v_y^2 + v_z^2 = c^2$$

in the unprimed frame and likewise

$$x' = x'_0 + v'_x(t' - t'_0); \qquad y' = y'_0 + v'_y(t' - t'_0); \qquad z' = z'_0 + v'_z(t' - t'_0) \tag{8.06}$$

where

$$v_x'^2 + v_y'^2 + v_z'^2 = c^2$$

in the primed one. Thus the second condition amounts to an additional requirement that, if in the equations for uniform rectilinear motion $v^2 = c^2$, then also $v'^2 = c^2$.

Our task amounts to finding the most general functions

$$\begin{aligned}
x' &= f_1(x, y, z, t) \\
y' &= f_2(x, y, z, t) \\
z' &= f_3(x, y, z, t) \\
t' &= f_4(x, y, z, t)
\end{aligned} \tag{8.07}$$

such that the primed equations given above follow from the analogous unprimed ones.†

Before tackling the problem we shall pass to a new, more symmetrical notation. We put

$$x = x_1, \qquad y = x_2, \qquad z = x_3 \tag{8.08}$$

and introduce instead of time a quantity proportional to it

$$x_0 = ct \tag{8.09}$$

which has the physical meaning of the distance that light would travel in the given time. (Note that in the new notation x_0 no longer denotes the initial value of a space coordinate.) We write the required transformation as

$$x'_i = f_i(x_0, x_1, x_2, x_3) \qquad (i = 0, 1, 2, 3) \tag{8.10}$$

† This problem has also been studied by Umov [4] and by Weyl [7].

We shall denote the initial values of x_0, x_1, x_2 and x_3 by ξ_0, ξ_1, ξ_2 and ξ_3 with a corresponding notation in the primed system. We introduce an arbitrary positive constant γ_0 and a parameter s given by $s = (c/\gamma_0)(t - t_0)$ and put

$$\gamma_i = \gamma_0 \frac{v_i}{c} \qquad (i = 1, 2, 3) \tag{8.11}$$

Then the equations of uniform straight line motion read as

$$x_i = \xi_i + \gamma_i s \qquad (i = 0, 1, 2, 3) \tag{8.12}$$

and our first condition requires that from (8.12) there should follow

$$x_i' = \xi_i' + \gamma_i' s' \qquad (i = 0, 1, 2, 3) \tag{8.13}$$

where the ξ_i' and the γ_i' are new constants and s' a new parameter which can be expressed in terms of the corresponding unprimed quantities as soon as the form of the functions f_i is known.

The second condition amounts to the requirement that from

$$\gamma_0^2 - (\gamma_1^2 + \gamma_2^2 + \gamma_3^2) = 0 \tag{8.14}$$

there should follow

$$\gamma_0'^2 - (\gamma_1'^2 + \gamma_2'^2 + \gamma_3'^2) = 0 \tag{8.15}$$

The transformation equations (8.10) must obviously be soluble for the old variables x_0, x_1, x_2 and x_3, so that the Jacobian of the transformation must not vanish

$$\text{Det} \frac{\partial f_i}{\partial x_k} \neq 0 \tag{8.16}$$

We now proceed to derive the equations for the functions f_i.

Considering the x_i as linear functions of the parameter s given by (8.12) we have

$$\frac{df_i}{ds} = \sum_{k=0}^{3} \gamma_k \frac{\partial f_i}{\partial x_k} \tag{8.17}$$

The derivative

$$\frac{dx_i'}{dx_0'} = \frac{\gamma_i'}{\gamma_0'} \tag{8.18}$$

must be a constant by our conditions, so we have

$$\frac{\sum\limits_{k=0}^{3} \gamma_k (\partial f_i/\partial x_k)}{\sum\limits_{k=0}^{3} \gamma_k (\partial f_0/\partial x_k)} = \frac{\gamma_i'}{\gamma_0'} = \text{const} \tag{8.19}$$

We equate to zero the logarithmic derivative of this expression with respect to s and obtain

$$\frac{\sum\limits_{k,l=0}^{3} \gamma_k \gamma_l (\partial^2 f_i/\partial x_k \partial x_l)}{\sum\limits_{k=0}^{3} \gamma_k (\partial f_i/\partial x_k)} = \frac{\sum\limits_{k,l=0}^{3} \gamma_k \gamma_l (\partial^2 f_0/\partial x_k \partial x_l)}{\sum\limits_{k=0}^{3} \gamma_k (\partial f_0/\partial x_k)} \tag{8.20}$$

In this equation the arguments on which the partial derivatives of f_0 and f_i

depend are the quantities (8.12) which in turn depend on the γ_i. However, since the ξ_i in (8.12) are arbitrary we can consider the γ_i and the x_i to be independent variables. (We can reach the same conclusion by putting $s = 0$ in (8.20) and then writing x_i instead of ξ_i.) Therefore the equations (8.20) must be satisfied identically in the γ_i and the x_i.

As functions of the γ_i the expressions (8.20) are rational fractions, but it is impossible for all four denominators, i.e. the four expressions (8.17) for $i = 0, 1, 2, 3$, to become zero simultaneously for any values of the γ_i, because the determinant (8.16) is always different from zero. Therefore each of the fractions always remains finite, even if its denominator becomes zero. This can only be so if the denominator is a factor of the numerator and, therefore, the expressions (8.20) are not, in fact, fractions but rational integral functions of the γ_i which we can write in the form

$$2 \sum_{l=0}^{3} \gamma_l \psi_l \tag{8.21}$$

Thus we have
$$\sum_{k,l=0}^{3} \gamma_k \gamma_l \frac{\partial^2 f_i}{\partial x_k \partial x_l} = 2 \sum_{k=0}^{3} \gamma_k \frac{\partial f_i}{\partial x_k} \sum_{l=0}^{3} \gamma_l \psi_l \tag{8.22}$$

As this is an identity in the γ_i, we have
$$\frac{\partial^2 f_i}{\partial x_k \partial x_l} = \psi_k \frac{\partial f_i}{\partial x_l} + \psi_l \frac{\partial f_i}{\partial x_k} \tag{8.23}$$

The conclusion is the following : in order that one uniform straight line motion should transform into another the transformation functions f_i must necessarily satisfy the system of partial differential equations (8.23) where the ψ_k are certain functions of x_0, x_1, x_2 and x_3.

We now find the condition that must be satisfied by the functions f_i in order that (8.15) should follow from (8.14). Owing to (8.19), equation (8.15) is equivalent to

$$\left(\sum_{k=0}^{3} \gamma_k \frac{\partial f_0}{\partial x_k} \right)^2 - \sum_{i=1}^{3} \left(\sum_{k=0}^{3} \gamma_k \frac{\partial f_i}{\partial x_k} \right)^2 = 0 \tag{8.24}$$

This must be a consequence of
$$\gamma_0^2 - (\gamma_1^2 + \gamma_2^2 + \gamma_3^2) = 0 \tag{8.14}$$

As the left-hand sides of both (8.24) and (8.14) are quadratic functions of the γ_i they must be proportional to each other. To state the consequences of this conveniently we introduce the four quantities.

$$e_0 = 1 ; \qquad e_1 = e_2 = e_3 = -1 \tag{8.25}$$

and write (8.24) and (8.14) in the form

$$\sum_{i,k,l=0}^{3} e_i \gamma_k \gamma_l \frac{\partial f_i}{\partial x_k} \frac{\partial f_i}{\partial x_l} = 0 \tag{8.26}$$

$$\sum_{k=0}^{3} e_k \gamma_k^2 = 0 \tag{8.27}$$

Taking the left-hand sides of (8.26) and (8.27) to be proportional we get

$$\sum_{i=0}^{3} e_i \frac{\partial f_i}{\partial x_k} \frac{\partial f_i}{\partial x_l} = \lambda e_k \delta_{kl} \tag{8.28}$$

where λ is some function of x_0, x_1, x_2 and x_3 and the symbol δ_{kl} has its familiar meaning

$$\delta_{kl} = 0 \quad \text{for} \quad k \neq l; \qquad \delta_{kk} = 1 \tag{8.29}$$

We differentiate (8.28) with respect to x_m, put

$$\frac{\partial \lambda}{\partial x_m} = 2\lambda \varphi_m \tag{8.30}$$

and have then

$$\sum_{i=0}^{3} e_i \left(\frac{\partial^2 f_i}{\partial x_k \partial x_m} \frac{\partial f_i}{\partial x_l} + \frac{\partial^2 f_i}{\partial x_l \partial x_m} \frac{\partial f_i}{\partial x_k} \right) = 2\lambda \varphi_m e_k \delta_{kl} \tag{8.31}$$

Inserting herein the expressions (8.23) for the second derivatives and using (8.28), we obtain

$$e_l \psi_k \delta_{lm} + e_k \psi_l \delta_{km} + 2 e_k \psi_m \delta_{kl} = 2 e_k \varphi_m \delta_{kl} \tag{8.32}$$

This relation must hold for all values of k, l, m. Putting $k = l$, $m \neq l$, this gives

$$\psi_m = \varphi_m \tag{8.33}$$

Then, putting $k = m$, $l = m$, we get $\psi_m = 0$, therefore

$$\psi_m = \varphi_m = 0. \tag{8.34}$$

The quantity λ in (8.28) and (8.30) must then be a constant and the equations (8.23) for the f_i become

$$\frac{\partial^2 f_i}{\partial x_k \partial x_l} = 0 \tag{8.35}$$

The final result is that the combination of the two conditions characterizing inertial frames requires the transformation formulae between the coordinates in the two frames to be linear.

The question as to how much follows as a consequence of each of the two conditions (i.e. of (8.23) and (8.28)), separately, is considered in Appendix A.

9. Determination of the Coefficients of the Linear Transformations and of a Scale Factor

Equations (8.28) for the function f_i involve a constant multiplier λ. In order to bring out explicitly[1] its influence on the transformation we shall write the linear functions f_i in the form

$$x_i' = f_i = \sqrt{\lambda} \left(a_i + \sum_{k=0}^{3} e_k a_{ik} x_k \right) \tag{9.01}$$

Equations (8.28) will be satisfied identically in λ if the coefficients a_{ik} satisfy the relation

$$\sum_{i=0}^{3} e_i a_{ik} a_{il} = e_k \delta_{kl} \tag{9.02}$$

from which it also follows that

$$\sum_{i=0}^{3} e_i a_{ki} a_{li} = e_k \delta_{kl} \tag{9.03}$$

The equations (9.01) can be solved for the x_i, leading to

$$x_i = \sum_{k=0}^{3} e_k a_{ki} \left(\frac{x'_k}{\sqrt{\lambda}} - a_k \right) \tag{9.04}$$

We also have

$$dx_0'^2 - (dx_1'^2 + dx_2'^2 + dx_3'^2) = \lambda[dx_0^2 - (dx_1^2 + dx_2^2 + dx_3^2)] \tag{9.05}$$

and, for an arbitrary function ω :

$$\left(\frac{\partial \omega}{\partial x'_0} \right)^2 - \left[\left(\frac{\partial \omega}{\partial x'_1} \right)^2 + \left(\frac{\partial \omega}{\partial x'_2} \right)^2 + \left(\frac{\partial \omega}{\partial x'_3} \right)^2 \right]$$
$$= \frac{1}{\lambda} \left\{ \left(\frac{\partial \omega}{\partial x_0} \right)^2 - \left[\left(\frac{\partial \omega}{\partial x_1} \right)^2 + \left(\frac{\partial \omega}{\partial x_2} \right)^2 + \left(\frac{\partial \omega}{\partial x_3} \right)^2 \right] \right\} \tag{9.06}$$

The factor λ, or rather $\sqrt{\lambda}$, evidently characterizes the ratio of the scales of measurement in the primed and unprimed frames ; in either frame the scale is a common one for space and time coordinates so that a change in it has no effect on the values of either angles in space or of velocities. We shall show that this factor should be equated to unity.

Consider a point at rest in the primed frame. In the unprimed frame the velocity of this point is then the velocity of the primed frame itself. We denote the components of this velocity (in the unprimed system) by V_1, V_2 and V_3, so that

$$V_i = \frac{dx_i}{dt} = c \frac{dx_i}{dx_0} \quad \text{for} \quad dx'_1 = dx'_2 = dx'_3 = 0 \tag{9.07}$$

But, from (9.04) we have

$$dx_i = \frac{1}{\sqrt{\lambda}} a_{0i} dx'_0; \qquad dx_0 = \frac{1}{\sqrt{\lambda}} a_{00} dx'_0 \tag{9.08}$$

and, therefore, $\quad V_i = c \dfrac{a_{0i}}{a_{00}} \quad (i = 1, 2, 3) \tag{9.09}$

It follows in the first place that the transformation (9.01) which gives the relation between the four coordinates in the two inertial frames, corresponds to passing from a given frame to another moving uniformly and in a straight line relative to the first, as it should be.

Further, it follows from (9.09) that the relative velocity of the motion is not at all connected with the scale factor λ and, therefore, that this factor cannot depend on the relative velocity.† Then one has only to assume that for vanishing relative velocity, length and time measurements in both systems are performed in the same way, in terms of the same units, and one finds $\lambda = 1$. Subject to such very natural requirements λ will be equal to 1 for *any* inertial frame, whatever its velocity.

† It is usually said, following Einstein, that the scale factor can " evidently " depend on nothing but the relative velocity, and it is subsequently proved that, in fact, it does not have any such dependence but is equal to 1.

Putting $\lambda = 1$ reduces our formulae (9.05) and (9.06) to the simpler form

$$dx_0'^2 - (dx_1'^2 + dx_2'^2 + dx_3'^2) = dx_0^2 - (dx_1^2 + dx_2^2 + dx_3^2) \tag{9.10}$$

and

$$\left(\frac{\partial\omega}{\partial x_0'}\right)^2 - \left[\left(\frac{\partial\omega}{\partial x_1'}\right)^2 + \left(\frac{\partial\omega}{\partial x_2'}\right)^2 + \left(\frac{\partial\omega}{\partial x_3'}\right)^2\right]$$
$$= \left(\frac{\partial\omega}{\partial x_0}\right)^2 - \left[\left(\frac{\partial\omega}{\partial x_1}\right)^2 + \left(\frac{\partial\omega}{\partial x_2}\right)^2 + \left(\frac{\partial\omega}{\partial x_3}\right)^2\right] \tag{9.11}$$

while the transformation equations from either frame to the other become:

$$x_i' = a_i + \sum_{k=0}^{3} e_k a_{ik} x_k \tag{9.12}$$

and

$$x_i = \sum_{k=0}^{3} e_k a_{ki} (x_k' - a_k) \tag{9.13}$$

These relations carry the name of Lorentz transformations. They constitute the formal basis of the whole theory of relativity.

One should note that the starting point of our discussion was the requirement that in every inertial frame the equation describing the propagation of an electromagnetic wave front should have the form (5.01). Thence it followed that the vanishing of the right-hand side of (9.11) led to the vanishing of the left-hand side. But by imposing an additional condition to the effect that a motion uniform and rectilinear in one frame should remain so in the other and that scales of measurement should not alter we found more : the left- and right-hand sides of (9.11) not only vanish together, they are identically equal.

10. Lorentz Transformations

A Lorentz transformation is a set of equations for transforming the space and time coordinates in one inertial frame into those of another that moves uniformly and in a straight line relative to the first. The transformation can be characterized by the fact that the quantity

$$ds^2 = dx_0^2 - (dx_1^2 + dx_2^2 + dx_3^2) \tag{10.01}$$

or

$$ds^2 = c^2 dt^2 - (dx^2 + dy^2 + dz^2) \tag{10.02}$$

remains invariant in the strict sense (not only the numerical value, but also the mathematical form of the expression remain unchanged.) The most general Lorentz transformation is of the form

$$x_i' = a_i + \sum_{k=0}^{3} e_k a_{ik} x_k \tag{10.03}$$

where the coefficients a_{ik} satisfy the relations

$$\sum_{i=0}^{3} e_i a_{ik} a_{il} = e_k \delta_{kl} \tag{10.04}$$

and

$$\sum_{i=0}^{3} e_i a_{ki} a_{li} = e_k \delta_{kl} \tag{10.05}$$

Let us investigate the physical meaning of the constants entering these transformation formulae.

First of all, the constant terms a_i evidently represent a change of origin for space and time coordinates. If we take it that at $t = 0$ the spatial origins of both frames coincide and $t' = 0$, we have

$$a_i = 0 \qquad (i = 0, 1, 2, 3) \tag{10.06}$$

In the following we shall make this assumption and shall write Lorentz transformations in the form

$$x_i' = \sum_{k=0}^{3} e_k a_{ik} x_k \qquad (10.07)$$

We have already discussed the physical significance of the coefficient ratios

$$\frac{a_{0i}}{a_{00}} = \frac{1}{c} V_i \qquad (10.08)$$

They give the relative velocity between the two systems, divided by the speed of light. More precisely, the V_i are the components in the unprimed frame of the vector giving the velocity of the primed frame relative to the unprimed one. Since the transformation inverse to (10.07) has the form

$$x_i = \sum_{k=0}^{3} e_k a_{ki} x_k' \qquad (10.09)$$

the quantities V_i' given by

$$\frac{a_{i0}}{a_{00}} = \frac{1}{c} V_i' \qquad (10.10)$$

are the components in the primed frame of the velocity vector of the unprimed frame relative to the primed one.

If in (10.04) and (10.05) we put $k = l = 0$, we obtain

$$a_{00}^2 - (a_{10}^2 + a_{20}^2 + a_{30}^2) = 1 \qquad (10.11)$$

and

$$a_{00}^2 - (a_{01}^2 + a_{02}^2 + a_{03}^2) = 1 \qquad (10.12)$$

Whence, using (10.08) and (10.10), it follows that

$$V_1^2 + V_2^2 + V_3^2 = V_1'^2 + V_2'^2 + V_3'^2 \qquad (10.13)$$

and

$$V^2 = V'^2 \qquad (10.14)$$

Here V^2 is understood to be the square of the magnitude of the velocity. Therefore the relative speed measured in either frame is the same—a result that is not obvious although it corresponds entirely with intuitive ideas.

It follows from (10.08) and (10.12) that

$$a_{00} = \frac{1}{\sqrt{(1 - V^2/c^2)}} \qquad (10.15)$$

The square root must be taken positive, for

$$a_{00} = \frac{\partial t'}{\partial t} > 0 \qquad (10.16)$$

A negative value of a_{00} would imply a change in the direction of time.

From (10.08) and (10.15) we get

$$a_{0i} = \frac{V_i}{\sqrt{(c^2 - V^2)}} \qquad (i = 1, 2, 3) \qquad (10.17)$$

and, similarly, from (10.10) and (10.15)

$$a_{i0} = \frac{V_i'}{\sqrt{(c^2 - V^2)}} \qquad (i = 1, 2, 3) \qquad (10.18)$$

Taking one suffix to be zero in the orthogonality relations (10.04) and (10.05) and using (10.17) and (10.18) one obtains

$$a_{00}V'_i = a_{i1}V_1 + a_{i2}V_2 + a_{i3}V_3 \qquad (i = 1, 2, 3) \tag{10.19}$$

and
$$a_{00}V_i = a_{1i}V_1 + a_{2i}V'_2 + a_{3i}V'_3 \qquad (i = 1, 2, 3) \tag{10.20}$$

If both suffixes are different from zero the orthogonality relations give

$$a_{1i}a_{1k} + a_{2i}a_{2k} + a_{3i}a_{3k} = \delta_{ik} + \frac{V_iV_k}{c^2 - V^2} \tag{10.21}$$

For i, $k = 1$, 2, 3 we shall now introduce new quantities α_{ik} instead of the a_{ik} by

$$\alpha_{ik} = -a_{ik} + \frac{a_{i0}a_{0k}}{a_{00} + 1} \tag{10.22}$$

or
$$\alpha_{ik} = -a_{ik} + (a_{00} - 1)\frac{V'_iV_k}{V^2} \tag{10.23}$$

It is easy to verify that as a result of (10.20) and (10.21) we have
$$\alpha_{1i}\alpha_{1k} + \alpha_{2i}\alpha_{2k} + \alpha_{3i}\alpha_{3k} = \delta_{ik} \qquad (i, k = 1, 2, 3) \tag{10.24}$$
Thus the α_{ik} are the coefficients of a three-dimensional orthogonal transformation and can be interpreted as direction cosines between the two sets of spatial axes with the first suffix referring to the new axes, the second to the old. Using (10.19) and (10.20) equations (10.22) give

$$\alpha_{i1}V_1 + \alpha_{i2}V_2 + \alpha_{i3}V_3 = -V'_i \tag{10.25}$$

and
$$\alpha_{1i}V'_1 + \alpha_{2i}V'_2 + \alpha_{3i}V'_3 = -V_i \tag{10.26}$$

These relations can be interpreted as saying that the vector **V'** (the velocity of the unprimed frame relative to the primed one) and the vector **V** (the velocity of the primed frame relative to the unprimed) are equal in magnitude and opposite in direction.

The equations obtained allow us to express all the coefficients of a Lorentz transformation in terms of the direction cosines α_{ik} (i, $k = 1$, 2, 3) and the three components V_1, V_2 and V_3 of the relative velocity. As the nine α_{ik} are subject to the six relations (10.24) and hence are expressible in terms of three independent quantities, the Lorentz transformation involves six parameters in all, not counting the constant displacement terms a_i that were set equal to zero.

We have already obtained the expressions (10.15) and (10.17) for the coefficients a_{00} and a_{0i}. For the a_{i0} we can take the expressions (10.18) in which the V'_i must be understood as expressed in the form (10.25), viz. :

$$a_{i0} = -\frac{1}{\sqrt{(c^2 - V^2)}} \sum_{l=1}^{3} \alpha_{il}V_l \qquad (i = 1, 2, 3) \tag{10.27}$$

For the a_{ik}, finally, we can put

$$a_{ik} = -\alpha_{ik} + (a_{00} - 1)\frac{V'_iV_k}{V^2} \tag{10.28}$$

or, more explicitly :

$$a_{ik} = -\alpha_{ik} - \left(\frac{1}{\sqrt{(1 - V^2/c^2)}} - 1\right) \frac{V_k}{V^2} \sum_{l=1}^{3} \alpha_{il} V_l \qquad (10.29)$$

Let us insert the values of transformation coefficients just found into (10.07), writing ct for x_0 to get back to more descriptive notation. We then get

$$t' = \frac{1}{\sqrt{(1 - V^2/c^2)}} \left(t - \frac{1}{c^2}(V_1 x_1 + V_2 x_2 + V_3 x_3)\right) \qquad (10.30)$$

The expressions for the spatial coordinates are most conveniently written as

$$x'_i = \sum_{m=1}^{3} \alpha_{im} x^*_m \qquad (10.31)$$

where

$$x^*_m = x_m - V_m t + \left(\frac{1}{\sqrt{(1 - V^2/c^2)}} - 1\right) \frac{V_m}{V^2} \sum_{k=1}^{3} V_k(x_k - V_k t) \qquad (10.32)$$

We see that the Lorentz transformation can be performed in two stages. The first consists in going from variables (x_1, x_2, x_3, t) to new variables $(x^*_1, x^*_2, x^*_3, t^*)$ where x^*_1, x^*_2 and x^*_3 are given by (10.32) and t^* is equal to t' and given by

$$t^* = \frac{1}{\sqrt{(1 - V^2/c^2)}} \left(t - \frac{1}{c^2}(V_1 x_1 + V_2 x_2 + V_3 x_3)\right) \qquad (10.33)$$

The second stage consists in going from $(x^*_1, x^*_2, x^*_3, t^*)$ to (x'_1, x'_2, x'_3, t') where by (10.30) and (10.31)

$$x'_i = \alpha_{i1} x^*_1 + \alpha_{i2} x^*_2 + \alpha_{i3} x^*_3; \qquad t' = t^* \qquad (10.34)$$

The second stage is evidently simply a rotation of the spatial reference frame, while the first is a transition to a frame moving with the velocity (V_1, V_2, V_3) without any rotation of spatial axes.

Of course we could also have performed the rotation of axes first and then gone over to the moving frame.

The reverse transformation can also be performed in two stages, firstly going from (x'_1, x'_2, x'_3, t') to $(x^*_1, x^*_2, x^*_3, t^*)$ by the equations

$$x^*_i = \alpha_{1i} x'_1 + \alpha_{2i} x'_2 + \alpha_{3i} x'_3; \qquad t^* = t' \qquad (10.35)$$

which represent simply a rotation of axes, and secondly passing from $(x^*_1, x^*_2, x^*_3, t^*)$ to (x_1, x_2, x_3, t) by means of

$$x_m = x^*_m + V_m t^* + \left(\frac{1}{\sqrt{(1 - V^2/c^2)}} - 1\right) \frac{V_m}{V^2} \sum_{k=1}^{3} V_k(x^*_k + V_k t^*) \qquad (10.36)$$

and

$$t = \frac{1}{\sqrt{(1 - V^2/c^2)}} \left(t^* + \frac{1}{c^2}(V_1 x^*_1 + V_2 x^*_2 + V_3 x^*_3)\right) \qquad (10.37)$$

which are the inverse formulae to (10.32), (10.33). The transformation from $(x^*_1, x^*_2, x^*_3, t^*)$ to (x_1, x_2, x_3, t) and its inverse go over into each other if the sign of the velocity **V** is reversed.

One should note that the Jacobian of these transformations is unity. As regards the substitution (10.34) and its inverse (10.35), the Jacobian will be $+1$ if they describe a rotation of axes in the proper sense, i.e. without an accompanying passage from a right-handed frame to a left-handed one, or vice versa. Therefore, if the direction of time is preserved and also the right-handed (or left-handed) character of the spatial frame, the Jacobian of the Lorentz transformation will be equal to 1. Such Lorentz transformations are customarily called proper. In the following we shall only use proper Lorentz transformations.

A rotation of axes is not properly a transition to a *new* inertial frame, so it is of no interest to us. The characteristic properties of a Lorentz transformation are contained in equations (10.32) and (10.33) and their inverses (10.36) and (10.37). These equations simplify if the directions of the axes are so chosen that one of them, e.g. the first, is in the direction of relative velocity. Putting

$$V_1 = V; \qquad V_2 = V_3 = 0 \tag{10.38}$$

we get from (10.32) and (10.33)

$$x_1^* = \frac{x_1 - Vt}{\sqrt{(1 - V^2/c^2)}}; \qquad x_2^* = x_2; \qquad x_3^* = x_3 \tag{10.39}$$

$$t^* = \frac{t - Vx_1/c^2}{\sqrt{(1 - V^2/c^2)}} \tag{10.40}$$

The inverse equations are obtained by replacing V by $-V$. For greater descriptiveness we shall write x, y, z instead of x_1, x_2, x_3. Replacing the asterisk by a prime, we then get

$$x' = \frac{x - Vt}{\sqrt{(1 - V^2/c^2)}}; \qquad y' = y; \qquad z' = z \tag{10.41}$$

and

$$t' = \frac{t - Vx/c^2}{\sqrt{(1 - V^2/c^2)}} \tag{10.42}$$

and, expressing x, t in terms of x', t' :

$$x = \frac{x' + Vt'}{\sqrt{(1 - V^2/c^2)}}; \qquad y = y'; \qquad z = z' \tag{10.43}$$

and

$$t = \frac{t' + Vx'/c^2}{\sqrt{(1 - V^2/c^2)}} \tag{10.44}$$

The transformation given by these formulae is of a special kind, but it contains all the characteristic features by which the new theory differs from the old.

It is convenient to write the formulae for Lorentz transformations in vectorial form. Using familiar three-dimensional vector notation we get

$$t' = \frac{1}{\sqrt{(1 - V^2/c^2)}}\left\{t - \frac{1}{c^2}(\mathbf{V} \cdot \mathbf{r})\right\} \tag{10.45}$$

$$\mathbf{r}' = \mathbf{r} - \mathbf{V}t + \left(\frac{1}{\sqrt{(1 - V^2/c^2)}} - 1\right)\frac{\mathbf{V}}{V^2}((\mathbf{V} \cdot \mathbf{r}) - V^2t) \tag{10.46}$$

11. Determination of Distances and Synchronization of Clocks within One Inertial Reference Frame

Before going on to discuss consequences of the Lorentz transformation, let us return to the questions already raised in Sections 1 and 2 concerning the measurement of distances and time differences in a single reference frame. We shall dwell a little more on the concept of simultaneity at different points in space and on the problem of synchronizing clocks at a distance from each other.

There are different methods of measuring distances between bodies at rest in an inertial frame : one can directly apply a graduated rule or " measuring rod ", one can use triangulation, or else one can use radar. The first method relies only on the properties of rigid bodies, the second depends also on the rectilinear propagation of light, in the third the knowledge of the speed of light plays an essential part. It goes without saying that all methods assume the validity of Euclidean geometry ; if it were not valid then, for instance, different triangulation procedures could give mutually contradictory results. We have stressed in Section 2 that the validity of the laws of Euclidean geometry should be taken as an experimental fact and not as an *a priori* assumption.

All three methods of measurement are based on the properties of solid bodies and of light. Since light is the simpler phenomenon one should consider it as the primary entity and should, for instance, check the constancy of a standard of length by optical means—by finding the number of wavelengths that fit on to the standard.

To measure the speed of light one must know how to measure distances and time intervals by methods independent of the knowledge of that speed. If, however, one assumes that the speed of light is the same in some direction and its reverse, it is enough to be able to measure time at one point. Any periodic process, in principle, gives one this ability, for instance, the vibration of an ammonia molecule or of a quartz crystal. We shall call a device that measures time a clock or chronometer, regardless whether it is in fact a mechanical contrivance, such as a common clock, or whether it works on some other principle.

The measurement of the speed of light basically amounts to the determination of the interval τ during which light passes to and fro along a path of length r, previously measured by triangulation or with a measuring rod ; the speed of light will be $c = 2r/\tau$. Thus the problem amounts essentially to finding a conversion factor from a distance expressed in units of length and measured by triangulation or by direct application of a measuring rod, to a distance expressed in units of time and measured by radar methods. This conversion factor can be determined once and for all.

We now pass to the question of comparing the readings of clocks at rest in the same inertial frame, but situated at a distance from each other. We assume that the clocks are of identical construction and run at the same rate, so that the question is simply that of synchronizing them. Let " clock A " be at the point A and " clock B " be at the point B, a given distance r from A. A light signal is emitted from A at time t_1 ; it is reflected by a mirror placed at B and returns to A at time t_2. What time should be indicated by the properly synchronized clock at B at the moment the signal reaches that point ? We shall assume that clock B is synchronous with clock A if at the moment the signal arrives it shows the time $t' = (t_1 + t_2)/2$. This is Einstein's definition of synchronization for two spatially separated clocks. It is a very natural definition and is in accord with the basic postulate of the Theory of Relativity that the speed of light is constant. For, if the signal leaves A at time t, it must reach B at the time

$$t = t_1 + \frac{r}{c}$$

having traversed the distance r with speed c. On the other hand, as it returns to A at time t_2, having previously traversed the distance r from B to A, it must have been reflected from B at the earlier time,

$$t = t_2 - \frac{r}{c}$$

It follows from these two equations that we must attribute to the time of reflection of the signal at B as measured by clock A the value $t = (t_1 + t_2)/2$, and if clock B is to be synchronous with clock A it should show the time $t' = t$ at the instant of reflection.

From the fact that the speed of light is the same going to and fro it follows that the above defined property of being synchronous is a reciprocal one of the two clocks : if clock B is synchronous with clock A, then clock A is also synchronous with clock B. Further, since Euclidean geometry is valid and the speed of light is the same for *any* direction of travel (both these facts are implied in the equation for the propagation of the front of a light wave), it follows that, if clock A is synchronous with several clocks B, C, $D \cdots$, all these clocks are mutually synchronous.

This last fact makes it possible to envisage as a model of an inertial reference frame a rigid scaffolding having at each of its junctions a clock, with all clocks synchronous. Using such a model the motion of any body relative to the inertial frame can be described as follows : let the body move in turn past the clocks that have spatial coordinates (x_1, y_1, z_1), (x_2, y_2, z_2), etc., with the clock at (x_i, y_i, z_i) showing time t_i at the instant of the body's passage. Then the coordinates $x(t)$, $y(t)$ and $z(t)$ of the body will be such functions of time as to have the values (x_i, y_i, z_i) at the times t_i.

For all its unwieldiness such a model can be of use and is often discussed in treatments of the Theory of Relativity. However, we prefer the model of a radar station because it allows a continuous determination both of the position of a moving body and of the corresponding time, by the station clock—a determination *based on a single point*, the position of the station. Because the speed of light is independent of the velocity of the source both models give the same values of space and time coordinates, the difference between them is merely that the radar model does not need any advance determination of distance, or synchronization of clocks, but instead, so to speak, performs these functions as the motion proceeds.

The radar model is the more flexible one and retains its intuitive value even in cases when the rigid scaffolding is quite inappropriate, for instance, when discussing astronomical distances. In addition, the radar model is one that permits of generalization.

The above exposition of Einstein's method of synchronization by light signals, with due account of retardation, appears so natural that one might think at first sight that it contains nothing characteristic of the Theory of Relativity. However, this is not so. The method indicated contains a *definition* of simultaneity at different points in space from the standpoint of a given inertial system. This definition rests on the laws of the Theory of Relativity and is not arbitrary, but, on the contrary, is the only rational one from the point of view of this theory.

In pre-relativistic physics it was assumed as self-evident that a single universal time exists and therefore it was tacitly supposed that there is no need to define simultaneity at different points in space. Consequently it was assumed that any method of synchronization, for instance by transport of clocks instead of by light signals, would give the same result. In fact this is not so.

We shall show later that the Theory of Relativity predicts that if clock A is synchronized with clock B by light signals and a chronometer C is checked at A with the clock there and then transported to point B, its reading when at B will not agree with that of clock B, even assuming ideal working of the chronometer. The readings of C will depend on the speed of its transport and will coincide only in the limit that this speed is infinitely small.

We shall return to this question in the next section. Here we wished to stress that even such a simple physical concept as simultaneity in a single inertial frame requires precise definition, and that all methods employed to measure the corresponding physical quantity must be in accord with this definition.

12. Time Sequence of Events in Different Reference Frames

The Lorentz transformations contain the formal basis of the views on space and time that follow from the Theory of Relativity.

Using these transformations we now consider the question of the time sequence of events in different reference frames. By " event " we mean an instantaneous occurrence that can be characterized by a point in space and a corresponding moment of time.

To have a concrete picture, we shall imagine that the " events " consist of the instantaneous flashing of light signals. Let the first flash happen at time t_1 at a point with coordinates x_1, y_1 and z_1 and the second at time t_2 at the point (x_2, y_2, z_2). Introducing ordinary three-dimensional vector notation we can characterize the place and time of the first event by the symbol $(\mathbf{r}_1, t_1)$ and those of the second by $(\mathbf{r}_2, t_2)$.

We first ask : which of the two flashes occurs first ? The answer will be unambiguous if the light from one of the flashes has time to arrive at the place of the other before the latter occurs. If

$$t_2 - t_1 > \frac{1}{c} \left| \mathbf{r}_2 - \mathbf{r}_1 \right| \tag{12.01}$$

the first flash is incontestably earlier than the second, and of course if

$$t_2 - t_1 < -\frac{1}{c} \left| \mathbf{r}_2 - \mathbf{r}_1 \right| \tag{12.02}$$

the flash $(\mathbf{r}_1, t_1)$ certainly takes place later than $(\mathbf{r}_2, t_2)$.

We shall talk of pairs of events for which either (12.01) or (12.02) is true as being *in time sequence*. In the case (12.01) we shall say that the second happening is *absolutely later* than the first and that, if (12.02) holds, it is *absolutely earlier*. In both cases one has

$$c^2(t_2 - t_1)^2 - (\mathbf{r}_2 - \mathbf{r}_1)^2 > 0 \tag{12.03}$$

The real positive quantity

$$T = \frac{1}{c} \sqrt{[c^2(t_2 - t_1)^2 - (\mathbf{r}_2 - \mathbf{r}_1)^2]} \tag{12.04}$$

is called the *time-like interval* between the two events. The interval between two events in time sequence is independent of the reference frame because the expression under the root in (12.04) is invariant under Lorentz transformations.

By the condition $\partial t'/\partial t > 0$, which expresses the conservation of the direction of time (see (10.16)), the relations (12.01) and (12.02) are also independent of the frame. This must be so because the question whether a signal has or has not arrived at the position of the other event is a physical one and cannot depend on any reference frame. Thus the notions " absolutely earlier " or " absolutely later ", applied to events in time sequence, are invariant.

Let us assume now that the light from one flash does not reach the place of the other flash before the latter occurs.

Then inequalities opposite to (12.01) and (12.02) will hold :

$$-\frac{1}{c}\,|\,\mathbf{r}_2 - \mathbf{r}_1\,| < t_2 - t_1 < \frac{1}{c}\,|\,\mathbf{r}_2 - \mathbf{r}_1\,| \qquad (12.05)$$

Pairs of events for which the inequality (12.05) is true will be called *quasi-simultaneous*. This name is justified by the fact that in this case the notions " earlier " and " later " become relative ones : one may find $t_2 - t_1 > 0$ in one reference frame and $t_2 - t_1 < 0$ in another. The question as to which flash happened first has now no unique answer.

Quasi-simultaneous events can be characterized by the invariant inequality

$$c^2(t_2 - t_1)^2 - (\mathbf{r}_2 - \mathbf{r}_1)^2 < 0 \qquad (12.06)$$

which follows from (12.05). The two relations, (12.05) and (12.06), are equivalent and, therefore, (12.05) is also invariant. We shall call the real positive quantity

$$R = \sqrt{[(\mathbf{r}_2 - \mathbf{r}_1)^2 - c^2(t_2 - t_1)^2]} \qquad (12.07)$$

the *space-like interval* between two quasi-simultaneous events.

We shall now show that if two events are quasi-simultaneous it is always possible to choose a frame of reference such that the events are simultaneous in it, and that if two events are in time sequence a frame can be found in which they occur at the same point in space.

We consider two quasi-simultaneous events with a given value for the time difference $t_2 - t_1$, which must, of course, satisfy (12.05). We introduce a new, primed, reference frame moving with speed V relative to the first frame. According to the transformation of time given by (10.30), the value of the difference $t' - t'_1$ in the new frame will be

$$t'_2 - t'_1 = \frac{1}{\sqrt{(1 - V^2/c^2)}}\left\{t_2 - t_1 - \frac{1}{c^2}\,(\mathbf{r}_2 - \mathbf{r}_1)\cdot\mathbf{V}\right\} \qquad (12.08)$$

The relative velocity $\mathbf{V}$ can be so chosen as to make the two events simultaneous in the new frame. To do this, we merely have to put

$$\mathbf{V} = (\mathbf{r}_2 - \mathbf{r}_1)\frac{c^2(t_2 - t_1)}{|\,\mathbf{r}_2 - \mathbf{r}_1\,|^2} \qquad (12.09)$$

By virtue of (12.06) we have

$$\mathbf{V}^2 = \frac{c^4(t_2 - t_1)^2}{|\,\mathbf{r}_2 - \mathbf{r}_1\,|^2} < c^2 \qquad (12.10)$$

so that the required relative speed is less than the speed of light, as is required for a Lorentz transformation.

To calculate the difference of the spatial coordinates of the two quasi-simultaneous events in the system in which they are actually simultaneous we write the equation (10.32) for the Lorentz transformation in the vectorial form :

$$\mathbf{r}' = \mathbf{r} - \mathbf{V}t + \left(\frac{1}{\sqrt{(1 - V^2/c^2)}} - 1\right)\frac{\mathbf{V}}{V^2}(\mathbf{V}\cdot\mathbf{r} - V^2 t) \qquad (12.11)$$

Inserting the difference $t_2 - t_1$ for t, the difference $\mathbf{r}_2 - \mathbf{r}_1$ for $\mathbf{r}$ and expression (12.09) for $\mathbf{V}$ we obtain for $\mathbf{r}' = \mathbf{r}'_2 - \mathbf{r}'_1$ the expression

$$\mathbf{r}'_2 - \mathbf{r}'_1 = (\mathbf{r}_2 - \mathbf{r}_1)\sqrt{\left(1 - \frac{c^2(t_2 - t_1)^2}{|\mathbf{r}_2 - \mathbf{r}_1|^2}\right)} = (\mathbf{r}_2 - \mathbf{r}_1)\sqrt{\left(1 - \frac{V^2}{c^2}\right)} \qquad (12.12)$$

In the primed system the spatial distance is thus seen to be

$$|\mathbf{r}'_2 - \mathbf{r}'_1| = R \qquad (12.13)$$

where R is the space-like interval defined in (12.07). Equation (12.13) also follows directly from the invariance of the expression (12.07) for R and the condition $t'_2 - t'_1 = 0$.

Thus the physical significance of the space-like interval between two quasi-simultaneous events is that it is their spatial distance in the frame in which they are simultaneous.

Let us now consider two events in time sequence ; for these either (12.01) or (12.02) must hold. We shall show that here a new, primed, frame can be introduced in which the spatial coordinates of both events coincide. To see this it is sufficient to introduce the difference $t_2 - t_1$ instead of t, and $\mathbf{r}_2 - \mathbf{r}_1$ instead of $\mathbf{r}$ into (12.11) and to put

$$\mathbf{V} = \frac{\mathbf{r}_2 - \mathbf{r}_1}{t_2 - t_1} \qquad (12.14)$$

Then the vector $\mathbf{r}' = \mathbf{r}'_2 - \mathbf{r}'_1$ vanishes, hence

$$\mathbf{r}'_2 = \mathbf{r}'_1 \qquad (12.15)$$

Because of the inequality (12.03) the magnitude of the velocity $\mathbf{V}$ is less than the speed of light

$$V^2 < c^2 \qquad (12.16)$$

as it should be.

In the new frame the time difference between the two events is, by (12.08) :

$$t'_2 - t'_1 = (t_2 - t_1)\sqrt{\left(1 - \frac{|\mathbf{r}_2 - \mathbf{r}_1|^2}{c^2(t_2 - t_1)^2}\right)} = (t_2 - t_1)\sqrt{\left(1 - \frac{V^2}{c^2}\right)} \qquad (12.17)$$

Hence, if $t_2 - t_1 > 0$, we get

$$t'_2 - t'_1 = T \qquad (12.18)$$

where T is the time-like interval (12.04).

In this way the physical significance of the time-like interval is put in evidence. It is the time elapsed between two events in time sequence, measured in that frame in which both events occur at the same point in space. This reference frame can be very directly visualized. It consists of, say, a clock moving uniformly in a straight line from the place of the first event to that of the second with such a speed as to be exactly at the first point when the event there occurs and likewise at the second point at the time of its event.

One should note that the relation of being in time sequence is transitive : given that a second event occurs absolutely later than a first and a third absolutely later than the second, it follows that the third is absolutely later than the first. This property is physically obvious, but can also be proved as follows : The two inequalities

$$t_2 - t_1 > \frac{1}{c}\left|\,\mathbf{r}_2 - \mathbf{r}_1\,\right|; \qquad t_3 - t_2 > \frac{1}{c}\left|\,\mathbf{r}_3 - \mathbf{r}_2\,\right| \qquad (12.19)$$

lead by addition to the third,

$$t_3 - t_1 > \frac{1}{c}\left|\,\mathbf{r}_3 - \mathbf{r}_1\,\right| \qquad (12.20)$$

since the sum of two sides of a triangle is greater than the third side. On the other hand the relation of being quasi-simultaneous is not transitive. If two events are quasi-simultaneous and a third is quasi-simultaneous with one of them, it may also be quasi-simultaneous with the other, but it could also be in time sequence with it, i.e. happen absolutely earlier or absolutely later.

Let us summarize. In the theory of relativity one divides events according to their instants of occurrence into quasi-simultaneous events and events in time sequence ; this distinction does not depend on any particular reference frame. Two events in time sequence possess an invariant *time-like interval*, equal to their time difference in a certain reference frame. Two quasi-simultaneous events possess an invariant *space-like interval* equal to their spatial distance in a certain frame.

This division in Relativity of pairs of events into two classes agrees with the notion of causality and makes it more precise. Given two quasi-simultaneous events neither can be the immediate cause or effect of the other. (Of course, they may both have as a common cause some third event that occurs absolutely earlier than either.) Only pairs of events in time sequence can be directly causally related, the one that occurs absolutely earlier may (but, of course, need not) be the cause of the other.

The concepts we have introduced are natural generalizations of the notions of pre-relativistic physics. The older ideas were not in accord with the fact that a finite limit exists for the speed of propagation of all kinds of action, the finite speed of light. They were not defined precisely enough and therefore gave rise to paradoxes. The new scheme of ideas incorporates the finiteness of the speed of light and so removes the paradoxes.

In older physics the idea of simultaneity was introduced *a priori*, without experimental justification. We shall consider one of the paradoxes to which the idea led. Assume we have two reference frames in uniform rectilinear relative motion and such that at a certain instant their origins coincide. Let a flash of light occur at that instant at the common origin. We consider the motion of the wave front from the point of view of the two frames. Seen from the first frame the wave front at any instant of time is a sphere centred at the origin of this frame ; but the same can be asserted with reference to the second frame—at any moment the wave front is a sphere centred at the other origin. The two origins only coincide at one instant, later they move apart, but a sphere can only have one centre. This discussion uses, on the one hand, the Principle of Relativity, i.e. that in two frames in uniform rectilinear relative motion all events occur in the same manner, on the other the principle that the speed of light is independent of the motion of the source—a consequence of the idea of a field. Both these principles are quite incontrovertible. How then is the paradox resolved ?

The resolution is to be found in the fact that the words " at any instant of time " have a different significance when applied to one or the other frame. The paradox arises only if the phrase is taken to mean " at any instant of a unique absolute time, common to both frames ". The existence of such a unique absolute time was taken for granted in pre-relativistic physics ; it is denied in Relativity. We have learnt that in Relativity time in one frame is not the same as time in another. In each frame the wave front is defined as the locus of all points reached by the light disturbance *simultaneously with respect to the given frame*. Since events that are simultaneous in one frame are not so in any other, the wave front in the one frame will consist of points different from those of the front in the other frame. If we make the picture that the wave propagation takes place in some rarified medium like a gas the wave fronts in the two systems will cover different sets of particles. Since we have two different wave fronts, it is not surprising that they have different centres.

This resolution of the paradox shows up vividly the logical necessity of renouncing the ideas of " absolute time " and " absolute simultaneity ".

Half a century ago when the Theory of Relativity was just emerging, this renunciation appeared to many as wellnigh unacceptable and it required great scientific boldness on the part of Einstein, who created the theory, to convince himself of its necessity. Today we accept the renunciation much more readily. The everyday notion of simultaneity is covered by the concept of quasi-simultaneity while in scientific matters, where we deal with great distances or great speeds, the necessity for a more precise definition of time appears quite natural.

13. Comparison of Time Differences in Moving Reference Frames. The Doppler Effect

Let us assume that a certain frame of reference or base is given, which is taken to be at rest. We observe from this base the development of some process occurring in a moving system. As such a process we could take the uniform running of a clock attached to a moving frame of reference. To follow the behaviour of the moving clock one could arrange for it to emit a light signal every second, or one might be able simply to observe its dial from a distance. In addition the base needs to be equipped with some means, say radar, to record continually the distance of the clock from base. We can then observe with a clock at the base the times of arrival of the light flashes from the moving clock and correct each of these recorded times for the time of travel of the signal. In this way we can determine the times t_n at which the supposedly second-by-second flashes were emitted. The correction mentioned is very easy to calculate.

Let $r(t)$ be the distance to the moving clock as measured from the base, expressed as a function of base time. Then t_n is obtained from the directly observed arrival time t_n^* by the equation

$$t_n + \frac{r(t_n)}{c} = t_n^* \tag{13.01}$$

The question is now whether the times t_n will be spaced at intervals of just one second. In other words, will the calculated times t_n coincide with the seconds of a clock at the base identical with the moving clock under observation ?

The equations of the Lorentz transformation answer this question. Assume that the clock is moving away from the base along a straight line passing through the origin of the base coordinates. (We take it that the signals are being received at the origin.) Taking this straight line as the x-axis and assuming that the moving clock was at the origin at $t = 0$, the position of the clock is given by the equations

$$x = vt ; \qquad y = 0 ; \qquad z = 0 \tag{13.02}$$

and x is just the distance of the clock from the base. Using equation (13.01) we see that the signal received at the base at time t was emitted at the instant

$$t_n = \frac{t_n^*}{1 + v/c} \tag{13.03}$$

reckoned by the base clock. Using the equations of the Lorentz transformation we now introduce a reference frame fixed to the moving clock :

$$x' = \frac{x - vt}{\sqrt{(1 - v^2/c^2)}} ; \qquad t' = \frac{t - vx/c^2}{\sqrt{(1 - v^2/c^2)}} \tag{13.04}$$

As we know, the equations inverse to these are :

$$x = \frac{x' + vt'}{\sqrt{(1 - v^2/c^2)}} ; \qquad t = \frac{t' + vx'/c^2}{\sqrt{(1 - v^2/c^2)}} \tag{13.05}$$

In the primed system the position of the clock that emits the signals will be $x' = 0$, $y' = 0$, $z' = 0$ and the instants of signal emission are

$$t_n' = n\tau \tag{13.06}$$

where the constant τ depends only on the structure of the clock, not on its motion ; it equals one second in the example of the text. Therefore we have

$$t_n = \frac{n\tau}{\sqrt{(1 - v^2/c^2)}} \tag{13.07}$$

On the other hand an identical clock at the base would record the times $n\tau$. Therefore if the moving clock is observed from the base it would appear to be running slow compared to the base clock. The emission times that are observed at base will be not τ (one second) apart, but less frequent; the spacing being given by

$$\Delta t = \frac{\tau}{\sqrt{(1 - v^2/c^2)}} \tag{13.08}$$

One should remember that this expression applies after correcting for the finite speed of the signal with the aid of (13.01). The actual instants at which the signals are observed to arrive at the base are given by

$$t_n^* = \left(1 + \frac{v}{c}\right) t_n = n\tau \sqrt{\left(\frac{1 + v/c}{1 - v/c}\right)} \tag{13.09}$$

so that their difference is
$$\Delta t^* = \tau \sqrt{\left(\frac{c+v}{c-v}\right)} \tag{13.10}$$

To make the discussion simple we have dealt with the case of the clock moving directly away from the observer (i.e. from the device registering the light signals). We now consider the more general case that the trajectory of the clock does not pass through the base. Let the receiving device still be situated at the origin, but let the moving clock coordinates now be given by the equations
$$x = vt ; \qquad y = y_0 ; \qquad z = z_0 \tag{13.11}$$
in the base frame. We may still put
$$x' = 0 ; \qquad y' = 0 ; \qquad z' = 0 \tag{13.12}$$
in the moving frame.

As before one passes from one frame to the other by means of the Lorentz transformation (13.04) or (13.05), the only difference being a shift $y - y' = y_0$, $z - z' = z_0$ along the axes of y and z. Therefore, the connection between t' and t and thus also (13.08), giving the rate of the moving clock, remain unchanged. A change appears only in the connection between t^* and t, i.e. between the instant of emission and the instant of reception. We shall now have instead of (13.09)
$$t_n^* = t_n + \frac{1}{c}\sqrt{(v^2 t_n^2 + y_0^2 + z_0^2)} \tag{13.13}$$

If we take the time difference τ to be small we can put
$$\Delta t^* = \frac{dt^*}{dt}\Delta t = \left(1 + \frac{v_r}{c}\right)\Delta t \tag{13.14}$$
where
$$v_r = \frac{dr}{dt} = \frac{v^2 t}{\sqrt{(v^2 t^2 + y_0^2 + z_0^2)}} \tag{13.15}$$
is the radial component of the clock velocity at the instant the signal is emitted. From (13.08) and (13.14) we get
$$\Delta t^* = \tau \cdot \frac{c + v_r}{\sqrt{(c^2 - v^2)}} \tag{13.16}$$
This replaces (13.10) in the general case.

The fact that Δt^* and τ are different is an expression of the well-known phenomenon of the Doppler effect, which is the following : if a periodic process of period τ takes place in a moving frame then the period Δt^* registered at some point in the rest frame proves to be greater than τ, if the motion of the system is away from the point and less if the motion is towards it. Equation (13.16) gives the relativistic expression for the Doppler effect in the case of light propagating *in vacuo*. The classical Doppler formula is obtained if no distinction is made between t' and t and Δt is replaced by τ in (13.14). This introduces a relative error of order v^2/c^2.

One might remark that historically the first determination of the speed of light in empty space was performed in 1675 by Olaf Roemer using a method essentially based on the Doppler effect. The system of Jupiter's satellites served as the moving clock and the periodic process observed consisted of their eclipses. During roughly half of its orbital motion the Earth approaches Jupiter, so that $v_r < 0$, and for the other half of the time it moves away and $v_r > 0$. Using the simplified expression (13.14) instead of (13.16) one can take for Δt the annual mean of the observed time between eclipses. On that part of the Earth's orbit on which $v_r < 0$, the time Δt^* will be less than Δt and the eclipses will be observed ahead of the expected time, while it will be greater on that part where $v_r > 0$ and the eclipses will then come late. Thus the relation (13.14) allows a calculation of the speed of light c. In this way Roemer found a value of $3 \cdot 1 \times 10^{10}$ cm sec^{-1}, very close to the now accepted value of $3 \cdot 0 \times 10^{10}$ cm sec^{-1}, which is obtained by much more accurate methods.

Let us stress once again that in the theory of the Doppler effect two considerations are taken into account: firstly, the connection between the instant t^* when the light signal arrives, and the instant t of its emission, and, secondly, the relation between the time t in the frame in which the signal is registered and the time t' in the frame moving with the emitting body. The first of these considerations, passing from t^* to t, introduces a factor depending on the radial component of the velocity; it was already known in pre-relativistic theory. The second consideration, transforming from t to t', introduces a factor depending on the magnitude of the velocity; it arises from the Lorentz transformation and is specific to the Theory of Relativity.

14. Comparison of Clock Readings in Moving Reference Frames

In the preceding section we examined a method of comparing time differences in different reference frames which relied on the use of light signals and took due account of their time of travel. However, it is also possible, in principle, to use another method in which one only compares the readings of clocks when, in the course of their motion, they are in immediate proximity of each other.

We imagine a row of clocks spaced out along a straight line and all belonging to the same frame. They are to be at rest in this frame and are supposed synchronized from the beginning. Suppose a clock A moves past the row of clocks. To obtain the rate of clock A it is sufficient to compare at any instant the reading of A with the reading of that base clock which A happens to be passing at the moment in question. Clearly it will be enough to consider two clocks in the base, so that we can think of the latter as formed of two clocks joined by a rigid bar.

Referred to the base, the coordinates of the two clocks at rest and of the moving clock A will be

$$
\begin{aligned}
x &= a \quad \text{(first base clock)} \\
x &= b \quad \text{(second base clock)} \\
x &= vt \quad \text{(clock } A\text{)}
\end{aligned}
\tag{14.01}
$$

Using the Lorentz transformation formulae (13.04) and (13.05) we can introduce a reference frame connected with clock A. In it the coordinates of the same three clocks will be

$$
\begin{aligned}
x' &= -vt' + a' \quad \text{(first base clock)} \\
x' &= -vt' + b' \quad \text{(second base clock)} \\
x' &= 0 \quad \text{(clock } A\text{)}
\end{aligned}
\tag{14.02}
$$

with the constants a' and b' related to the a and b of (14.01) by

$$
a' = a\sqrt{\left(1 - \frac{v^2}{c^2}\right)}; \qquad b' = b\sqrt{\left(1 - \frac{v^2}{c^2}\right)}
\tag{14.03}
$$

Without making any choice between the two reference frames we can register the following objective facts : first, the readings of clock A and of the first base clock at the instant when they are coincident and, second, the readings of A and the second base clock when in turn they coincide. We denote the two described readings of A by t_1' and t_2' and by t_1 and t_2 the corresponding readings of the first and second base clocks respectively. Then we get, using (14.01) and (14.02)

$$t_1 = \frac{a}{v}; \qquad t_1' = \frac{a'}{v}$$

$$t_2 = \frac{b}{v}; \qquad t_2' = \frac{b'}{v} \tag{14.04}$$

whereby, owing to (14.03)

$$t_1' = t_1 \sqrt{\left(1 - \frac{v^2}{c^2}\right)}; \qquad t_2' = t_2 \sqrt{\left(1 - \frac{v^2}{c^2}\right)} \tag{14.05}$$

These results enable us to check, on the one hand, the rate of clock A observed from the base, and on the other hand, the rate of the base clocks observed from a frame fixed to A. We mean by the rate of a periodic process as observed from a particular frame, the rate expressed in terms of that time variable which is defined by the synchronization appropriate to the frame.

The quantities t_1 and t_2 are readings of different base clocks, but as the two clocks are synchronized in the base frame, we can maintain that when the second clock read t_2, so did the first, using the word " when " *in the sense of that particular synchronization.* Therefore the difference $t_2 - t_1$ is just the time elapsed in the base frame reckoning during which the reading of clock A advanced by $t_2' - t_1'$. Thus the rate of clock A observed from the base is determined by the equation

$$t_2' - t_1' = (t_2 - t_1) \sqrt{\left(1 - \frac{v^2}{c^2}\right)} \tag{14.06}$$

Since $| t_2' - t_1' | < | t_2 - t_1 |$, clock A will be *slow* to an observer at the base. Putting $t_2' - t_1' = \tau$, and $t_2 - t_1 = \Delta t$, our equation coincides with (13.08).

We now consider the rate of a base clock observed from a frame attached at A. To check this rate it is now essential to observe the readings of *one and the same* clock at base, either the first or the second. For definiteness let us consider the second. We have only one *direct* reading for it, namely the one for the instant when it was coincident with clock A, and then it read t_2, while clock A read t_2'. The other reading of the second clock must be *calculated* from the available data. We therefore ask : where was the second clock and what was its reading when the first clock was coincident with clock A ? It is essential to remember that the words " where " and " when " in the above must now be used in the sense appropriate to the frame of A, the primed frame. The question is readily answered. When the first clock and A coincided, the latter indicated the time $t_1 = a'/v$, and then, according to (14.02) the second clock was at the point $x' = b' - a'$. The reading of the second clock is then obtained by inserting $t' = t_1$ and $x' = b' - a'$ into the Lorentz transformation (13.05).

We get
$$t = \frac{t_1' + (v/c^2)(b' - a')}{\sqrt{(1 - v^2/c^2)}} = t_1 + \frac{v}{c^2}(b - a) \tag{14.07}$$

or
$$t = t_1 + (t_2 - t_1)\frac{v^2}{c^2} \tag{14.08}$$

(The reading of the second clock now does not agree with the reading of the first, which is t_1, because now simultaneity is understood in the frame of A and not of the base.) From the reading of the second clock, as given by (14.08), together with the directly observed reading t_2, one finds the rate of the second clock in the frame of A. We have

$$t_2 - t = (t_2 - t_1)\left(1 - \frac{v^2}{c^2}\right) \tag{14.09}$$

whence, finally,
$$t_2 - t = (t_2' - t_1')\sqrt{\left(1 - \frac{v^2}{c^2}\right)} \tag{14.10}$$

Thus in the frame of A the clocks at base are again slow ; we have complete reciprocity between the two frames.

It is sometimes said that time passes more slowly in the moving frame than in the frame at rest. As the Principle of Relativity allows one to interchange the roles of the two frames, this formulation is contradictory.

The nature of the kind of misunderstanding here involved can best be clarified by means of a mathematical illustration which has a direct bearing on our question. We saw in Section 10 that in a Lorentz transformation

$$\frac{\partial t'}{\partial t} = a_{00} = \frac{1}{\sqrt{(1 - v^2/c^2)}} > 1 \tag{14.11}$$

but that for the reverse transformation also

$$\frac{\partial t}{\partial t'} = a_{00} = \frac{1}{\sqrt{(1 - v^2/c^2)}} > 1 \tag{14.12}$$

If one forgets that in (14.11) the differentiation takes place at constant x, y, z and in (14.12) at constant x', y' and z', it seems strange that $\partial t/\partial t'$ is not the reciprocal of $\partial t'/\partial t$ but equal to it. It is clear, however, that there is in fact no paradox.

Returning to the physical side of the matter one can say that the problem in question is not concerned with " passage of time " in different frames but with the description of some *localized process* within different frames. Let the process be localized at a point at rest in the unprimed system so that x, y and z are constant. Then we conclude from $\partial t'/\partial t > 1$ that the duration, or period of the process in " its own ", unprimed frame will be less than in any other (primed) frame that is in motion relative to the former. If, however, the process is localized at a point with constant coordinates x', y', z' then its " own " or " proper " system will be the primed one and we have $\partial t/\partial t' > 1$, but the conclusion is the same.

If the duration of the process in its " proper " system was $d\tau$, then it will be $dt > d\tau$ in another system moving with speed V relative to the first where

$$d\tau = \sqrt{\left(1 - \frac{V^2}{c^2}\right)}\, dt \tag{14.13}$$

Here **V** is the velocity that enters the Lorentz transformation which relates the two frames. The magnitude of **V** is equal to that of **v** the velocity of motion of the point at which the process is localized. The components of **v** are

$$v_x = \frac{dx}{dt}; \qquad v_y = \frac{dy}{dt}; \qquad v_z = \frac{dz}{dt} \qquad (14.14)$$

We can therefore write, instead of (14.13)

$$d\tau = \sqrt{\left(1 - \frac{v^2}{c^2}\right)} \, dt \qquad (14.15)$$

It is easy to see that this expression is invariant under Lorentz transformations. The quantity $d\tau$ can be thought of as the differential of a " proper time " τ given by

$$\tau = \int_0^t \sqrt{\left(1 - \frac{v^2}{c^2}\right)} \, dt \qquad (14.16)$$

where we have assumed that $\tau = 0$ at $t = 0$. If the velocity **v** is constant then τ is the duration as measured in its " proper " frame of the process associated with the moving point–hence the name " proper time ". If, however, **v** is a variable velocity the physical meaning of τ is not obvious. Even so it can be looked upon as an auxiliary mathematical quantity which it is convenient to use because of its invariance under Lorentz transformations. One still retains the name " proper time " for it in the case of variable velocity **v**.

If a moving body, a clock, is in a gravitational field which is the cause of its acceleration, one can give a different expression for the time shown by this clock, an expression which in addition to the velocity **v**, also involves the gravitational potential (see (62.03)). The expression (14.16) will not be correct in this case. The correct expression may be justified in Einstein's theory of gravitation, although it is not a direct consequence of that theory (see Section 62). As for the ordinary theory of relativity, it allows one to draw conclusions in a general form (i.e. without going deeply into the nature of the processes occurring) only in relation to *unaccelerated* motion. In general, however, no theory is capable of predicting how a clock will behave when subjected to impacts or arbitrary accelerations without entering into the details of the clock's construction. This cannot be achieved by the theory of gravitation either; the expression given in Section 62 for the time shown by a clock in accelerated motion relates to the case when the acceleration is caused by the gravitational field.

One could also introduce the notion of clocks nearly or, in the limit, entirely insensitive to impacts and accelerations (for instance atomic systems with large internal frequencies). One could then propose to measure proper time τ by the readings of such an ideally insensitive clock, this being just the physical meaning of proper time. But one should note that such a proposal, although not in contradiction with the theory of relativity, does not follow from it and represents a special hypothesis. We shall return to this question in Sections 61 and 62.

15. Comparison of Distances and Lengths in Moving Reference Frames

If an object is at rest in a given frame of reference the determination of its geometrical shape or dimensions need not be performed instantaneously. An object at rest may be measured gradually, by noting the positions of various points one by one. On the other hand, if one has to measure the dimensions and shape of a moving object it is absolutely necessary that the observations of all its points should relate to the same instant, otherwise one obtains a distorted picture.

It is thus clear that the concepts of dimensions and shape of a moving object are closely related to the concept of simultaneity. We know already that the notion of simultaneity is not something absolute but depends on the reference frame. Therefore we must expect that the shape and size of an object is also not absolute, but must be stated in relation to a definite frame.

As the simplest example, let us consider the length of a rod measured in different frames of reference.

Let two frames be in relative motion in the direction of their common x-axis. Their space and time coordinates are then connected by a Lorentz transformation which we restate :

$$x' = \frac{x - vt}{\sqrt{(1 - v^2/c^2)}}; \qquad t' = \frac{t - vx/c^2}{\sqrt{(1 - v^2/c^2)}} \qquad (15.01)$$
$$y' = y; \qquad z' = z$$

Let the direction of the rod be the same as the direction of the relative velocity of the two frames—i.e. as the x-axis—and let the rod be at rest in the unprimed system. At all times the coordinates of the ends of the rod in that system will be

$$\begin{array}{llll} x = a, & y = 0, & z = 0 & \text{(first end of rod)} \\ x = b, & y = 0, & z = 0 & \text{(second end of rod)} \end{array} \qquad (15.02)$$

and if $b > a$ the length of the rod is

$$l = b - a \qquad (15.03)$$

In the primed frame, which moves relative to the rod, the coordinates of its ends will be

$$\begin{array}{llll} x' = -vt' + a', & y' = 0, & z' = 0 & \text{(first end)} \\ x' = -vt' + b', & y' = 0, & z' = 0 & \text{(second end)} \end{array} \qquad (15.04)$$

where
$$a' = a\sqrt{\left(1 - \frac{v^2}{c^2}\right)}; \qquad b' = b\sqrt{\left(1 - \frac{v^2}{c^2}\right)} \qquad (15.05)$$

The length of the rod is the distance between simultaneous positions of its ends. In the primed system simultaneity means equal values of t' and distance is expressed in the usual way as a difference of primed coordinates. Therefore the length of the rod in the primed frame will be

$$l' = b' - a' \qquad (15.06)$$

Hence
$$l' = l\sqrt{\left(1 - \frac{v^2}{c^2}\right)} \qquad (15.07)$$

Thus, in the frame in which the rod has a velocity v in the direction of its length it appears shortened ; its length l' is less than the length l obtained for the rod at rest.

If we were to take into consideration the transverse dimensions of the rod (those in the directions of the y and z-axes and perpendicular to the velocity), we could verify that they do not change. Consequently the volume of the rod decreases proportionally with its longitudinal dimension. The same result is true for a body of any shape. If V is the volume of a body in the system in which it is at rest, its volume V' in a frame relative to which it moves with speed v will be

$$V' = V \cdot \sqrt{\left(1 - \frac{v^2}{c^2}\right)} \tag{15.08}$$

Assume we have two identical rods parallel to each other with a relative velocity directed along their axes. Then, in the frame connected with the first rod the second will appear shortened, and *vice versa*. This state of affairs is the same as in the clock example and, as before, there is no paradox. The difference in the measured lengths comes from the different definitions of simultaneity. The positions of the ends of the rod that were simultaneous in one frame are not simultaneous, but only quasi-simultaneous in the other. Let x_a be the position of the end A at the instant t_a and x_b the position of the end B at t_b. The corresponding quantities in the other frame will be denoted by the corresponding primed symbols. By the invariance of the space-like interval we have

$$(x_a - x_b)^2 - c^2(t_a - t_b)^2 = (x'_a - x'_b)^2 - c^2(t'_a - t'_b)^2 \tag{15.09}$$

If we here put $t_a = t_b$ we shall have $t'_a \neq t'_b$ and hence

$$|x_a - x_b| < |x'_a - x'_b| \tag{15.10}$$

On the left we have the length of the rod in the unprimed system ; the quantity on the right will be the length of the rod in the primed frame provided it is at rest in it, for then it is immaterial whether $x'_a(t')$ and $x'_b(t')$ refer to the same time t' or not and we can take $x'_a = x'_a(t'_a)$ and $x'_b = x'_b(t'_b)$ with $t'_a \neq t'_b$.

If we put $t'_a = t'_b$ we have $t_a \neq t_b$ and hence

$$|x_a - x_b| > |x'_a - x'_b| \tag{15.11}$$

but now the left-hand side is the length of the rod in the frame in which it rests whereas the right-hand side is the length in an arbitrary primed frame.

In these considerations the symmetry of the equations with respect to primed and unprimed frames is evident from the beginning and, therefore, the considerations themselves may appear trivial. We have given them in order to emphasize once again the close relation between the concepts of simultaneity and of length.

16. Relative Velocity

In pre-relativistic mechanics the relative velocity of two bodies was defined as the difference of their velocities. Let the velocities of two bodies, both measured in the same frame of reference, be **u** and **v** respectively. Then the velocity of the second body relative to the first used to be defined as **w** = **v** − **u**. This definition is invariant with respect to Galileo transformations but not Lorentz transformations. Therefore it is not suitable in the Theory of Relativity and must be replaced by another. The fact that **w** = **v** − **u** has no physical meaning becomes evident by examining the following example. Let the velocities **u** and **v** have opposite directions and have magnitudes near to the speed of light or equal to it. Then the " velocity " **w** will have a magnitude near or equal to twice the speed of light, which is evidently absurd.

We shall, therefore, give a new definition of relative velocity which is in accord with the requirements of Relativity and has a direct physical meaning. Let the velocities of two bodies in some frame of reference be **u** and **v** as before. We can introduce a primed frame of reference in which the velocity of one, say the first, body vanishes. Then we can interpret the velocity **v'** of the second body in this frame as the relative velocity of the two bodies. We shall see that the magnitude of **v'** will depend symmetrically on **u** and **v**, so that the so defined relative velocity of two bodies does not depend upon which body was chosen to be at rest in the new frame.

To illustrate the physical significance of our definition we consider an example. Imagine we are observing two aeroplanes from the ground and let their velocities be **u** and **v** respectively. Assume that the first plane has radar equipment permitting a measurement of the speed of the other plane relative to itself. The velocity so measured will be the relative velocity of our definition.

We must express this relative velocity in terms of the components of the velocities **u** and **v** of the two planes, as observed from the ground. For this purpose we write down the general formulae for a Lorentz transformation deduced in Section 10. These are

$$\mathbf{r'} = \mathbf{r} - \mathbf{V}t + (a_{00} - 1)\frac{\mathbf{V}}{V^2}(\mathbf{V}\cdot\mathbf{r} - V^2t),$$

$$t' = a_{00}\left(t - \frac{\mathbf{r}\cdot\mathbf{V}}{c^2}\right) \tag{16.01}$$

and their inverse is

$$\mathbf{r} = \mathbf{r'} + \mathbf{V}t' + (a_{00} - 1)\frac{\mathbf{V}}{V^2}(\mathbf{V}\cdot\mathbf{r'} + V^2t'),$$

$$t = a_{00}\left(t' + \frac{\mathbf{r'}\cdot\mathbf{V}}{c^2}\right) \tag{16.02}$$

where we have used the notation of (10.15), putting

$$a_{00} = \frac{1}{\sqrt{(1 - V^2/c^2)}} \tag{16.03}$$

To have the first plane (the one of velocity **u**, relative to the ground) at rest in the primed system we must choose

$$V_x = u_x; \qquad V_y = u_y; \qquad V_z = u_z \tag{16.04}$$

The velocity of the second plane measured from the ground is

$$\mathbf{v} = \frac{d\mathbf{r}}{dt} \tag{16.05}$$

while its velocity measured from the other plane is

$$\mathbf{v'} = \frac{d\mathbf{r'}}{dt'} \tag{16.06}$$

The relation between these two quantities is found by differentiating equation (16.01) and (16.02). We have

$$\mathbf{v'} = \frac{\mathbf{v} - \mathbf{u} + (a_{00} - 1)(\mathbf{u}/u^2)\{(\mathbf{u} \cdot \mathbf{v}) - u^2\}}{a_{00}(1 - \mathbf{u} \cdot \mathbf{v}/c^2)} \tag{16.07}$$

and

$$\mathbf{v} = \frac{\mathbf{v'} + \mathbf{u'} + (a_{00} - 1)(\mathbf{u}/u^2)\{(\mathbf{u} \cdot \mathbf{v'}) + u^2\}}{a_{00}(1 + \mathbf{u} \cdot \mathbf{v'}/c^2)} \tag{16.08}$$

where, by (16.03) and (16.04)

$$a_{00} = \frac{1}{\sqrt{(1 - u^2/c^2)}} \tag{16.09}$$

Equation (16.08) is the solution of (16.07) for $\mathbf{v}$. As the Lorentz transformation is linear with respect to space and time coordinates the primed components v'_x, v'_y and v'_z are linear fractional functions of the unprimed component v_x, v_y and z_z. Let us calculate the square of the vector $\mathbf{v'}$, i.e. the square of the relative velocity of the two planes. We have

$$v'^2 = \frac{(\mathbf{u} - \mathbf{v})^2 - (1/c^2)[\mathbf{u} \times \mathbf{v}]^2}{(1 - \mathbf{u} \cdot \mathbf{v}/c^2)^2} \tag{16.10}$$

As we have already noted, this expression is symmetrical with respect to $\mathbf{u}$ and $\mathbf{v}$. We shall now verify that the inequalities $u^2 < c^2$ and $v^2 < c^2$ imply $v'^2 < c^2$ whatever the direction of the velocity vectors $\mathbf{u}$ and $\mathbf{v}$. Indeed we have

$$1 - \frac{v'^2}{c^2} = \frac{(1 - u^2/c^2)(1 - v^2/c^2)}{(1 - \mathbf{u} \cdot \mathbf{v}/c^2)^2} \tag{16.11}$$

Because $u^2 < c^2$ and $v^2 < c^2$ the right-hand side is always positive, so the left-hand side must also be positive and hence $v'^2 < c^2$. In the limit when one or other of the velocities $\mathbf{u}$ and $\mathbf{v}$ is equal to light velocity the relative velocity $\mathbf{v''}$ will also be equal to it. This agrees with our basic assumption on which the whole of Relativity Theory is based.

It should be noted that the square of the relative velocity is invariant under Lorentz transformations. This means that if in (16.10) we replace the quantities $\mathbf{u}$ and $\mathbf{v}$ by the velocities $\mathbf{u''}$ and $\mathbf{v''}$ of the two aeroplanes relative to some other frame, say a third plane, the value (16.10) will not be affected by the change. It is evident that this must be so by the meaning of v'^2 as the square of a relative velocity.

Equation (16.07) simplifies if in the given frame the two velocities $\mathbf{u}$ and $\mathbf{v}$ are either parallel or perpendicular. In the first case we get

$$\mathbf{v'} = \frac{\mathbf{v} - \mathbf{u}}{1 - \mathbf{u} \cdot \mathbf{v}/c^2} \qquad \{\text{for } [\mathbf{u} \times \mathbf{v}] = 0\} \tag{16.12}$$

and in the second

$$\mathbf{v'} = \mathbf{v}\sqrt{\left(1 - \frac{u^2}{c^2}\right)} - \mathbf{u} \qquad \{\text{for } (\mathbf{u} \cdot \mathbf{v}) = 0\} \tag{16.13}$$

Equation (16.12) with the opposite sign before $\mathbf{u}$ is usually called Einstein's Addition Theorem for Velocities.

In the general case one can assert the following: If " velocity space " is considered as a Lobachevsky space the relativistic addition theorem for velocities coincides with the vector addition theorem in Lobachevsky geometry.

This will be proved in the following section.

17. The Lobachevsky-Einstein Velocity Space

Let us consider the relative velocity of two bodies moving with infinitesimally differing velocities $\mathbf{v}$ and $\mathbf{v} + d\mathbf{v}$. Let ds be the magnitude of this relative velocity, divided by c. Inserting $\mathbf{u} = \mathbf{v} + d\mathbf{v}$ into (16.10) and dividing by c^2 we get

$$ds^2 = \frac{c^2(d\mathbf{v})^2 - [\mathbf{v} \times d\mathbf{v}]^2}{(c^2 - v^2)^2} \tag{17.01}$$

or

$$ds^2 = \frac{(c^2 - v^2)(d\mathbf{v})^2 + (\mathbf{v} \cdot d\mathbf{v})^2}{(c^2 - v^2)^2} \tag{17.02}$$

By the physical meaning of (17.01) as being proportional to the square of an infinitesimal relative velocity it must be invariant under Lorentz transformations. This can be directly verified, by expressing v_x, v_y and v_z by (16.08) as fractional linear functions of v'_x, v'_y and v'_z. This makes ds^2 the same function of (v'_x, v'_y, v'_z) and (dv'_x, dv'_y, dv'_z) as it was of (v_x, v_y, v_z) and (dv_x, dv_y, dv_z).

We shall consider (17.01) and (17.02) as the squared element of length in a certain *velocity space*. This is the space in which the velocity hodograph of ordinary mechanics is constructed. This space possesses all the properties of Lobachevsky space, and the velocity components v_x, v_y, v_z divided by c are the so-called Beltrami coordinates in it (see V. F. Kagan [9], eq. CVIII p. 453). The properties of Lobachevsky space can be derived by examining the expression (17.01)

A curve in Lobachevsky space can be given by stating v_x, v_y and v_z as functions of some parameter p. If the values p_1 and p_2 of p correspond to the end points of the curve, the arc length along the curve is given by the formula

$$s = \int_{p_1}^{p_2} \sqrt{(2F)}\, dp \tag{17.03}$$

where

$$F = \frac{1}{2} \frac{\dot{\mathbf{v}}^2}{c^2 - v^2} + \frac{1}{2} \frac{(\mathbf{v} \cdot \dot{\mathbf{v}})^2}{(c^2 - v^2)^2} \tag{17.04}$$

differentiation with respect to p being denoted by a dot. We determine the equation of a Lobachevsky straight line, i.e. of the shortest curve joining the points p_1 and p_2. This is done by equating to zero the variation of the integral (17.03), or, in other words, by writing down Lagrange's equations for the Lagrangian

$$L = \sqrt{(2F)} \tag{17.05}$$

These equations are

$$\frac{d}{dp} \frac{\partial L}{\partial \dot{v}_x} - \frac{\partial L}{\partial v_x} = 0, \quad \text{etc.} \tag{17.06}$$

or

$$\frac{d}{dp} \left(\frac{1}{\sqrt{(2F)}} \frac{\partial F}{\partial \dot{v}_x} \right) - \frac{1}{\sqrt{(2F)}} \frac{\partial F}{\partial v_x} = 0, \quad \text{etc.} \tag{17.07}$$

Up to now the parameter p was arbitrary. We now choose it so that

$$\frac{dF}{dp} = 0, \qquad F = \text{const.} \tag{17.08}$$

With this choice equations (17.07) are equivalent to

$$\frac{d}{dp}\frac{\partial F}{\partial \dot{v}_x} - \frac{\partial F}{\partial v_x} = 0, \qquad \text{etc.} \tag{17.09}$$

Since F does not contain p explicitly, we have

$$\dot{v}_x \frac{\partial F}{\partial \dot{v}_x} + \dot{v}_y \frac{\partial F}{\partial \dot{v}_y} + \dot{v}_z \frac{\partial F}{\partial \dot{v}_z} - F = \text{const.} \tag{17.10}$$

i.e. the quantity (17.10) is an integral of the Lagrange equations. But F is a homogeneous quadratic function of $\dot{v}_x$, $\dot{v}_y$ and $\dot{v}_z$, so that (17.10) is equal to F and thus condition (17.08) is a consequence of the Lagrange equations (17.09).

We now proceed to write equations (17.09) in more detail and to find their integrals. We have

$$\frac{\partial F}{\partial \dot{v}_x} = \frac{\dot{v}_x}{c^2 - v^2} + v_x \frac{(\mathbf{v} \cdot \dot{\mathbf{v}})}{(c^2 - v^2)^2} \tag{17.11}$$

$$\frac{\partial F}{\partial v_x} = v_x\left(\frac{\dot{\mathbf{v}}^2}{(c^2 - v^2)^2} + \frac{2(\mathbf{v} \cdot \dot{\mathbf{v}})^2}{(c^2 - v^2)^3}\right) + \dot{v}_x \frac{(\mathbf{v} \cdot \dot{\mathbf{v}})}{(c^2 - v^2)^2} \tag{17.12}$$

We introduce a vector $\mathbf{w}$ with components

$$w_x = \frac{\dot{v}_x}{c^2 - v^2}; \qquad w_y = \frac{\dot{v}_y}{c^2 - v^2}; \qquad w_z = \frac{\dot{v}_z}{c^2 - v^2} \tag{17.13}$$

Then equations (17.11) and (17.12) become

$$\frac{\partial F}{\partial \dot{v}_x} = w_x + v_x \frac{(\mathbf{v} \cdot \mathbf{w})}{c^2 - v^2} \tag{17.14}$$

$$\frac{\partial F}{\partial v_x} = v_x\left(w^2 + 2\frac{(\mathbf{v} \cdot \mathbf{w})^2}{c^2 - v^2}\right) + w_x(\mathbf{v} \cdot \mathbf{w}) \tag{17.15}$$

Differentiating (17.14) with respect to the parameter p and expressing $\dot{\mathbf{v}}$ in terms of $\mathbf{w}$ we get

$$\frac{d}{dp}\frac{\partial F}{\partial \dot{v}_x} = \dot{w}_x + v_x \frac{(\mathbf{v} \cdot \dot{\mathbf{w}})}{c^2 - v^2} + v_x\left(w^2 + 2\frac{(\mathbf{v} \cdot \mathbf{w})^2}{c^2 - v^2}\right) + w_x(\mathbf{v} \cdot \mathbf{w}) \tag{17.16}$$

Inserting (17.15) and (17.16) into Lagrange's equations (17.09) we see that they take on the form

$$\dot{w}_x + v_x \frac{(\mathbf{v} \cdot \dot{\mathbf{w}})}{c^2 - v^2} = 0, \qquad \text{etc.} \tag{17.17}$$

It is easily seen that as an algebraic consequence of these equations (17.17) we have $(\mathbf{v} \cdot \dot{\mathbf{w}}) = 0$ whence it follows that (17.17) is equivalent to

$$\dot{w}_x = 0, \qquad \dot{w}_y = 0, \qquad \dot{w}_z = 0 \tag{17.18}$$

or, vectorially,

$$\dot{\mathbf{w}} = 0 \tag{17.19}$$

Thus Lagrange's equations amount to the requirement that the vector $\mathbf{w}$ (defined by (17.13)) should be constant. But $\mathbf{w}$ is proportional to $\dot{\mathbf{v}}$; if it is constant, so is the vector product

$$[\mathbf{w} \times \mathbf{v}] = \text{const.} \qquad (17.20)$$

This gives two further linearly independent integrals of Lagrange's equations.

From the integrals found we see that the equation of a Lobachevsky straight line in velocity space is a set of *linear* relations between the velocity components v_x, v_y and v_z. We know that Lorentz transformations lead to a fractional linear substitution for the velocity components. It is, therefore, evident that after a transformation the linear relations remain linear.

We now determine the length along a Lobachevsky straight line between the points $\mathbf{v} = \mathbf{v}_1$ and $\mathbf{v} = \mathbf{v}_2$, and also establish a connection between this length and the relative velocity of two bodies of velocities $\mathbf{v}_1$ and $\mathbf{v}_2$ respectively. As the coordinates of points on the straight line are given by linear relations they can be represented parametrically in the form

$$\mathbf{v} = \mathbf{v}_1 + \mu(\mathbf{v}_2 - \mathbf{v}_1) \qquad (0 \leqslant \mu \leqslant 1) \qquad (17.21)$$

Inserting this expression for $\mathbf{v}$ into (17.04) we get

$$2F = \frac{c^2(\mathbf{v}_2 - \mathbf{v}_1)^2 - [\mathbf{v}_1 \times \mathbf{v}_2]^2}{(c^2 - v^2)^2} \dot{\mu}^2 \qquad (17.22)$$

Putting for brevity

$$a = \sqrt{\{c^2(\mathbf{v}_2 - \mathbf{v}_1)^2 - [\mathbf{v}_1 \times \mathbf{v}_2]^2\}} \qquad (17.23)$$

we obtain from (17.03) an expression for the length along the line from $\mathbf{v}_1$ to $\mathbf{v}_2$

$$s = \int_0^1 \frac{a \, d\mu}{(c^2 - v^2)} \qquad (17.24)$$

This integral is evaluated most simply by means of the substitution

$$\mu = \frac{(c^2 - v_1^2)\xi}{c^2 - \mathbf{v}_1 \cdot \mathbf{v}_2 + (\mathbf{v}_1 \cdot \mathbf{v}_2 - v_1^2)\xi} \qquad (17.25)$$

giving

$$s = \int_0^1 \frac{ab \, d\xi}{b^2 - a^2\xi^2} = \frac{1}{2} \log \frac{b + a}{b - a} \qquad (17.26)$$

where

$$b = c^2 - \mathbf{v}_1 \cdot \mathbf{v}_2 \qquad (17.27)$$

The coefficients of the substitution were so chosen as to have 0 and 1 for the limits of ξ and so that the denominator in (17.26) does not involve the first power of ξ. Hence we obtain

$$\frac{a}{b} = \tanh s \qquad (17.28)$$

and, after squaring and multiplying by c^2, this can be written as

$$\frac{(\mathbf{v}_2 - \mathbf{v}_1)^2 - (1/c^2)[\mathbf{v}_1 \times \mathbf{v}_2]^2}{[1 - (\mathbf{v}_1 \cdot \mathbf{v}_2/c^2)]^2} = c^2 \tanh^2 s \qquad (17.29)$$

Comparing this expression with (16.10) we see that the left-hand side is the square of the relative velocity. Thus the relative velocity is related to the length of the corresponding segment of the Lobachevsky straight line by

$$|\mathbf{v}'| = c \tanh s \qquad (17.30)$$

Let us assume that the velocities $\mathbf{v}_1$ and $\mathbf{v}_2$ have the same direction. Expressing their magnitudes in terms of segments of a Lobachevsky straight line we have

$$v_1 = c \tanh s_1; \qquad v_2 = c \tanh s_2 \qquad (17.31)$$

The length of Lobachevsky line corresponding to the relative velocity will be equal to the difference of the lengths s_2 and s_1. Therefore, if $s_2 > s_1$, the relative velocity will be

$$v' = c \tanh(s_2 - s_1) = c \frac{\tanh s_2 - \tanh s_1}{1 - \tanh s_2 \tanh s_1} \qquad (17.32)$$

or

$$v' = \frac{v_2 - v_1}{1 - (v_2 v_1 / c^2)} \qquad (17.33)$$

This is just the Einstein addition, or rather in our case subtraction, formula.

Let us now consider the angle between the relative velocities of two bodies. If the velocities are taken relative to a point assumed at rest the cosine of the angle is given by the usual formula

$$\cos (\mathbf{v}_1, \mathbf{v}_2) = \frac{\mathbf{v}_1 \cdot \mathbf{v}_2}{|v_1|\, |v_2|} \qquad (17.34)$$

but if the velocities are given relative to a point that is itself in motion with a velocity $\mathbf{u}$, the angle between the relative velocities is given by a more complicated formula, which, however, can easily be obtained as follows. We make a Lorentz transformation to bring to rest the point that was moving with velocity $\mathbf{u}$. Then we can apply the usual formula (17.37), getting

$$\cos \alpha = \cos (\mathbf{v}'_1, \mathbf{v}'_2) = \frac{\mathbf{v}'_1 \cdot \mathbf{v}'_2}{|v'_1|\, |v'_2|} \qquad (17.35)$$

with $\mathbf{v}'_1$ and $\mathbf{v}'_2$ denoting the velocities of the two bodies after the Lorentz transformation. These velocities are obtained from (16.07), replacing $\mathbf{v}$ by $\mathbf{v}_1$ and by $\mathbf{v}_2$. Expressing $\mathbf{v}'_1$ and $\mathbf{v}'_2$ by $\mathbf{v}_1$ and $\mathbf{v}_2$, we obtain after some manipulation

$$\cos \alpha = \frac{(\mathbf{v}_1 - \mathbf{u}) \cdot (\mathbf{v}_2 - \mathbf{u}) - (1/c^2)[\mathbf{v}_1 \times \mathbf{u}][\mathbf{v}_2 \times \mathbf{u}]}{\sqrt{\{(\mathbf{v}_1 - \mathbf{u})^2 - (1/c^2)[\mathbf{v}_1 \times \mathbf{u}]^2\}} \cdot \sqrt{\{(\mathbf{v}_2 - \mathbf{u})^2 - (1/c^2)[\mathbf{v}_2 \times \mathbf{u}]^2\}}} \qquad (17.36)$$

This, however, is just the expression for the cosine of the angle of a triangle in Lobachevsky space. (It is the angle at $\mathbf{u}$ in a triangle whose vertices are at the points $\mathbf{u}$, $\mathbf{v}_1$ and $\mathbf{v}_2$.)

Indeed our initial expression (17.01) for the square of the element of length in Lobachevsky space has the form

$$ds^2 = \frac{c^2(d\mathbf{v})^2 - [\mathbf{v} \times d\mathbf{v}]^2}{(c^2 - v^2)^2} \qquad (17.37)$$

This expression corresponds to a "displacement" $d\mathbf{v}$ from the "point" $\mathbf{v}$. For the displacement $\delta\mathbf{v}$ from the same point we have

$$\delta s^2 = \frac{c^2(\delta\mathbf{v})^2 - [\mathbf{v} \times \delta\mathbf{v}]^2}{(c^2 - v^2)^2} \qquad (17.38)$$

The cosine of the angle between the displacements can be stated in an invariant manner by means of the equation

$$ds \, \delta s \cos \alpha = \frac{c^2 d\mathbf{v} \, \delta \mathbf{v} - [\mathbf{v} \times d\mathbf{v}][\mathbf{v} \times \delta \mathbf{v}]}{(c^2 - v^2)^2} \tag{17.39}$$

(This formula can be considered as the definition of an angle in Lobachevsky geometry.) If now in (17.36) we write $\mathbf{v}$ instead of $\mathbf{u}$ and if we insert into (17.39) the displacements

$$d\mathbf{v} = \varepsilon(\mathbf{v}_1 - \mathbf{v}) \, ; \qquad \delta \mathbf{v} = \eta(\mathbf{v}_2 - \mathbf{v}) \tag{17.40}$$

along two sides of a triangle starting from the vertex $\mathbf{v}$, the expression for $\cos \alpha$ obtained from (17.39) is the same as in (17.36).

Thus the angle between relative velocities can be thought of as an angle in Lobachevsky geometry. Given three bodies moving with velocities $\mathbf{v}_1$, $\mathbf{v}_2$ and $\mathbf{v}_3$ the corresponding triangle has its vertices at the points $\mathbf{v}_1$, $\mathbf{v}_2$ and $\mathbf{v}_3$; the relative velocities will correspond to the sides of the triangle and the angles between the velocities to the angles of the triangle. A similar construction is possible in non-relativistic kinematics, but there the geometry of velocity space is Euclidean whereas in the Theory of Relativity it is Lobachevskian.

The validity of Lobachevsky geometry in velocity space has its experimental verification. We refer to Fizeau's experiment which measures the speed of light in a moving medium and to the phenomenon of astronomical aberration discovered by Bradley.

Fizeau's experiment aims at comparing the velocity of light propagation in a moving and in a stationary medium. The propagation of light in a medium is a rather complicated process involving the charges within the medium ; a velocity c/n can be attributed to the propagation where n is the index of re-fraction of the medium. If the medium itself moves in the direction of the propagation with a speed v then $w = c/n$ will be the speed of light propagation relative to the medium. The speed relative to a frame at rest can then be obtained by Einstein's equation

$$w' = \frac{w + v}{1 + (wv/c^2)} \tag{17.41}$$

Inserting here $w = c/n$ and retaining terms of first and zero order in c we get

$$w' = \frac{c}{n} + v\left(1 - \frac{1}{n^2}\right) = w + v\left(1 - \frac{1}{n^2}\right) \tag{17.42}$$

The coefficient of v bears the name Fresnel's convection coefficient.

The fact that this coefficient is not unity shows that the addition of velocities must be performed according to Einstein's addition formula, corresponding to Lobachevsky geometry, and not according to the pre-relativistic rule based on Euclidean geometry.

The phenomenon of astronomical aberration consists basically in the fact that in two frames in relative motion the directions to one and the same star do not coincide but differ by the aberration. To find this quantity one should construct a Lobachevsky triangle with vertices at the points $\mathbf{v}_1$, $\mathbf{v}_2$ and $\mathbf{v}_3 = \mathbf{a}c$ where $\mathbf{v}_1$ and $\mathbf{v}_2$ are the velocities of bodies fixed in the two frames and $\mathbf{a}$ is a unit vector in the direction of the light wave emitted by the star. In the triangle $\mathbf{v}_1$, $\mathbf{v}_2$, $\mathbf{v}_3$ the angle at the vertex $\mathbf{v}_3$ will be zero (see equation (17.44) below), and the sum of the two angles at v_1 and v_2 will be less than two right angles by the magnitude of the aberration. (If the geometry were Euclidean the sum of these angles would be equal to two right angles.)

The required trigonometrical calculation can easily be performed using the formula

$$\cos \alpha_1 = \frac{(\mathbf{v}_2 - \mathbf{v}_1)(\mathbf{v}_3 - \mathbf{v}_1) - (1/c^2)[\mathbf{v}_2 \times \mathbf{v}_1][\mathbf{v}_3 \times \mathbf{v}_1]}{\sqrt{\{(\mathbf{v}_2 - \mathbf{v}_1)^2 - (1/c^2)[\mathbf{v}_2 \times \mathbf{v}_1]^2\}} \cdot \sqrt{\{(\mathbf{v}_3 - \mathbf{v}_1)^2 - (1/c^2)[\mathbf{v}_3 \times \mathbf{v}_1]^2\}}} \tag{17.43}$$

and two other formulae obtained from (17.43) by cyclic permutation of the suffixes 1, 2 and 3.

First of all, since $v_3^2 = c^2$, we have

$$\cos \alpha_3 = 1; \qquad \alpha_3 = 0 \tag{17.44}$$

We then choose a frame such that

$$\mathbf{v}_1 + \mathbf{v}_2 =: 0 \tag{17.45}$$

and put $\qquad |\mathbf{v}_1| = |\mathbf{v}_2| = v; \qquad \mathbf{a} \cdot \mathbf{v}_1 = -\mathbf{a} \cdot \mathbf{v}_2 = v \cos \beta \tag{17.46}$

The relative speed of the two systems will be

$$v_{12} = \frac{2v}{1 + v^2/c^2} \tag{17.47}$$

From (17.43) we get

$$\cos \alpha_1 = \frac{v - c \cos \beta}{c - v \cos \beta}; \qquad \sin \alpha_1 = \frac{\{\sqrt{(c^2 - v^2)}\} \sin \beta}{c - v \cos \beta} \tag{17.48}$$

and, by analogy,

$$\cos \alpha_2 = \frac{v + c \cos \beta}{c + v \cos \beta}; \qquad \sin \alpha_2 = \frac{\{\sqrt{(c^2 - v^2)}\} \sin \beta}{c + v \cos \beta} \tag{17.49}$$

Denoting the magnitude of aberration by δ we can put

$$\delta = \pi - \alpha_1 - \alpha_2 - \alpha_3 = \pi - \alpha_1 - \alpha_2 \tag{17.50}$$

The previous equations give

$$2 \sin^2 \tfrac{1}{2}\delta = 1 + \cos (\alpha_1 + \alpha_2) = \frac{2v^2 \sin^2 \beta}{c^2 - v^2 \cos^2 \beta} \tag{17.51}$$

whence $\qquad \tan \tfrac{1}{2}\delta = \dfrac{v \sin \beta}{\sqrt{(c^2 - v^2)}} \tag{17.52}$

In astronomical observations one compares the apparent position of a star at times of different direction of the Earth's orbital motion (annual aberration). Since only the relative velocities of the bodies that receive the starlight enter our considerations, the overall motion of the Solar System relative to the stars considered will evidently have no effect as long as its velocity is constant during the lengths of time involved. It is, therefore, not possible to determine the velocity of a star relative to the Earth or the Sun by observing its aberration.

CHAPTER II

THE THEORY OF RELATIVITY IN TENSOR FORM

18. Some Remarks on the Covariance of Equations

In Section 6, when we discussed the basic postulates of the Theory of Relativity, we established certain general requirements to which any equations must conform, which determine the course of physical processes and do not involve initial conditions. These requirements fix the rules according to which such equations must transform on passing from one inertial frame to another.

According to the Principle of Relativity the rules for transforming the independent variables and the unknown functions entering the equations must be such that the equations stated in one inertial frame are equivalent to equations *of the same form* in any other inertial frame.

We have already used this requirement in discussing the Lorentz transformation. Indeed, we obtained this transformation from the condition that the equation for wave front propagation

$$\frac{1}{c^2}\left(\frac{\partial \omega}{\partial t}\right)^2 - \left[\left(\frac{\partial \omega}{\partial x}\right)^2 + \left(\frac{\partial \omega}{\partial y}\right)^2 + \left(\frac{\partial \omega}{\partial z}\right)^2\right] = 0 \qquad (18.01)$$

should preserve its form and also that uniform rectilinear motion should remain uniform and rectilinear in all inertial frames. Thus the rules for transforming the independent variables, i.e. the space and time coordinates, have already been fixed, by the above requirements, but we have yet to consider the transformation rules for the unknown functions occurring in the equations.

The simplest transformation rule is simple invariance. For instance, in the case of equation (18.01) ω is the unknown function. It is determined by the wave front equation

$$\omega(x, y, z, t) = 0 \qquad (18.02)$$

The transformed function ω', giving the wave front equation in the new variables

$$\omega'(x', y', z', t') = 0 \qquad (18.03)$$

is simply equal to the old function; its form is determined by the condition

$$\omega'(x', y', z', t') \equiv \omega(x, y, z, t) \qquad (18.04)$$

However, in the majority of problems the form of an equation is only conserved if the Lorentz transformation on the independent variables is accompanied by certain transformations of the unknown functions. If a transformation exists such that the new functions, expressed in the terms of the new variables, satisfy equations of the same form as do the old functions in the old variables, the equations are termed *covariant*.

The requirement of covariance of equations under Lorentz transformations is a necessary consequence of the Principle of Relativity. On the other hand, it is clear that not all equations are covariant. We shall have to examine the equations used in the physical description of various processes, e.g. the equations of electrodynamics and of mechanics, in order to decide whether they are covariant or not. If some of them are not, we shall have to alter them to a covariant form.

A preliminary to investigating covariance and to formulating covariant equations is the study of the quantities with the simplest transformation laws. Only linear laws need be considered. The complete classification of quantities according to their transformation laws is a question for Group Theory. We cannot here deal with it in its full generality and shall confine ourselves to what is essential for the formulation of the basic equations of mechanics and electrodynamics.

19. Definition of a Tensor in Three Dimensions and some Remarks on Covariant Quantities

The equations describing a rotation of the axes of a spatial coordinate frame are

$$x'_i = \sum_{k=1}^{3} \alpha_{ik} x_k \qquad (i, k = 1, 2, 3) \tag{19.01}$$
$$x_i = \sum_{k=1}^{3} \alpha_{ik} x'_i$$

where the α_{ik} are the direction cosines relating the old and the new axes. Formally we can define a three-dimensional vector as a set of quantities (A_1, A_2, A_3), called components, which transform according to

$$A'_i = \sum_{k=1}^{3} \alpha_{ik} A_k \tag{19.02}$$

when the axes are rotated. A special case of a vector is the coordinate vector for which $A_1 = x_1$, $A_2 = x_2$ and $A_3 = x_3$.

Let us assume that two vectors are given and that their components A_i and B_i are connected by the linear relation

$$B_i = \sum_{k=1}^{3} T_{ik} A_k \tag{19.03}$$

After a rotation of the axes the new vector components will be connected by the analogous relation

$$B'_i = \sum_{k=1}^{3} T'_{ik} A'_k \tag{19.04}$$

with

$$T'_{ik} = \sum_{j,\,l=1}^{3} \alpha_{ij} \alpha_{kl} T_{jl} \tag{19.05}$$

For the old and the new components of the vector B_i must be connected by the same transformation as those of A_i. If first we express the B'_i in terms of the B_i; and then in (19.03) express the A_i in terms of the A'_i, we obtain (19.04) and (19.05).

Thus the set of quantities T_{ik} transforms according to (19.05) when the axes are rotated. Such a set is called a tensor, or more precisely a tensor of the second rank. (In general the rank of a tensor is equal to the number of suffixes attached to it.)

Examples of tensors occur even in non-relativistic mechanics. Thus the components of the angular momentum of a rigid body (B_i) are connected with the components of its angular velocity (A_i) by relations of the form (19.03) where T_{ik} is the inertia tensor. Another example occurs in the theory of elasticity, where similar relations give the connection between the components (dF_x, dF_y, dF_z) of the force on some surface element and the projections (dS_x, dS_y, dS_z) of the surface element on to the coordinate planes. In this case the set of coefficients is the stress tensor. In both these examples the tensor T_{ik} is symmetric in its suffixes, but tensors also exist which do not have this property.

Equation (19.05) shows that the components of a tensor transform like the products $x_i \xi_k$ of the coordinates (x_1, x_2, x_3) and (ξ_1, ξ_2, ξ_3) of two points, which may be coincident $(x_i = \xi_i)$.

Let us consider an antisymmetric tensor, i.e. one whose components satisfy the relation

$$T_{ik} + T_{ki} = 0 \tag{19.06}$$

An example of such a tensor is the set of antisymmetric combinations formed from the products of the coordinates of two points

$$T_{ik} = x_i \xi_k - \xi_i x_k \tag{19.07}$$

As the suffixes we are here concerned with can only take on the three values (1, 2, 3), we can replace any pair of suffixes by the single missing one and put

$$\begin{aligned}
T_{23} &= -T_{32} = T_1 \\
T_{31} &= -T_{13} = T_2 \\
T_{12} &= -T_{21} = T_3
\end{aligned} \tag{19.08}$$

We introduce the antisymmetric system of quantities defined as
$\varepsilon_{ikl} = +1$, if (i, k, l) is an even permutation of (1, 2, 3);
$\varepsilon_{ikl} = -1$, if (i, k, l) is an odd permutation of (1, 2, 3);
$\varepsilon_{ikl} = 0$ if any of the suffixes are equal.
Then (19.08) may be written as

$$T_l = \frac{1}{2} \sum_{i,k=1}^{3} \varepsilon_{ikl} T_{ik} \tag{19.09}$$

The properties of the ε_{ikl} ensure that in fact the sum in (19.09) has only two terms and if (i, k, l) is an even permutation of (1, 2, 3) the previous equation may be written as

$$T_l = T_{ik} \tag{19.09*}$$

Using the antisymmetry condition we can replace (19.05) by

$$T'_{ik} = \frac{1}{2} \sum_{p,q=1}^{3} (\alpha_{ip}\alpha_{kq} - \alpha_{iq}\alpha_{kp}) T_{pq} \tag{19.10}$$

In this sum three of the nine terms vanish, namely those with $p = q$. The other six are equal in pairs, so that only three essentially different terms occur.

Let (i, k, l) and (p, q, r) be even permutations of $(1, 2, 3)$. Using the notation (19.09) and putting

$$\alpha_{ip}\alpha_{kq} - \alpha_{iq}\alpha_{kp} = \beta_{lr} \tag{19.11}$$

we can rewrite equation (19.10) as

$$T'_l = \sum_{r=1}^{3} \beta_{lr} T_r \tag{19.12}$$

Let us now consider the determinant

$$\Delta = \begin{vmatrix} \alpha_{11} & \alpha_{12} & \alpha_{13} \\ \alpha_{21} & \alpha_{22} & \alpha_{23} \\ \alpha_{31} & \alpha_{32} & \alpha_{33} \end{vmatrix} \tag{19.13}$$

By the orthogonality of the transformation $\Delta^2 = 1$, and, in particular, if the transformation is purely a rotation of the axes $\Delta = +1$, while if the rotation is accompanied by a reflexion, i.e. a reversal of one or of three axes, $\Delta = -1$. In both cases

$$\beta_{lr} = \Delta \cdot \alpha_{lr} \tag{19.14}$$

Thus for a simple rotation of the axes we have

$$T'_l = \sum_{r=1}^{3} \alpha_{lr} T_r \tag{19.15}$$

and for an "improper orthogonal transformation", i.e. a rotation with reflexion,

$$T'_l = - \sum_{r=1}^{3} \alpha_{lr} T_r \tag{19.16}$$

. Equations (19.15) and (19.16) show that in a pure rotation the set of quantities (19.08) transforms as a vector and in a rotation with reflexion their transformation is the same as for a vector except for a change of sign of all components. A set of quantities having this transformation law is conventionally called an *axial* vector as distinct from a *polar* vector which is one that obeys (19.02) in all transformations. The vector product of two polar vectors is easily seen to be an axial vector. To give physical examples (in terms of three dimensional vector algebra), the vector of electric field intensity is polar and the vector of magnetic field intensity is axial. Equations (19.08) show that an axial vector is in essence a tensor of the second rank, therefore if the terms " vector " and " tensor " are used in the sense of definitions (19.02) and (19.05) one can do without the term " axial vector ".

Tensors of higher rank in three dimensional Euclidean space can be defined similarly. For instance, a tensor of the third rank is a set of quantities T_{ijk} which transform on rotation according to the law

$$T'_{ijk} = \sum_{l, m, n=1}^{3} \alpha_{il}\alpha_{jm}\alpha_{kn} T_{lmn} \tag{19.17}$$

Further, a quantity that does not change when the axes are rotated can also be considered to be a tensor, namely a tensor of zero rank. Such a quantity is called a *scalar* or an *invariant*.

Given a tensor of the second rank one can find a linear combination of its components which does not change when the axes are rotated, and thus is a scalar. The linear combination having this property is the sum of the diagonal elements of the tensor, i.e. the quantity

$$T = \sum_i T_{ii} \tag{19.18}$$

Using the property

$$\sum_i \alpha_{ij}\alpha_{il} = \delta_{jl} \tag{19.19}$$

of the coefficients of an orthogonal transformation one verifies easily that (19.05) leads to

$$T' = T \tag{19.20}$$

so that T is a scalar. Similarly, from the components of a third rank tensor, one can obtain three vectors, namely

$$A_l = \sum_m T_{lmm} ; \qquad B_l = \sum_m T_{mlm} ; \qquad C_l = \sum_m T_{mml} \tag{19.21}$$

One can ask whether it is possible to replace tensors by other quantities of various ranks in such a way that it is no longer possible to form from components of one rank any linear combinations that transform like quantities of lower rank.

This can indeed be done and the resulting quantities have the transformation properties of solid harmonics. We recall that a solid harmonic $P_{lm}(x, y, z)$ is a harmonic polynomial which, expressed in terms of spherical polar coordinates

$$x = r \sin \vartheta \cos \varphi ; \qquad y = r \sin \vartheta \sin \varphi ; \qquad z = \cos \vartheta$$

becomes a product of r^l with a surface harmonic

$$r^l Y_{lm}(\vartheta, \varphi) = P_{lm}(x, y, z)$$

The order l is equal to the rank of the corresponding tensor, but the number of linearly independent " components " will be less than for a tensor. If the coordinate frame is rotated the new polynomial $P_{lm}(x', y', z')$ can be expressed as a linear combination of the old polynomials $P_{lm}(x, y, z)$, all with the same l, and with m taking on the values $m = -l, -l+1, \ldots, l$. The coefficients of this linear transformation determine the desired transformation law for quantities of rank l.

One final remark : We have assumed in our discussions that the tensors or related quantities are, by their physical meaning, completely determined, including their signs. Correspondingly, the coefficients in our transformation formulae were single-valued functions of the cosines α_{ik}. However, one can also imagine quantities that are only defined except for a sign, so that only quadratic expressions in them are fully determined. In this case the coefficients of their transformations need not be uniquely fixed by the α_{ik} but may instead be chosen to be determined only apart from their sign (the same in all coefficients). This leads to a new type of physical quantity, the so-called spinor, and to a corresponding generalization of spherical harmonics and their transformation law. Such quantities are used in quantum mechanics.

Tensors are thus not the only geometrical quantities with a definite transformation law, but in ordinary, non-quantal applications of the Theory of Relativity the consideration of tensors is sufficient.

20. Definition of a Four-Dimensional Vector

In the preceding section we summarized the definition of tensors in Euclidean space. We must now generalize this definition to apply to the four-dimensional space-time manifold. The part played before by rotations of the axes is now taken over by Lorentz transformations. An essentially new feature is the difference of sign between the space terms and the time term in the expression

$$ds^2 = c^2dt^2 - dx^2 - dy^2 - dz^2 \tag{20.01}$$

which gives the square of an infinitesimal four-dimensional interval. We have seen that the invariance of (20.01) characterizes Lorentz transformations in the same way as the invariance of

$$dl^2 = dx^2 + dy^2 + dz^2 \tag{20.02}$$

characterizes rotations of spatial axes.

The difference in sign is extremely important for the whole theory because it reflects the existence of a deep distinction between space and time.

It would be possible to impose the same sign on all terms of ds^2 by introducing imaginary quantities—imaginary space coordinates or imaginary time. This course was adopted by Minkowski and by Umov; but we believe that it is not appropriate to introduce a symmetry between space and time into our equations in this manner because it obscures the actually existing distinction between them and does not have any mathematical advantages. Therefore we shall continue to use real space variables and a real time.

If we put

$$ct = x_0; \qquad x = x_1; \qquad y = x_2; \qquad z = x_3 \tag{20.03}$$

the expression for ds^2 becomes

$$ds^2 = dx_0^2 - dx_1^2 - dx_2^2 - dx_3^2 = \sum_{k=0}^{3} e_k \, dx_k^2 \tag{20.04}$$

where the quantities e_k are equal to ± 1 (see (8.25)). The direct and inverse Lorentz transformations can be written as

$$x_i' = \sum_{k=0}^{3} e_k a_{ik} x_k \tag{20.05}$$

and

$$x_i = \sum_{k=0}^{3} e_k a_{ki} x_k' \tag{20.06}$$

Therefore the differentials of old and new coordinates will be connected by

$$dx_i' = \sum_{k=0}^{3} e_k a_{ik} dx_k \tag{20.07}$$

and the partial derivatives of any function φ with respect to the old and the new coordinates by

$$\frac{\partial \varphi}{\partial x_i'} = \sum_{k=0}^{3} e_i a_{ik} \frac{\partial \varphi}{\partial x_k} \tag{20.08}$$

If the quadratic form (20.04) were definite, all the numbers e_k would be equal and so would the coefficients in (20.07) and (20.08). In fact, we have

$$e_0 = 1; \qquad e_1 = e_2 = e_3 = -1 \tag{20.09}$$

and some of the corresponding coefficients in the two equations differ in sign.

In contrast to the case of purely spatial rotations, the transformation laws are different for coordinate differentials and for partial derivatives with respect to the coordinates. This must be remembered when defining a vector. We must distinguish between vectors whose components transform like the partial derivatives of the coordinates and those for which they transform like coordinate differentials. The former will be called *covariant*, the latter *contravariant*. We shall write the components of a covariant vector with *suffixes*, or lower indices, and the components of a contravariant one with *superfixes*, or upper indices. Thus the transformation law for a covariant vector is written as

$$A'_i = \sum_{k=0}^{3} e_i a_{ik} A_k \tag{20.10}$$

and for a contravariant one as

$$A'^i = \sum_{k=0}^{3} e_k a_{ik} A^k \tag{20.11}$$

These relations can also be expressed as

$$A'_i = \sum_{k=0}^{3} \frac{\partial x_k}{\partial x_i} A_k \tag{20.12}$$

and

$$A'^i = \sum_{k=0}^{3} \frac{\partial x'_i}{\partial x_k} A^k \tag{20.13}$$

One should note that the coordinates and their differentials are exceptional in violating the rule of index positioning. The notation dx_0, dx_1, dx_2, dx_3 is customary although by the general rule one should write $(dx)^0$, $(dx)^1$, $(dx)^2$ and $(dx)^3$.

If a covariant vector A_i is given we can always introduce a corresponding contravariant vector by putting

$$A^i = e_i A_i \tag{20.14}$$

The two vectors are not essentially different and we shall speak not of two vectors but of the covariant and contravariant components of the same vector and denote them by the same letter.

The scalar product of two vectors A_i and B_i is defined as the sum

$$\sum_{i=0}^{3} e_i A_i B_i = \sum_{i=0}^{3} e_i A^i B^i \tag{20.15}$$

It can also be written as

$$\sum_{i=0}^{3} A_i B^i = \sum_{i=0}^{3} A^i B_i \tag{20.16}$$

This quantity is invariant under Lorentz transformations.

The scalar product of a vector with itself

$$\sum_{i=0}^{3} A_i A^i = (A_0)^2 - (A_1)^2 - (A_2)^2 - (A_3)^2 \tag{20.17}$$

can be positive or negative. A vector for which (20.17) is positive is called " *time-like* " and a vector for which this expression is negative is called " *space-like* ".

As an example of a time-like vector we can mention the four-dimensional velocity, whose components are defined by the equations

$$u^0 = \frac{c}{\sqrt{(1 - v^2/c^2)}}; \qquad u^i = \frac{v_i}{\sqrt{(1 - v^2/c^2)}} \qquad (i = 1, 2, 3) \qquad (20.18)$$

The fact that this set of quantities is a vector can be seen as follows : We know that the quantity

$$c \, d\tau = ds = \{\sqrt{(c^2 - v^2)}\} \, dt \qquad (20.19)$$

is invariant ; on the other hand the quantities (20.18) can be written in the form

$$u^0 = c \frac{dt}{d\tau} = \frac{dx_0}{d\tau}; \qquad u^i = \frac{dx_i}{d\tau} \qquad (i = 1, 2, 3) \qquad (20.20)$$

Hence it is clear that u^0, u^1, u^2 and u^3 transform like the differentials of the coordinates x_0, x_1, x_2, x_3. They are thus components of a contravariant vector. That the velocity vector is time-like follows from the identity

$$(u^0)^2 - (u^1)^2 - (u^2)^2 - (u^3)^2 = c^2 \qquad (20.21)$$

The four-dimensional vector of acceleration whose components are defined by

$$w^0 = \frac{du^0}{d\tau}; \qquad w^i = \frac{du^i}{d\tau} \qquad (i = 1, 2, 3) \qquad (20.22)$$

is an example of a space-like vector. In more detail, we can write

$$w^0 = \frac{1}{\sqrt{(1 - v^2/c^2)}} \frac{d}{dt}\left(\frac{c}{\sqrt{(1 - v^2/c^2)}}\right)$$

$$w^i = \frac{1}{\sqrt{(1 - v^2/c^2)}} \frac{d}{dt}\left(\frac{1}{\sqrt{(1 - v^2/c^2)}} \frac{dx_i}{dt}\right) \qquad (i = 1, 2, 3) \qquad (20.23)$$

The space-like nature of this vector is proved by differentiating the identity (20.21) with respect to time, or to τ, which gives

$$u^0 w^0 - u^1 w^1 - u^2 w^2 - u^3 w^3 = 0 \qquad (20.24)$$

or
$$c w^0 - v_1 w^1 - v_2 w^2 - v_3 w^3 = 0 \qquad (20.25)$$

Hence we get the inequality

$$(w^0)^2 < \frac{v^2}{c^2} \{(w^1)^2 + (w^2)^2 + (w^3)^2\} < (w^1)^2 + (w^2)^2 + (w^3)^2 \qquad (20.26)$$

which proves our statement that w is space-like.

21. Four-Dimensional Tensors

One can define tensors of the second and higher ranks in the four-dimensional space time manifold just as in three-dimensional space.

A set of quantities transforming under Lorentz transformations according to the law

$$T'_{ik} = \sum_{j,l=0}^{3} \frac{\partial x_j}{\partial x'_i} \frac{\partial x_l}{\partial x'_k} T_{jl} \qquad (21.01)$$

or
$$T'_{ik} = \sum_{j,l=0}^{3} e_i e_k a_{ij} a_{kl} T_{jl} \qquad (21.02)$$

is called a covariant tensor of the second rank. Similarly a set of quantities transforming according to

$$T'^{ik} = \sum_{j,\,l=0}^{3} \frac{\partial x'_i}{\partial x_j} \frac{\partial x'_k}{\partial x_l} T^{jl} \tag{21.03}$$

or
$$T'^{ik} = \sum_{j,\,l=0}^{3} e_j e_l a_{ij} a_{kl} T^{jl} \tag{21.04}$$

is called a contravariant tensor. Lastly, one can also define a mixed tensor of the second rank as one that is covariant in one index and contravariant in the other. Its components transform according to

$$T'^{i}_{k} = \sum_{j,\,l=0}^{3} \frac{\partial x'_i}{\partial x_j} \frac{\partial x_l}{\partial x'_k} T^{j}_{l} \tag{21.05}$$

or
$$T'^{i}_{k} = \sum_{j,\,l=0}^{3} e_j e_k a_{ij} a_{kl} T^{j}_{l} \tag{21.06}$$

If all four numbers e_i were equal, the coefficients in (21.02), (21.04) and (21.06) would be the same, in fact there are sign differences between corresponding coefficients.

The transformation formulae (21.02), (21.04) and (21.06) are not essentially different, and one can easily pass from quantities transforming according to one of them to others transforming according to either of the other two. To do this one simply puts

$$T^{ik} = e_i e_k T_{ik} \tag{21.07}$$

while T^i_k may be defined either as

$$T^i_{\cdot k} = e_i T_{ik} \tag{21.08}$$

or as
$$T^i_{\cdot k} = e_i T_{ki} \tag{21.09}$$

If the tensor is symmetric the quantities (21.08) and (21.09) are the same. Just as for a vector, we shall not speak of different tensors but of covariant, contravariant and mixed components of one and the same tensor.

Similarly, tensors of the third and higher ranks may be introduced. For example a tensor of third rank with three covariant indices transforms according to the law

$$T'_{ikm} = \sum_{j,\,l,\,n=0}^{3} \frac{\partial x_j}{\partial x'_i} \frac{\partial x_l}{\partial x'_k} \frac{\partial x_n}{\partial x'_m} T_{jln} \tag{21.10}$$

or
$$T'_{ikm} = \sum_{j,\,l,\,n=0}^{3} e_i e_k e_m a_{ij} a_{kl} a_{mn} T_{jln} \tag{21.11}$$

As in the three-dimensional case, one can form a scalar from components of a second rank tensor, namely

$$T = \sum_{i=0}^{3} e_i T_{ii} \tag{21.12}$$

and three vectors can be constructed from the components of a tensor of the third rank :

$$A_i = \sum_k e_k T_{ikk} ; \qquad B_i = \sum_k e_k T_{kik} ; \qquad C_i = \sum_k e_k T_{kki} \tag{21.13}$$

We shall not dwell on the question touched on at the end of Section 19 concerning quantities other than tensors whose transformation laws are the simplest in a certain sense. This is because in all non-quantal applications of the Theory of Relativity the main role is played by tensors.

Given two tensors other tensors can be constructed of a rank equal to the sum, or to the difference, of the ranks of the given tensors and also tensors of ranks intermediate between these, but of the same parity as the sum and difference. We shall show this by examples. In Section 20 we saw that two vectors A_i and B_i can form the scalar

$$C = \sum_{i=0}^{3} e_i A_i B_i \tag{21.14}$$

Vectors are to be thought of as tensors of the first rank and scalars as tensors of zero rank. We can also use the same vectors to construct two tensors of second rank, namely

$$C_{ik} = A_i B_k \quad \text{and} \quad C_{ik} = B_i A_k \tag{21.15}$$

Given a tensor of second rank T_{ik} and a vector A_i, the quantity

$$B_i = \sum_{k} e_k A_k T_{ik} \tag{21.16}$$

will be a vector and the quantity

$$C_{ikl} = A_i T_{kl} \tag{21.17}$$

a third rank tensor; so will the quantities obtained by interchanging suffixes on the right of (21.17).

As a last example we take second rank tensors T_{ik} and U_{ik} and form the scalar

$$C = \sum_{i,k=0}^{3} e_i e_k T_{ik} U_{ik} \tag{21.18}$$

the second rank tensor

$$C_{ik} = \sum_{m} e_m T_{im} U_{km} \tag{21.19}$$

and the fourth rank tensor

$$C_{iklm} = T_{ik} U_{lm} \tag{21.20}$$

In this case, evidently

$$C_{ik} = \sum_{m} e_m C_{imkm} \tag{21.21}$$

and

$$C = \sum_{i} e_i C_{ii} \tag{21.22}$$

The tensor character of all these quantities is readily verified from the properties of the coefficients of a Lorentz transformation as given by (10.04) and (10.05).

It should be observed that in all sums containing products of covariant tensor components these products are multiplied by the sign factors, e_i, e_k, ... where i, k, etc., are suffixes over which a summation is performed. Instead one can write these sums so as to have each index occurring once as the covariant suffix of one tensor, and the other time as the contravariant superfix of a second tensor. In this form the sign factors do not appear. Thus, for example, the scalar product (21.14) can be written in the form (20.16) and the sum (21.18), using (21.07), as

$$C = \sum_{i,k=0}^{3} T^{ik} U_{ik} \tag{21.23}$$

Given a tensor, other tensors can be obtained not only by multiplication by a second tensor but also by differentiation. The operation of differentiating with respect to a coordinate x_i then appears in place of multiplication by a covariant component of some vector. For instance, the quantity

$$C = \sum_{i=0}^{3} e_i \frac{\partial A_i}{\partial x_i} = \sum_{i=0}^{3} \frac{\partial A^i}{\partial x_i} \tag{21.24}$$

is a scalar and the set of quantities

$$B_i = \sum_{k=0}^{3} e_k \frac{\partial T_{ik}}{\partial x_k} \tag{21.25}$$

is a vector (the divergence of the tensor T_{ik}). If in particular

$$A_i = \frac{\partial \varphi}{\partial x_i} \tag{21.26}$$

where φ is some scalar, the result of inserting A_i into (21.24),

$$\Box \varphi = \sum_{i=0}^{3} e_i \frac{\partial^2 \varphi}{\partial x_i^2} = \frac{\partial^2 \varphi}{\partial x_0^2} - \frac{\partial^2 \varphi}{\partial x_1^2} - \frac{\partial^2 \varphi}{\partial x_2^2} - \frac{\partial^2 \varphi}{\partial x_3^2} \tag{21.27}$$

must also be a scalar. The symbol $\Box$ is the d'Alembert operator.

22. Pseudo-Tensors

In addition to tensors it is convenient to consider other quantities whose transformation law depends on the sign of the determinant

$$D = \frac{D(x_0, x_1, x_2, x_3)}{D(x_0', x_1', x_2', x_3')} = \text{Det}\,(e_i a_{ik}) \tag{22.01}$$

of the transformation. The properties of the coefficients in a Lorentz transformation ensure that the square of D is always unity. D itself will be $+1$ for proper Lorentz transformations, i.e. those which preserve the sense of time and also the right- or left-handedness of the spatial axes, but -1 for improper transformations. Although we agreed to consider proper transformations only, it is useful for the classification of geometric quantities to know also their behaviour for improper transformations.

We consider a set of quantities ε_{iklm}, antisymmetric with respect to all suffixes and with $\varepsilon_{0123} = 1$. It follows that if two or more suffixes are equal ε_{iklm} must vanish, that $\varepsilon_{iklm} = +1$ if $(i\,k\,l\,m)$ is an even permutation of $(0\,1\,2\,3)$ and that $\varepsilon_{iklm} = -1$ if it is an odd permutation.

The identity

$$\sum_{pqrs=0}^{3} \varepsilon_{pqrs} \frac{\partial x_p}{\partial x_i'} \frac{\partial x_q}{\partial x_k'} \frac{\partial x_r}{\partial x_l'} \frac{\partial x_s}{\partial x_m'} = D \cdot \varepsilon_{iklm} \tag{22.02}$$

is readily verified, for the left-hand side is the expansion of the determinant

$$\begin{vmatrix} \dfrac{\partial x_0}{\partial x_i'} & \dfrac{\partial x_0}{\partial x_k'} & \dfrac{\partial x_0}{\partial x_l'} & \dfrac{\partial x_0}{\partial x_m'} \\ \cdot & \cdot & \cdot & \cdot \\ \cdot & \cdot & \cdot & \cdot \\ \dfrac{\partial x_3}{\partial x_i'} & \dfrac{\partial x_3}{\partial x_k'} & \dfrac{\partial x_3}{\partial x_l'} & \dfrac{\partial x_3}{\partial x_m'} \end{vmatrix}$$

which is obtained from D by permuting columns, provided all four suffixes $(i\,k\,l\,m)$ are different, and which vanishes otherwise.

Equation (22.02) shows that if $D = 1$ the ε transform like components of a tensor, but that if $D = -1$ their transformation law differs in sign from the tensor rule. A set of quantities having such transformation laws is called a *pseudo-tensor*.

We can consider the ε_{iklm} to be covariant components of an antisymmetric pseudo-tensor of fourth rank. Its contravariant components are, by the general rule,

$$\varepsilon^{iklm} = e_i e_k e_l e_m \varepsilon_{iklm} \tag{22.03}$$

but since the ε are only different from zero if all suffixes are different, in which case $e_i e_k e_l e_m = e_0 e_1 e_2 e_3 = -1$, we have more simply

$$\varepsilon^{iklm} = -\varepsilon_{iklm} \tag{22.04}$$

If φ is a scalar the set of quantities

$$\varphi_{iklm} = \varphi \varepsilon_{iklm} \tag{22.05}$$

is an antisymmetrical pseudo-tensor of fourth rank. Such a pseudo-tensor has only one component, just like a scalar. Hence it is customarily known as a pseudo-scalar.

To every antisymmetric tensor A_{ik} of the second rank one can adjoin an antisymmetric pseudo-tensor $\overset{*}{A}{}^{ik}$ of the same rank by the equation

$$\overset{*}{A}{}^{ik} = \frac{1}{2} \sum_{l,\,m=0}^{3} \varepsilon^{iklm} A_{lm} \tag{22.06}$$

It is called the dual of the given tensor. Only two terms in the sum (22.06) differ from zero and these terms are equal, therefore we have

$$\overset{*}{A}{}^{10} = A_{23}; \qquad \overset{*}{A}{}^{20} = A_{31}; \qquad \overset{*}{A}{}^{30} = A_{12}$$

$$\overset{*}{A}{}^{23} = A_{10}; \qquad \overset{*}{A}{}^{31} = A_{20}; \qquad \overset{*}{A}{}^{12} = A_{30} \tag{22.07}$$

Similarly there corresponds to any antisymmetric tensor of the third rank a pseudo-vector—i.e. a pseudo-tensor of the first rank, given by the equation

$$\overset{*}{A}{}^{i} = \frac{1}{6} \sum_{k,\,l,\,m=0}^{3} \varepsilon^{iklm} A_{klm} \tag{22.08}$$

There are six non-vanishing terms in the sum, but all six are equal. Therefore we obtain the explicit form

$$\overset{*}{A}{}^{0} = -A_{123}; \qquad \overset{*}{A}{}^{1} = A_{230}; \qquad \overset{*}{A}{}^{2} = A_{310}; \qquad \overset{*}{A}{}^{3} = A_{120} \tag{22.09}$$

for the components of the pseudo-vector.

We shall refer for short to the " product of a tensor with a tensor ", meaning a tensor obtained by multiplying the components of two given tensors according to the rules of Section 21. Then we can say that the product of two pseudo-tensors, like the product of two tensors, is a tensor, but the product of a tensor with a pseudo-tensor is a pseudo-tensor. We have, in fact, already used this rule in forming the pseudo-tensor $\overset{*}{A}{}^{ik}$ and the pseudo-vector $\overset{*}{A}{}^{i}$.

23. Infinitesimal Lorentz Transformations

The general Lorentz transformation, including a shift of origin, has the form

$$x'_i = a_i + \sum_{k=0}^{3} e_k a_{ik} x_k \qquad (23.01)$$

We examine the case when this transformation is only infinitesimally different from the identity. In this case the constants a_i are infinitesimal and the coefficients a_{ik} may be written as

$$a_{ik} = e_k \delta_{ik} + \omega^{ik} \qquad (23.02)$$

where the ω^{ik} are infinitesimal. To stress the fact that the coordinates form a contravariant vector, we shall, in this section, write them with *superfixes*.

$$x^0 = ct; \qquad x^1 = x, \qquad x^2 = y, \qquad x^3 = z \qquad (23.03)$$

We shall likewise write the infinitesimal constants describing the shift of origin as a^i instead of a_i. In this notation the result of inserting (23.02) into (23.01) is

$$x'^i = x^i + a^i + \sum_{k=0}^{3} e_k \omega^{ik} x^k \qquad (23.04)$$

For an infinitesimal transformation the distinction between the given and the transformed frame is not important and therefore the differences

$$\Delta x^i = x'^i - x^i \qquad (23.05)$$

can be treated as the components of a vector referred to either system, say to the first one. So the expressions

$$\Delta x^i = a^i + \sum_{k=0}^{3} e_k \omega^{ik} x^k \qquad (23.06)$$

represent an infinitesimal contravariant vector. Hence the constants a^i themselves form such a vector and the quantities ω^{ik} a contravariant tensor. This tensor is antisymmetric, for on inserting (23.02) into the orthogonality conditions for the coefficients of a Lorentz transformation

$$\sum_{i=0}^{3} e_i a_{ik} a_{il} = e_k \delta_{kl} \qquad (23.07)$$

and neglecting terms of second order in the infinitesimals we get

$$\omega^{ik} + \omega^{ki} = 0 \qquad (23.08)$$

An antisymmetric tensor of rank 2 has six independent components. These six quantities together with the four components of the infinitesimal displacement vector a^i are the ten independent parameters that characterize the infinitesimal Lorentz transformation.

Let us perform two infinitesimal transformations consecutively, one with the parameters a^i, ω^{ik}, the other with parameters b^i, φ^{ik}. It is easy to see that, neglecting second order terms, the combined result of the transformations is equivalent to a single transformation with the parameters

$$c^i = a^i + b^i; \qquad \psi^{ik} = \omega^{ik} + \varphi^{ik} \qquad (23.09)$$

This shows in particular that the result of two infinitesimal transformations does not depend on the order in which they are performed. We can therefore consider a displacement of origin, a change to a moving frame and an infinitesimal rotation of the axes separately and in turn.

Putting

$$a^0 = c\tau; \qquad a^1 = a_x; \qquad a^2 = a_y; \qquad a^3 = a_z \qquad (23.10)$$

we get a transformation describing a change of time origin by τ to an *earlier* instant and a shift of spatial origin *backward* along the vector **a** and a distance equal to the magnitude of **a**. The passage to a frame moving with an infinitesimal velocity **V** is represented by the transformation

$$
\begin{aligned}
x' - x = \Delta x &= -V_x t \\
y' - y = \Delta y &= -V_y t \\
z' - z = \Delta z &= -V_z t
\end{aligned}
\qquad (23.11)
$$

of the space coordinates together with the transformation

$$
t' - t = \Delta t = -\frac{1}{c^2}(xV_x + yV_y + zV_z) \qquad (23.12)
$$

of the time.

Going from three- to four-dimensional symbols and comparing coefficients in (23.11) and (23.06) we get

$$
\omega^{10} = -\frac{V_x}{c}; \qquad \omega^{20} = -\frac{V_y}{c}; \qquad \omega^{30} = -\frac{V_z}{c} \qquad (23.13)
$$

On the other hand, comparing coefficients in (23.12) and (23.06) gives

$$
\omega^{01} = \frac{V_x}{c}; \qquad \omega^{02} = \frac{V_y}{c}; \qquad \omega^{03} = \frac{V_z}{c} \qquad (23.14)
$$

a result that is obvious from the antisymmetry of the tensor ω^{ik}.

Let us finally consider an infinitesimal rotation of spatial axes. By a well-known formula in kinematics we have

$$
\Delta \mathbf{r} = [\boldsymbol{\omega} \times \mathbf{r}] \qquad (23.15)
$$

where $\boldsymbol{\omega}$ is the vector of an infinitesimal rotation, having components equal to the angles of rotation about the axes of x, y and z.

Comparing (23.15) with (23.06) we get

$$
\omega^{23} = -\omega^{32} = \omega_x; \qquad \omega^{31} = -\omega^{13} = \omega_y; \qquad \omega^{12} = -\omega^{21} = \omega_z \qquad (23.16)
$$

We also write down the covariant components ω_{ik}. Lowering indices by the usual rule we get

$$
\omega_{10} = \frac{V_x}{c}; \qquad \omega_{20} = \frac{V_y}{c}; \qquad \omega_{30} = \frac{V_z}{c}
$$
$$
\omega_{23} = \omega_x; \qquad \omega_{31} = \omega_y; \qquad \omega_{12} = \omega_z \qquad (23.17)
$$

with all other components following from antisymmetry.

In conclusion we remark that it is possible to obtain the equations of finite Lorentz transformations from a study of the infinitesimal transformations, but we shall not discuss this question here.

24. The Transformation Laws for the Electromagnetic Field and the Covariance of Maxwell's Equations

Our derivation of the basic laws of the Theory of Relativity started from the propagation law for an electromagnetic wave front. This law is a result of Maxwell's equations as was shown in Section 3. We must now verify that Maxwell's equations are really covariant with respect to Lorentz transformations. To do this we must first find the law according to which an electromagnetic field transforms in going from one reference frame to another.

It is well known that the electromagnetic field can be expressed in terms of a scalar and a vector potential by the equations

$$H_1 = \frac{\partial A_3}{\partial x_2} - \frac{\partial A_2}{\partial x_3}; \qquad E_1 = -\frac{1}{c}\frac{\partial A_1}{\partial t} - \frac{\partial \Phi}{\partial x_1}$$

$$H_2 = \frac{\partial A_1}{\partial x_3} - \frac{\partial A_3}{\partial x_1}; \qquad E_2 = -\frac{1}{c}\frac{\partial A_2}{\partial t} - \frac{\partial \Phi}{\partial x_2} \qquad (24.01)$$

$$H_3 = \frac{\partial A_2}{\partial x_1} - \frac{\partial A_1}{\partial x_2}; \qquad E_3 = -\frac{1}{c}\frac{\partial A_3}{\partial t} - \frac{\partial \Phi}{\partial x_3}$$

The field becomes zero when, and only when, the linear differential form

$$\delta\varphi = -c\Phi\, dt + A_1\, dx_1 + A_2\, dx_2 + A_3\, dx_3 \qquad (24.02)$$

is a total differential. We assume that this linear form is invariant or scalar. This is so if A_1, A_2 and A_3 are the spatial (covariant) components of a four-dimensional vector whose fourth component is

$$A_0 = -\Phi \qquad (24.03)$$

Bearing in mind that $ct = x_0$ we can write $\delta\varphi$ in the form

$$\delta\varphi = \sum_{i=0}^{3} A_i\, dx_i \qquad (24.04)$$

The condition

$$\mathrm{div}\, \mathbf{A} + \frac{1}{c}\frac{\partial \Phi}{\partial t} = 0 \qquad (24.05)$$

usually imposed on the potentials is invariant under Lorentz transformations because it can be written as

$$\sum_{i=0}^{3} e_i \frac{\partial A_i}{\partial x_i} = 0 \qquad (24.06)$$

or, with the introduction of contravariant components, by

$$A^0 = A_0 = -\Phi; \qquad A^1 = -A_1; \qquad A^2 = -A_2; \qquad A^3 = -A_3 \qquad (24.07)$$

as

$$\sum_{i=0}^{3} \frac{\partial A^i}{\partial x_i} = 0 \qquad (24.08)$$

Inserting $x_0 = ct$ and $A_0 = -\Phi$ into (24.01) we rewrite the expressions for the fields in the new notation. For the electric field we get

$$E_1 = \frac{\partial A_0}{\partial x_1} - \frac{\partial A_1}{\partial x_0}$$

$$E_2 = \frac{\partial A_0}{\partial x_2} - \frac{\partial A_2}{\partial x_0} \qquad (24.09)$$

$$E_3 = \frac{\partial A_0}{\partial x_3} - \frac{\partial A_3}{\partial x_0}$$

while the expressions for the magnetic field remain unchanged. All the equations can be combined in the short form

$$F_{ik} = \frac{\partial A_k}{\partial x_i} - \frac{\partial A_i}{\partial x_k} \qquad (24.10)$$

where we have

$$\begin{aligned} H_1 &= F_{23} & E_1 &= F_{10} \\ H_2 &= F_{31} & E_2 &= F_{20} \\ H_3 &= F_{12} & E_3 &= F_{30} \end{aligned} \tag{24.11}$$

If (A_i) is a covariant vector, then (F_{ik}) is an antisymmetric tensor of second rank. Thus our assumption as to the vectorial nature of the potentials leads to the conclusion that the electromagnetic field is an antisymmetric tensor in the four-dimensional space-time manifold. From this it is easy to verify that Maxwell's equations are covariant for Lorentz transformations. We construct from derivatives of field components the third rank tensor

$$F_{ikl} = \frac{\partial F_{ik}}{\partial x_l} + \frac{\partial F_{kl}}{\partial x_i} + \frac{\partial F_{li}}{\partial x_k} \tag{24.12}$$

It is evidently antisymmetric. By (22.09) we can adjoin to it the pseudo-vector

$$\overset{*}{F}{}^0 = -F_{123}; \qquad \overset{*}{F}{}^1 = F_{230}; \qquad \overset{*}{F}{}^2 = F_{310}; \qquad \overset{*}{F}{}^3 = F_{120} \tag{24.13}$$

We calculate the components of this pseudo-vector and find

$$\begin{aligned}
\overset{*}{F}{}^0 &= -\frac{\partial F_{23}}{\partial x_1} - \frac{\partial F_{31}}{\partial x_2} - \frac{\partial F_{12}}{\partial x_3} = -\frac{\partial H_1}{\partial x_1} - \frac{\partial H_2}{\partial x_2} - \frac{\partial H_3}{\partial x_3} = -\operatorname{div} \mathbf{H} \\
\overset{*}{F}{}^1 &= \frac{\partial F_{23}}{\partial x_0} + \frac{\partial F_{02}}{\partial x_3} + \frac{\partial F_{30}}{\partial x_2} = \frac{1}{c}\frac{\partial H_1}{\partial t} - \frac{\partial E_2}{\partial x_3} + \frac{\partial E_3}{\partial x_2} \\
\overset{*}{F}{}^2 &= \frac{\partial F_{31}}{\partial x_0} + \frac{\partial F_{03}}{\partial x_1} + \frac{\partial F_{10}}{\partial x_3} = \frac{1}{c}\frac{\partial H_2}{\partial t} - \frac{\partial E_3}{\partial x_1} + \frac{\partial E_1}{\partial x_3} \\
\overset{*}{F}{}^3 &= \frac{\partial F_{12}}{\partial x_0} + \frac{\partial F_{01}}{\partial x_2} + \frac{\partial F_{20}}{\partial x_1} = \frac{1}{c}\frac{\partial H_3}{\partial t} - \frac{\partial E_1}{\partial x_2} + \frac{\partial E_2}{\partial x_1}
\end{aligned} \tag{24.14}$$

For ease of interpretation we have replaced x_0 by ct on the right-hand sides. By Maxwell's equations

$$\operatorname{curl} \mathbf{E} + \frac{1}{c}\frac{\partial \mathbf{H}}{\partial t} = 0; \qquad \operatorname{div} \mathbf{H} = 0 \tag{24.15}$$

so that the right-hand sides of all equations (24.14) are zero.

Therefore the first set of Maxwell's equations can be written in the covariant form

$$\overset{*}{F}{}^i = 0 \tag{24.16}$$

or

$$F_{ikl} = 0 \tag{24.17}$$

We now turn to the second set of Maxwell's equations, passing first from covariant field components to contravariant ones:

$$\begin{aligned} F^{23} &= H_1 & F^{10} &= -E_1 \\ F^{31} &= H_2 & F^{20} &= -E_2 \\ F^{12} &= H_3 & F^{30} &= -E_3 \end{aligned} \tag{24.18}$$

We form the contravariant vector

$$s^i = \sum_{k=0}^{3} \frac{\partial F^{ik}}{\partial x_k} \tag{24.19}$$

Then

$$s^0 = 0 + \frac{\partial F^{01}}{\partial x_1} + \frac{\partial F^{02}}{\partial x_2} + \frac{\partial F^{03}}{\partial x_3} = \frac{\partial E_1}{\partial x_1} + \frac{\partial E_2}{\partial x_2} + \frac{\partial E_3}{\partial x_3}$$

$$s^1 = \frac{\partial F^{10}}{\partial x_0} + 0 + \frac{\partial F^{12}}{\partial x_2} + \frac{\partial F^{13}}{\partial x_3} = -\frac{1}{c}\frac{\partial E_1}{\partial t} + \frac{\partial H_3}{\partial x_2} - \frac{\partial H_2}{\partial x_3}$$

$$s^2 = \frac{\partial F^{20}}{\partial x_0} + \frac{\partial F^{21}}{\partial x_1} + 0 + \frac{\partial F^{23}}{\partial x_3} = -\frac{1}{c}\frac{\partial E_2}{\partial t} + \frac{\partial H_1}{\partial x_3} - \frac{\partial H_3}{\partial x_1} \qquad (24.20)$$

$$s^3 = \frac{\partial F^{30}}{\partial x_0} + \frac{\partial F^{31}}{\partial x_1} + \frac{\partial F^{32}}{\partial x_2} + 0 = -\frac{1}{c}\frac{\partial E_3}{\partial t} + \frac{\partial H_2}{\partial x_1} - \frac{\partial H_1}{\partial x_2}$$

so that the zero component of s^i is

$$s^0 = \operatorname{div} \mathbf{E} \qquad (24.21)$$

while the spatial components are equal to the components of the three-dimensional vector

$$(s^1, s^2, s^3) = -\frac{1}{c}\frac{\partial \mathbf{E}}{\partial t} + \operatorname{curl} \mathbf{H} \qquad (24.22)$$

In free space the right-hand sides of these equations are zero and therefore the second set of Maxwell's equations in free space can be stated in the form

$$s^i \equiv \sum_{k=0}^{3} \frac{\partial F^{ik}}{\partial x_k} = 0 \qquad (24.23)$$

In a space occupied by charge of density ρ the Maxwell-Lorentz equations have the form

$$\operatorname{div} \mathbf{E} = 4\pi\rho ; \qquad \operatorname{curl} \mathbf{H} - \frac{1}{c}\frac{\partial \mathbf{E}}{\partial t} = \frac{4\pi}{c}\mathbf{j} \qquad (24.24)$$

where $\mathbf{j}$ is the current density. The covariance of Maxwell's equations is therefore assured if the quantities

$$s^0 = 4\pi\rho ; \qquad s^i = \frac{4\pi}{c}j_i \qquad (i = 1, 2, 3) \qquad (24.25)$$

represent the contravariant components of a four-dimensional vector. By the identity

$$\sum_{i,k=0}^{3} \frac{\partial^2 F^{ik}}{\partial x_i \partial x_k} = 0 \qquad (24.26)$$

we have

$$\sum_{i=0}^{3} \frac{\partial s^i}{\partial x_i} = 0 \qquad (24.27)$$

whence

$$\frac{\partial \rho}{\partial t} + \operatorname{div} \mathbf{j} = 0 \qquad (24.28)$$

As is well known, this equation expresses the law of conservation of charge.

The fact that the quantities (24.25) form a four-dimensional vector is perfectly consistent with the physical interpretation given to them by Lorentz. According to him $\mathbf{j} = \rho\mathbf{v}$ where ρ is the density of the charge and $\mathbf{v}$ its velocity. The four-dimensional current vector

$$\rho c, \rho v_1, \rho v_2, \rho v_3 \qquad (24.29)$$

is proportional to the four-dimensional velocity vector

$$u^0 = \frac{c}{\sqrt{(1 - v^2/c^2)}}; \qquad u^1 = \frac{v_1}{\sqrt{(1 - v^2/c^2)}}$$

$$u^2 = \frac{v_2}{\sqrt{(1 - v^2/c^2)}}; \qquad u^3 = \frac{v_3}{\sqrt{(1 - v^2/c^2)}}$$

$$(24.30)$$

(see (20.18)) with the coefficient of proportionality

$$\rho^* = \rho \sqrt{\left(1 - \frac{v^2}{c^2}\right)} \qquad (24.31)$$

This quantity is an invariant which has the physical significance of the charge density in that reference frame in which the charge is momentarily at rest.

We have verified the covariance of Maxwell's equations and have established that the transformations undergone by the electromagnetic field when going from one reference frame to another are those of an antisymmetric tensor of the second rank. We shall now state the transformation laws in an explicit form, introducing for the general coefficients of the Lorentz transformation their values for the case that the transformation does not involve a spatial rotation. We then have

$$a_{00} = \frac{1}{\sqrt{(1 - V^2/c^2)}}$$

$$a_{0i} = \frac{a_{00}}{c} V_i; \qquad a_{i0} = -\frac{a_{00}}{c} V_i \qquad (i = 1, 2, 3) \qquad (24.32)$$

$$a_{ik} = -\delta_{ik} - (a_{00} - 1)\frac{V_i V_k}{V^2} \qquad (i, k = 1, 2, 3)$$

Inserting these values into the general expression

$$F'_{ik} = e_i e_k \sum_{j, l=0}^{3} a_{ij} a_{kl} F_{jl} \qquad (24.33)$$

and using the antisymmetry of F_{ik} we get

$$F'_{23} = a_{00} F_{23} - (a_{00} - 1) \frac{V_1}{V^2} (V_1 F_{23} + V_2 F_{31} + V_3 F_{12})$$

$$- \frac{1}{c} a_{00} (V_2 F_{30} - V_3 F_{20}) \qquad (24.34)$$

and two similar expressions obtained from (24.34) by cyclic permutation of the suffixes 1, 2 and 3. We also get

$$F'_{10} = a_{00} F_{10} - (a_{00} - 1) \frac{V_1}{V^2} (V_1 F_{10} + V_2 F_{20} + V_3 F_{30})$$

$$+ \frac{1}{c} a_{00} (V_2 F_{12} - V_3 F_{31}) \qquad (24.35)$$

and two expressions obtained by cyclic permutation. Using (24.11) to pass to the usual notation for the electric and the magnetic fields and using three-dimensional vector algebra, we may write

$$E_1' = a_{00}E_1 - (a_{00} - 1)\frac{V_1}{V^2}(\mathbf{V} \cdot \mathbf{E}) + \frac{a_{00}}{c}[\mathbf{V} \times \mathbf{H}]_1$$

$$H_1' = a_{00}H_1 - (a_{00} - 1)\frac{V_1}{V^2}(\mathbf{V} \cdot \mathbf{H}) - \frac{a_{00}}{c}[\mathbf{V} \times \mathbf{E}]_1$$

(24.36)

Passing from the components to the vectors, replacing a_{00} by its value and regrouping terms a little, we obtain the final expressions

$$\mathbf{E}' = \frac{\mathbf{V}}{V^2}(\mathbf{V} \cdot \mathbf{E}) + \frac{1}{\sqrt{(1 - V^2/c^2)}}\left(\mathbf{E} - \frac{\mathbf{V}}{V^2}(\mathbf{V} \cdot \mathbf{E}) + \frac{1}{c}[\mathbf{V} \times \mathbf{H}]\right) \quad (24.37)$$

and $$\mathbf{H}' = \frac{\mathbf{V}}{V^2}(\mathbf{V} \cdot \mathbf{H}) + \frac{1}{\sqrt{(1 - V^2/c^2)}}\left(\mathbf{H} - \frac{\mathbf{V}}{V^2}(\mathbf{V} \cdot \mathbf{H}) - \frac{1}{c}[\mathbf{V} \times \mathbf{E}]\right) \quad (24.38)$$

For comparison we shall also state the transformation formulae for a four-dimensional covariant vector, using the usual vector notation for its space components.

$$A_0' = \frac{1}{\sqrt{(1 - V^2/c^2)}}\left(A_0 + \frac{1}{c}(\mathbf{V} \cdot \mathbf{A})\right) \quad (24.39)$$

and $$\mathbf{A}' = \mathbf{A} - \frac{\mathbf{V}}{V^2}(\mathbf{V} \cdot \mathbf{A}) + \frac{1}{\sqrt{(1 - V^2/c^2)}} \cdot \frac{\mathbf{V}}{V^2}\left((\mathbf{V} \cdot \mathbf{A}) + \frac{V^2}{c}A_0\right) \quad (24.40)$$

We note that the equations for the transformation of the fields give

$$\mathbf{E}' \cdot \mathbf{V} = \mathbf{E} \cdot \mathbf{V}; \qquad \mathbf{H}' \cdot \mathbf{V} = \mathbf{H} \cdot \mathbf{V} \quad (24.41)$$

This means that those parts of the electric and the magnetic field which are *parallel* to the velocity $\mathbf{V}$ remain unchanged. On the other hand for the spatial part of a four-dimensional vector the part *perpendicular* to the velocity remains invariant, for we have

$$\mathbf{A}' - \frac{\mathbf{V}}{V^2}(\mathbf{V} \cdot \mathbf{A}') = \mathbf{A} - \frac{\mathbf{V}}{V^2}(\mathbf{V} \cdot \mathbf{A}) \quad (24.42)$$

If we consider the particular Lorentz transformation with

$$V_x = V; \qquad V_y = V_z = 0 \quad (24.43)$$

the transformation equations simplify, giving

$$E_x' = E_x; \qquad\qquad\qquad H_x' = H_x$$

$$E_y = \frac{1}{\sqrt{(1 - V^2/c^2)}}\left(E_y - \frac{V}{c}H_z\right); \qquad H_y' = \frac{1}{\sqrt{(1 - V^2/c^2)}}\left(H_y + \frac{V}{c}E_z\right)$$

$$E_z' = \frac{1}{\sqrt{(1 - V^2/c^2)}}\left(E_z + \frac{V}{c}H_y\right); \qquad H_z' = \frac{1}{\sqrt{(1 - V^2/c^2)}}\left(H_z - \frac{V}{c}E_y\right)$$

(24.44)

One can construct two combinations from the field components that are invariant under Lorentz transformations. We have

$$E'^2 - H'^2 = E^2 - H^2 \quad (24.45)$$

and $$\mathbf{E}' \cdot \mathbf{H}' = \mathbf{E} \cdot \mathbf{H} \quad (24.46)$$

The first of these quantities is also invariant under improper Lorentz transformations (see Section 22) and is a scalar. The second changes sign in improper transformations, and therefore is a pseudo-scalar. This can easily be seen in tensor notation. We have

$$\mathbf{E}^2 - \mathbf{H}^2 = -\frac{1}{2} \sum_{i,k=0}^{3} F_{ik} F^{ik} \tag{24.47}$$

and

$$\mathbf{E} \cdot \mathbf{H} = \frac{1}{4} \sum_{i,k=0}^{3} F_{ik} \overset{*}{F}{}^{ik} \tag{24.48}$$

where $\overset{*}{F}{}^{ik}$ is an antisymmetric pseudo-tensor related to the field tensor by equations analogous to (22.06) and (22.07). We note that for a plane wave the quantities (24.45) and (24.46) vanish (in all frames).

As do Maxwell's equations themselves, the transformation equations for the field reveal a very close relation between the electric and the magnetic field. For instance, a field due to charges at rest in some frame will be an electrostatic one in that frame; but in another reference frame which moves relative to the first, a magnetic field is found in addition to the electric one. This is readily understood since a moving charge represents a current. Similarly a field that is purely magnetic in one frame will appear in another frame as a superposition of a magnetic and an electric field.

25. The Motion of a Charged Mass-Point in a given External Field

We now consider the motion of a particle of mass m and charge e in a given external field. As we already saw (Eq. (20.23)) the four-dimensional vector of acceleration has the components

$$w^0 = \frac{1}{\sqrt{(1 - v^2/c^2)}} \frac{d}{dt} \left(\frac{c}{\sqrt{(1 - v^2/c^2)}} \right);$$

$$w^i = \frac{1}{\sqrt{(1 - v^2/c^2)}} \frac{d}{dt} \left(\frac{1}{\sqrt{(1 - v^2/c^2)}} \frac{dx_i}{dt} \right) \qquad (i = 1, 2, 3) \tag{25.01}$$

The quantities here being differentiated with respect to time are the components of four-dimensional velocity

$$u^0 = \frac{c}{\sqrt{(1 - v^2/c^2)}}; \qquad u^i = \frac{1}{\sqrt{(1 - v^2/c^2)}} \frac{dx_i}{dt} \qquad (i = 1, 2, 3) \tag{25.02}$$

with

$$v^2 = \left(\frac{dx_1}{dt} \right)^2 + \left(\frac{dx_2}{dt} \right)^2 + \left(\frac{dx_3}{dt} \right)^2 \tag{25.03}$$

We introduce a primed reference frame such that in it the instantaneous velocity of the particle is zero. We then make the assumption that in this frame, which is instantaneously travelling with the particle, the acceleration as usually defined is proportional to the electric field

$$\frac{d^2 x_i'}{dt'^2} = \frac{e}{m} E_i' \tag{25.04}$$

This equation must now be stated in the original frame.

In the primed frame the four-dimensional velocity and acceleration are

$$u'^0 = c, \qquad u'^1 = u'^2 = u'^3 = 0 \tag{25.05}$$

and
$$w'^0 = 0, \qquad w'^i = \frac{d^2 x'^i}{dt'^2} \tag{25.06}$$

Thus in the primed frame the relation between the four-dimensional acceleration and the field is

$$w'^0 = 0, \qquad w'^i = \frac{e}{m} E'_i \tag{25.07}$$

Using the transformation rules for a contravariant vector (which are the same as the transformation rules for the coordinates) we find that

$$w^i = \sum_{k=0}^{3} e_k a_{ki} w'^k \tag{25.08}$$

Inserting into the right-hand side the values for w'^k from (25.07) we get for the four-dimensional acceleration in the original system

$$w^i = -\frac{e}{m} (a_{1i} E'_1 + a_{2i} E'_2 +_{3i} a E'_3) \tag{25.09}$$

The values of the a_{ik} must be inserted into this from (24.32), giving

$$w^0 = \frac{e}{m} \cdot \frac{a_{00}}{c} (\mathbf{V} \cdot \mathbf{E'}) \tag{25.10}$$

and
$$w^i = \frac{e}{m} \left(E'_i + (a_{00} - 1) \frac{V_i}{V^2} (\mathbf{V} \cdot \mathbf{E'}) \right) \tag{25.11}$$

Finally $\mathbf{E'}$ must be expressed in terms of $\mathbf{E}$ and $\mathbf{H}$. Since $\mathbf{V} \cdot \mathbf{E'} = \mathbf{V} \cdot \mathbf{E}$, equation (24.36), with a_{00} replaced by its explicit value, gives

$$w^0 = \frac{e}{m} \frac{1}{\sqrt{(c^2 - V^2)}} (\mathbf{V} \cdot \mathbf{E}) \tag{25.12}$$

and
$$w^i = \frac{e}{m} \frac{c}{\sqrt{(c^2 - V^2)}} \left(\mathbf{E} + \frac{1}{c} [\mathbf{V} \times \mathbf{H}] \right)_i \tag{25.13}$$

Here $\mathbf{V}$ is the velocity of the frame moving with the particle; at the instant under consideration $\mathbf{V}$ coincides with $\mathbf{v}$, the velocity of the particle. Therefore we can rewrite the previous equations as

$$w^0 = \frac{e}{m} \frac{1}{\sqrt{(c^2 - v^2)}} (\mathbf{v} \cdot \mathbf{E}) \tag{25.14}$$

and
$$w^i = \frac{e}{m} \frac{c}{\sqrt{(c^2 - v^2)}} \left(\mathbf{E} + \frac{1}{c} [\mathbf{v} \times \mathbf{H}] \right)_i \tag{25.15}$$

Now we can abandon the moving frame and take it that the equations just obtained are valid at any instant of time. They are thus the equations of motion of the particle. However, the form of the equations (25.14) and (25.15) is inconvenient owing to the mixed notation used; on the left we have a four-dimensional vector while the right-hand side involves three-dimensional quantities. We now make the notation uniform, by first stating the equation entirely in four-dimensional and then entirely in three-dimensional terms.

Using the equation (25.02) for the four-dimensional velocity and equation (24.11) for the field, we can write equations (25.14) and (25.15) in the form

$$w^0 = \frac{e}{mc} (u^1 F_{10} + u^2 F_{20} + u^3 F_{30}) \tag{25.16}$$

and $\qquad w^i = \dfrac{e}{mc}(u^0 F_{i0} + u^1 F_{i1} + u^2 F_{i2} + u^3 F_{i3}) \qquad (i = 1, 2, 3) \qquad (25.17)$

Because of the antisymmetry of the tensor F_{ik} the right-hand sides of all equations (25.17) contain in fact three and not four terms. Passing to the covariant vector of acceleration

$$ w_0 = w^0 ; \qquad w_1 = -w^1 ; \qquad w_2 = -w^2 ; \qquad w_3 = -w^3 \qquad (25.18) $$

we have for all four values of i

$$ w_i = -\frac{e}{mc} \sum_{k=0}^{3} u^k F_{ik} \qquad (25.19) $$

On either side of this equation we have a covariant vector so that it is obvious that the equations of motion, written in this form, are valid in any reference frame, as it should be. It is easy to verify that

$$ \sum_{i=0}^{3} u^i w_i = 0 \qquad (25.20) $$

in agreement with (20.24). This means that the first equation of motion is a consequence of the three others.

In view of the covariance of equations (25.19) it would have been sufficient for proof of their validity, to verify that in the primed frame they reduce to the form (25.07).

We now pass to the three-dimensional statement of the equations. Using the expression (25.01) for the four-dimensional vector of acceleration and introducing three-dimensional vector notation we have

$$ \frac{d}{dt}\left(\frac{mc^2}{\sqrt{(1 - v^2/c^2)}}\right) = e\,(\mathbf{v} \cdot \mathbf{E}) \qquad (25.21) $$

and $\qquad \dfrac{d}{dt}\left(\dfrac{m\mathbf{v}}{\sqrt{(1 - v^2/c^2)}}\right) = e\left(\mathbf{E} + \dfrac{1}{c}\,[\mathbf{v} \times \mathbf{H}]\right) \qquad (25.22)$

In (25.21) the right-hand side is the power, or rate of work done by the field on the particle ; by general mechanical principles one should therefore interpret the left-hand side as the rate of increase of the kinetic energy of the particle. In (25.22) the right-hand side is the Lorentz force on a moving charge and the left-hand side the rate of increase of particle momentum.

Thus the kinetic energy and the momentum of the particle can differ only by constants from the expressions

$$ W = \frac{mc^2}{\sqrt{(1 - v^2/c^2)}} \qquad (25.23) $$

and $\qquad \mathbf{P} = \dfrac{m\mathbf{v}}{\sqrt{(1 - v^2/c^2)}} \qquad (25.24)$

whose time derivatives occur in the equations of motion.

The values of the constants can be determined by a covariance requirement ; one must postulate that the energy and the momentum of a particle[†] form a four-dimensional vector.

Now, the quantities (25.23) and (25.24) are themselves a four vector, for

---

† More accurately the energy divided by c and the momentum.

they are respectively proportional to the temporal and spatial components of the four-dimensional velocity. Therefore the constants must vanish.‡ Consequently the quantities (25.23) and (25.24) are the energy and momentum of the particle.

If we take $v = 0$ then, in agreement with older ideas, $P = 0$, the momentum of a body at rest is zero ; but for $v = 0$ the energy W takes on a value different from zero, namely

$$W_0 = mc^2 \qquad (25.25)$$

This result disagrees with older notions, but is fully confirmed by experiment : any body of mass m represents a store of energy W_0 (see Section 34, below). A similar relation

$$W = Mc^2 \qquad (25.26)$$

between the mass and the energy of a body holds also at arbitrary velocity if M is understood to mean the quantity

$$M = \frac{m}{\sqrt{(1 - v^2/c^2)}} \qquad (25.27)$$

which is itself a function of the speed. The quantity M must be taken as the rational generalization of the concept of mass. It enters as the multiplier of the velocity in expression (25.24) for the momentum and so describes the inertia, or inertial mass, of the body. M is usually called simply the mass while m is termed the rest-mass. Correspondingly W is referred to as energy and W_0 as rest energy.

The rest-mass m is a constant independent of the state of motion of the particle as a whole, which may, however, depend on the internal state of the particle, if the latter has some complex structure and some internal degrees of freedom. The rest-mass can be expressed in terms of the invariant of the four-dimensional vector of energy-momentum. Indeed, this invariant is independent of velocity and equal to

$$\frac{W^2}{c^2} - P^2 = m^2 c^2 \qquad (25.28)$$

The mass M depends on velocity in such a way that if the particle approaches the speed of light its mass increases without limit. Consequently no body having a rest-mass different from zero can attain the speed of light in any frame of reference. This fact confirms strikingly the limiting property of the speed of light.

If the speed of a particle is small compared to the speed of light the difference

$$W - mc^2 = \frac{1}{2} mv^2 + \frac{3}{8} m \frac{v^4}{c^2} + \ldots \qquad (25.29)$$

will only differ by small quantities from the usual expression for the kinetic energy.

The foregoing relations were derived for the equations of motion of a charged

‡ A more detailed argument goes as follows : the constants must on the one hand form a vector, on the other they must be independent of the state of motion and, hence, of the frame of reference. However, a constant vector different from zero, with components independent of the frame, does not exist.

particle but they have more general validity. The relation (25.26) between mass and energy holds not only for the present case of a particle of invariable rest-mass, but also for any complex body or system of bodies in which internal processes can effect changes of rest-mass. The relation expresses the fundamental law of proportionality of mass and energy. We shall return to a discussion of it in Section 34.

26. Approximate Description of a System of Moving Point Charges

The problem of the motion of a system of charged mass points requires a simultaneous determination of the motions of the charges and of the electromagnetic field in which they move ; only an external field can be considered as predetermined. The field transmits the interactions between the charges with a finite velocity, namely c. Consequently the force acting on a given charge will depend not on the momentary state but rather on the past state of motion of all the other charges. The field arising in the accelerated motion of charges not only carries the interaction but also radiates into outside space, therefore the energy of the charges will be spent in part on radiation and the system of charges is not a conservative one. Also it must be borne in mind that the field possesses an infinite number of degrees of freedom and therefore the system of charges with their field is strictly speaking one with infinite degrees of freedom and thus not a purely mechanical one.

Nevertheless the problem of the motion of charges can be approximately formulated in mechanical terms, involving only the degrees of freedom of the charges themselves. To do this one must express the field, or rather the potentials, of each charge in terms of its position and velocity and, further, one must find an approximate way of relating quantities at an earlier to quantities at a later instant. The potentials at a given place and given time are in this way expressed approximately in terms of the positions and velocities of the particles at the same instead of at an earlier time. An approximate Lagrangian for a system of charged particles may thus be constructed.

We find first the Lagrangian form of the equations of motion of a single charged particle. It is easy to verify that equations (25.22) can be derived from the Lagrangian

$$L = -mc^2 \sqrt{\left(1 - \frac{v^2}{c^2}\right)} - e\Phi + \frac{e}{c}(\mathbf{A} \cdot \mathbf{v}) \qquad (26.01)$$

where $\Phi = -A_0$ and A_k are the scalar and vector potentials respectively. For, since $\dot{x}_i = v_i$ we have

$$
\begin{aligned}
\frac{\partial L}{\partial \dot{x}_i} &= \frac{mv_i}{\sqrt{(1 - v^2/c^2)}} + \frac{e}{c}A_i \\
\frac{\partial L}{\partial x_i} &= -e\frac{\partial \Phi}{\partial x_i} + \frac{e}{c}\sum_{k=1}^{3}\frac{\partial A_k}{\partial x_i}v_k
\end{aligned}
\qquad (26.02)
$$

Inserting these expressions into Lagrange's equations

$$\frac{d}{dt}\left(\frac{\partial L}{\partial \dot{x}_i}\right) - \frac{\partial L}{\partial x_i} = 0 \tag{26.03}$$

and remembering how the fields are expressed in terms of the potentials by (24.01) we get

$$\frac{d}{dt}\left(\frac{mv_i}{\sqrt{(1 - v^2/c^2)}}\right) - e\left(E_i + \frac{1}{c}\,[\mathbf{v} \times \mathbf{H}]_i\right) = 0 \tag{26.04}$$

which is the same as equation (25.22) and of which we also know (25.21) to be a consequence.

We now pass to the case of a system of particles. We seek an approximate expression for the fields of particles of known motion. Considering first a spatial distribution of charge we can write down the equations for the potentials as

$$\Delta\Phi - \frac{1}{c^2}\frac{\partial^2\Phi}{\partial t^2} = -4\pi\rho \tag{26.05}$$

and

$$\Delta\mathbf{A} - \frac{1}{c^2}\frac{\partial^2\mathbf{A}}{\partial t^2} = -\frac{4\pi}{c}\,\mathbf{j} \tag{26.06}$$

The solution of (26.05) that is required is the retarded potential

$$\Phi = \int \frac{[\rho]\,dV'}{|\mathbf{r} - \mathbf{r}'|} \tag{26.07}$$

where
$$[\rho] = \rho(\mathbf{r}',\, t'); \qquad t' = t - \frac{1}{c}\,|\mathbf{r} - \mathbf{r}'| \tag{26.08}$$

If the motion of the particle is sufficiently slow and sufficiently smooth† then for not too great distances the expression for $[\rho]$ may be replaced by the first few terms in an expansion in inverse powers of c

$$[\rho] = \rho(\mathbf{r}',\, t) - \frac{1}{c}\,|\mathbf{r} - \mathbf{r}'|\,\frac{\partial}{\partial t}\,\rho(\mathbf{r}',\, t) + \frac{1}{2c^2}\,|\mathbf{r} - \mathbf{r}'|^2\,\frac{\partial^2}{\partial t^2}\,\rho(\mathbf{r}',\, t) + \ldots \tag{26.09}$$

Inserting this expansion into (26.07) and using the fact that the integral

$$\int \rho(\mathbf{r}',\, t)\,dV' = e_a \tag{26.10}$$

is the charge of the particle and therefore independent of time, we get

$$\Phi = \int \frac{\rho(\mathbf{r}',\, t)\,dV'}{|\mathbf{r} - \mathbf{r}'|} + \frac{1}{2c^2}\frac{d^2}{dt^2}\int \rho(\mathbf{r}',\, t)\cdot|\mathbf{r} - \mathbf{r}'|\,dV' + \ldots \tag{26.11}$$

If we now assume that the charge is concentrated near the point‡

$$\mathbf{r}' = \mathbf{r}_a = \mathbf{r}_a(t) \tag{26.12}$$

we obtain from (26.11)

$$\Phi = \frac{e_a}{|\mathbf{r} - \mathbf{r}_a|} + \frac{e_a}{2c^2}\frac{\partial^2}{\partial t^2}\,|\mathbf{r} - \mathbf{r}_a| \tag{26.13}$$

† These requirements impose a limitation on the speed of the particle ($v^2 \ll c^2$), on its acceleration and on higher time derivatives.

‡ The suffix a in e_a, $\mathbf{r}_a$, $\mathbf{v}_a$, etc., now denotes the number of the particle.

Putting $$\dot{\mathbf{r}}_a(t) = \mathbf{v}_a \tag{26.14}$$

and performing one of the time differentiations in (26.13) we have

$$\Phi = \frac{e_a}{|\mathbf{r} - \mathbf{r}_a|} - \frac{e_a}{2c^2} \frac{\partial}{\partial t} \left(\frac{\mathbf{v}_a \cdot (\mathbf{r} - \mathbf{r}_a)}{|\mathbf{r} - \mathbf{r}_a|} \right) \tag{26.15}$$

Here the first term gives the Coulomb potential, as for a charge at rest, while the second is a retardation correction.

In the expression for the vector potential we need not include any correction terms§ and we may write it as

$$A_i = \frac{e_a v_{ai}}{c |\mathbf{r} - \mathbf{r}_a|} \tag{26.16}$$

(This expression for the vector potential is obtained if in (26.06) second derivatives with respect to time are neglected, if the current density $\mathbf{j}$ is replaced by $\rho \mathbf{v}_a$ and if the transition to a concentrated charge is made.)

The form (26.13) of the scalar potential is inconvenient because it involves not only the velocity $\mathbf{v}_a$ but also the acceleration $\dot{\mathbf{v}}_a$ of the particle which produces the field. This inconvenience can easily be removed by using the fact that the fields are not changed by a " gauge transformation " of the potentials, i.e. by the substitution

$$\Phi \to \Phi + \frac{1}{c} \frac{\partial \chi}{\partial t}$$
$$A_i \to A_i - \frac{\partial \chi}{\partial x_i} \tag{26.17}$$

where χ is an arbitrary function of space and time coordinates. We choose

$$\chi = \frac{e_a}{2c} \frac{\mathbf{v}_a \cdot (\mathbf{r} - \mathbf{r}_a)}{|\mathbf{r} - \mathbf{r}_a|} \tag{26.18}$$

and thereby cancel the second term in (26.15) at the expense of complicating the expression for A_i a little. The result is

$$\Phi = \frac{e_a}{|\mathbf{r} - \mathbf{r}_a|} \tag{26.19}$$

and

$$A_i = \frac{e_a}{2c} \left(\frac{v_{ai}}{|\mathbf{r} - \mathbf{r}_a|} + \sum_{k=1}^{3} \frac{v_{ak}(x_k - x_{ak})(x_i - x_{ai})}{|\mathbf{r} - \mathbf{r}_a|^3} \right) \tag{26.20}$$

It is easy to verify that the new expression for the vector potential has vanishing divergence :

$$\sum_{i=1}^{3} \frac{\partial A_i}{\partial x_i} = 0 \tag{26.21}$$

Insertion of these values for the potentials into the last two terms of the Lagrangian (26.01) gives

$$-e\Phi + \frac{e}{c}(\mathbf{A} \cdot \mathbf{v}) = -\frac{ee_a}{|\mathbf{r} - \mathbf{r}_a|} + \frac{ee_a}{2c^2} \left(\frac{(\mathbf{v} \cdot \mathbf{v}_a)}{|\mathbf{r} - \mathbf{r}_a|} + \frac{\{\mathbf{v}_a \cdot (\mathbf{r} - \mathbf{r}_a)\}\{\mathbf{v} \cdot (\mathbf{r} - \mathbf{r}_a)\}}{|\mathbf{r} - \mathbf{r}_a|^3} \right) \tag{26.22}$$

§ In the Lagrangian and in the equations of motion the terms in the vector potential are of the same order as the terms involving corrections to the scalar potential.

This expression is symmetric in the particle producing the field and the particle being acted on. We can consider it to be an approximate statement of the interaction law for two particles. It allows us to write the Lagrangian of a system of particles as

$$
L = -\sum_a m_a c^2 \sqrt{\left(1 - \frac{v_a^2}{c^2}\right)} - \frac{1}{2} \sum_{\substack{a,\,b \\ (a \neq b)}} \frac{e_a e_b}{|\mathbf{r}_a - \mathbf{r}_b|}
$$

$$
+ \frac{1}{4c^2} \sum_{\substack{a,\,b \\ (a \neq b)}} e_a e_b \left(\frac{(\mathbf{v}_a \cdot \mathbf{v}_b)}{|\mathbf{r}_a - \mathbf{r}_b|} + \frac{\{\mathbf{v}_a \cdot (\mathbf{r}_a - \mathbf{r}_b)\}\{\mathbf{v}_b \cdot (\mathbf{r}_a - \mathbf{r}_b)\}}{|\mathbf{r}_a - \mathbf{r}_b|^3} \right) \qquad (26.23)
$$

Incidentally, since quantities of order v^2/c^2 are assumed small in the interaction law it will be more consistent to neglect higher terms in this quantity everywhere. Therefore taking only the first terms in the expansion of the square root we can replace (26.23) by

$$
L = -W_0 + \sum_a \left(\frac{1}{2} m_a v_a^2 + \frac{1}{8} m_a \frac{v_a^4}{c^2} \right) - \frac{1}{2} \sum_{\substack{a,\,b \\ a \neq b}} \frac{e_a e_b}{|\mathbf{r}_a - \mathbf{r}_b|}
$$

$$
+ \frac{1}{4c^2} \sum_{\substack{a,\,b \\ (a \neq b)}} e_a e_b \left(\frac{(\mathbf{v}_a \cdot \mathbf{v}_b)}{|\mathbf{r}_a - \mathbf{r}_b|} + \frac{\{\mathbf{v}_a \cdot (\mathbf{r}_a - \mathbf{r}_b)\}\{\mathbf{v}_b \cdot (\mathbf{r}_a - \mathbf{r}_b)\}}{|\mathbf{r}_a - \mathbf{r}_b|^3} \right) \qquad (26.24)
$$

where

$$
W_0 = c^2 \sum_a m_a \qquad (26.25)
$$

is the sum of the rest energies of all the particles.

We now consider the question of Lorentz transformations in the problem of the motion of a system of particles. Assume the problem to be solved in some frame of reference. This means that in the given frame the spatial coordinates of each particle are known as functions of the time in the frame:

$$
\mathbf{r}_a = \mathbf{r}_a(t) \qquad (26.26)
$$

We now perform a Lorentz transformation and seek to express the new space coordinates x_a', y_a', z_a' as functions of the new time t'. The equations of the Lorentz transformation have the form

$$
\mathbf{r}' = \mathbf{r} - \mathbf{V}t + \left(\frac{1}{\sqrt{(1 - V^2/c^2)}} - 1 \right) \frac{\mathbf{V}}{V^2} \{\mathbf{V} \cdot (\mathbf{r} - \mathbf{V}t)\} \qquad (26.27)
$$

and

$$
t' = \frac{1}{\sqrt{(1 - V^2/c^2)}} \left(t - \frac{1}{c^2} (\mathbf{V} \cdot \mathbf{r}) \right) \qquad (26.28)
$$

Therefore the new functions of the new time can be obtained by eliminating the variable t from the equations

$$
\mathbf{r}'_a = \mathbf{r}_a(t) - \mathbf{V}t + \left(\frac{1}{\sqrt{(1 - V^2/c^2)}} - 1 \right) \frac{\mathbf{V}}{V^2} (\mathbf{V} \cdot \{\mathbf{r}_a(t) - \mathbf{V}t\}) \qquad (26.29)
$$

and

$$
t' = \frac{1}{\sqrt{(1 - V^2/c^2)}} \left(t - \frac{1}{c^2} \{\mathbf{V} \cdot \mathbf{r}_a(t)\} \right) \qquad (26.30)
$$

In other words, the solution of (26.30) for t must be found and inserted in (26.29). This can only be done approximately taking V^2/c^2 to be small compared with unity. The approximate solution of (26.30) is

$$t = \left(1 - \frac{V^2}{2c^2}\right)t' + \frac{1}{c^2}\{\mathbf{V} \cdot \mathbf{r}_a(t')\} \tag{26.31}$$

Before inserting this into (26.29) we write the latter in the simplified form

where
$$\mathbf{r}'_a = \mathbf{r}_a(t) - \mathbf{V}t + \frac{\mathbf{V}}{2c^2}(\{\mathbf{V} \cdot \mathbf{r}_a(t)\} - V^2 t) \tag{26.32}$$

Inserting now, we get approximately

$$\mathbf{r}'_a(t') = \mathbf{r}_a(t') - \mathbf{V}t' + \frac{1}{c^2}\mathbf{v}_a(t') \cdot \left(-\frac{1}{2}V^2 t' + \{\mathbf{V} \cdot \mathbf{r}_a(t')\}\right) - \frac{\mathbf{V}}{2c^2}\{\mathbf{V} \cdot \mathbf{r}_a(t')\}$$
$$\tag{26.33}$$

$$\mathbf{v}_a(t') = \left(\frac{d\mathbf{r}_a(t)}{dt}\right)_{t=t'} \tag{26.34}$$

Differentiating (26.33) with respect to t' we obtain the corresponding expression for the velocity

$$\mathbf{v}'_a(t') = \mathbf{v}_a(t') - \mathbf{V} + \frac{1}{c^2}\mathbf{v}_a(t')\left(-\frac{1}{2}V^2 + \{\mathbf{V} \cdot \mathbf{v}_a(t')\}\right)$$
$$- \frac{\mathbf{V}}{2c^2}\{\mathbf{V} \cdot \mathbf{v}_a(t')\} + \frac{1}{c^2}\dot{\mathbf{v}}_a(t')\left(-\frac{1}{2}V^2 t' + \{\mathbf{V} \cdot \mathbf{r}_a(t')\}\right) \tag{26.35}$$

where $\dot{\mathbf{v}}_a$ is the derivative of $\mathbf{v}_a$ with respect to its argument.

We note that the relation between t and t' depends on the number a of the particle ; this is understandable because the transition to the new definition of simultaneity requires the introduction of different corrections for different particles. The old definition of simultaneity used in the original frame involved taking the same value of t for all particles (so that the t' values were different), but with the definition of simultaneity used in the new frame the values of t' for all particles are taken equal, so that the t are different. We can therefore omit the suffix a on t'. We can also replace t' by the unprimed symbol t and omit this argument from all functions in (26.33) and (26.35). We can then write these equations more briefly as

$$\mathbf{r}'_a = \mathbf{r}_a - \mathbf{V}t + \frac{1}{c^2}\mathbf{v}_a\left(-\frac{1}{2}V^2 t + (\mathbf{V} \cdot \mathbf{r}_a)\right) - \frac{\mathbf{V}}{2c^2}(\mathbf{V} \cdot \mathbf{r}_a) \tag{26.36}$$

and

$$\mathbf{v}'_a = \mathbf{v}_a - \mathbf{V} + \frac{1}{c^2}\mathbf{v}_a\left(-\frac{1}{2}V^2 + (\mathbf{V} \cdot \mathbf{v}_a)\right) - \frac{\mathbf{V}}{2c^2}(\mathbf{V} \cdot \mathbf{v}_a)$$
$$+ \frac{1}{c^2}\dot{\mathbf{v}}_a\left(-\frac{1}{2}V^2 t + (\mathbf{V} \cdot \mathbf{r}_a)\right) \tag{26.37}$$

This is the form of the new functions $\mathbf{r}'_a$ and $\mathbf{v}'_a$ expressed as functions of the new independent variable which, however, we have denoted by the same symbol as the old one.

The equations derived are approximate but on the assumption that the speeds V and v_a are of the same order the terms omitted are of the same order as those that are inevitably neglected in the construction of the retarded Lagrangian. Thus the omissions are in conformity with the nature of the problem.

It is well known that equations of motion are obtained by varying the action integral

$$S = \int_{(1)}^{(2)} L \, dt \tag{26.38}$$

and that in the usual case that the Lagrangian depends only on the coordinates and the velocities, and possibly the time, the equations of motion are

$$\frac{d}{dt} \frac{\partial L}{\partial \dot{x}_a} - \frac{\partial L}{\partial x_a}, = 0, \quad \text{etc.} \tag{26.39}$$

If the accelerations also enter the Lagrangian the equations of motion take on the form

$$-\frac{d^2}{dt^2} \frac{\partial L}{\partial \ddot{x}_a} + \frac{d}{dt} \frac{\partial L}{\partial \dot{x}_a} - \frac{\partial L}{\partial x_a} = 0, \quad \text{etc.} \tag{26.40}$$

where $\ddot{x}_a$, $\ddot{y}_a$ and $\ddot{z}_a$ are the components of acceleration of the a-th particle.

If the action integral S is invariant with respect to a Lorentz transformation the equations of motion will obviously be covariant.

Let us consider, for example, the equation of motion of a single particle, as derived from the Lagrangian (26.01). In this case the action integral can be written as

$$S = -mc^2 \int d\tau + \frac{e}{c} \int \sum_{k=0}^{3} A_k \, dx_k \tag{26.41}$$

(with $x_0 = ct$). Its invariance follows from the invariance of the differential of proper time and of the differential form (24.02) in the potentials.

However, the invariance of the action integral is not a necessary condition for the invariance of the equations of motion; it is sufficient that a Lorentz transformation should leave the *variation* of the action integral unchanged. This can be seen for example in (26.41) if one subjects the potentials to a gauge transformation of the type (26.17) with some function χ. Then S changes into

$$S' = S - \frac{e}{c} (\chi^{(2)} - \chi^{(1)}) \tag{26.42}$$

where $\chi^{(1)}$ and $\chi^{(2)}$ are the values of χ at the two limits of the integration. Since the variations vanish at the limits, we have

$$\delta S' = \delta S \tag{26.43}$$

and the equations of motion do not change, as it should be, since a gauge transformation of the potentials does not affect the fields.

We apply these considerations to our case of the motion of interacting charges and to the Lagrangian (26.23). We denote by $L'(t')$ the expression obtained for the Lagrangian $L(t)$ by replacing $\mathbf{r}_a(t)$ by $\mathbf{r}'_a(t')$ and $\mathbf{v}_a(t)$ by $\mathbf{v}'_a(t')$ from (26.33) and (26.35). If the original action integral was

$$S = \int_{(1)}^{(2)} L(t) \, dt \tag{26.44}$$

the transformed integral will be

$$S' = \int_{(1)}^{(2)} L'(t') \, dt' \tag{26.45}$$

and the change in the action integral due to the Lorentz transformation is

$$S' - S = \int_{(1)}^{(2)} L'(t')\, dt' - \int_{(1)}^{\cdot(2)} L(t)\, dt \qquad (26.46)$$

or, if we call the integration variable t in both integrals

$$S' - S = \int_{(1)}^{(2)} L'(t)\, dt - \int_{(1)}^{(2)} L(t)\, dt \qquad (26.47)$$

Here $L'(t)$ is the expression obtained from $L(t)$ by replacing $\mathbf{r}_a$ by $\mathbf{r}'_a$ and $\mathbf{v}_a$ by $\mathbf{v}'_a$ according to (26.36) and (26.37).

It follows from (26.47) that in order to ensure the covariance of the equations of motion it is sufficient that the difference

$$\{L'(t) - L(t)\}\, dt = dF \qquad (26.48)$$

is a total differential of some function F. For then

$$S' - S = F^{(2)} - F^{(1)} \qquad (26.49)$$

where $F^{(2)}$ and $F^{(1)}$ are the values of the function at the limits, so that the variations of the two integrals will be equal.

By performing the calculation we can verify that (26.48) really holds with the function F given by

$$F = \sum_a \left(-m_a + \frac{1}{2} m_a \frac{v_a^2}{c^2} - \frac{e_a}{2c^2} \sum_{\substack{b \\ (b \neq a)}} \frac{e_b}{|\mathbf{r}_a - \mathbf{r}_b|} \right) \left((\mathbf{V} \cdot \mathbf{r}_a) - \frac{V^2}{2} t \right)$$

$$- \frac{1}{c^2} \sum_a m_a (\mathbf{V} \cdot \mathbf{r}_a)(\mathbf{V} \cdot \mathbf{v}_a) + \frac{V^2}{2c^2} \sum_a m_a (\mathbf{V} \cdot \mathbf{r}_a) + \frac{V^4}{8c^2} \sum_a m_a t \qquad (26.50)$$

This also proves that the equations of motion derived from the Lagrangian (26.23) or (26.24) are indeed Lorentz covariant to the approximation stated.

27. Derivation of the Conservation Laws in the Mechanics of Point Systems

We now turn to the derivation of integrals of the equations of motion. To this end we consider the infinitesimal Lorentz transformations studied in Section 23 in the form involving all ten parameters. We recall that a transformation with these parameters expressed the following: a change τ of time origin, a displacement $\mathbf{a}$ of the origin of the spatial coordinates, a transition to a new reference frame moving with velocity $\mathbf{V}$ relative to the original frame and an infinitesimal rotation of the spatial axes characterized by the quantity $\boldsymbol{\omega}$. We have to calculate the change, resulting from such transformations, in the functions of time that represent the coordinates of each particle. This variation $\delta \mathbf{r}_b$ has two causes, the first arising from the vectorial nature of $\mathbf{r}_b$ and the second from the change in the argument t.

According to (23.06) and (23.17) the former variation is

$$\Delta \mathbf{r}_b = \mathbf{a} - \mathbf{V}t + [\boldsymbol{\omega} \times \mathbf{r}_b] \qquad (27.01)$$

The argument t appearing in quantities that refer to the b-th particle is varied by

$$\Delta t_b = \tau - \frac{1}{c^2}(\mathbf{V} \cdot \mathbf{r}_b) \qquad (27.02)$$

where the first term comes from the change in the time origin and the second from the transition to the moving frame. (Equation (27.02) is one of the equations of (23.06)).

The variation $\Delta^*\mathbf{r}_b$ due to the change of the argument of $\mathbf{r}_b(t)$ is obtained from the equation

$$\mathbf{r}_b(t) = \mathbf{r}'_b(t') \qquad (t' = t + \Delta t_b) \tag{27.03}$$

whence
$$\mathbf{r}'_b(t) = \mathbf{r}_b(t - \Delta t_b) = \mathbf{r}_b(t) - \mathbf{v}_b \Delta t_b \tag{27.04}$$

and, therefore,
$$\Delta^*\mathbf{r}_b = \mathbf{r}'_b(t) - \mathbf{r}_b(t) = -\mathbf{v}_b \Delta t_b \tag{27.05}$$

Thus the total variation in the form of the function $\mathbf{r}_a(t)$ is

$$\delta \mathbf{r}_b = \Delta \mathbf{r}_b + \Delta^* \mathbf{r}_b = \Delta \mathbf{r}_b - \mathbf{v}_b \Delta t_b \tag{27.06}$$

Using (27.01) and (27.02) the total variation $\delta \mathbf{r}_b$ can now be expressed in terms of the parameters of the infinitesimal Lorentz transformation as follows :

$$\delta \mathbf{r}_b = -\mathbf{v}_b \tau + \mathbf{a} - \mathbf{V}t + \frac{1}{c^2} \mathbf{v}_b(\mathbf{V} \cdot \mathbf{r}_b) + [\boldsymbol{\omega} \times \mathbf{r}_b] \tag{27.07}$$

and evidently the total variation $\delta \mathbf{v}_b$ of the velocity $\mathbf{v}_b$ will be

$$\delta \mathbf{v}_b = \frac{d}{dt} \delta \mathbf{r}_b \tag{27.08}$$

In the expression for $\delta \mathbf{r}_b$ the terms containing $\mathbf{V}$ are the same as the terms of first order in $\mathbf{V}$ in equation (26.36), as was to be expected.

We now calculate by two methods the variation of the Lagrangian in an infinitesimal Lorentz transformation. The first method is based on the use of the equations of motion, the second on direct transformation and the use of (26.48) and (26.50). We have

$$\delta L = \sum_a \left(\frac{\partial L}{\partial \mathbf{v}_a} \cdot \delta \mathbf{v}_a + \frac{\partial L}{\partial \mathbf{r}_a} \cdot \delta \mathbf{r}_a \right) \tag{27.09}$$

since the Lagrangian does not involve time explicitly.

Here $\partial L/\partial \mathbf{r}_a$ is to be understood to mean the three-dimensional vector with the components $\partial L/\partial x_a$, $\partial L/\partial y_a$ and $\partial L/\partial z_a$ and $\partial L/\partial \mathbf{v}_a$ is defined correspondingly. Using the equations of motion and also the relation (27.08) we can write

$$\delta L = \frac{d}{dt} \sum_a \frac{\partial L}{\partial \mathbf{v}_a} \cdot \delta \mathbf{r}_a \tag{27.10}$$

On the other hand, as mentioned before, we can evaluate the variation in the Lagrangian L without using the equations of motion. Evidently L does not vary when the spatial origin is displaced or when the spatial axes are rotated. If the zero of time is changed L varies by $-\tau \cdot dL/dt$ for if $L'(t') = L(t)$ where $t' = t + \tau$, then

$$L'(t) = L(t - \tau) = L(t) - \tau \frac{dL}{dt} \tag{27.11}$$

The change in L as a result of passing to a moving frame is given by (26.48) where it is sufficient to take for F the terms of (26.50) which are of first order in $\mathbf{V}$, namely

$$F = \sum_a \left(-m_a + \frac{1}{2} m_a \frac{v_a^2}{c^2} - \frac{e_a}{2c^2} \sum_{\substack{b \\ (a \neq b)}} \frac{e_b}{|\mathbf{r}_a - \mathbf{r}_b|} \right) (\mathbf{V} \cdot \mathbf{r}_a) \tag{27.12}$$

Thus
$$\delta L = -\tau \frac{dL}{dt} + \frac{dF}{dt} = \frac{d}{dt}(-\tau L + F) \tag{27.13}$$

Equating (27.10) and (27.13) we get

$$\frac{d}{dt} \left(\sum_a \frac{\partial L}{\partial \mathbf{v}_a} \cdot \delta \mathbf{r}_a + L\tau - F \right) = 0 \tag{27.14}$$

whence

$$\sum_a \frac{\partial L}{\partial \mathbf{v}_a} \cdot \delta \mathbf{r}_a + L\tau - F = \text{const.} \tag{27.15}$$

The left-hand side of this expression is a linear function of the ten parameters of the Lorentz transformation. Inserting into (27.15) the expressions (27.07) for $\delta \mathbf{r}_a$ and (27.12) for F we can put

$$I \equiv -\tau W + \mathbf{a} \cdot \mathbf{P} + \mathbf{V} \cdot \mathbf{K} + \boldsymbol{\omega} \cdot \mathbf{M} = \text{const.} \tag{27.16}$$

where W, $\mathbf{P}$, $\mathbf{K}$ and $\mathbf{M}$ do not depend on the parameters and are given by

$$W = \sum_a \mathbf{v}_a \cdot \frac{\partial L}{\partial \mathbf{v}_a} - L \tag{27.17}$$

$$\mathbf{P} = \sum_a \frac{\partial L}{\partial \mathbf{v}_a} \tag{27.18}$$

$$\mathbf{K} = \sum_a \left(m_a - \frac{1}{2} m_a \frac{v_a^2}{c^2} + \frac{e_a}{2c^2} \sum_{\substack{b \\ (b \neq a)}} \frac{e_b}{|\mathbf{r}_a - \mathbf{r}_b|} + \frac{1}{c^2} \mathbf{v}_a \cdot \frac{\partial L}{\partial \mathbf{v}_a} \right) \mathbf{r}_a - t \sum_a \frac{\partial L}{\partial \mathbf{v}_a} \tag{27.19}$$

$$\mathbf{M} = \sum_a \left[\mathbf{r}_a \times \frac{\partial L}{\partial \mathbf{v}_a} \right] \tag{27.20}$$

The left-hand side of (27.16) must be constant whatever the values of the parameters τ, $\mathbf{a}$, $\mathbf{V}$ and $\boldsymbol{\omega}$. This can only be if the quantities, W, $\mathbf{P}$, $\mathbf{K}$ and $\mathbf{M}$ are themselves constant. Thus we have obtained ten integrals each of which is connected with a particular one of the ten parameters of the infinitesimal Lorentz transformation. The physical meaning of these integrals is easy to see. W is the energy, $\mathbf{P}$ the momentum, $\mathbf{K}$ the integral of mass centre motion and $\mathbf{M}$ the angular momentum. Thus the ten integrals we have found are the classic integrals of the theory of systems of mass points, but with corrections for Relativity.

Let us write down the integrals explicitly. We have

$$W = c^2 \sum_a m_a + \frac{1}{2} \sum_a m_a v_a^2 + \frac{3}{8} \sum_a m_a \frac{v_a^4}{c^2} + \frac{1}{2} \sum_{\substack{a, b \\ (a \neq b)}} \frac{e_a e_b}{|\mathbf{r}_a - \mathbf{r}_b|}$$

$$+ \frac{1}{4c^2} \sum_{\substack{a, b \\ a \neq b}} \frac{e_a e_b (\mathbf{v}_a \cdot \mathbf{v}_b)}{|\mathbf{r}_a - \mathbf{r}_b|} + \frac{1}{4c^2} \sum_{\substack{a, b \\ (a \neq b)}} \frac{e_a e_b}{|\mathbf{r}_a - \mathbf{r}_b|^3} \{\mathbf{v}_a \cdot (\mathbf{r}_a - \mathbf{r}_b)\}\{\mathbf{v}_b \cdot (\mathbf{r}_a - \mathbf{r}_b)\} \tag{27.21}$$

This is the energy of the system.

If we put

$$W = c^2 \sum_a m_a + E \tag{27.22}$$

the quantity E will be the energy as it is usually defined, namely, so as to vanish for zero velocities and infinite distances between particles. Side by side with the energy we shall consider the corresponding mass

$$M = \frac{W}{c^2} = \sum_a m_a + \frac{E}{c^2} \tag{27.23}$$

which may be called the total mass of the system. By the definition just given the total mass of a system is equal to the sum of the rest-masses of all the separate particles and of the mass corresponding to their kinetic and interaction energies.

Let us now discuss the other integrals of motion. By (27.18) the integral of momentum is

$$\mathbf{P} = \sum_a m_a \mathbf{v}_a\left(1 + \frac{v_a^2}{2c^2}\right) + \frac{1}{2c^2} \sum_{\substack{a,\,b \\ (a \neq b)}} \frac{e_a e_b}{|\mathbf{r}_a - \mathbf{r}_b|} \left(\mathbf{v}_a + \frac{(\mathbf{r}_a - \mathbf{r}_b)\{\mathbf{v}_b \cdot (\mathbf{r}_a - \mathbf{r}_b)\}}{|\mathbf{r}_a - \mathbf{r}_b|^2}\right) \tag{27.24}$$

To write the integral of the mass centre motion in an explicit form we introduce for brevity

$$M_a^* = m_a\left(1 + \frac{v_a^2}{2c^2}\right) + \frac{e_a}{2c^2} \sum_{\substack{b \\ (a \neq b)}} \frac{e_b}{|\mathbf{r}_a - \mathbf{r}_b|} \tag{27.25}$$

Then we have

$$\mathbf{K} = \sum_a M_a^* \mathbf{r}_a - t\mathbf{P} \tag{27.26}$$

It should be noted that

$$\sum_a M_a^* = M \tag{27.27}$$

where M is understood to mean the expression (27.23) taken to the same approximation as that in which M_a^* is given: this corresponds to the non-relativistic approximation for the energy E.

Introducing the position vector $\mathbf{R}$ of the mass centre of the system by the relation

$$M\mathbf{R} = \sum_a M_a^* \mathbf{r}_a \tag{27.28}$$

expression (27.26) for $\mathbf{K}$ takes on the form

$$\mathbf{K} = M\mathbf{R} - t\mathbf{P} \tag{27.29}$$

the fact that $\mathbf{K}$ is constant represents the law of motion of the mass centre.

Finally, the integrals of the angular momentum of the system are

$$\mathbf{M} = \sum_a m_a\left(1 + \frac{v_a^2}{2c^2}\right)[\mathbf{r}_a \times \mathbf{v}_a]$$

$$+ \frac{1}{2c^2} \sum_{\substack{a,\,b \\ (a \neq b)}} \frac{e_a e_b}{|\mathbf{r}_a - \mathbf{r}_b|} \left([\mathbf{r}_a \times \mathbf{v}_b] - \frac{[\mathbf{r}_a \times \mathbf{r}_b]\{\mathbf{v}_b \cdot (\mathbf{r}_a - \mathbf{r}_b)\}}{|\mathbf{r}_a - \mathbf{r}_b|^2}\right) \tag{27.30}$$

28. The Tensor Character of the Integrals of Motion

We must now investigate the behaviour of the integrals of motion under Lorentz transformations. If we knew from the start that

$$I = -\tau W + \mathbf{a} \cdot \mathbf{P} + \mathbf{V} \cdot \mathbf{K} + \boldsymbol{\omega} \cdot \mathbf{M} \tag{28.01}$$

was an invariant we could decide the tensor character of W, $\mathbf{P}$, $\mathbf{K}$ and $\mathbf{M}$ from the properties of the parameters τ, $\mathbf{a}$, $\mathbf{V}$ and $\boldsymbol{\omega}$, of the infinitesimal Lorentz transformation. Since, however, we have not proved the invariance of (28.01) we shall adopt a more direct approach, though it involves rather tedious calculations which we shall refrain from elaborating. We shall subject W, $\mathbf{P}$, $\mathbf{K}$ and $\mathbf{M}$ to a finite Lorentz transformation and see how they can be expressed in terms of the initial quantities.

We shall denote by W', $\mathbf{P}'$, $\mathbf{K}'$ and $\mathbf{M}'$ the quantities resulting from putting $\mathbf{r}'_a$ and $\mathbf{v}'_a$ in place of $\mathbf{r}_a$ and $\mathbf{v}_a$, with the use of (26.36) and (26.37). We obtain

$$W' = \left(1 + \frac{1}{2}\frac{V^2}{c^2} + \frac{3}{8}\frac{V^4}{c^4}\right)W - \left(1 + \frac{1}{2}\frac{V^2}{c^2}\right)(\mathbf{V} \cdot \mathbf{P}) \tag{28.02}$$

and

$$\mathbf{P}' = \mathbf{P} - \mathbf{V}\frac{W}{c^2} + \frac{\mathbf{V}}{2c^2}\left\{\mathbf{V} \cdot \left(\mathbf{P} - \mathbf{V}\frac{W}{c^2}\right)\right\} \tag{28.03}$$

or, in terms of the total mass,

$$c^2 M' = \left(c^2 + \frac{1}{2}V^2 + \frac{3}{8}\frac{V^4}{c^2}\right)M - \left(1 + \frac{1}{2}\frac{V^2}{c^2}\right)(\mathbf{V} \cdot \mathbf{P}) \tag{28.04}$$

and

$$\mathbf{P}' = \mathbf{P} - \mathbf{V}M + \frac{\mathbf{V}}{2c^2}\{\mathbf{V} \cdot (\mathbf{P} - \mathbf{V}M)\} \tag{28.05}$$

To the same approximation these equations can also be written as

$$c^2 M' = \frac{c^2 M - (\mathbf{V} \cdot \mathbf{P})}{\sqrt{(1 - V^2/c^2)}} \tag{28.06}$$

and

$$\mathbf{P}' = \mathbf{P} - \mathbf{V}M + \left(\frac{1}{\sqrt{(1 - V^2/c^2)}} - 1\right)\frac{\mathbf{V}}{V^2}\{\mathbf{V} \cdot (\mathbf{P} - \mathbf{V}M)\} \tag{28.07}$$

Comparing these equations with the usual ones for Lorentz transformations (26.27) and (26.28), it is apparent that the components P_x, P_y and P_z of the vector $\mathbf{P}$ transform like the coordinates x, y and z, and the total mass like the time t. This means that the set of quantities

$$P^0 = Mc = \frac{W}{c}; \qquad P^1 = P_x, \qquad P^2 = P_y; \qquad P^3 = P_z \tag{28.08}$$

is a contravariant vector. The covariant components of this four-dimensional vector are

$$P_0 = Mc = \frac{W}{c}; \qquad P_1 = -P_x; \qquad P_2 = -P_y; \qquad P_3 = -P_z \tag{28.09}$$

If we consider the whole system of charges as one compound body, we must ascribe to this body the mass M and the momentum $\mathbf{P}$. We can also ascribe to it, or more exactly to its mass centre, the velocity

$$\mathbf{v} = \frac{\mathbf{P}}{M} \tag{28.10}$$

and the rest-mass

$$\mu = \sqrt{\left(M^2 - \frac{P^2}{c^2}\right)} \tag{28.11}$$

The quantity μ is equal to M' in that frame of reference in which $\mathbf{P}' = 0$. It is evident from this example that the rest-mass of a body depends on its internal state, in the present example on the state of motion of the constituent particles.

We now turn to the transformation law for **K** and **M**. Making the same insertions from (26.36) and (26.37) we get for **K'** and **M'**

$$\mathbf{K'} = \left(1 + \frac{V^2}{2c^2}\right)\mathbf{K} - \frac{1}{2c^2}\mathbf{V}(\mathbf{V}\cdot\mathbf{K}) - \frac{1}{c^2}[\mathbf{V}\times\mathbf{M}] \qquad (28.12)$$

and $$\mathbf{M'} = \left(1 + \frac{V^2}{2c^2}\right)\mathbf{M} - \frac{1}{2c^2}\mathbf{V}(\mathbf{V}\cdot\mathbf{M}) + \left(1 + \frac{V^2}{2c^2}\right)[\mathbf{V}\times\mathbf{K}] \qquad (28.13)$$

To the same approximation we can also put

$$\mathbf{K'} = \frac{\mathbf{V}}{V^2}(\mathbf{V}\cdot\mathbf{K}) + \frac{1}{\sqrt{(1 - V^2/c^2)}}\left(\mathbf{K} - \frac{\mathbf{V}}{V^2}(\mathbf{V}\cdot\mathbf{K}) - \frac{1}{c^2}[\mathbf{V}\times\mathbf{M}]\right) \qquad (28.14)$$

and $$\mathbf{M'} = \frac{\mathbf{V}}{V^2}(\mathbf{V}\cdot\mathbf{M}) + \frac{1}{\sqrt{(1 - V^2/c^2)}}\left(\mathbf{M} - \frac{\mathbf{V}}{V^2}(\mathbf{V}\cdot\mathbf{M}) + [\mathbf{V}\times\mathbf{K}]\right) \qquad (28.15)$$

We compare these relations with those describing the transformation of an antisymmetric tensor, bearing in mind that in the three-dimensional sense **K** is a polar vector and **M** an axial one. The required transformation equations have been stated in Section 24 for the case of the electromagnetic field tensor (equations (24.37) and (24.38)). To make the two sets of equations coincide we must take it that the vector **M** transforms like **H** and the vector **K** like $-\mathbf{E}/c$. The other possibility $\mathbf{M} \sim \mathbf{E}$, $\mathbf{K} \sim \mathbf{H}/c$ is excluded because **K** and **E** are polar and **M** and **H** axial vectors. We can therefore introduce an antisymmetric tensor in terms of its covariant components

$$M_{23} = M_x ; \qquad M_{31} = M_y ; \qquad M_{12} = M_z,$$
$$M_{10} = -cK_x ; \qquad M_{20} = -cK_y ; \qquad M_{30} = -cK_z \qquad (28.16)$$

or equally well in terms of its contravariant components

$$M^{23} = M_x ; \qquad M^{31} = M_y ; \qquad M^{12} = M_z$$
$$M^{10} = cK_x ; \qquad M^{20} = cK_y ; \qquad M^{30} = cK_z \qquad (28.17)$$

A check on the correctness of this is the observation that for a single particle

$$M_x = m(x^2 u^3 - x^3 u^2), \qquad \text{etc.}$$
$$cK_x = m(x^1 u^0 - x^0 u^1), \qquad \text{etc.} \qquad (28.18)$$

where u^0, u^1, u^2 and u^3 denote the components of the four-dimensional velocity and where, to stress their contravariance, space and time coordinates have been written with superfixes : $x^0 = ct$, $x^1 = x$, $x^2 = y$ and $x^3 = z$.

We have thus shown that of the ten integrals of motion four, namely energy and momentum, form a four-dimensional vector and the remaining six, the integrals of mass centre motion and the angular momentum, an antisymmetric tensor. This allows one to assert that if these quantities are constant in any one frame of reference they will be constant in all frames. The circumstance that we deduced the conservation laws from approximate equations is related to the approximate character of the statement of the whole problem. We have already remarked that strictly speaking the energy and the momentum of a system of charges do not remain constant but may be dissipated as radiation.

Having established the tensor character of the integrals of motion we can verify that the expression (28.01) is really invariant. To do this it is sufficient to rewrite the expression for I in four-dimensional notation. According to Section 23 we have

$$\tau = \frac{1}{c} a_0; \qquad a_x = -a_1; \qquad a_y = -a_2; \qquad a_z = -a_3 \qquad (28.19)$$

where a_0, a_1, a_2 and a_3 form a covariant vector.

Further

$$V_x = c\omega_{10}; \qquad V_y = c\omega_{20}; \qquad V_z = c\omega_{30} \qquad (28.20)$$

and

$$\omega_x = \omega_{23}; \qquad \omega_y = \omega_{31}; \qquad \omega_z = \omega_{12} \qquad (28.21)$$

where the ω_{ik} are the covariant components of an antisymmetric tensor. Using the four-dimensional notation (28.08) and (28.17) for the integrals of motion we get in place of (28.01)

$$I = - a_0 P^0 - a_1 P^1 - a_2 P^2 - a_3 P^3$$
$$+ \omega_{10} M^{10} + \omega_{20} M^{20} + \omega_{30} M^{30} + \omega_{23} M^{23} + \omega_{31} M^{31} + \omega_{12} M^{12} \qquad (28.22)$$

or, more briefly,

$$I = - \sum_{i=0}^{3} a_i P^i + \frac{1}{2} \sum_{i,\,k=0}^{3} \omega_{ik} M^{ik} \qquad (28.23)$$

proving our assertion that I is invariant.

29. A Remark on the Conventional Formulation of the Conservation Laws

In this section we make some remarks of a critical nature on the conventional formulation of the conservation laws. For definiteness we shall deal with the conservation laws for energy and momentum as they are the ones most frequently discussed.

One writes expressions for the energy, or the total mass, and for the momentum in the form

$$W = Mc^2 = \sum_a \frac{m_a c^2}{\sqrt{(1 - v_a^2/c^2)}} \qquad (29.01)$$

and

$$\mathbf{P} = \sum_a \frac{m_a \mathbf{v}_a}{\sqrt{(1 - v_a^2/c^2)}} \qquad (29.02)$$

and makes two statements about them: first that these quantities form a four-dimensional vector and, second, that they remain constant.

In fact both statements are only correct in the case that the particles do not interact. Then, however, the velocity of each particle separately remains constant and each quartet of quantities

$$W^{(a)} = \frac{m_a c^2}{\sqrt{(1 - v_a^2/c^2)}}; \qquad \mathbf{P}^{(a)} = \frac{m_a \mathbf{v}_a}{\sqrt{(1 - v_a^2/c^2)}} \qquad (29.03)$$

is a constant four-dimensional vector. Thus, in the absence of interaction the constancy of the sums (29.01) and (29.02) follows trivially from the constancy of their separate terms (29.03); the summation tells one nothing new.

On the other hand, when interactions are present the expressions (29.01) and (29.02) do not remain constant and do not form a four-dimensional vector. The first part of this statement is easy to understand, for even in non-relativistic theory it is not the kinetic energy but the total energy of a system of particles that remains constant.

The Theory of Relativity introduces corrections that take care of interactions not only into the expression for the energy but also into the one for the momentum of the system (see (27.21) and (27.24)). Only with the inclusion of these corrections will the two expressions be constant. As for vectorial properties, the following state of affairs might at first sight seem paradoxical. We saw in Section 25 (equations (25.23) and (25.24)) that the set of quantities (29.03) is, for a single particle, a four-dimensional vector even for accelerated motion ; further, it would seem that a sum of vectors must also be a vector. In spite of this we assert that the sums (29.01) and (29.02) do not represent the components of a four-dimensional vector. The paradox is removed by the consideration that the quantities $W^{(a)}$ and $\mathbf{P}^{(a)}$ are functions of a time common to all particles. Their sums W and $\mathbf{P}$ are in fact sums of the values of $W^{(a)}$ and $\mathbf{P}^{(a)}$ *simultaneous in the given frame.* In a different frame of reference these values will no longer be simultaneous ones. Therefore, when passing to a new frame one has not only to form linear combinations of the $W^{(a)}$ and $\mathbf{P}^{(a)}$ according to the vector rule but must also recalculate these quantities appropriately to the new simultaneity, as was elaborated in Section 26. Such a recalculation changes nothing only in the case of constant $W^{(a)}$, $\mathbf{P}^{(a)}$; the general case involves the change of these quantities during the time that corresponds to the change from old to new simultaneity, as was shown approximately in Section 26. It is therefore clear that the sums $W = \sum_a W^{(a)}$ and $\mathbf{P} = \sum_a \mathbf{P}^{(a)}$ will have vectorial properties only in the case of non-interacting particles and not in general.

In the presence of interactions the quantities that are vectors and also constant are, to the approximation considered, the integrals of motion derived in Section 27. Those expressions differ from (29.01) and (29.02) on the one hand by their inclusion of interaction terms, on the other hand by the fact that the quantities $m_a/\sqrt{(1 - v_a^2/c^2)}$ are replaced by the leading terms of the expansions of these quantities in powers of v_a^2/c^2, the expansions being taken to the same order as in the interaction terms.

It may, however, happen that with all particles a large distance apart, the interaction terms contribute negligibly but that at the same time the speeds of the particles are very great. In such a limiting case of weakly interacting particles the expressions (29.01) and (29.02) can be used but it must be borne in mind that they are applicable only *before the beginning* and *after the end* of the interaction, and not in the intervening time.

In the limiting case stated one can use conservation laws for energy and momentum in the usual form

$$\sum_a \frac{m_a c^2}{\sqrt{(1 - v_a^2/c^2)}} = \sum_a \frac{m_a c^2}{\sqrt{(1 - v_a^{*2}/c^2)}} \tag{29.04}$$

and

$$\sum_a \frac{m_a \mathbf{v}_a}{\sqrt{(1 - v_a^2/c^2)}} = \sum_a \frac{m_a \mathbf{v}_a^*}{\sqrt{(1 - v_a^{*2}/c^2)}} \tag{29.05}$$

where v_a and v_a^* respectively are the values of the velocity of the a-th particle before and after the interaction. It is clear from what has been said that the left-hand sides of these expressions do not remain constant during the whole time of interaction, but that after the interaction they regain the values they had in the beginning.

The remarks made in this section are equally true in relation to the conventional formulation of the conservation law for angular momentum, in which also interaction terms are not considered.

30. The Vector of Energy Current (Umov's Vector).

Let us consider the familiar non-relativistic equations of motion in the mechanics of continuous media. They have the form

$$\rho \frac{dv_i}{dt} = \rho F_i + \sum_{k=1}^{3} \frac{\partial p_{ik}}{\partial x_k} \qquad (i = 1, 2, 3) \tag{30.01}$$

and

$$\frac{\partial \rho}{\partial t} + \sum_{i=1}^{3} \frac{\partial (\rho v_i)}{\partial x_i} = 0 \tag{30.02}$$

Here v_1, v_2 and v_3 are the components of the velocities of the particles constituting the medium, ρ is the density, p_{ik} the stress tensor† and F_i the components of the external force acting on a unit of mass. The accelerations dv/dt appearing on the left-hand side of (30.01) are the so-called substantial derivatives, given by

$$\frac{dv_i}{dt} = \frac{\partial v_i}{\partial t} + \sum_{k=1}^{3} v_k \frac{\partial v_i}{\partial x_k} \tag{30.03}$$

The equation (30.02) is usually called the equation of continuity. It is well known that it expresses the conservation of mass.

The system of equations (30.01) and (30.02) is not in itself complete; it does not allow one to determine the motion of the medium from given initial and boundary conditions. Two steps are needed to obtain a complete system of equations : first, one has to express the stress tensor in terms of other quantities such as deformations, velocities, pressure, temperature and electromagnetic and other fields and, second, if the number of unknown functions is greater than four—i.e. greater than the number of equations in (30.01) and (30.02)—one must add to these equations some others such as the equation of state, the equation of heat flow, field equations, etc.

In the following we shall confine ourselves to the case of a conservative system in the absence of external forces.

We consider first a compressible elastic medium. Then we can introduce Π, the potential energy per unit mass of the medium and express the stress tensor in terms of it. Let a_1, a_2 and a_3 be some Lagrange variables, say the initial coordinates of a particle. At time t the coordinates of the particle will then be

$$x_i = x_i(a_1, a_2, a_3, t) \qquad (i = 1, 2, 3) \tag{30.04}$$

---

† In this section we use the terms "vector" and "tensor" in their three-dimensional meaning.

and the deformation of the medium is characterized by the set of quantities

$$A_{mn} = \sum_{i=1}^{3} \frac{\partial x_i}{\partial a_m} \frac{\partial x_i}{\partial a_n} \tag{30.05}$$

The potential energy Π is a function of the deformation and if one puts

$$d\Pi = \frac{1}{2\rho} \sum_{m,n=1}^{3} P_{mn}\, dA_{mn} \qquad (P_{mn} = P_{nm}) \tag{30.06}$$

the components p_{ik} of the stress tensor can be expressed in terms of the coefficients P_{mn} as follows

$$p_{ik} = \sum_{m,n=1}^{3} P_{mn} \frac{\partial x_i}{\partial a_m} \frac{\partial x_k}{\partial a_n} \qquad (p_{ik} = p_{ki}) \tag{30.07}$$

From these equations it is readily deduced that

$$\rho \frac{d\Pi}{dt} = \rho \left(\frac{\partial \Pi}{\partial t} + \sum_{i=1}^{3} v_i \frac{\partial \Pi}{\partial x_i} \right) = \sum_{i,k=1}^{3} p_{ik} \frac{\partial v_i}{\partial x_k} \tag{30.08}$$

In the case of a fluid

$$p_{ik} = -p\delta_{ik} \tag{30.09}$$

where p is the pressure, so that the tensor p_{ik} reduces to a scalar. In this case equation (30.08) becomes

$$\rho \frac{d\Pi}{dt} = -p \operatorname{div} \mathbf{v} = \frac{p}{\rho} \frac{d\rho}{dt} \tag{30.10}$$

by virtue of (30.02), and this leads to the usual expression

$$\Pi = \int \frac{p\, d\rho}{\rho^2} = \int \frac{dp}{\rho} - \frac{p}{\rho} \tag{30.11}$$

for the potential energy of a unit mass of fluid. For infinitesimal deformations, when the usual theory of elasticity applies, relation (30.08) can equally well be verified directly without recourse to Lagrange variables.

It is interesting to consider the relation (30.08) in conjunction with the thermodynamic identity

$$\rho \frac{du}{dt} = \sum_{i,k=1}^{3} p_{ik} \frac{\partial v_i}{\partial x_k} + \rho T \frac{d\sigma}{dt} \tag{30.12}$$

in which u is the internal energy, σ the entropy and T the temperature. For isothermal processes one can put

$$\Pi = u - T\sigma = F \tag{30.13}$$

where F is the free energy, and for adiabatic processes

$$\Pi = u \tag{30.14}$$

We now turn to the equations of motion. Using the equation of continuity we can write the three equations (30.01) in the form

$$\frac{\partial(\rho v_i)}{\partial t} + \sum_{k=1}^{3} \frac{\partial}{\partial x_k} (\rho v_i v_k - p_{ik}) = 0 \tag{30.15}$$

Just as the equation of continuity

$$\frac{\partial \rho}{\partial t} + \sum_{k=1}^{3} \frac{\partial(\rho v_k)}{\partial x_k} = 0 \tag{30.02}$$

expresses the law of mass conservation, so one can take (30.15) to express the law of conservation of momentum. In the equation of continuity the scalar quantity ρ is the mass density and the vector with the components ρv_i ($i = 1$, 2, 3) is the mass current density. Similarly in (30.15) the vector ρv_i is the momentum density and the tensor

$$S_{ik} = \rho v_i v_k - p_{ik} \tag{30.16}$$

the momentum current density. So the vector ρv_i enters once as the mass current density and again as momentum density. Similarly, remembering that $S_{ik} = S_{ki}$, this quantity enters once as the i-th component of the current of ρv_k and again as the k-th component of the current of ρv_i. We have just seen that the equation of continuity and the equations of motion can be interpreted as laws of conservation of mass and of momentum. It is natural to try to express in an analogous manner the law of conservation of energy. This was first done by Umov who introduced the important notion of energy current as early as 1874 [4, 5].

We introduce a scalar

$$S = \frac{1}{2} \rho v^2 + \rho \Pi \tag{30.17}$$

and a vector with the components

$$S_i = v_i \left(\frac{1}{2} \rho v^2 + \rho \Pi \right) - \sum_{k=1}^{3} p_{ik} v_k \tag{30.18}$$

In these equations Π denotes as before the potential energy per unit mass. It is obvious that the two terms in S are respectively the densities of kinetic and of potential energy, so that S is the volume density of total energy. The vector S_i which we shall call Umov's vector† can be interpreted as the vector of energy current. For, using the equations of motion, the equation of continuity and the relation (30.08), it is easy to verify that

$$\frac{\partial S}{\partial t} + \sum_{i=1}^{3} \frac{\partial S_i}{\partial x_i} = 0 \tag{30.19}$$

This can obviously be interpreted as the conservation law for energy.

One should note that if the equations of motion (30.15) are given, then of the two equations: (30.02), the continuity equation, and (30.19), the equation describing energy flow, only one is independent. Either can be obtained from the other by using the equations of motion. Instead of either of them one could also take any linear combination of them. This would bring in a quantity

---

† The quantities S and S_i actually discussed by Umov differed from those introduced here by the absence of potential energy terms. Therefore, the right-hand side of the relation given by Umov, which corresponds to (30.19), was not zero but the negative of (30.08), i.e. the work done by the elastic forces in unit volume and unit time.

$\rho + \lambda S$ and the corresponding current $\rho v_i + \lambda S_i$ (with a constant λ having the dimensions of $(\text{velocity})^{-2}$). In the following section we shall see that the relativistic form of the equations of motion for a continuous medium corresponds approximately to choosing such a linear combination with $\lambda = 1/c^2$.

In conclusion, we point out the following circumstance. In the foregoing discussion the flux of a certain quantity S was determined (by means of the appropriate conservation law) from its divergence which was assumed given. This does not determine the flux uniquely. According to its physical meaning, however, the flux vector is a completely determined quantity. Therefore we must expect that if the requirements of the theory of relativity are met, it should be formally possible to make the definition of the flux unique, provided certain additional conditions are imposed on it. One of these conditions is the requirement that the flux vector of the function of state S, should itself be a function of state. This requirement will be formulated more precisely and discussed in detail in the two following sections. In the examples here discussed the requirement is satisfied by the energy flux (Umov's vector), the mass flux and the momentum flux.

31. The Mass Tensor

In the previous section we saw that for a conservative system the usual non-relativistic equations of motion of a continuous medium can be stated as four equations in each of which a sum of derivatives with respect to the spatial coordinates and to the time is equated to zero. This form of equation leads us to surmise that in Relativity they possess a generalization of the form

$$\frac{\partial T^{00}}{\partial x_0} + \sum_{k=1}^{3} \frac{\partial T^{0k}}{\partial x_k} = 0$$
$$\frac{\partial T^{i0}}{\partial x_0} + \sum_{k=1}^{3} \frac{\partial T^{ik}}{\partial x_k} = 0 \tag{31.01}$$

where $T^{ik}(i, k = 0, 1, 2, 3)$ is some tensor.

The first of these equations should express conservation of mass or energy and the other three, for $i = 1$, 2 and 3, the conservation of momentum. If T^{00} is the density of total mass, including the rest-mass and the mass of the kinetic energy, then cT^{0i} is the mass current density. Also, if cT^{i0} is the density of the i-th component of momentum, then $c^2 T^{ik}$ ($k = 1, 2, 3$) will be its current density. The mass M contained in some volume and the energy W corresponding to it will be expressible in terms of T^{00} as the volume integral

$$M = \frac{W}{c^2} = \int T^{00} \, dV \tag{31.02}$$

Similarly the momentum contained in the same volume will be

$$P^i = c \int T^{i0} \, dV \tag{31.03}$$

The equations (31.01) express the fact that any increase of the energy or the momentum contained in a volume is due to an influx of energy or momentum from outside the volume, i.e. through the closed surface enclosing the volume in question. The integrals (31.02) and (31.03) taken over all space are the total mass and the total momentum of the system. They remain constant in time.

In addition to the laws of conservation of mass, energy and momentum, conservation laws must also hold for the angular momentum and for the mass centre motion of the system. They can be written in a form analogous to (31.01). It follows directly from that set of equations that

$$\frac{\partial}{\partial x_0}(x_i T^{k0} - x_k T^{i0}) + \sum_{m=1}^{3} \frac{\partial}{\partial x_m}(x_i T^{km} - x_k T^{im}) = T^{ki} - T^{ik} \quad (31.04)$$
$$(i, k = 0, 1, 2, 3)$$

and these relations have the form of the required additional conservation laws if their right-hand sides vanish. Hence we get the condition

$$T^{ik} = T^{ki} \quad (31.05)$$

i.e. the tensor T^{ik} must be symmetric. This means in particular that the mass current must equal the momentum not only in the equations of mechanics, but quite generally. We shall now state the relations (31.04) for a symmetric tensor separately for $k = 1, 2, 3$ and for $k = 0$:

$$\frac{\partial}{\partial x_0}(x_i T^{k0} - x_k T^{i0}) + \sum_{m=1}^{3} \frac{\partial}{\partial x_m}(x_i T^{km} - x_k T^{im}) = 0 \quad (31.06)$$

and

$$\frac{\partial}{\partial x_0}(x_i T^{00} - x_0 T^{i0}) + \sum_{m=1}^{3} \frac{\partial}{\partial x_m}(x_i T^{0m} - x_0 T^{im}) = 0 \quad (31.07)$$

Here $i, k = 1, 2, 3$. The equations (31.06) can be considered to be the laws of angular momentum conservation and the equations (31.07) as the laws of motion of the mass-centre. In both cases these are the laws in differential form; integration of the equations over some volume gives the corresponding integral relations.

If the integrals

$$M^{ik} = c \int (x_i T^{k0} - x_k T^{i0})\, dV \quad (31.08)$$

and

$$K^i = \frac{1}{c} M^{i0} = \int (x_i T^{00} - x_0 T^{i0})\, dV \quad (31.09)$$

are taken over all space they will remain constant; the quantities M^{23}, M^{31}, and M^{12} are the components of angular momentum of the system and the quantities M^{10}, M^{20} and M^{30} divided by c can be interpreted as the products of the mass of the system and the initial coordinates of its mass centre.

The tensor we are discussing will be called the mass tensor.† Its invariant has the dimensions of a mass density. When multiplied by c^2 the tensor T^{ik} is also called the energy tensor, its invariant then has the dimensions of energy density.

We shall impose on the mass tensor another condition which can be stated in the form of a physical principle, as follows : *The mass tensor must be a function of the state of the system.* We must define what we mean by state of a system. Let us assume that the equations of motion and field equations are written

† We prefer this name to the often used "matter-tensor". The notion of "matter" is of a very general character and should not be identified with the notion of mass.

as a system of n first order equations for the unknown functions $\varphi_1, \ldots, \varphi_n$ and that these equations can be solved for the time derivatives of the functions. If initial values are prescribed for the functions $\varphi_1, \ldots, \varphi_n$ this, together with boundary or similar conditions, determines their values at any subsequent time. This is the principle of causality. We shall say that the functions $\varphi_1, \ldots, \varphi_n$ characterize the state of the system. Any function of $\varphi_1, \ldots, \varphi_n$ which does not contain their time derivatives and also does not contain the coordinates explicitly will be called a function of the state. (We may note that in the Theory of Relativity derivatives with respect to spatial coordinates and to time enter symmetrically and therefore if some scalar, vector or tensor does not contain any time derivatives it will also not contain any space derivatives.)

Let us give some examples. In the mechanics of mass points a state is characterized by the coordinates and velocities of the particles, therefore any function of coordinates and velocities is a function of the state. In hydrodynamics a state is characterized by the three components of velocity, the density and the pressure, with the two last quantities related by some equation. In the theory of the electromagnetic field a state is characterized by the antisymmetric field tensor.

Thus our physical principle‡ requires that the components of the mass tensor should be functions only of the quantities that characterize the system. Derivatives of these quantities must not enter nor should the coordinates appear explicitly. (We assume of course that cartesian coordinates are used.)

We now inquire to what extent the mass tensor is determined by the conditions we have stated. We take first the equation expressing the fact that the divergence of the mass tensor vanishes

$$\sum_{k=0}^{3} \frac{\partial T^{ik}}{\partial x_k} = 0 \tag{31.10}$$

together with symmetry condition $T^{ik} = T^{ki}$. In addition we make the condition that the ten integrals of these equations, i.e. W, P^i and M^{ik} should have fixed values.

Let $A^{im,nk}$ be a tensor of fourth rank having the following symmetry properties : antisymmetry with respect to the first pair of indices

$$A^{im,\, nk} = - A^{mi,\, nk} \tag{31.11}$$

antisymmetry with respect to the second pair

$$A^{im,\, nk} = - A^{im,\, kn} \tag{31.12}$$

and the cyclic symmetry

$$A^{im,\, nk} + A^{in,\, km} + A^{ik,\, mn} = 0 \tag{31.13}$$

From these properties it follows that

$$A^{im,\, nk} = A^{nk,\, im} \tag{31.14}$$

In terms of second derivatives of $A^{im,nk}$ we can construct the tensor

---

‡ It seems that this principle has never been explicitly formulated. However, it is satisfied by all forms of the mass tensor in common use.

$$B^{ik} = \sum_{m,\, n=0}^{3} \frac{\partial^2 A^{im,\,nk}}{\partial x_m \, \partial x_n} \tag{31.15}$$

which we shall call Krutkov's tensor.† It is easy to see that it is symmetric and that the antisymmetry of $A^{im,nk}$ in n and k results in the identity

$$\sum_{k=0}^{3} \frac{\partial B^{ik}}{\partial x_k} = 0 \tag{31.16}$$

In addition, Krutkov's tensor has the following property. If the tensor T^{ik} is replaced by B^{ik} in the volume integrals of the form of M, P^i, M^{ik} and K^i (equations (31.02), (31.03), (31.08) and (31.09)) these all reduce to surface integrals. The integrals formed with B^{ik} will thus all vanish if the tensor $A^{im,nk}$ and its first derivatives become zero on the surface enclosing the volume, or, when the volume considered is all space, if they tend to zero sufficiently fast at infinity.

Let T^{ik} be a given mass tensor. Adding to it a **Krutkov tensor** we get a new tensor

$$\overset{*}{T}{}^{ik} = T^{ik} + B^{ik} \tag{31.17}$$

which has the following properties. Firstly, it will be symmetric, secondly, by (31.10) and (31.16) it will satisfy the equation

$$\sum_{k=0}^{3} \frac{\partial \overset{*}{T}{}^{ik}}{\partial x_k} = 0 \tag{31.18}$$

Thirdly, the integrals $\overset{*}{M}$, $\overset{*}{P}{}^i$, $\overset{*}{M}{}^{ik}$ and $\overset{*}{K}{}^i$ formed from $\overset{*}{T}{}^{ik}$ will be equal to similar integrals formed with the given tensor T^{ik}.

Thus, apart from the condition that the mass tensor should be a function of the state, the tensor $\overset{*}{T}{}^{ik}$ obtained by (31.17) from T^{ik} will satisfy all requirements. In other words, the mass tensor would not be determined uniquely if no further condition were imposed.

However, the condition that the mass tensor should be a function of the state completely changes the situation and ensures that the definition of the mass tensor is unique in principle. The following circumstance can be considered an indication of this. Let us assume that the tensor T^{ik} is a function of the state, so that it satisfies all the conditions imposed, including the requirement just discussed. Even if the fourth rank tensor $A^{im,\,nk}$ is also a function of state, its second derivatives will not possess the same property and addition of the quantities B^{ik} to T^{ik} is not permissible. It is true that these considerations cannot be considered a proof, but a full proof of our statement can be constructed by other means. We shall discuss this in the following section.

The uniqueness of the mass tensor becomes particularly important in the theory of gravitation because the equations of this theory contain the mass tensor itself, not only its divergence.

† In three dimensions a fourth rank tensor $A^{im,nk}$ with the properties given reduces to a symmetric tensor of second rank with the components $\gamma_{11} = A^{23,23}$, $\gamma_{22} = A^{31,31}$, $\gamma_{33} = A^{12,12}$, $\gamma_{23} = A^{31,12}$, $\gamma_{31} = A^{12,23}$, $\gamma_{12} = A^{23,31}$. The tensor γ_{pq} was introduced and widely used by G. Krutkov in his book [10].

When expressing equations of motion as the vanishing of four-dimensional divergences we imply that the physical system under consideration is conservative. A general remark on non-conservative systems should be made.

As the law of energy conservation is a universal one, a non-conservative system should be regarded as one in which some forms of energy, such as heat, have not been explicitly taken into account. If there is some form of energy partaking in the general balance but not included in the tensor T^{ik} the divergence of this tensor will not vanish; the equations (31.01) will then have on their right-hand sides the flux into unit volume of this form of energy, and of the corresponding momentum. In the following we shall deal only with conservative systems.

31*. A System of Equations for the Components of the Mass Tensor as Functions of the Field †

Let us assume that the state of a physical system is described by the set of functions $\varphi_1, \varphi_2, \ldots, \varphi_n$. This set of functions may be called a field and the equations of motion relating these functions may be called field equations. We have already given examples of physical fields (the fields of velocity, density and pressure, the electromagnetic field, etc.).

The statement made in the previous section concerning the mass tensor can be made more precise in the following manner. The symmetric tensor T^{ik}, the components of which are functions of state (i.e. functions of the field), and whose divergence vanishes as a consequence of the field equations, is determined by these equations (which are purely local) apart from two constants. The tensor T^{ik} will be defined apart from a constant multiplying factor, provided local conditions are supplemented by a condition at infinity. This latter usually amounts to the requirement that the mass tensor should become zero where the field is zero (i.e. where all or some of the functions φ_s become zero). The constant factor evidently depends on the choice of energy or mass units, and its value is determined if these units are fixed.

Thus finally the mass tensor is uniquely determined for every physical system.

The proof of this statement can be given in each individual case by considering two systems of differential equations satisfied by the components of T^{ik} considered as functions of $\varphi_1, \varphi_2, \ldots, \varphi_n$. The first of these systems expresses the fact that T^{ik} is a tensor and the second the fact that the divergence of this tensor vanishes.

To derive the first system of equations, let us examine an infinitesimal Lorentz transformation.

Equation (23.06) shows that in such a transformation the components of a vector receive the increment

$$\delta A^i = \sum_{k=0}^{3} e_k \omega^{ik} A^k \qquad (31^*.01)$$

† This section and Section 49* have been added to the second Russian edition. To preserve the numbering of the original edition, equations appearing in these two sections are marked with asterisks. In the first English edition part of the present Section 31* was included at the end of Section 31.

The corresponding relation for the increment of tensor components is

$$\delta T^{ik} = \sum_{m=0}^{3} e_m \omega^{im} T^{mk} + \sum_{m=0}^{3} e_m \omega^{km} T^{im} \tag{31*.02}$$

Since the functions of state φ_s are also subject to a definite transformation law (they are always expressed in terms of some scalars, vectors and tensors), they will also obey relations of the form

$$\delta \varphi_s = \frac{1}{2} \sum_{l,\,m=0}^{3} e_l e_m \omega^{lm} \psi_s^{lm} \tag{31*.03}$$

or

$$\delta \varphi_s = \frac{1}{2} \sum_{l,\,m=0}^{3} \omega_{lm} \psi_s^{lm} \tag{31*.04}$$

where

$$\psi_s^{lm} = -\psi_s^{ml} \tag{31*.05}$$

are some known functions of $\varphi_1, \varphi_2, \ldots, \varphi_n$.

We consider certain general properties of the coefficients ψ_s^{lm}. It can be shown that they satisfy the relation

$$\sum_{r=1}^{m} \left(\psi_r^{pq} \frac{\partial \psi_s^{lm}}{\partial \varphi_r} - \psi_r^{lm} \frac{\partial \psi_s^{pq}}{\partial \varphi_r} \right) = e_p \delta_{mp} \psi_s^{lq} + e_q \delta_{mq} \psi_s^{pl} + e_p \delta_{lp} \psi_s^{qm} + e_q \delta_{lq} \psi_s^{mp} \tag{31*.06}$$

To prove this we note first of all that this relation is functionally invariant in the following sense. If in place of the functions $\varphi_1, \varphi_2, \ldots, \varphi_n$ we introduce new functions of state $\overset{*}{\varphi}_1, \overset{*}{\varphi}_2, \ldots, \overset{*}{\varphi}_n$ (each set being expressible in terms of the other) and if we also introduce corresponding coefficients $\overset{*}{\psi}_s^{lm}$ related to the ψ_s^{lm} by

$$\overset{*}{\psi}_s^{lm} = \sum_{r=1}^{n} \psi_r^{lm} \frac{\partial \overset{*}{\varphi}_s}{\partial \varphi_r} \tag{31*.07}$$

then equation (31*.06) will be satisfied for the starred quantities. On the other hand relation (31*.06) is easily verified directly if the φ_r form a scalar, a vector or a tensor (or a set of scalars, vectors or tensors). Since ultimately all functions of state must be expressed in terms of scalars, vectors and tensors it follows from the functional invariance of (31*.06) that this relation is generally valid. We shall not go into the detailed exposition of the manipulations involved in this proof.

The foregoing equations can be written in a more elegant form by introducing the operators X^{lm} defined by the equations

$$X^{lm}(f) = \sum_{r=1}^{n} \psi_r^{lm} \frac{\partial f}{\partial \varphi_r} \tag{31*.08}$$

Then we have, in particular

$$X^{lm}(\varphi_s) = \psi_s^{lm}. \tag{31*.09}$$

Using (31*.06) it is easy to prove the operator equation

$$X^{pq}X^{lm} - X^{lm}X^{pq} = e_p\delta_{mp}X^{lq} + e_q\delta_{mq}X^{pl} + e_p\delta_{lp}X^{qm} + e_q\delta_{lq}X^{mp} \tag{31*.10}$$

If this equation is applied to a function φ_s, relation (31*.06) follows conversely from it.

The change of any field function (i.e. any function of the $\varphi_1, \varphi_2, \ldots, \varphi_n$) in an infinitesimal Lorentz transformation can be expressed in terms of the operators X^{lm}. Indeed, if $f = f(\varphi_1, \ldots, \varphi_n)$ it follows from (31*.04) that

$$\delta f = \frac{1}{2}\sum_{l,\, m=0}^{3} \omega_{lm}X^{lm}(f) \tag{31*.11}$$

Putting $f = \varphi_s$ and using (31*.09) we return to equation (31*.04). The formula (31*.11) is convenient because of the fact that it is independent of the choice of functions $\varphi_1, \ldots, \varphi_n$.

We apply equation (31*.11) to one of the components of T^{ik}. We have

$$\delta T^{ik} = \frac{1}{2}\sum_{l,\, m=0}^{3} \omega_{lm}X^{lm}(T^{ik}) \tag{31*.12}$$

On the other hand, since T^{ik} is a tensor, equation (31*.02) holds; it can be written in the form

$$\delta T^{ik} = \sum_{l,\, m=0}^{3} \omega_{lm}(e_i\delta_{il}T^{mk} + e_k\delta_{kl}T^{im}) \tag{31*.13}$$

Both expressions for T^{ik} must be equal identically, i.e. for any choice of anti-symmetric quantities ω_{lm}. Equating the antisymmetric part of the coefficients of the ω_{lm} in the two expressions we obtain

$$X^{lm}(T^{ik}) = e_i\delta_{il}T^{mk} - e_i\delta_{im}T^{lk} + e_k\delta_{kl}T^{im} - e_k\delta_{km}T^{il} \tag{31*.14}$$

or, in more detail

$$\sum_{s=1}^{n} \psi_s^{lm}\frac{\partial T^{ik}}{\partial \varphi_s} = e_i\delta_{il}T^{mk} - e_i\delta_{im}T^{lk} + e_k\delta_{kl}T^{im} - e_k\delta_{km}T^{il} \tag{31*.15}$$

This is the first of the two aforementioned systems of differential equations for the T^{ik} as functions of the field.

The second set of equations is obtained from the condition that the divergence of the mass tensor vanishes. It follows from this requirement that

$$\sum_{k=0}^{3}\sum_{s=1}^{n} \frac{\partial T^{ik}}{\partial \varphi_s}\frac{\partial \varphi_s}{\partial x_k} = 0 \tag{31*.16}$$

and this equation must hold for all values of the φ_s and of the $\partial\varphi_s/\partial x_k$ which are connected by the equations of motion (and possibly by other relations, if not all these quantities are independent). When the φ_s and the $\partial\varphi_s/\partial x_k$ are expressed in terms of independent quantities equation (31.27) must reduce to an identity in these latter variables. Since the T^{ik} contain only the functions φ_s themselves, but not their derivatives with respect to the x_m this identity leads to a set of relations for the $\partial T^{ik}/\partial \varphi_s$ which involves only the φ_r not the

$\partial \varphi_r / \partial x_m$. These relations are just the second system of equations for the mass tensor. We note that both systems are satisfied by the values

$$T^{ik} = \lambda e_i \delta_{ik} \tag{31*.17}$$

where λ is a constant.

The complete system of equations for T^{ik} consists of these two sub-systems: equations (31*.15), which express the fact that the T^{ik} form a tensor and further equations which state that the divergence of this tensor vanishes; the latter are obtained from (31*.16) by eliminating the derivatives $\partial \varphi_s / \partial x_k$ with the aid of the field equations. The complete system can be discussed in a simple form in particular cases that correspond to given physical systems. When this is done, the uniqueness of the mass tensor is confirmed every time. Examples of uniqueness proofs are given in Appendices B and C. Further examples can be found in the literature [11].

To conclude this section we shall show that if the mass density T^{00} is known as a function of the field $\varphi_1, \ldots, \varphi_n$, equations (31*.14) or (31*.15) also permit the unique determination of all other components of the mass tensor. Indeed, if we assume that T^{00} is known and if in (31*.14) we put $i = k = l = 0$; $m = 1, 2, 3$ we get

$$T^{0m} = T^{m0} = \tfrac{1}{2} X^{0m}(T^{00}) \tag{31*.18}$$

where the operator X^{0m} has the value given by (31*.08). Thus, the mass flux density has been expressed in terms of the mass density. Further, putting $i = l = 0; \; k, m = 1, 2, 3$ we get

$$T^{mk} = X^{0m}(T^{0k}) - \delta_{mk} T^{00} \tag{31*.19}$$

or, using (31*.18),

$$T^{mk} = (\tfrac{1}{2} X^{0m} X^{0k} - \delta_{mk}) T^{00} \tag{31*.20}$$

This expression is in fact symmetric in m and k. Indeed, we have the operator relation

$$X^{0m} X^{0k} - X^{0k} X^{0m} = X^{mk} \qquad (m, k = 1, 2, 3) \tag{31*.21}$$

and from (31*.14) it follows that the result of applying this operator to T^{00} is zero (this last fact means that T^{00} is a three-dimensional scalar).

Thus in order to obtain all components of the mass tensor it is sufficient to know the component T^{00}.

32. Examples of the Mass Tensor

In this section and the following we shall discuss the explicit form of the mass tensor in some concrete cases, without dwelling on the proof of its uniqueness. Examples of such proofs will be given in Appendices B and C.

We begin with the simplest case of " dustlike " matter, by which we mean an assembly of non-interacting particles which nevertheless have a continuous variation of velocity so that a velocity field can be defined. In this case, we introduce the special notation Θ^{ik} for the mass tensor. We denote by ρ^* the invariant mass density, i.e. the density in that frame of reference relative to which the particles of the particular volume element in question are momentarily at rest. This frame might also be described as travelling with the particles of this volume. Let u^i be components of the four-dimensional velocity of the particles. We put

$$\Theta^{ik} = \frac{1}{c^2} \rho^* u^i u^k \tag{32.01}$$

By definition Θ^{ik} is a four-dimensional contravariant tensor. Its zero-zero component is

$$\Theta^{00} = \frac{1}{c^2}\rho^*(u^0)^2 = \frac{\rho^*}{1 - v^2/c^2} \tag{32.02}$$

This component must be equal to the density of total mass, including the mass of the kinetic energy. We shall show that this is so : if ρ^* is the density of rest-mass in the frame moving with the particles, then the density of rest-mass in the "laboratory frame" relative to which a particle moves with velocity $\mathbf{v}$, is

$$\rho = \frac{\rho^*}{\sqrt{(1 - v^2/c^2)}} \tag{32.03}$$

Further, if ρ is the rest-mass density, the density of the total mass, including kinetic energy, is

$$\frac{\rho}{\sqrt{(1 - v^2/c^2)}} = \frac{\rho^*}{1 - v^2/c^2} = \Theta^{00} \tag{32.04}$$

This expression for density corresponds to the usual expression

$$M = \frac{m}{\sqrt{(1 - v^2/c^2)}} \tag{32.05}$$

for the mass of a single particle. The other components of the mass tensor are, in three-dimensional notation

$$\Theta^{0i} = \frac{1}{c}\frac{\rho^* v_i}{1 - v^2/c^2} = \frac{1}{c}\frac{\rho v_i}{\sqrt{(1 - v^2/c^2)}} \tag{32.06}$$

and

$$\Theta^{ik} = \frac{1}{c^2}\frac{\rho^* v_i v_k}{1 - v^2/c^2} = \frac{1}{c^2}\frac{\rho v_i v_k}{\sqrt{(1 - v^2/c^2)}} \tag{32.07}$$

Let us form the divergence of the tensor Θ^{ik}. We have

$$\sum_{k=0}^{3} \frac{\partial \Theta^{ik}}{\partial x_k} = \frac{1}{c^2} u^i \sum_{k=0}^{3} \frac{\partial(\rho^* u^k)}{\partial x_k} + \frac{\rho^*}{c^2} \sum_{k=0}^{3} u^k \frac{\partial u^i}{\partial x_k} \tag{32.08}$$

We introduce special symbols for the sums in (32.08), putting

$$Q^* = \sum_{k=0}^{3} \frac{\partial(\rho^* u^k)}{\partial x_k} \tag{32.09}$$

and

$$w^i = \sum_{k=0}^{3} u^k \frac{\partial u^i}{\partial x_k} \tag{32.10}$$

These can also be written as

$$Q^* = \frac{\partial \rho}{\partial t} + \operatorname{div}(\rho \mathbf{v}) \tag{32.11}$$

and

$$w^i = \frac{1}{\sqrt{(1 - v^2/c^2)}}\left(\frac{\partial u^i}{\partial t} + \sum_{k=0}^{3} v_k \frac{\partial u^i}{\partial x_k}\right) = \frac{1}{\sqrt{(1 - v^2/c^2)}}\frac{du^i}{dt} \tag{32.12}$$

where d/dt is the substantial derivative. This shows that the invariant Q^*

is the rate of increase of rest mass in unit fluid volume† and the vector w^i is the four-dimensional acceleration, the space components of which become the ordinary acceleration in non-relativistic approximation. Thus

$$\sum_{k=0}^{3} \frac{\partial \Theta^{ik}}{\partial x_k} = \frac{Q^*}{c^2} u^i + \frac{\rho^*}{c^2} w^i \tag{32.13}$$

By the equation of motion this expression must be zero. But we have the identities

$$\sum_{i=0}^{3} u_i u^i = c^2 ; \qquad \sum_{i=0}^{3} u_i w^i = 0 \tag{32.14}$$

so that the equation

$$Q^* u^i + \rho^* w^i = 0 \tag{32.15}$$

is equivalent to the two separate ones

$$Q^* = 0 \quad \text{and} \quad w^i = 0 \tag{32.16}$$

The first of these is the equation of continuity which expresses the constancy of the rest-mass of the particles. In the case we are considering the rest-mass does not change because the particles do not interact and their internal energy remains constant. The second equation of (32.16) expresses the constancy of the four-dimensional, and hence also of the three-dimensional, velocity. That non-interacting particles move with constant velocity is, of course, physically obvious. As the equations of motion are of first order in ρ^* and u^i and as Θ^{ik} is expressed as a function of these quantities this mass tensor is clearly a function of the state. Therefore the form of the mass tensor for dustlike matter may be considered established.

Let us now seek to generalize the equations of perfect fluid hydrodynamics. In non-relativistic theory this case is characterized by the stress tensor reducing to a scalar. This readily permits a relativistic generalization. Let us assume that the energy tensor, i.e. the mass tensor times c^2, has the form

$$c^2 T^{ik} = \left(\mu^* + \frac{p}{c^2} \right) u^i u^k - p e_k \delta_{ik} \tag{32.17}$$

where μ^* and p are four-dimensional scalars connected by the relation

$$\mu^* = f(p) \tag{32.18}$$

In the frame, relative to which the velocity at the point and at the moment in question is zero, the component T^{00} of the mass tensor is equal to μ^*. Therefore μ^* is the rest-mass density of the fluid. As the fluid is assumed elastic and can possess compressional potential energy, this rest-mass includes the mass corresponding to that energy. Since the compressional energy may change, the rest-mass of a volume of fluid will not stay constant. With this fact in mind we introduced a special symbol μ^* for this rest-mass density leaving the symbol ρ^* to refer to that part of the rest-mass density which does not change in the course of the motion.

† By " fluid volume " we mean the volume of an element of fluid always consisting of the same particles.

We now state the equations of motion. Putting for brevity

$$Q = \sum_{k=0}^{3} \frac{\partial}{\partial x_k} \left[\left(\mu^* + \frac{p}{c^2} \right) u^k \right] \tag{32.19}$$

and using the notation w^i for acceleration as before, we have

$$c^2 \sum_{k=0}^{3} \frac{\partial T^{ik}}{\partial x_k} = Q u^i + \left(\mu^* + \frac{p}{c^2} \right) w^i - e_i \frac{\partial p}{\partial x_i} \tag{32.20}$$

In the absence of external forces this expression will be equal to zero.

Using equation (32.14) we can get from (32.20) another expression for Q, namely

$$Q = \frac{1}{c^2} \sum_{k=0}^{3} u^k \frac{\partial p}{\partial x_k} = \frac{1}{c^2 \sqrt{(1 - v^2/c^2)}} \frac{dp}{dt} = \frac{1}{c^2} \frac{dp}{d\tau} \tag{32.21}$$

Here dp/dt is the substantial derivative of p and $d\tau$ the differential of the particle proper time. As for p itself, a comparison of these equations of motion with the non-relativistic ones shows readily that it is the pressure. Equating the two expressions for Q we obtain

$$\sum_{k=0}^{3} \left\{ \left(\mu^* + \frac{p}{c^2} \right) \frac{\partial u^k}{\partial x_k} + u^k \frac{\partial \mu^*}{\partial x_k} \right\} = 0 \tag{32.22}$$

As we assume μ^* to be a function of p we can introduce a new quantity ρ^* by the differential relation

$$\frac{d\rho^*}{\rho^*} = \frac{d\mu^*}{\mu^* + p/c^2} \tag{32.23}$$

We can choose the constant of integration in such a way, say, as to make $\rho^* = \mu^*$ when $p = 0$. Using (32.23) we can write (32.22) as

$$\sum_{k=0}^{3} \frac{\partial}{\partial x_k} (\rho^* u^k) = 0 \tag{32.24}$$

Hence we see that ρ^* can be interpreted as the invariant density of that part of the rest-mass which does not change in the motion. This quantity, like μ^*, is a function of p.

Let us put

$$\mu^* = \rho^* \left(1 + \frac{\Pi}{c^2} \right) \tag{32.25}$$

Then we get from the differential relation between μ^* and ρ^* that

$$d\Pi = \frac{p \, d\rho^*}{\rho^{*2}} \tag{32.26}$$

whence

$$\Pi = \int_0^p \frac{dp}{\rho^*} - \frac{p}{\rho^*} \tag{32.27}$$

The quantity Π can be interpreted in analogy with (30.11) as the potential energy of a unit mass of fluid, with mass meaning that part of the rest-mass which does not vary during the motion. Expressing μ^* in terms of ρ^* and Π we can write the energy tensor as

$$c^2 T^{ik} = \left[\rho^* + \frac{1}{c^2} (\rho^* \Pi + p) \right] u^i u^k - p e_k \delta_{ik} \tag{32.28}$$

while the equations of motion appear as

$$\left[\rho^* + \frac{1}{c^2} (\rho^* \Pi + p) \right] w^i = e_i \frac{\partial p}{\partial x_i} - \frac{1}{c^2} \frac{dp}{d\tau} u^i \tag{32.29}$$

The equation for the zero component of acceleration can be replaced by the equation of continuity in the form (32.24).

One may note that the invariant of the mass tensor is

$$\sum_{i=0}^3 e_i T^{ii} = \rho^* \left(1 + \frac{\Pi}{c^2} \right) - \frac{3p}{c^2} = \mu^* - \frac{3p}{c^2} \tag{32.30}$$

Comparing the equations of motion (32.29) with equation (32.28) for T^{ik} one sees that the mass tensor T^{ik} is a function of the state, as it should be.

We now write down the components of the mass tensor in non-relativistic approximation, but retaining in T^{00} and T^{0i} terms of an order of $1/c^2$ compared with the main terms. In the main terms we put

$$\rho^* = \rho - \frac{1}{2} \rho \frac{v^2}{c^2} \tag{32.31}$$

in agreement with (32.03). Here ρ is the usual density that satisfies the equation of continuity (30.02). We then have

$$T^{00} = \rho + \frac{1}{c^2} \left(\frac{1}{2} \rho v^2 + \rho \Pi \right)$$

$$T^{0i} = \frac{1}{c} \rho v_i + \frac{v_i}{c^3} \left(\frac{1}{2} \rho v^2 + \rho \Pi + p \right) \tag{32.32}$$

$$T^{ik} = \frac{1}{c^2} (\rho v_i v_k + p \delta_{ik})$$

Comparing the correction terms in T^{00} and T^{0i} with Umov's scalar and vector (30.17) and (30.18) we see that the components T^{00} and T^{0i} of the mass tensor can be written as

$$T^{00} = \rho + \frac{1}{c^2} S ; \qquad T^{0i} = \frac{1}{c} \rho v_i + \frac{1}{c^3} S_i \tag{32.33}$$

Thus Umov's scalar and vector give the second order relativistic corrections to the usual expressions for mass density and momentum density. As for the spatial components of T^{ik}, they are proportional to the three-dimensional tensor of momentum current density which was considered in Section 30.

Using these results we can also write down approximate expressions for the mass tensor for the case of an elastic body. We have

$$T^{00} = \rho + \frac{1}{c^2}\left(\frac{1}{2}\,\rho v^2 + \rho\Pi\right)$$

$$T^{0i} = \frac{1}{c}\,\rho v_i + \frac{1}{c^3}\left\{v_i\left(\frac{1}{2}\,\rho v^2 + \rho\Pi\right) - \sum_{k=1}^{3} p_{ik}v_k\right\} \qquad (32.34)$$

$$T^{ik} = \frac{1}{c^2}\,(\rho v_i v_k - p_{ik})$$

If here we put $p_{ik} = -p\delta_{ik}$ as in (30.09), we get back to the case of a perfect fluid.

We shall not discuss the relativistic formulation of the theory of elasticity. We shall only make one remark concerning the possibility of using the concept of an absolutely rigid body in Relativity. In non-relativistic mechanics this concept is introduced as an abstraction, according to which the shape and size of such a body does not change, whatever the forces acting on it. In particular, a blow imparted at some instant to one end of an absolutely rigid body immediately sets the other end of the body in motion. In fact, in a physical solid body the blow produces a wave in the body that spreads with the speed of sound. Therefore the abstraction implies the assumption that the speed of sound may be treated as infinitely great.† However, it is evident that if the speed of sound is assumed infinitely great, the speed of light, which is actually some hundred thousand times greater, must also be taken as infinite. It is thus clear that the abstraction involved in defining an absolutely rigid body is permissible only in a non-relativistic theory. As the Theory of Relativity is based on the fact that any kind of action propagates with finite speed, this abstraction must inevitably lead to contradictions. Therefore the notion of an absolutely rigid body may not be used in Relativity Theory.

However, this does not preclude the use of the notion of a rigid measuring rod in discussions of Relativity. For this notion merely presupposes the existence of rigid bodies whose shape and size remain unchanged under certain particular external conditions such as the absence of accelerations or impulses, constancy of temperature, etc. Such rigid rods can be realized with sufficient accuracy by solid bodies existing in nature and they can serve as standards of length. As we showed in Section 2 the constancy of their length can be checked, say by comparison with the wave length of some spectral line.

33. The Energy Tensor of the Electromagnetic Field

In the preceding sections we discussed the mass tensor, and the energy tensor which is proportional to it, for a substance consisting of particles interacting by means of elastic forces. We now consider the energy tensor for a substance of particles interacting only by means of the electromagnetic field. As we are dealing with macroscopic theory we can imagine the substance to be a continuous medium with a continuous charge distribution.

We start from Maxwell's equations in the form given by Lorentz. We put for the components of the electric and of the magnetic field

---

† One reaches the same conclusion if one considers the absolutely rigid body as the limiting case of an elastic body in which the elastic moduli are infinite.

$$E_1 = F_{10}; \qquad E_2 = F_{20}; \qquad E_3 = F_{30}$$
$$H_1 = F_{23}; \qquad H_2 = F_{31}; \qquad H_3 = F_{12} \tag{33.01}$$

As we saw in Section 24, the four-dimensional statement of Maxwell's equations is

$$F_{ikl} \equiv \frac{\partial F_{ik}}{\partial x_l} + \frac{\partial F_{kl}}{\partial x_i} + \frac{\partial F_{li}}{\partial x_k} = 0 \tag{33.02}$$

and

$$\sum_{k=0}^{3} \frac{\partial F^{ik}}{\partial x_k} = s^i \tag{33.03}$$

where the

$$F^{ik} = e_i e_k F_{ik} \tag{33.04}$$

are the contravariant components of the antisymmetric field tensor and where the four-dimensional vector s^i has the components

$$s^0 = 4\pi\rho; \qquad s^i = \frac{4\pi}{c} j_i = \frac{4\pi}{c} \rho v_i \qquad (i = 1, 2, 3) \tag{33.05}$$

Here ρ denotes the charge density, v^i the three-dimensional velocity and $j_i = \rho v_i$ the electric current density. Introducing the invariant charge density ρ^* and the four-dimensional velocity u^i, we may replace (33.05) by

$$s^i = \frac{4\pi}{c} \rho^* u^i \qquad (i = 0, 1, 2, 3) \tag{33.06}$$

We saw in Section 25 that the equations of motion of a particle of charge e and rest-mass m is of the form

$$mw_i = -\frac{e}{c} \sum_{k=0}^{3} F_{ik} u^k \tag{33.07}$$

Here we have on the right the Lorentz force acting on the charge e. To pass from a single particle to a substance with continuous charge and mass distribution we must introduce the invariant charge density ρ^* in place of the charge and the invariant mass density μ^* in place of the mass. We then get

$$\mu^* w_i = -\frac{\rho^*}{c} \sum_{k=0}^{3} F_{ik} u^k \tag{33.08}$$

or

$$\mu^* w_i = -\frac{1}{4\pi} \sum_{k=0}^{3} F_{ik} s^k \tag{33.09}$$

As we have introduced two new functions, ρ^* and μ^* which are not necessarily proportional, we must adjoin to the equations of motion two further equations for these functions. The equation for ρ^* is already implied by Maxwell's equations and is an expression of the law of charge conservation

$$\sum_{k=0}^{3} \frac{\partial(\rho^* u^k)}{\partial x_k} = 0 \tag{33.10}$$

The equation for μ^* must be stated separately. We assume that the rest-mass of the particles does not change in the motion; (this assumption implies that no Joule heat is developed). Then we have

$$Q^* \equiv \sum_{k=0}^{3} \frac{\partial(\mu^* u^k)}{\partial x_k} = 0 \tag{33.11}$$

Of the equations of motion (33.09) only three are independent, because we have the identity

$$\mu^* \sum_{i=0}^{3} u^i w_i = -\frac{\rho^*}{c} \sum_{i,k=0}^{3} F_{ik} u^i u^k = 0 \tag{33.12}$$

Thus the equations of motion (33.09) together with the equation of rest-mass conservation represent four independent equations. Our problem is to write them in the form of the divergence of some tensor. To do this we first use equation (32.13) according to which

$$\mu^* w^i + Q^* u^i = c^2 \sum_{k=0}^{3} \frac{\partial \Theta^{ik}}{\partial x_k} \tag{33.13}$$

where

$$\Theta^{ik} = \frac{1}{c^2} \mu^* u^i u^k \tag{33.14}$$

(Note that now the invariant rest-mass is denoted by μ^* and not by ρ^* as in (32.01)). On the other hand the equations (33.09) and (33.11) can be combined into the four independent ones

$$\mu^* w_i + Q^* u_i = -\frac{1}{4\pi} \sum_{k=0}^{3} F_{ik} s^k \tag{33.15}$$

which are equivalent to (33.09) and (33.11), as a consequence of (33.12). The left-hand sides of the last set of equations, or rather their contravariant forms, have already been expressed as the divergence of a tensor. It remains therefore to do the same with the right-hand sides.

For this purpose let us consider the tensor

$$U_{ik} = -\frac{1}{4\pi} \sum_{m=0}^{3} e_m F_{im} F_{km} + \frac{1}{16\pi} e_i \delta_{ik} \sum_{m,n=0}^{3} F^{mn} F_{mn} \tag{33.16}$$

and denote by f_i the negative of its divergence. We have then

$$f_i = -\sum_{k=0}^{3} e_k \frac{\partial U_{ik}}{\partial x_k} \tag{33.17}$$

Performing the differentiations, some simple calculation gives

$$f_i = -\frac{1}{4\pi} \sum_{k,l=0}^{3} F_{ik} \frac{\partial F^{kl}}{\partial x_l} - \frac{1}{8\pi} \sum_{k,l=0}^{3} F^{kl} F_{ikl} \tag{33.18}$$

where the F_{ikl} are the quantities defined in (33.02). By virtue of Maxwell's equations (33.02) and (33.03) we find

$$f_i = -\frac{1}{4\pi} \sum_{k=0}^{3} F_{ik} s^k \tag{33.19}$$

which is the Lorentz force as it appeared on the right-hand side of (33.15).

Thus both members of (33.15) have been represented in the form of divergences. Passing to contravariant components we can write the equations

$$\mu^* w^i + Q^* u^i - f^i = 0 \tag{33.20}$$

as

$$\sum_{k=0}^{3} \frac{\partial T^{ik}}{\partial x_k} = 0 \tag{33.21}$$

where

$$c^2 T^{ik} = c^2 \Theta^{ik} + U^{ik} \tag{33.22}$$

is the energy tensor of the whole system, comprising the material medium and the field. In the last equation the first term on the right is the energy tensor of the medium and the second that of the field.

The tensor T^{ik} involves the invariant density μ^*, the velocity components u^i and the field components F_{ik}. Since these quantities characterize the state of the system, this mass tensor is evidently a function of the state.

We now examine the field energy tensor in a little more detail.

In three-dimensional notation the components of the energy tensor of the electromagnetic field have the following form

$$U^{00} = U_{00} = \frac{1}{8\pi} (E^2 + H^2) \tag{33.23}$$

$$U^{0i} = -U_{0i} = \frac{1}{4\pi} [\mathbf{E} \times \mathbf{H}]_i \tag{33.24}$$

and

$$U^{ik} = U_{ik} = -\frac{1}{4\pi} (E_i E_k + H_i H_k) + \frac{1}{8\pi} \delta_{ik} (E^2 + H^2) \tag{33.25}$$

We note that the invariant of the energy tensor vanishes.

$$\sum_{i=0}^{3} e_i U_{ii} = 0 \tag{33.26}$$

As always the component U^{00} represents the energy density, and the components U^{0i} multiplied by c the energy current vector, i.e. Umov's vector. It can be written as

$$\mathbf{S} = \frac{c}{4\pi} [\mathbf{E} \times \mathbf{H}] \tag{33.27}$$

and is usually called the Umov-Poynting vector, or simply Poynting's vector, because Poynting was the first to give the explicit expression for the energy current density of the electromagnetic field resulting from Maxwell's equations.

Quite generally, the energy current divided by c^2 is equal to the corresponding mass current and the mass current is in turn equal to the momentum. Therefore the Umov-Poynting vector divided by c^2 is equal to the electromagnetic momentum density. The fact that the electromagnetic field carries momentum gives rise to the forces of radiation pressure first discovered experimentally in 1900 by P. N. Lebedev [13]. Equations (33.25) show that if a body is situated in an electromagnetic field a surface element $d\sigma$ normal to the x_i-axis is acted on by a force with the components

$$F_k \, d\sigma = + U_{ik} \, d\sigma \qquad (k = 1, 2, 3) \tag{33.28}$$

We consider a totally reflecting body, part of whose boundary surface is flat. Let the equation of this flat part be $x_1 = 0$, with the body extending into the region $x_1 > 0$. We assume that a plane wave of the form

$$
\begin{aligned}
E_1^0 &= -\sin\vartheta f & H_1^0 &= \sin\vartheta g \\
E_2^0 &= \cos\vartheta f & H_2^0 &= -\cos\vartheta g \\
E_3^0 &= g & H_3^0 &= f
\end{aligned}
\tag{33.29}
$$

impinges on the body, where

$$
f = f\left(t - \frac{1}{c}(x_1 \cos\vartheta + x_2 \sin\vartheta)\right)
$$

$$
g = g\left(t - \frac{1}{c}(x_1 \cos\vartheta + x_2 \sin\vartheta)\right)
\tag{33.30}
$$

We add to the field (33.29) the reflected wave which is obtained by replacing ϑ by $\pi - \vartheta$ and g by $-g$ in the preceding equations and so get the complete field, satisfying all boundary conditions. The values of the field components on the surface of the body will be

$$
\begin{aligned}
E_1 &= -2\sin\vartheta f & H_1 &= 0 \\
E_2 &= 0 & H_2 &= -2\cos\vartheta g \\
E_3 &= 0 & H_3 &= 2f
\end{aligned}
\tag{33.31}
$$

where the functions f and g are taken at $x_1 = 0$. Inserting these values in (33.25) we obtain for the force acting on unit surface area of the body

$$
F_1 = U_{11} = \frac{1}{2\pi}(f^2 + g^2)\cos^2\vartheta; \quad F_2 = U_{12} = 0; \quad F_3 = U_{13} = 0 \tag{33.32}
$$

Hence, whatever the direction of the incident wave, the force acts in the direction of the inward normal to the surface and thus is a normal pressure (see [12]).

Let us now consider another case. Let the electromagnetic field consist of a superposition of waves, uniformly distributed over all directions. Then the statistical mean of the products of field components will be

$$
\overline{E_i E_k} = \frac{1}{3}\overline{E^2}\delta_{ik}; \quad \overline{H_i H_k} = \frac{1}{3}\overline{H^2}\delta_{ik} \tag{33.33}
$$

The space components of the energy tensor will then be

$$
\overline{U}_{ik} = \frac{1}{24\pi}(\overline{E^2} + \overline{H^2})\delta_{ik} = \frac{1}{3}\overline{U}_{00}\delta_{ik} \tag{33.34}
$$

In this case the electromagnetic field produces an isotropic pressure equal in magnitude to one-third of the electromagnetic energy density. This result is of great importance in the theory of black body radiation.

34. Mass and Energy

According to the terminology in use in mechanics the mass of a body is a measure of its inertia (inertial mass). On the other hand the word "mass" is also used to mean the ability of a body to produce a gravitational field and to experience forces in such a field (gravitational mass). Inertia and the property of producing a gravitational field are entirely distinct manifestations of the nature of matter. It is, however, no accident that the measures of these two distinct manifestations carry the same name. The reason is that both properties are always present together and are always proportional to each other so that with a suitable choice of units one and the same number can be used to measure them both. The equality of inertial and gravitational mass is an experimental fact which has been verified with enormous accuracy by Eötvös, but the definitions of the two concepts are quite different, corresponding as they do to quite different manifestations of the properties of matter. There exists a physical theory, namely Einstein's Theory of Gravitation, in which the fundamental law of the equality of inertial and gravitational mass is accounted for automatically in the sense that one and the same constant appearing in the solution of Einstein's equations figures as inertial and as gravitational mass.

How should one answer the question : are inertial and gravitational mass the same thing or not? Their manifestations are different but their numerical characteristics are proportional. Such a state of affairs is customarily described by the word " equivalence ".

An analogous question arises in connection with the concepts of mass and energy. (For definiteness we shall discuss the inertial mass.) We have just recalled the definition of mass. Energy is usually defined as the ability to do work. For its definition the essentials are, first, the law of conservation of energy and, second, the ability of different forms of energy to transform into each other. Both together are known as the law of conservation and transmutation of energy. Because this universal law is valid, a measurement of any kind of energy can be reduced to a measurement of one particular kind, e.g. mechanical energy, and one and the same unit, e.g. a mechanical one, can be used to measure all kinds of energy.

Thus the manifest properties of matter corresponding to mass and to energy are undoubtedly different. However, the Theory of Relativity asserts that mass and energy are indissolubly connected and are proportional. Any change of energy of a system is accompanied by a change of inertial mass. This is true not only for the kinetic energy of a body in a change in which rest-mass remains unaltered, but also for changes of all kinds of internal energy in which the rest-mass also changes.

Phenomena are known in physics in which the whole of the energy corresponding to the rest-mass of a body can transmute into radiative energy, which, of course, possesses the same mass. Conversely rest-mass energy may be created at the expense of radiative energy. An example of this is the conversion of an electron-positron pair into a gamma quantum and the reverse phenomenon of the creation of such a pair by a quantum.

In the preceding sections we have studied in detail the relation between mass and energy. We saw that to any energy W one should ascribe a mass $M = W/c^2$ and to every mass one should ascribe an energy $W = Mc^2$. The two quantities are always proportional and if they are both expressed in the same units, say those of energy, they may be measured by the same number.

Further, we saw that the energy tensor differs only by the factor c^2 from the mass tensor and that the law of conservation of energy is at the same time the law of conservation of mass.

Thus to the question posed above whether mass and energy are the same thing or not we can give the same answer as to the question of the relation of inertial and gravitational mass. The properties of matter manifest as mass and as energy are different but their numerical characteristics are proportional. Thus in this case we also can talk of equivalence–the equivalence of mass and energy. But it is better to call this fundamental law simply the law of proportionality of mass and energy.

We have just stated that the law of energy conservation is at the same time the law of mass conservation. A question arises immediately. Experiment shows that for an enormous majority of known physical processes the mass of a body, determined by weighing, and its energy, determined by work done, are conserved separately. One observes *two* conservation laws. How does this relate to the fact that in the Theory of Relativity only *one* law is formulated ?

This question can be answered as follows. There is but one rigorous conservation law, which applies to the entire mass of a body M and to the corresponding entire energy $W = Mc^2$. But an overwhelmingly large part of the energy (and of the corresponding rest-mass) does not usually take part in transformations and is conserved separately. It follows then that the remaining part of the energy, which is active in transformations is also conserved separately.

The division of energy into a " passive " part which does not undergo any transformation in a process and an active part which is capable of changing into different forms can be followed through in the examples of the hydrodynamical equations discussed in Section 32. There, by use of the frame travelling with the fluid particle in question we separated out the kinetic energy and then considered two rest-mass densities, the total density μ^* and the density ρ^* of the passive part. The two quantities were connected by (32.35) which gives

$$\mu^* = \rho^* + \frac{1}{c^2}\rho^*\Pi \tag{34.01}$$

where the second term on the right is the density of compressional potential energy divided by c^2.

The division is still more clearly apparent in the approximate equations (32.32) and (32.34) which give the total mass density T^{00} and the total mass current density cT^{0i}. By (32.33) these equations can be stated as

$$T^{00} = \rho + \frac{1}{c^2}S ; \qquad cT^{0i} = \rho v_i + \frac{1}{c^2}S_i \tag{34.02}$$

Here ρ and ρv_i are the density and current density of that part of the mass which does not take part in any transformation while Umov's scalar and vector represent the density and current density of the active part of the energy, or, when divided by c^2, of the active part of the mass.

We spoke above of the fact that the total mass of a body as determined by weighing, including the variable part, is practically conserved although the body may emit or absorb energy. This is explained simply by insufficient accuracy of weighing and by the fact that in ordinary bodies a predominant part of the mass is passive. A change in the active part, on the other hand, can be detected with much greater accuracy by measuring the corresponding part of the energy, i.e. by calorimetric methods rather than by weighing.

It is natural to inquire into the deeper reason for the fact that in normal conditions the predominant part of the energy is bound so durably as to be in a completely passive state. Why does even a negligible part of it never leave this state and destroy the separate balance of the active part? The Theory of Relativity by itself is unable to answer this question. One should look for the answer in the domain of quantal laws, which have as one of their main features the existence of stable states with discrete energy levels. With elementary particles the energy corresponding to their rest-mass can only transform into the active form of radiation as a whole, or not at all. A small loss of mass is impossible. This has been verified experimentally in the electron-positron case but is also believed to be true for all other elementary particles. As the predominant part of the mass of atoms has the form of the mass of elementary particles the impossibility of a small change of mass must also hold for atoms.

Thus the reason for the particular stability with which the passive part of the energy is bound is of quantal character.

It is worth noting that the division of energy, or mass, into an active and a passive part is of a relative nature. In ordinary chemical reactions not only intranuclear energy but also the energy of the inner electronic shells behaves passively. At very high temperatures, when a complete or nearly complete ionization of atoms becomes possible, the energy of the inner electron shells becomes active. Finally, in processes involving rearrangements within atomic nuclei the intranuclear energy becomes active as well. However, even then the energy corresponding to the rest-masses of the heavy elementary particles that form the nucleus remains in a passive state.

The particularly durable binding of the predominant part of all energy, or mass, is the reason why one can speak of the laws of conservation of mass and of energy as two separate laws, although in Relativity the two laws coalesce into one.

The law of mass conservation in chemical reactions was discovered and experimentally proved by Lomonosov and then confirmed by Lavoisier. As for the law of energy conservation, its precise formulation was only given in the nineteenth century by R. Mayer. However, Huygens in the seventeenth century and Johann and, especially, Daniel Bernoulli in the eighteenth century already used it in mechanics and Lomonosov was aware of its general character, as can be seen from his famous letter to Euler written in 1748.

CHAPTER III

GENERAL TENSOR ANALYSIS

35. Permissible Transformations for Space and Time Coordinates

As the basis of our mathematical formulation of Relativity Theory we chose the wave front equation

$$(\nabla\omega)^2 \equiv \frac{1}{c^2}\left(\frac{\partial\omega}{\partial t}\right)^2 - \left[\left(\frac{\partial\omega}{\partial x}\right)^2 + \left(\frac{\partial\omega}{\partial y}\right)^2 + \left(\frac{\partial\omega}{\partial z}\right)^2\right] = 0 \qquad (35.01)$$

and the related expression for the square of the interval

$$ds^2 = c^2 dt^2 - (dx^2 + dy^2 + dz^2) \qquad (35.02)$$

$((\nabla\omega)^2$ is to be understood as an abbreviation for the differential expression on the left-hand side of the wave front equation.) If we introduce our usual variables

$$x_0 = ct; \qquad x_1 = x; \qquad x_2 = y; \qquad x_3 = z \qquad (35.03)$$

and also the numbers

$$e_0 = 1; \qquad e_1 = e_2 = e_3 = -1 \qquad (35.04)$$

the expressions $(\nabla\omega)^2$ and ds^2 can be written as

$$(\nabla\omega)^2 = \sum_{k=0}^{3} e_k \left(\frac{\partial\omega}{\partial x_k}\right)^2 \qquad (35.05)$$

and

$$ds^2 = \sum_{k=0}^{3} e_k (dx_k)^2 \qquad (35.06)$$

We know that both these expressions are invariant under Lorentz transformations. If new coordinates

$$x_0' = ct'; \qquad x_1' = x'; \qquad x_2' = y'; \qquad x_3' = z' \qquad (35.07)$$

are introduced which are connected with the previous ones by a Lorentz transformation, we get

$$(\nabla\omega)^2 = \sum_{k=0}^{3} e_k \left(\frac{\partial\omega}{\partial x_k'}\right)^2 \qquad (35.08)$$

and

$$ds^2 = \sum_{k=0}^{3} e_k (dx_k')^2 \qquad (35.09)$$

Variables such as (35.03) or (35.07) in which $(\nabla\omega)^2$ and ds^2 have the forms (35.05) and (35.06) or (30.08) and (30.09) will be called Galilean coordinates, this term now being understood to include the time.

We now assume that while x_0', x_1', x_2' and x_3' are given by (35.07) as before, and so are Galilean coordinates, the quantities x_0, x_1, x_2 and x_3 are no longer equal to (35.03) but instead are some auxiliary variables connected to x_0', x_1', x_2 and x_3' by relations of the form

$$x_\alpha' = f_\alpha(x_0, x_1, x_2, x_3) \qquad (\alpha = 0, 1, 2, 3) \qquad (35.10)$$

where the f_α are arbitrary functions subject only to some general conditions. We shall assume that the equations (35.10) can be solved for x_0, x_1, x_2 and x_3 so that their Jacobian must be non-zero

$$D = \frac{D(x_0', x_1', x_2', x_3')}{D(x_0, x_1, x_2, x_3)} \neq 0 \qquad (35.11)$$

Further we suppose that the functions f_α have continuous derivatives of the first three orders. There will be other conditions on the f_α which arise from physical considerations ; these will be examined later.

If this change of variables is made $(\nabla\omega)^2$ becomes a homogeneous quadratic form in the first derivatives with respect to the variables x_0, x_1, x_2 and x_3. We write this form as

$$(\nabla\omega)^2 = \sum_{\alpha, \beta=0}^{3} g^{\alpha\beta} \frac{\partial\omega}{\partial x_\alpha} \frac{\partial\omega}{\partial x_\beta} \qquad (35.12)$$

where

$$g^{\alpha\beta} = \sum_{k=0}^{3} e_k \frac{\partial x_\alpha}{\partial x_k'} \frac{\partial x_\beta}{\partial x_k'} \qquad (35.13)$$

Similarly, if the change of variables is made in ds^2 the result is

$$ds^2 = \sum_{\alpha, \beta=0}^{3} g_{\alpha\beta}\, dx_\alpha\, dx_\beta \qquad (35.14)$$

with

$$g_{\alpha\beta} = \sum_{k=0}^{3} e_k \frac{\partial x_k'}{\partial x_\alpha} \frac{\partial x_k'}{\partial x_\beta} \qquad (35.15)$$

It is readily deduced from (35.13) and (35.15) that

$$\sum_{\alpha=0}^{3} g_{\mu\alpha} g^{\nu\alpha} = \delta_\mu^\nu = \begin{cases} 1 & \text{if } \nu = \mu \\ 0 & \text{if } \nu \neq \mu \end{cases} \qquad (35.16)$$

Hence if g is defined as the determinant

$$g = \mathrm{Det}\, g_{\alpha\beta} \qquad (35.17)$$

the quantities $g^{\alpha\beta}$ will be the first minors of this determinant divided by g itself. Using the rule of determinant multiplication we get

$$\mathrm{Det}\left(e_k \frac{\partial x_k'}{\partial x_\alpha}\right) \cdot \mathrm{Det}\left(\frac{\partial x_i'}{\partial x_\beta}\right) = \mathrm{Det}\, g_{\alpha\beta} \qquad (35.18)$$

Here the second factor is equal to the Jacobian D of (35.11) and since

$$e_0 e_1 e_2 e_3 = -1 \qquad (35.19)$$

the first factor is $-D$. Consequently

$$g = -D^2 \qquad (35.20)$$

It is useful to restrict the choice of variables x_0, x_1, x_2 and x_3 by conditions which ensure that x_0, like x_0', is of the nature of a time whereas x_1, x_2 and x_3 are of the nature of spatial coordinates. These conditions must be formulated precisely. As before, we mean by the term " event " a spatial point considered at a particular moment in time ; it may be called a " point-instant ". We demand that two events having the same values of the spatial coordinate parameters x_1, x_2 and x_3 but different values x_0^* and x_0^{**} for their time parameters shall be in time sequence in the sense of Section 12. We know that for events in time sequence the squared interval is positive. This must be true in particular for an infinitesimal interval, so if we take the difference $x_0^{**} - x_0^*$ to be infinitesimal and put

$$x_0^* = x_0; \qquad x_0^{**} = x_0 + dx_0 \qquad (35.21)$$

we must have

$$ds^2 = g_{00}dx_0^2 > 0 \qquad (35.22)$$

whence

$$g_{00} > 0 \qquad (35.23)$$

Assume further that we have two events with the same time parameter x_0 but different values of the spatial parameters, namely (x_1, x_2, x_3) and $(x_1 + dx_1, x_2 + dx_2, x_3 + dx_3)$. We require that two such events shall be quasi-simultaneous in the sense of Section 12. For quasi-simultaneous events ds^2 is negative, therefore we must have

$$ds^2 = \sum_{i, k=1}^{3} g_{ik} \, dx_i \, dx_k < 0 \qquad (35.24)$$

whatever the values of dx_1, dx_2 and dx_3, provided not all three are zero. It follows that the quadratic form (35.24) must be negative-definite. It is a well known algebraic fact that the necessary and sufficient conditions for this are the inequalities

$$\begin{vmatrix} g_{11} & g_{12} & g_{13} \\ g_{21} & g_{22} & g_{23} \\ g_{31} & g_{32} & g_{33} \end{vmatrix} < 0 \qquad (35.25)$$

$$\begin{vmatrix} g_{11} & g_{12} \\ g_{21} & g_{22} \end{vmatrix} > 0; \qquad \begin{vmatrix} g_{22} & g_{23} \\ g_{32} & g_{33} \end{vmatrix} > 0; \qquad \begin{vmatrix} g_{11} & g_{13} \\ g_{31} & g_{33} \end{vmatrix} > 0 \qquad (35.26)$$

$$g_{11} < 0; \qquad g_{22} < 0; \qquad g_{33} < 0 \qquad (35.27)$$

which, incidentally, are not all independent. An independent set of conditions is, for instance (35.25), the first inequality of (35.26) and the first of (35.27).

It is not difficult to show that if all these conditions are imposed on the coefficients $g_{\alpha\beta}$ then, regardless of whether they are given by (35.15) or not, it is possible to represent ds^2 in the neighbourhood of any point as the sum of four squared terms, one with a positive and the remaining three with negative signs. The set of signs of the terms is called the signature of the quadratic form. In our case the signature can be written as (e_0, e_1, e_2, e_3) or as $(+ - - -)$.

It follows from the inequalities (35.25) to (35.27) that the determinant g is always negative and also that similar inequalities involving the $g^{\alpha\beta}$ with upper indices hold, consequently we have

$$g^{00} > 0 \qquad (35.28)$$

and

$$\sum_{i, k=1}^{3} g^{ik}\omega_i\omega_k < 0 \qquad (35.29)$$

where ω_1, ω_2 and ω_3 are any three numbers, not all zero. We shall not give the proofs of these purely algebraic statements.

Thus, in order that the parameter x_0 should have the character of time and the other three, x_1, x_2 and x_3, the character of spatial coordinates, it is necessary and sufficient that g_{00} should be positive and that the quadratic form with the coefficients g_{ik} ($i, k = 1, 2, 3$) should be negative-definite. There is no need to impose any restriction on the quantities g_{10}, g_{20} and g_{30}.

Let us now consider the geometrical meaning of the equations $x_0 = $ const. and $x_k = $ const. We shall derive a condition under which the equation

$$\omega(x, y, z, t) = 0 \qquad (35.30)$$

can be interpreted as the equation of a surface in motion. It follows from this equation that the differentials of space and time coordinates, are related by

$$\omega_x \, dx + \omega_y \, dy + \omega_z \, dz + \omega_t \, dt = 0 \qquad (35.31)$$

where ω_x, ω_y, ω_z and ω_t denote the derivatives of ω with respect to x, y, z and t. We take a displacement (dx, dy, dz) in the direction of the normal to the surface and put

$$dx = \frac{\omega_x}{|\text{grad } \omega|} \, dn \, ; \qquad dy = \frac{\omega_y}{|\text{grad } \omega|} \, dn \, ; \qquad dz = \frac{\omega_z}{|\text{grad } \omega|} \, dn \qquad (35.32)$$

so that $|dn|$ is the absolute value of the displacement. Inserting into (35.31) we get

$$|\text{grad } \omega| \, dn + \omega_t dt = 0 \qquad (35.33)$$

and therefore the square of the displacement velocity

$$v^2 = \left(\frac{dn}{dt}\right)^2 \qquad (35.34)$$

will be given by

$$v^2 = \frac{\omega_t^2}{(\text{grad } \omega)^2} \qquad (35.35)$$

Thus (35.30) can be interpreted as the equation of a surface, each point of which moves normally with a speed given by (35.35). However, such an interpretation is only possible as long as this speed does not exceed that of light. According to (35.35) and (35.01) this means that we must have

$$(\nabla\omega)^2 \leqslant 0 \qquad (35.36)$$

The equality sign is valid for motion with the speed of light.
  On the other hand, if

$$(\nabla\omega)^2 > 0 \qquad (35.37)$$

equation (35.30) can be solved for the time and written in the form

$$t = \frac{1}{c} f(x, y, z) \qquad (35.38)$$

with

$$(\text{grad } f)^2 < 1 \qquad (35.39)$$

Equation (35.38) assigns to every point in space a definite instant of time in such a way that all the four-dimensional " point-instants " are quasi-simultaneous. Such an equation may be called a " time-equation ". We recall that time equations occurred in Section 3 in connection with the question of the characteristics of Maxwell's equations.

  As we remarked in Section 3, an equation $\omega = 0$ can be considered as the equation of a hypersurface in the four-dimensional space-time manifold. Such hypersurfaces can then be divided into two classes.

  If $(\nabla\omega)^2 < 0$ we can say that one of the dimensions of the hypersurface is time-like (the inaccurate phrase " the surface is time-like " is sometimes used).

By (35.35) this describes an ordinary two-dimensional surface† moving with a velocity less than that of light.

If $(\nabla\omega)^2 > 0$, on the other hand, we say that the hypersurface is space-like. It then represents the whole of infinite space, the various points of which are all taken at different instants of time, the time t at which the point (x, y, z) is taken, being determined by the time equation, i.e. the equation of the hypersurface; the instants of time assigned to any two points in space must be so close that the corresponding four-dimensional interval is always space-like.

We use the fact that $(\nabla\omega)^2$ is an invariant and in turn put $\omega = x_0$, $\omega = x_1$, $\omega = x_2$ and $\omega = x_3$. This gives

$$(\nabla x_0)^2 = g^{00} > 0 \tag{35.40}$$

and $\quad (\nabla x_1)^2 = g^{11} < 0 \; ; \quad (\nabla x_2)^2 = g^{22} < 0 \; ; \quad (\nabla x_3)^2 = g^{33} < 0 \tag{35.41}$

Hence the equation $x_0 = $ const. is a time equation and the three equations $x_k = $ const. ($k = 1, 2, 3$) represent surfaces moving in the direction of their normals with less than light velocity. These latter are thus equations of moving spatial coordinate surfaces.

It follows also from our conditions on the transformations of space and time coordinates that constant values of x_1, x_2 and x_3 correspond, in any inertial frame of reference, to motion of a point with less than light velocity.

In classical Newtonian mechanics one often uses a time dependent coordinate transformation which is interpreted as passing to a moving frame of reference. In comparing coordinate transformations in Newtonian mechanics with the transformations of space and time coordinates in the Theory of Relativity it is essential to realize the following. Firstly, in the general case of accelerated motion the very notion of a frame of reference in Newtonian mechanics is not the same as in Relativity. The Newtonian concept involves the idea of an absolutely rigid body and the instantaneous propagation of light. In Relativity, on the other hand, the notion of a rigid body is used, if at all, not in an absolute sense but only for non-accelerated motions and in the absence of external forces, and is of an auxiliary nature; the concept of a frame of reference is not based on it but on the law of wave front propagation. The prototype of a Newtonian frame of reference is a rigid scaffolding, the prototype of a Relativistic one is the radar station. Secondly, the class of transformations permissible in Newtonian mechanics is much wider than in the Theory of Relativity; Newtonian mechanics does not have to consider the limitations, discussed above, which arise from the existence of a limiting speed.

As an example we consider a transformation which can be interpreted in Newtonian mechanics as going over to a uniformly accelerated frame. Let x', y', z' and t' be the space and time coordinates in an inertial frame, i.e. Galilean coordinates. We put

$$x' = x - \frac{1}{2} at^2 \; ; \qquad y' = y \; ; \qquad z' = z \tag{35.42}$$

and also

$$t' = t - \frac{a}{c^2} tx. \tag{35.43}$$

---

† In the four-dimensional manifold a hypersurface has three dimensions but in the present case only two of these are spatial.

The variables x, y, z and t can be interpreted as space and time coordinates in a certain accelerated frame (in the Newtonian sense and in the corresponding approximation). Inserting (35.42) and (35.43) into the expression for ds^2 we get

$$ds^2 = (c^2 - 2ax - a^2t^2)\, dt^2 - dx^2 - dy^2 - dz^2 + \frac{a^2}{c^2}\,(x\,dt + t\,dx)^2 \quad (35.44)$$

The required inequalities for the coefficients will hold if the conditions

$$1 - \frac{a^2t^2}{c^2} > 0\,; \qquad \left(1 - \frac{ax}{c^2}\right)^2 - \frac{a^2t^2}{c^2} > 0 \qquad (35.45)$$

are satisfied. In addition we can require that

$$\frac{\partial t'}{\partial t} = 1 - \frac{ax}{c^2} > 0 \qquad (35.46)$$

These inequalities show that the substitutions (35.42), (35.43) are permissible only in a part of space and only for a limited length of time.

Another example is the transformation corresponding to the introduction of a uniformly rotating frame. We put

$$\begin{aligned} x' &= x \cos \omega t + y \sin \omega t\,; & z' &= z \\ y' &= -x \sin \omega t + y \cos \omega t\,; & t' &= t \end{aligned} \qquad (35.47)$$

and obtain

$$ds^2 = [c^2 - \omega^2(x^2 + y^2)]\, dt^2 - 2\omega(y\,dx - x\,dy)\, dt - dx^2 - dy^2 - dz^2$$
$$(35.48)$$

The conditions on the coefficients require

$$c^2 - \omega^2(x^2 + y^2) > 0 \qquad (35.49)$$

which is satisfied only for distances from the axis of rotation less than that where the linear velocity of the rotation equals the speed of light.

We stress once again that the examples given here have physical sense only in a region in which Newtonian mechanics is applicable (see also Section 61).

It is obvious that the introduction of ordinary curvilinear spatial coordinates is always an allowed transformation. As long as the transformations do not involve time they have the same geometrical meaning as in non-relativistic theory. Therefore we refrain from discussing them.

36. General Tensor Analysis and Generalized Geometry

In the previous section we considered the expressions

$$(\nabla\omega)^2 = \sum_{\alpha,\,\beta=0}^{3} g^{\alpha\beta}\,\frac{\partial\omega}{\partial x_\alpha}\,\frac{\partial\omega}{\partial x_\beta} \qquad (36.01)$$

and

$$ds^2 = \sum_{\alpha,\,\beta=0} g_{\alpha\beta}\, dx_\alpha\, dx_\beta \qquad (36.02)$$

which were obtained from the usual expressions of Relativity Theory by introducing variables x_1, x_2, x_3 and x_0 in place of the space and time coordinates x, y, z and t. We established the conditions subject to which the variable x_0 can characterize a sequence of events in time and the variables x_1, x_2 and x_3 their location in space.

By itself, the introduction of new variables can naturally not influence the physical consequences of the theory ; it is merely a mathematical device. However, the development of a formalism which permits the statement of equations of mathematical physics (such as equations of motion and field equations) directly in terms of arbitrary variables without the use of cartesian spatial coordinates and time, is not only useful as a device for convenient computation but is also important in principle. The existence of such a formalism can show the way to generalize physical theories.

We shall call equations generally covariant, if they are valid for any arbitrary choice of independent variables. The formalism that allows one to write down generally covariant tensor equations will be called " general tensor analysis. "

Generally covariant equations are already used in Newtonian mechanics. We refer to Lagrange's equations (of the second kind) which describe the motion of a system of mass points in generalized coordinates and also their generalization for continuous media. While they state nothing physically new as compared to equations in cartesian coordinates, Lagrange's equations nevertheless play an important part both in practical applications and in theoretical investigations. In the Theory of Relativity general tensor analysis has a similar purpose.

In general tensor analysis the starting point is the pair of equations (36.01) and (36.02) giving the square of the four-dimensional gradient and the square of the interval. One says that these expressions characterize the *metric* of space-time. The coefficients $g^{\alpha\beta}$ and $g_{\alpha\beta}$ entering the equations are thought of as functions of the variables x_0, x_1, x_2 and x_3.

We have so far assumed that the expressions (36.01) and (36.02) are derived from (35.01) and (35.02), or from (35.08) and (35.09), by introduction of new variables, so that the coefficients $g^{\alpha\beta}$ and $g_{\alpha\beta}$ can be represented in the forms (35.13) and (35.15). In this case the ten coefficients $g_{\alpha\beta}$ can be expressed in terms of the four functions f_0, f_1, f_2 and f_3 as follows :

$$g_{\alpha\beta} = \sum_{k=0}^{3} e_k \frac{\partial f_k}{\partial x_\alpha} \frac{\partial f_k}{\partial x_\beta} \tag{36.03}$$

By virtue of (35.16) the $g^{\alpha\beta}$ can be expressed in terms of the same four functions.

However, it is important to note that the equations of general tensor anlaysis are hardly any more complicated if it is not assumed that the $g_{\alpha\beta}$ can be represented in the form (36.03) but that instead they are taken simply as given functions of the coordinates, i.e. of the variables, x_0, x_1, x_2 and x_3. This more general point of view corresponds to the introduction of non-Euclidean geometry and a non-Euclidean metric in space time. Such a step takes one beyond the limits of ordinary (so-called " Special ") Relativity and is connected with the formulation of a new physical theory, namely Einstein's Theory of Gravitation. Later chapters of this book are devoted to this theory, but in this chapter, we adopt a purely formal point of view and develop general tensor analysis on the assumption that the metric is given and the $g_{\alpha\beta}$ are known functions of the coordinates. Such a presentation has two advantages. In the first place we can find the conditions which the $g_{\alpha\beta}$ must satisfy in order to be expressible in the form (36.03) ; this gives us a generally covariant formulation of the usual Theory of Relativity. In the second place we obtain in this way the mathematical apparatus for formulating Einstein's Theory of Gravitation.

Before going on to a systematic exposition of general tensor analysis we establish the connection between the expressions $(\nabla\omega)^2$ and ds^2 which exists if

$$\sum_{\alpha=0}^{3} g_{\mu\alpha}g^{\nu\alpha} = \delta_{\mu}^{\nu} \qquad (36.04)$$

regardless of whether the $g_{\alpha\beta}$ are of the form (36.03) or not. We show that if a function $\omega(x_0, x_1, x_2, x_3)$ satisfies $(\nabla\omega)^2 = 0$ then differentials of the coordinates related by the condition $\omega = \text{const.}$ satisfy $ds^2 = 0$.

Putting

$$\omega_\alpha = \frac{\partial \omega}{\partial x_\alpha} \qquad (\alpha = 0, 1, 2, 3) \qquad (36.05)$$

We write $(\nabla\omega)^2 = 0$ in the form

$$G \equiv \sum_{\alpha,\,\beta=0}^{3} g^{\alpha\beta}\omega_\alpha\omega_\beta = 0 \qquad (36.06)$$

This partial differential equation for ω is of the same type as the Hamilton-Jacobi equation of classical mechanics and can be solved similarly to the latter. If we solve it for ω_0 and write

$$\omega_0 = -H(\omega_1, \omega_2, \omega_3) \qquad (36.07)$$

the function H will correspond to the Hamiltonian and Hamilton's equations will be

$$\frac{dx_k}{dx_0} = \frac{\partial H}{\partial \omega_k}; \qquad \frac{d\omega_k}{dx_0} = -\frac{\partial H}{\partial x_k} \qquad (k = 1,\ 2,\ 3) \qquad (36.08)$$

But

$$\frac{\partial H}{\partial \omega_k} = -\frac{\partial \omega_0}{\partial \omega_k} = \frac{(\partial G/\partial \omega_k)}{(\partial G/\partial \omega_0)} \qquad (36.09)$$

and the first three equations of (36.05) show that the differentials dx_α ($\alpha = 0,$ 1, 2, 3) are proportional to the partial derivatives of G with respect to the ω_α. Denoting the infinitesimal coefficient of proportionality by $\tfrac{1}{2}dp$, we have

$$dx_\alpha = \frac{dp}{2}\frac{\partial G}{\partial \omega_\alpha} = dp \sum_{\beta=0}^{3} g^{\alpha\beta}\omega_\beta \qquad (36.10)$$

Solving for ω_α with the use of (36.04) we get

$$\omega_\alpha\, dp = \sum_{\beta=0}^{3} g_{\alpha\beta}\, dx_\beta \qquad (36.11)$$

and the obvious relation

$$\sum_{\alpha=0}^{3} \omega_\alpha\, dx_\alpha = 0 \qquad (36.12)$$

then gives

$$ds^2 = \sum_{\alpha,\,\beta=0}^{3} g_{\alpha\beta}\, dx_\alpha\, dx_\beta = 0 \qquad (36.13)$$

as required. Thus if we continue to consider the equation $(\nabla\omega)^2 = 0$ as describing a wave front we can take it that for points on the wave front the differentials of space and time coordinates are related by $ds^2 = 0$.

In the following we shall consider the $g_{\alpha\beta}$ as given functions of the variables x_0, x_1, x_2 and x_3 and shall merely assume that they have continuous derivatives of all orders considered and that they satisfy the inequalities stated in Section

35. In addition to the $g_{\alpha\beta}$ we shall consider the $g^{\alpha\beta}$, their connection being (36.04). The conditions under which the $g_{\alpha\beta}$ can be represented in the form (36.03) will be established in Section 42 below.

37. The Definitions of a Vector and of a Tensor. Tensor Algebra

In tensor analysis one frequently has to deal with sums similar to those in (36.01) and (36.02), in which the summation index appears twice. Following a suggestion by Einstein we introduce an abbreviated notation for such sums which consists of omitting the summation sign, summation over indices appearing twice being understood. We further agree to sum from 0 to 3 if the indices are Greek characters such as $(\alpha, \beta, \ldots)$ and from 1 to 3 if they are Roman ones, such as $(i, k, \ldots)$. Using this notation we can, for instance, replace

$$ds^2 = \sum_{\alpha, \beta=0}^{3} g_{\alpha\beta} \, dx_\alpha \, dx_\beta \tag{37.01}$$

simply by

$$ds^2 = g_{\alpha\beta} \, dx_\alpha \, dx_\beta \tag{37.02}$$

or, if we wish to single out the time-like coordinate x_0,

$$ds^2 = g_{00} \, dx_0^2 + 2g_{0i} \, dx_0 \, dx_i + g_{ik} \, dx_i \, dx_k \tag{37.03}$$

This short notation proves very convenient and does not lead to misunderstandings. In the rare cases when summation over a double index is not to be understood we shall state this explicitly. For instance, in the special case when (36.02) reduces to

$$ds^2 = dx_0^2 - dx_1^2 - dx_2^2 - dx_3^2 \tag{37.04}$$

we write

$$g_{\alpha\beta} = e_\alpha \delta_{\alpha\beta} \quad \text{(no summation)} \tag{37.05}$$

In Section 20 we gave the definitions of a covariant and of a contravariant vector for the case (37.05). Equations (20.12) and (20.13) can now be written as

$$A'_\alpha = \frac{\partial x_\beta}{\partial x'_\alpha} A_\beta \tag{37.06}$$

and

$$A'^\alpha = \frac{\partial x'_\alpha}{\partial x_\beta} A^\beta \tag{37.07}$$

and they can also serve as definitions of a vector in the general case. As before, covariant vectors will be written as letters carrying a suffix while for contravariant ones a superfix is used. However, for the coordinate differentials we make an exception to this rule, writing them as dx_α although they form a contravariant vector.

Thus a covariant vector can be defined as a set of four quantities that transform like the four partial derivatives of some function with respect to the coordinates. Similarly, a contravariant vector is a set of four quantities that transform like the four coordinate differentials.

In the case when ds^2 has the form (37.04) and when we consider only Lorentz transformations, the coefficients in the transformation formulae (37.06) and (37.07) are constants. In the more general case of arbitrary transformations the coefficients are variable. In the case of Lorentz transformations a vector need not necessarily refer to a definite point in space-time but may be " free ". An example of a free vector is the energy-momentum vector of a material system. (Similarly the tensor of angular momentum and mass centre motion is a free tensor.) By contrast, if one considers general coordinate transformation, then, just as for ordinary curvilinear spatial coordinates, a vector must necessarily be related to a particular point in space. Examples of bound vectors are any field vectors, such as the velocity vector for a continuous medium, whose components are functions of a point, i.e. of the coordinates x_0, x_1, x_2 and x_3. However, a bound vector need not be defined throughout a finite region of space-time; it may be defined only on some curve as is the case for the tangent vector of a curve, or on some surface as for the normal to a surface. The same remarks apply to tensors, and in general tensor analysis we shall always have to do with bound tensors as well as bound vectors. When these are transformed the quantities $\partial x'_\alpha / \partial x_\beta$ entering the transformation must always be taken at the same point as the vector or tensor to be transformed.†

This definition of a tensor is analogous to the one given in Section 21 for the case of Lorentz transformations. Equations (21.01), (21.03) and (21.05) which give the transformation rules for second order covariant, contravariant and mixed tensors respectively remain valid in general tensor analysis. In our present notation they read:

$$T'_{\mu\nu} = \frac{\partial x_\alpha}{\partial x'_\mu} \frac{\partial x_\beta}{\partial x'_\nu} T_{\alpha\beta} \tag{37.08}$$

$$T'^{\mu\nu} = \frac{\partial x'_\mu}{\partial x_\alpha} \frac{\partial x'_\nu}{\partial x_\beta} T^{\alpha\beta} \tag{37.09}$$

and

$$T'^{\mu}_{\nu} = \frac{\partial x'_\mu}{\partial x_\alpha} \frac{\partial x_\beta}{\partial x'_\nu} T^{\alpha}_{\beta} \tag{37.10}$$

Thus a covariant, contravariant or mixed tensor of the second order is a set of quantities transforming, respectively, according to (37.08), (37.09) or (37.10).

Covariant or contravariant, but not mixed, tensors which have either of the properties of symmetry or antisymmetry, retain that property after transformation. For on renaming the suffixes in (37.08) we obtain

$$T'_{\nu\mu} = \frac{\partial x_\alpha}{\partial x'_\mu} \frac{\partial x_\beta}{\partial x'_\nu} T_{\beta\alpha} \tag{37.11}$$

Therefore, putting

$$2S_{\alpha\beta} = T_{\alpha\beta} + T_{\beta\alpha} \tag{37.12}$$

and

$$2A_{\alpha\beta} = T_{\alpha\beta} - T_{\beta\alpha} \tag{37.13}$$

and defining $S'_{\mu\nu}$ and $A'_{\mu\nu}$ correspondingly we get

$$S'_{\mu\nu} = \frac{\partial x_\alpha}{\partial x'_\mu} \frac{\partial x_\beta}{\partial x'_\nu} S_{\alpha\beta} \tag{37.14}$$

and

$$A'_{\mu\nu} = \frac{\partial x_\alpha}{\partial x'_\mu} \frac{\partial x_\beta}{\partial x'_\nu} A_{\alpha\beta} \tag{37.15}$$

The quantity $S_{\alpha\beta}$ can be called the symmetric part and $A_{\alpha\beta}$ the antisymmetric part of the tensor $T_{\alpha\beta}$. Equations (37.14) and (37.15) show that each of these two parts separately is a tensor. Therefore, if the tensor $T_{\alpha\beta}$ is itself symmetric, so that $A_{\alpha\beta} = 0$, then also $A'_{\mu\nu} = 0$, i.e. the transformed tensor $T'_{\mu\nu}$ is also symmetric. Similarly, if $T_{\alpha\beta}$ is antisymmetric so that $S_{\alpha\beta} = 0$ then likewise $S'_{\mu\nu} = 0$ and the transformed tensor $T'_{\mu\nu}$ remains antisymmetric. The same

† For further discussion of free vectors see Section 49.

considerations apply to a contravariant tensor, but for a mixed tensor the upper and the lower index enter the transformation equation (37.10) differently and therefore it has no invariant meaning to divide a mixed tensor into a symmetric and an antisymmetric part.

An extremely important example of a symmetric tensor of second rank is the set of coefficients $g_{\alpha\beta}$ in ds^2. The fact that the $g_{\alpha\beta}$ are symmetric in their two suffixes follows directly from their definition. That they form a tensor follows from the invariance of ds^2. For on passing to new variables x_0', x_1', x_2' and x_3' we have

$$g_{\mu\nu}' \, dx_\mu' \, dx_\nu' = g_{\alpha\beta} \, dx_\alpha \, dx_\beta \tag{37.16}$$

whence

$$g_{\mu\nu}' = g_{\alpha\beta} \frac{\partial x_\alpha}{\partial x_\mu'} \cdot \frac{\partial x_\beta}{\partial x_\nu'} \tag{37.17}$$

which is just the tensor transformation rule. The tensor $g_{\alpha\beta}$ is called the fundamental or metric tensor.

The set of quantities $g^{\alpha\beta}$ defined by the equation

$$g^{\alpha\beta} g_{\beta\gamma} = \delta_\gamma^\alpha \tag{37.18}$$

also form a tensor, which in this case is contravariant. We proceed to prove this. In the primed coordinate system the $g_{\mu\nu}'$ are given by (37.17) and the $g'^{\mu\nu}$ have to be calculated from the equation

$$g'^{\mu\lambda} g_{\lambda\nu}' = \delta_\nu^\mu \tag{37.19}$$

On the other hand, if $g^{\alpha\beta}$ is to be a contravariant tensor, we must have

$$g'^{\mu\lambda} = g^{\alpha\beta} \frac{\partial x_\mu'}{\partial x_\alpha} \frac{\partial x_\lambda'}{\partial x_\beta} \tag{37.20}$$

We must show that both definitions of the $g'^{\mu\nu}$ give the same. Since the solution of (37.19) for the $g'^{\mu\nu}$ must be unique it is sufficient to verify that the quantities given by (37.20) satisfy (37.19). This is simply done by use of the equations

$$\frac{\partial x_\alpha}{\partial x_\lambda'} \frac{\partial x_\lambda'}{\partial x_\rho} = \frac{\partial x_\alpha}{\partial x_\rho} = \delta_\rho^\alpha \tag{37.21}$$

and

$$g_{\lambda\nu}' \frac{\partial x_\lambda'}{\partial x_\rho} = g_{\rho\sigma} \frac{\partial x_\sigma}{\partial x_\nu'} \tag{37.22}$$

Inserting (37.20) into (37.19) and using first (37.22) and then (37.18) we obtain the sequence of equations

$$g'^{\mu\lambda} g_{\lambda\nu}' = g^{\alpha\beta} g_{\lambda\nu}' \frac{\partial x_\mu'}{\partial x_\alpha} \frac{\partial x_\lambda'}{\partial x_\beta} = g^{\alpha\beta} g_{\beta\sigma} \frac{\partial x_\mu'}{\partial x_\alpha} \frac{\partial x_\sigma}{\partial x_\nu'} = \delta_\sigma^\alpha \frac{\partial x_\mu'}{\partial x_\alpha} \frac{\partial x_\sigma}{\partial x_\nu'} = \frac{\partial x_\mu'}{\partial x_\alpha} \frac{\partial x_\alpha}{\partial x_\nu'} = \delta_\nu^\mu \tag{37.23}$$

which finally leads to (37.19).

The $g^{\alpha\beta}$ are called the contravariant components of the fundamental tensor, the $g_{\alpha\beta}$ being its covariant components.

The equation

$$\delta_\sigma^\alpha \frac{\partial x_\mu'}{\partial x_\alpha} \frac{\partial x_\sigma}{\partial x_\nu'} = \delta_\nu^\mu \tag{37.24}$$

which forms part of (37.23) shows that the set of quantities

$$\delta_\nu^\mu = \begin{cases} 1 & \text{if } \mu = \nu \\ 0 & \text{if } \mu \neq \nu \end{cases} \tag{37.25}$$

which are the same in all coordinate systems, satisfy the definition of a mixed tensor of second rank.

Given a covariant vector A_ν the set of quantities

$$A^\mu = g^{\mu\nu}A_\nu \tag{37.26}$$

will transform as a contravariant vector, as is easily verified. We do not consider two vectors so related as essentially different and refer to the A_ν and the A^μ as the covariant and contravariant components of the same vector. The operation described by (37.26) is referred to briefly as raising the index of the vector A_ν and the inverse operation

$$A_\nu = g_{\nu\mu}A^\mu \tag{37.27}$$

is called lowering the index. Raising and lowering of indices can also be performed on tensors. For instance, from the covariant tensor $T_{\mu\nu}$ we can obtain the contravariant tensor

$$T^{\mu\nu} = g^{\mu\alpha}g^{\nu\beta}T_{\alpha\beta} \tag{37.28}$$

by raising both indices, and the original tensor can be restored by the inverse operation

$$T_{\mu\nu} = g_{\mu\alpha}g_{\nu\beta}T^{\alpha\beta} \tag{37.29}$$

It is evident that the properties of symmetry and antisymmetry are not affected by this. In forming a mixed tensor we must observe which of the indices is raised or lowered. For clarity we can mark the position of the raised or lowered index by a dot. For example, the tensors

$$T^\mu_{\cdot\nu} = g^{\mu\alpha}T_{\alpha\nu} \tag{37.30}$$

and

$$T_\nu^{\cdot\mu} = g^{\mu\alpha}T_{\nu\alpha} \tag{37.31}$$

are identical only if $T_{\alpha\beta}$ is symmetric, in which case the dots are unnecessary and we can write

$$T^\mu_\nu = g^{\mu\alpha}T_{\alpha\nu} = g^{\mu\alpha}T_{\nu\alpha} \tag{37.32}$$

For the sake of brevity we have hitherto discussed only vectors and second rank tensors, but tensors of higher rank may be defined correspondingly.

A set of quantities is called a covariant tensor of rank n if it undergoes the transformation

$$A'_{\beta_1\beta_2\ldots\beta_n} = A_{\alpha_1\alpha_2\ldots\alpha_n} \frac{\partial x_{\alpha_1}}{\partial x'_{\beta_1}} \frac{\partial x_{\alpha_2}}{\partial x'_{\beta_2}} \cdots \frac{\partial x_{\alpha_n}}{\partial x'_{\beta_n}} \tag{37.33}$$

Similarly a set of quantities is a contravariant tensor of rank n if it transforms as follows

$$B'^{\beta_1\beta_2\ldots\beta_n} = B^{\alpha_1\alpha_2\ldots\alpha_n} \frac{\partial x'_{\beta_1}}{\partial x_{\alpha_1}} \frac{\partial x'_{\beta_2}}{\partial x_{\alpha_2}} \cdots \frac{\partial x'_{\beta_n}}{\partial x_{\alpha_n}} \tag{37.34}$$

Finally a mixed tensor of rank n with k covariant and m contravariant indices, where $k + m = n$, is a set of quantities transforming according to the rule

$$C'^{\mu_1\ldots\mu_m}_{\nu_1\ldots\nu_k} = C^{\alpha_1\ldots\alpha_m}_{\beta_1\ldots\beta_k} \frac{\partial x'_{\mu_1}}{\partial x_{\alpha_1}} \cdots \frac{\partial x'_{\mu_m}}{\partial x_{\alpha_m}} \frac{\partial x_{\beta_1}}{\partial x'_{\nu_1}} \cdots \frac{\partial x_{\beta_k}}{\partial x'_{\nu_k}} \tag{37.35}$$

From a covariant tensor of rank n we obtain a contravariant tensor of the same rank by the relation

$$A^{\mu_1 \cdots \mu_n} = A_{\alpha_1 \cdots \alpha_n} g^{\alpha_1 \mu_1} \cdots g^{\alpha_n \mu_n} \qquad (37.36)$$

and we can speak of these quantities as the covariant and contravariant components of one and the same tensor. If only some, but not all, indices are raised we can obtain mixed tensors of the same rank and, in general, we should indicate the position of the indices that are raised by the use of dots. If we have two tensors of rank k and m we can construct a tensor of the higher rank $n = k + m$ by multiplying components. For covariant tensors we may put

$$A_{\alpha_1 \cdots \alpha_k} B_{\alpha_{k+1} \cdots \alpha_n} = C_{\alpha_1 \cdots n} \qquad (37.37)$$

and similar equations hold for contravariant and mixed tensors.

Given a tensor $A_{\alpha_1 \cdots \alpha_n}$ of rank n we can construct another tensor $B_{\alpha_1 \cdots \alpha_{n-2}}$ by the rule

$$A_{\alpha_1 \cdots \alpha_{n-2} \beta \gamma} g^{\beta \gamma} = B_{\alpha_1 \cdots \alpha_{n-2}} \qquad (37.38)$$

The rank of the new tensor is two less than the rank of the original one. This operation is called contraction with respect to the two indices involved. In (37.38) the contraction is with respect to the last two indices and it is evident that the result of contraction will depend on which pair of indices is chosen. Contraction may be performed in two stages. First one of the suffixes is raised according to the rule

$$A_{\alpha_1 \cdots \alpha_{n-2} \alpha_{n-1} \gamma} g^{\beta \gamma} = A_{\alpha_1 \cdots \alpha_{n-1}}^{\qquad\quad\cdots\cdots\,\beta} \qquad (37.39)$$

and then the other suffix, α_{n-1}, is equated with the raised index β and the summation is performed

$$A_{\alpha_1 \cdots \alpha_{n-2} \beta}^{\qquad\quad\cdots\cdots\,\beta} = B_{\alpha_1 \cdots \alpha_{n-2}} \qquad (37.40)$$

Contracting a second rank tensor produces a scalar

$$T_{\mu\nu} g^{\mu\nu} = T \qquad (37.41)$$

which can also be given as

$$T_{\cdot\nu}^{\nu\cdot} = T_{\nu\cdot}^{\cdot\nu} = T \qquad (37.42)$$

That the contraction of either of the two tensors (37.30) and (37.31) leads to the same result is easily understandable because the scalar T depends only on the symmetric part of the tensor $T_{\mu\nu}$ and for a symmetric covariant tensor both the related mixed tensors are the same.

A vector cannot be contracted because it has only one index, but from two vectors one can construct a second rank tensor which may then be contracted. The result is the scalar

$$g^{\mu\nu} A_\mu B_\nu = A_\mu B^\mu = A^\nu B_\nu \qquad (37.43)$$

which can be called the scalar product of the two vectors A_μ and B_ν. If the two vectors coincide, the scalar is

$$g^{\mu\nu} A_\mu A_\nu = A_\mu A^\mu \qquad (37.44)$$

According to the sign of the scalar product of a vector with itself, all vectors may be classified as being time-like, if $A_\mu A^\mu > 0$, space-like if $A_\mu A^\mu < 0$, or nul vectors if $A_\mu A^\mu = 0$. This classification is the same as that discussed in Section 20.

If two time-like vectors A^μ and B^μ both have unit invariants the absolute value of their scalar product will be greater than unity. In other words the conditions

$$g_{\mu\nu}A^\mu A^\nu = 1 \; ; \qquad g_{\mu\nu}B^\mu B^\nu = 1 \qquad (37.45)$$

lead to the inequality

$$|g_{\mu\nu}A^\mu B^\nu| \geqslant 1 \qquad (37.46)$$

This will now be proved. Condition (37.45) for A^μ can be written as

$$\left(\sqrt{(g_{00})}A^0 + \frac{1}{\sqrt{g_{00}}}\, g_{0i}A^i\right)^2 - \left(\frac{g_{0i}g_{0k}}{g_{00}} - g_{ik}\right)A^i A^k = 1 \qquad (37.47)$$

or more briefly as

$$\frac{1}{g_{00}}(A_0)^2 - a_{ik}A^i A^k = 1 \qquad (37.48)$$

with

$$a_{ik} = \frac{g_{0i}g_{0k}}{g_{00}} - g_{ik} \qquad (37.49)$$

Similarly

$$B_\mu B^\mu \equiv \frac{1}{g_{00}}(B_0)^2 - a_{ik}B^i B^k = 1 \qquad (37.50)$$

On the other hand the scalar product $A_\mu B^\mu$ is equal to

$$A_\mu B^\mu \equiv \frac{1}{g_{00}}\, A_0 B_0 - a_{ik}\, A^i B^k \qquad (37.51)$$

By virtue of the inequalities for the $g_{\mu\nu}$ proved in Section 35 the quantities a_{ik} are the coefficients of a positive definite quadratic form. Therefore

$$|a_{ik}A^i B^k| \leqslant \sqrt{(a_{ik}A^i A^k)} \cdot \sqrt{(a_{ik}B^i B^k)} \qquad (37.52)$$

and if we put

$$A = \sqrt{(a_{ik}A^i A^k)}\; ; \qquad B = \sqrt{(a_{ik}B^i B^k)} \qquad (37.53)$$

we obtain $\quad |A_0| = \sqrt{g_{00}}\sqrt{(1 + A^2)}\; ; \qquad |B_0| = \sqrt{g_{00}}\sqrt{(1 + B^2)}$

$$|a_{ik}A^i B^k| \leqslant AB \qquad (37.54)$$

Therefore

$$|A_\mu B^\mu| \geqslant \sqrt{(1 + A^2)}\sqrt{(1 + B^2)} - AB \geqslant 1 \qquad (37.55)$$

as required.

For general time-like vectors it follows from (37.46) that

$$|g_{\mu\nu}A^\mu B^\nu| \geqslant \sqrt{(g_{\mu\nu}A^\mu A^\nu)} \cdot \sqrt{(g_{\mu\nu}B^\mu B^\nu)} \qquad (37.56)$$

and it should be noted that this relation is analogous to (37.52) except for a reversal of sign. This is due to the indefiniteness of the metric.

For a time-like vector the covariant and the contravariant components of index zero always have the same sign. Assuming that $A_0 > 0$ and $B_0 > 0$, and thus also $A^0 > 0$ and $B^0 > 0$, we can write (37.56) in the form

$$A_\nu B^\nu \geqslant \sqrt{(A_\nu A^\nu)} \cdot \sqrt{(B^\mu B_\mu)} \qquad (37.57)$$

To conclude this section we discuss the concept of a pseudo-tensor in general tensor analysis. In Section 22 we introduced the set of quantities $\varepsilon_{\alpha\beta\gamma\delta}$ which are antisymmetric in all their suffixes with $\varepsilon_{0123} = 1$. These quantities satisfy (22.02) which, in somewhat different notation, can be written as

$$\varepsilon_{\alpha\beta\gamma\delta}\frac{\partial x'_\alpha}{\partial x_\mu}\frac{\partial x'_\beta}{\partial x_\nu}\frac{\partial x'_\gamma}{\partial x_\rho}\frac{\partial x'_\delta}{\partial x_\sigma} = D\varepsilon_{\mu\nu\rho\sigma} \qquad (37.58)$$

Here D is the Jacobian† (35.11). On the other hand we can easily show by use of the rule of determinant multiplication that

$$\text{Det } g_{\alpha\beta} = D^2 \text{ Det } g'_{\lambda\mu} \tag{37.59}$$

This is a generalization of (35.18). Rewriting this equation in the form

$$g = D^2 g' \tag{37.60}$$

and taking the square root, after first changing the sign, we get

$$\sqrt{(-g)} = |D|\sqrt{(-g')} \tag{37.61}$$

This is the transformation law for the determinant g. We now multiply both sides of (37.58) by $\sqrt{(-g')}$ and put

$$E_{\mu\nu\rho\sigma} = \sqrt{(-g)} \cdot \varepsilon_{\mu\nu\rho\sigma} \tag{37.62}$$

and

$$E'_{\alpha\beta\gamma\delta} = \sqrt{(-g')} \cdot \varepsilon_{\alpha\beta\gamma\delta} \tag{37.63}$$

Then we can write (37.58) in the form

$$E'_{\alpha\beta\gamma\delta} \frac{\partial x'_\alpha}{\partial x_\mu} \frac{\partial x'_\beta}{\partial x_\nu} \frac{\partial x'_\gamma}{\partial x_\rho} \frac{\partial x'_\delta}{\partial x_\sigma} = \text{sgn } D \cdot E_{\mu\nu\rho\sigma} \tag{37.64}$$

where $\text{sgn } D = \pm 1$ is the sign of the Jacobian D. This equation shows that for transformations with positive Jacobian the quantities $E_{\mu\nu\rho\sigma}$ transform as a covariant fourth-rank tensor while for transformations with negative Jacobian their transformation rule differs only by a sign from the rule for such a tensor. A set of quantities with such a transformation law will be called a *pseudo-tensor*. The corresponding contravariant pseudo-tensor is obtained by the general formula

$$E^{\mu\nu\rho\sigma} = \sqrt{(-g)} \cdot g^{\mu\alpha}g^{\nu\beta}g^{\rho\gamma}g^{\sigma\delta}\varepsilon_{\alpha\beta\gamma\delta} \tag{37.65}$$

and is

$$E^{\mu\nu\rho\sigma} = -\frac{1}{\sqrt{(-g)}} \varepsilon_{\mu\nu\rho\sigma} \tag{37.66}$$

The antisymmetric fourth-rank pseudo-tensor allows us to derive from any antisymmetric tensor $A_{\gamma\delta}$ of second rank a dual pseudo-tensor

$$\overset{*}{A}{}^{\alpha\beta} = \frac{1}{2} E^{\alpha\beta\gamma\delta} A_{\gamma\delta} \tag{37.67}$$

and from any antisymmetric tensor $A_{\beta\gamma\delta}$ of third rank a dual pseudo-vector

$$\overset{*}{A}{}^{\alpha} = \frac{1}{6} E^{\alpha\beta\gamma\delta} A_{\beta\gamma\delta} \tag{37.68}$$

If we construct an antisymmetric tensor $A_{\beta\gamma\delta}$ from the three vectors a_μ, b_μ, c_μ according to the rule

$$A_{\beta\gamma\delta} = a_\beta b_\gamma c_\delta + a_\gamma b_\delta c_\beta + a_\delta b_\beta c_\gamma - a_\gamma b_\beta c_\delta - a_\beta b_\delta c_\gamma - a_\delta b_\gamma c_\beta \tag{37.69}$$

the dual pseudo-vector has the components

$$\overset{*}{A}{}^0 = -\frac{1}{\sqrt{(-g)}}\begin{vmatrix} a_1 & a_2 & a_3 \\ b_1 & b_2 & b_3 \\ c_1 & c_2 & c_3 \end{vmatrix}; \qquad \overset{*}{A}{}^1 = +\frac{1}{\sqrt{(-g)}}\begin{vmatrix} a_0 & a_2 & a_3 \\ b_0 & b_2 & b_3 \\ c_0 & c_2 & c_3 \end{vmatrix}$$

$$\overset{*}{A}{}^2 = -\frac{1}{\sqrt{(-g)}}\begin{vmatrix} a_0 & a_1 & a_3 \\ b_0 & b_1 & b_3 \\ c_0 & c_1 & c_3 \end{vmatrix}; \qquad \overset{*}{A}{}^3 = +\frac{1}{\sqrt{(-g)}}\begin{vmatrix} a_0 & a_1 & a_2 \\ b_0 & b_1 & b_2 \\ c_0 & c_1 & c_2 \end{vmatrix} \tag{37.70}$$

† In (22.02) D denoted the Jacobian of the inverse transformation.

These are proportional to the minors complementary to the elements ξ_0, ξ_1, ξ_2 and ξ_3 of the determinant

$$\Delta = \begin{vmatrix} \xi_0 & \xi_1 & \xi_2 & \xi_3 \\ a_0 & a_1 & a_2 & a_3 \\ b_0 & b_1 & b_2 & b_3 \\ c_0 & c_1 & c_2 & c_3 \end{vmatrix} \tag{37.71}$$

Obviously $\qquad \overset{*}{A}{}^{\alpha} a_{\alpha} = 0 ; \qquad \overset{*}{A}{}^{\alpha} b_{\alpha} = 0 ; \qquad \overset{*}{A}{}^{\alpha} c_{\alpha} = 0 \tag{37.72}$

so that the pseudo-vector A^{α} is perpendicular to all three vectors a_{α}, b_{α} and c_{α}. It may be called the vector product of these three vectors.

38. The Equation of a Geodesic

We consider two point-instants corresponding to two events in time sequence and we denote their coordinates by $x_{\alpha}^{(1)}$ and $x_{\alpha}^{(2)}$ respectively. Let a material point move along some curve in such a way that when $x_0 = x_0^{(1)}$ its spatial coordinates are $x_k = x_k^{(1)}$ and when $x_0 = x_0^{(2)}$ they are $x_k = x_k^{(2)}$.

As the events $x_{\alpha}^{(1)}$ and $x_{\alpha}^{(2)}$ are assumed to be in time sequence such motion is possible with a speed less than that of light. The time x_0 and the spatial coordinates x_k corresponding to it can be expressed parametrically in terms of an auxiliary variable p, by putting

$$x_{\alpha} = \varphi^{\alpha}(p) \tag{38.01}$$

with $\qquad x_{\alpha}^{(1)} = \varphi^{\alpha}(p_1); \qquad x_{\alpha}^{(2)} = \varphi^{\alpha}(p_2) \tag{38.02}$

Since the speed of the motion is less than that of light the inequality

$$ds^2 = g_{\alpha\beta}\dot{\varphi}^{\alpha}\dot{\varphi}^{\beta}\, dp^2 > 0 \tag{38.03}$$

must hold for any infinitesimal interval along the path. Here a dot denotes differentiation with respect to p. The finite interval between the two events in time sequence which is proportional to the interval of proper time τ, will be denoted by $s = c\tau$ and we have

$$s = c\tau = \int_{p_1}^{p_2} \sqrt{(g_{\alpha\beta}\dot{\varphi}^{\alpha}\dot{\varphi}^{\beta})} \cdot dp \tag{38.04}$$

We now consider two quasi-simultaneous events. The two points in space at which the events take place can be joined by some curve and to each point on this curve we can assign a definite instant of time, i.e. we can write down the " time equation " for each point, taking care that any two intermediate space-instants are quasi-simultaneous. The analytic expressions for the curve and the time equation may again be stated in the form of equations (38.01) and (38.02), but we can no longer interpret these equations as describing the *motion* of a point along a curve ; they now give a *static* description of the curve as a whole. For any pair of intermediate points, infinitesimally separated, we have

$$ds^2 = g_{\alpha\beta}\dot{\varphi}^{\alpha}\dot{\varphi}^{\beta}\, dp^2 < 0 \tag{38.05}$$

and the space-like interval

$$l = \int_{p_1}^{p_2} \sqrt{(-g_{\alpha\beta}\dot{\varphi}^{\alpha}\dot{\varphi}^{\beta})} \cdot dp \tag{38.06}$$

characterizes the length of the curve.

The question arises of the extremal values of both the time-like interval (38.04) between two events in time sequence and the space-like interval (38.06) between two quasi-simultaneous events. Both these variational problems lead to equations of the same form, whether the interval is time-like or space-like. The variational equations are called the equations of the geodesic by analogy with the theory of surfaces. However, it is important to note that whereas in the theory of surfaces, where the square of an infinitesimal distance is a positive definite quadratic form of the coordinate differentials, the geodesic is, generally speaking†, a *shortest* line; in the four-dimensional space-time manifold the situation is different: the extremal value of the interval is a *maximum* for a time-like interval and neither a maximum nor a minimum for a space-like interval. This can easily be verified in the special case of the Galilean metric where ds^2 has the form (37.04). For events in time sequence we can then choose a reference frame so that the spatial coordinates of the initial and final points are the same and we can choose the time t as the parameter. We then have

$$s = \int_{t^{(1)}}^{t^{(2)}} \sqrt{(c^2 - v^2)} \cdot dt \tag{38.07}$$

where

$$v^2 = \left(\frac{dx}{dt}\right)^2 + \left(\frac{dy}{dt}\right)^2 + \left(\frac{dz}{dt}\right)^2 \tag{38.08}$$

The solution of the variational problem in this case is given by constant values of x, y and z, so that $v^2 = 0$. For any other trajectory v^2 will somewhere be greater than zero, so that $\sqrt{(c^2 - v^2)} < c$ and therefore

$$s < s_{\max} = c(t^{(2)} - t^{(1)}) \tag{38.09}$$

For the space-like interval we can choose a frame of reference such that

$$t^{(2)} = t^{(1)} ; \qquad y^{(2)} = y^{(1)} ; \qquad z^{(2)} = z^{(1)} \tag{38.10}$$

while $x^{(2)} > x^{(1)}$. Taking the coordinate x as the parameter we obtain

$$l = \int_{x^{(1)}}^{x^{(2)}} \sqrt{\left\{1 + \left(\frac{dy}{dx}\right)^2 + \left(\frac{dz}{dx}\right)^2 - c^2 \left(\frac{dt}{dx}\right)^2\right\}} \cdot dx \tag{38.11}$$

The solution of the variational problem is now given by constant values of y, z and t for which then

$$l_{\text{extr}} = x^{(2)} - x^{(1)} \tag{38.12}$$

However, for other curves $y(x)$, $z(x)$ or other time equations $t(x)$ we may find either $l > l_{\text{extr}}$ or $l < l_{\text{extr}}$ depending on whether the square root in (38.11) is in the mean greater or less than unity.

We now derive the differential equations of the geodesic. The **Lagrangian** of the variational problem is

$$L = \sqrt{(\dot{g}_{\alpha\beta}\dot{\varphi}^\alpha\dot{\varphi}^\beta)} \tag{38.13}$$

or, writing x_α instead of φ^α

$$L = \sqrt{(g_{\alpha\beta}\dot{x}_\alpha\dot{x}_\beta)} \tag{38.14}$$

† i.e. for sufficiently near terminal points.

The extremal condition for the integral

$$s = \int_{p_1}^{p_2} L \, dp \tag{38.15}$$

leads to the Euler-Lagrange equations

$$\frac{d}{dp} \frac{\partial L}{\partial \dot{x}_\alpha} - \frac{\partial L}{\partial x_\alpha} = 0 \tag{38.16}$$

We now put

$$F = \frac{1}{2} g_{\alpha\beta} \dot{x}_\alpha \dot{x}_\beta \tag{38.17}$$

so that

$$L = \sqrt{(2F)} \tag{38.18}$$

By the same reasoning as in Section 17 we can choose a parameter p so that

$$\frac{dF}{dp} = 0 ; \qquad F = \text{const} \tag{38.19}$$

and with this choice (38.16) is equivalent to

$$\frac{d}{dp} \frac{\partial F}{\partial \dot{x}_\alpha} - \frac{\partial F}{\partial x_\alpha} = 0 \tag{38.20}$$

These last equations possess the integral

$$\dot{x}_\alpha \frac{\partial F}{\partial \dot{x}_\alpha} - F = F = \text{const} \tag{38.21}$$

so that the condition (38.19) is a consequence of (38.21). Inserting the explicit expression for F we obtain from (38.20)

$$\frac{d}{dp} (g_{\alpha\beta} \dot{x}_\beta) - \frac{1}{2} \frac{\partial g_{\beta\gamma}}{\partial x_\alpha} \dot{x}_\beta \dot{x}_\gamma = 0 \tag{38.22}$$

or, performing the differentiations,

$$g_{\alpha\beta} \ddot{x}_\beta + \frac{\partial g_{\alpha\beta}}{\partial x_\gamma} \dot{x}_\beta \dot{x}_\gamma - \frac{1}{2} \frac{\partial g_{\beta\gamma}}{\partial x_\alpha} \dot{x}_\beta \dot{x}_\gamma = 0 \tag{38.23}$$

The coefficient of $\dot{x}_\beta \dot{x}_\gamma$ can be symmetrized with respect to β and γ; if we put

$$[\beta\gamma, \alpha] = \frac{1}{2} \left(\frac{\partial g_{\alpha\beta}}{\partial x_\gamma} + \frac{\partial g_{\alpha\gamma}}{\partial x_\beta} - \frac{\partial g_{\beta\gamma}}{\partial x_\alpha} \right) \tag{38.24}$$

the differential equation of the geodesic becomes

$$g_{\alpha\beta} \ddot{x}_\beta + [\beta\gamma, \alpha] \dot{x}_\beta \dot{x}_\gamma = 0 \tag{38.25}$$

The expression (38.24) is called a Christoffel symbol of the first kind. In order to solve equations (38.25) for the second derivatives we multiply them by $g^{\alpha\nu}$ and sum over α. Then with the new symbol

$$\{\beta\gamma, \nu\} = g^{\alpha\nu}[\beta\gamma, \alpha] \tag{38.26}$$

we obtain

$$\ddot{x}_\nu + \{\beta\gamma, \nu\} \dot{x}_\beta \dot{x}_\gamma = 0 \tag{38.27}$$

The expression (38.26) is called a Christoffel symbol of the second kind and is often represented by an alternative symbol

$$\{\beta\gamma, \nu\} = \Gamma^\nu_{\beta\gamma} \tag{38.28}$$

For uniformity we can also introduce a corresponding form of notation for Christoffel symbols of the first kind :

$$[\alpha\beta, \gamma] = \Gamma_{\gamma, \alpha\beta} \tag{38.29}$$

but this is less common practice.

We have thus

$$\Gamma_{v, \alpha\beta} = \frac{1}{2}\left(\frac{\partial g_{v\alpha}}{\partial x_\beta} + \frac{\partial g_{v\beta}}{\partial x_\alpha} - \frac{\partial g_{\alpha\beta}}{\partial x_v}\right) \tag{38.30}$$

and

$$\Gamma^v_{\alpha\beta} = \frac{1}{2} g^{v\mu}\left(\frac{\partial g_{\mu\alpha}}{\partial x_\beta} + \frac{\partial g_{\mu\beta}}{\partial x_\alpha} - \frac{\partial g_{\alpha\beta}}{\partial x_\mu}\right) \tag{38.31}$$

In this notation the equation of a geodesic takes on the form

$$\frac{d^2x_v}{dp^2} + \Gamma^v_{\alpha\beta}\frac{dx_\alpha}{dp}\frac{dx_\beta}{dp} = 0 \tag{38.32}$$

If the Christoffel symbols correspond to a metric tensor that can be written in the form (35.15) equations (38.32) are equivalent to the relations

$$\frac{d^2x'_k}{dp^2} = 0 \qquad (k = 0, 1, 2, 3) \tag{38.33}$$

for the Galilean coordinates x'_k. This follows from the covariance of the equations and the fact that in Galilean coordinates the Christoffel symbols vanish. In this case, therefore, the equation of a geodesic leads to linear dependence of the Galilean coordinates on the parameter p.

It is not difficult to verify that the development leading to (38.32) remains valid whatever the sign of F. If $F > 0$ the " geodesic " joins two events in time sequence and equations (38.32) can be interpreted as the equation of motion of a free mass point moving with a speed less than that of light. The increment dp of p is proportional to the increment $d\tau$ of the proper time τ and (38.32) may be replaced by

$$\frac{d^2x_v}{d\tau^2} + \Gamma^v_{\alpha\beta}\frac{dx_\alpha}{d\tau}\frac{dx_\beta}{d\tau} = 0 \tag{38.34}$$

The length of the geodesic gives the interval of proper time between the " departure " and the " arrival " of the mass point. If on the other hand $F < 0$, the geodesic joins two quasi-simultaneous events and we can put dp equal to the increment of the spatial interval. Equations (38.32) then appear as

$$\frac{d^2x_v}{dl^2} + \Gamma^v_{\alpha\beta}\frac{dx_\alpha}{dl}\frac{dx_\beta}{dl} = 0 \tag{38.35}$$

The case $F = 0$ corresponds to a point moving along a ray with the speed of light. In this case the Lagrangian (38.18) is zero and the above derivation of the geodesic equation is no longer valid. However, the equations (38.32) themselves retain their meaning and as they possess the integral (38.21) they are compatible with the condition $F = 0$. To justify the equations in this case we can start from the Hamiltonian equations that were discussed in Section 36. According to (36.08) we have

$$\frac{dx_k}{dx_0} = \frac{\partial H}{\partial \omega_k}; \qquad \frac{d\omega_k}{dx_0} = -\frac{\partial H}{\partial x_k} \qquad (k = 1. 2, 3) \tag{38.36}$$

where the Hamiltonian $H = -\omega_0$ is obtained by solving for ω_0 the equation

$$G \equiv g^{\alpha\beta}\omega_\alpha\omega_\beta = 0 \tag{38.37}$$

Therefore we have

$$dH = -d\omega_0 = \frac{1}{(\partial G/\partial \omega_0)}\left(\frac{\partial G}{\partial x_\alpha} dx_\alpha + \frac{\partial G}{\partial \omega_k} d\omega_k\right) \tag{38.38}$$

Using the fact that

$$\frac{d\omega_0}{dx_0} = -\frac{dH}{dx_0} = -\frac{\partial H}{\partial x_0} \tag{38.39}$$

and expressing the derivatives of H in terms of the derivatives of G we can write equations (38.36) in a symmetric fashion :

$$\frac{dx_\alpha}{dp} = \frac{1}{2}\frac{\partial G}{\partial \omega_\alpha}; \qquad \frac{d\omega_\alpha}{dp} = -\frac{1}{2}\frac{\partial G}{\partial x_\alpha} \qquad (\alpha = 0, 1, 2, 3) \tag{38.40}$$

Here dp is considered to be the differential of the independent variable p. The first four equations of (38.40) have already been given in Section 36. Writing the right-hand sides explicitly we get

$$\frac{dx_\alpha}{dp} = g^{\alpha\beta}\omega_\beta; \qquad \frac{d\omega_\alpha}{dp} = -\frac{1}{2}\frac{\partial g^{\mu\nu}}{\partial x_\alpha}\omega_\mu\omega_\nu \tag{38.41}$$

It is readily seen that these equations are equivalent to (38.32), for we have

$$\omega_\mu = g_{\mu\lambda}\frac{dx_\lambda}{dp} \tag{38.42}$$

and therefore

$$\frac{\partial g^{\mu\nu}}{\partial x_\alpha}\omega_\mu = \frac{\partial g^{\mu\nu}}{\partial x_\alpha}g_{\mu\lambda}\frac{dx_\lambda}{dp} = -g^{\mu\nu}\frac{\partial g_{\mu\lambda}}{\partial x_\alpha}\frac{dx_\lambda}{dp} \tag{38.43}$$

since

$$\frac{\partial g^{\mu\nu}}{\partial x_\alpha}g_{\mu\lambda} + g^{\mu\nu}\frac{\partial g_{\mu\lambda}}{\partial x_\alpha} = \frac{\partial}{\partial x_\alpha}(g^{\mu\nu}g_{\mu\lambda}) = \frac{\partial}{\partial x_\alpha}(\delta_\lambda^\nu) = 0 \tag{38.44}$$

Inserting (38.43) into (38.41) we get

$$\frac{d\omega_\alpha}{dp} = \frac{1}{2}g^{\mu\nu}\omega_\nu\frac{\partial g_{\mu\lambda}}{\partial x_\alpha}\frac{dx_\lambda}{dp} \tag{38.45}$$

or, in consequence of the first set of equations in (38.41),

$$\frac{d\omega_\alpha}{dp} = \frac{1}{2}\frac{\partial g_{\mu\lambda}}{\partial x_\alpha}\frac{dx_\mu}{dp}\frac{dx_\lambda}{dp} \tag{38.46}$$

Eliminating the ω_α from these equations and (38.42) we finally obtain

$$\frac{d}{dp}\left(g_{\alpha\beta}\frac{dx_\beta}{dp}\right) = \frac{1}{2}\frac{\partial g_{\mu\lambda}}{\partial x_\alpha}\frac{dx_\mu}{dp}\frac{dx_\lambda}{dp} \tag{38.47}$$

These equations are the same as the equations (38.22) from which the equations of the geodesic in the form (38.32) were derived. The passage from (38.41) to (38.47) is the usual one from Hamilton's to Lagrange's equations.

We have thus proved that the geodesic of zero length is likewise determined by the equations (38.22) but with the condition $F = 0$ adjoined.

It should be noted that because F is constant, a geodesic retains its character for its entire length; it may always describe the motion of a point with a speed less than that of light or it may be a null-line or, finally, it may be everywhere space-like.

For a null-geodesic the relation (38.37) with $\omega_\alpha = \partial\omega/\partial x_\alpha$ may be considered to be the Hamilton-Jacobi equation for the action function ω. (See Section 36.) The Hamilton-Jacobi equation for the general case can also be readily obtained. For definiteness we consider the case of a point moving with a speed less than that of light.

Choosing the time $t = x_0$ as the parameter and denoting differentiation with respect to it by a dot we can write the Lagrangian of the problem[†] in the form

$$L = + \sqrt{(g_{00} + 2g_{0i}\dot{x}_i + g_{ik}\dot{x}_i\dot{x}_k)} \tag{38.48}$$

The generalized momenta are

$$\frac{\partial L}{\partial \dot{x}_i} = p_i = + \frac{1}{L}(g_{0i} + g_{ik}\dot{x}_k) \tag{38.49}$$

and the Hamiltonian is found by the usual rule to be the expression

$$H = \dot{x}_i p_i - L = -\frac{1}{L}(g_{00} + g_{0k}\dot{x}_k) \tag{38.50}$$

with the velocities x_k expressed in terms of the momenta p_i by (38.49).

If we put

$$p_0 = \frac{1}{L}(g_{00} + g_{0k}\dot{x}_k) \tag{38.51}$$

and observe that

$$L\, dt = ds \tag{38.52}$$

where s is the length of arc, the four quantities p_i, p_0 can be uniformly written as

$$p_\alpha = g_{\alpha\beta}\frac{dx_\beta}{ds} \tag{38.53}$$

The identity

$$g_{\alpha\beta}\frac{dx_\alpha}{ds}\frac{dx_\beta}{ds} = 1 \tag{38.54}$$

leads to the relation

$$g^{\mu\nu}p_\mu p_\nu = 1 \tag{38.55}$$

which can be regarded as the result of eliminating the three velocities $\dot{x}_1$, $\dot{x}_2$ and $\dot{x}_3$ from the four equations (38.49) and (38.51). The Hamiltonian $H = -p_0$ is obtained by solving (38.55) for p_0. The Hamilton-Jacobi equation is obtained by the usual rule of expressing p_1, p_2, p_3 and H as partial derivatives of S with respect to the spatial coordinates and to time, as follows:

$$H = -\frac{\partial S}{\partial t}; \qquad p_k = \frac{\partial S}{\partial x_k} \tag{38.56}$$

These equations can also be written as

$$p_\nu = \frac{\partial S}{\partial x_\nu} \tag{38.57}$$

Thus the Hamilton-Jacobi form of the equation of a geodesic is

$$g_{\mu\nu}\frac{\partial S}{\partial x_\mu}\frac{\partial S}{\partial x_\nu} = 1 \tag{38.58}$$

If a complete integral of the Hamilton-Jacobi equation

$$S = S(x_0, x_1, x_2, x_3, c_1, c_2, c_3) + c_0 \tag{38.59}$$

---

† It is convenient to introduce the Lagrangian with opposite sign to the usual convention in mechanics. As a result, the sign of the energy will be opposite to the sign of the Hamiltonian.

is known, which contains three arbitrary constants c_1, c_2 and c_3, not counting the additive constant c_0, the derivatives of S with respect to the constants,

$$\frac{\partial S}{\partial c_k} = b_k \qquad (k = 1, 2, 3) \tag{38.60}$$

are also constants, as is proved in mechanics. They are determined from the conditions of the problem.

A comparison of (38.58) with (38.37) shows that the equations of a null-geodesic are obtained from (38.58) by replacing the right-hand side by zero. For a space-like geodesic the right-hand side of the Hamilton-Jacobi equation is a negative constant which can be set equal to -1.

39. Parallel Transport of a Vector

In Euclidean space it is very easy to define what is meant by saying that two vectors at different points are equal and parallel. It simply means that their cartesian components are equal. Obviously this same definition holds for vectors in a plane, and it can immediately be generalized to the case of vectors in a curved surface, provided the surface is developable. However, for a general non-developable surface parallelism of two vectors in it can be defined only if the points of application of the two vectors are infinitely close to each other. We can regard a vector on a surface as being a vector in space which is tangential to the surface at its point of application. Given a vector on the surface at a point P a vector at the adjacent point Q of the surface and parallel to the first vector in the sense of the geometry of the surface can be constructed as follows. We consider the given vector at P as a vector in space and we construct at Q the vector that is parallel to it in space in the usual sense. We then project this vector on to the tangent plane to the surface at Q. The tangential vector at Q is taken to be parallel to the given vector at P.

This construction can be performed analytically as follows. Let y_1, y_2 and y_3 be cartesian coordinates in Euclidean space and x_1 and x_2 the coordinate parameters on the surface. Then the parametric equations of the surface have the form

$$y_1 = y_1(x_1, x_2); \qquad y_2 = y_2(x_1, x_2); \qquad y_3 = y_3(x_1, x_2) \tag{39.01}$$

and the square of the element of arc on the surface is

$$ds^2 = g_{11} \, dx_1^2 + 2g_{12} \, dx_1 \, dx_2 + g_{22} \, dx_2^2 \tag{39.02}$$

where

$$g_{ik} = \sum_{n=1}^{3} \frac{\partial y_n}{\partial x_i} \frac{\partial y_n}{\partial x_k} \tag{39.03}$$

Let A_1 and A_2 be the covariant components of some vector at the point $P(x_1, x_2)$ on the surface and A^1 and A^2 its contravariant components. We can look upon this vector as a vector in space with the cartesian components

$$Y_n = \frac{\partial y_n}{\partial x_1} A^1 + \frac{\partial y_n}{\partial x_2} A^2 \qquad (n = 1, 2, 3) \tag{39.04}$$

and we have

$$A_l = \sum_{n=1}^{3} Y_n \frac{\partial y_n}{\partial x_l} \qquad (l = 1, 2) \tag{39.05}$$

If on passing to the point $Q(x_1 + dx_1, x_2 + dx_2)$ we do not change the cartesian components Y_n we get a vector in space which is no longer tangential to the surface. However, its tangential components define a vector on the surface, namely

$$A_l + \delta A_l = \sum_{n=1}^{3} Y_n \left(\frac{\partial y_n}{\partial x_l} + \sum_{k=1}^{2} \frac{\partial^2 y_n}{\partial x_k \partial x_l} \delta x_k \right) \tag{39.06}$$

and this vector is taken by definition to be the result of parallel transport of A_l to the point Q, in the sense of the geometry on the surface. The normal component of Y_n evidently drops out of equation (39.06).

The expression that appears as an addition to $\partial y_n / \partial x_l$ in that equation takes account of the change of this quantity in going from P to Q. Owing to this additional term the component A_l receives the increment

$$\delta A_l = \sum_{n=1}^{3} Y_n \sum_{k=1}^{2} \frac{\partial^2 y_n}{\partial x_k \partial x_l} \delta x_k \tag{39.07}$$

Insertion of Y_n from (39.04) gives

$$\delta A_l = \sum_{i,k=1}^{2} A^i \delta x_k \sum_{n=1}^{3} \frac{\partial y_n}{\partial x_i} \frac{\partial^2 y_n}{\partial x_k \partial x_l} \tag{39.08}$$

It is readily shown using the expression (39.03) for the g_{ik} that the sum over n in (39.09) is

$$\sum_{n=1}^{3} \frac{\partial y_n}{\partial x_i} \frac{\partial^2 y_n}{\partial x_k \partial x_l} = \frac{1}{2} \left(\frac{\partial g_{ik}}{\partial x_l} + \frac{\partial g_{il}}{\partial x_k} - \frac{\partial g_{kl}}{\partial x_i} \right) \tag{39.09}$$

or, using the definition (39.30) for the Christoffel symbols,

$$\sum_{n=1}^{3} \frac{\partial y_n}{\partial x_i} \frac{\partial^2 y_n}{\partial x_k \partial x_l} = \Gamma_{i,kl} \tag{39.10}$$

Thus the increment of the components of any vector in parallel transport is

$$\delta A_l = \sum_{i,k=1}^{2} \Gamma_{i,kl} A^i \delta x_k \tag{39.11}$$

It is important to note that this increment depends only on the internal properties of the surface, which are determined by the expression (39.02) for ds^2.

The theory of the parallel transport of vectors was developed by Levi-Civita [14] and his pupils; it can be formulated almost without change for the case of the four-dimensional space-time manifold.

Let the coefficients of the quadratic form

$$ds^2 = g_{\alpha\beta} \, dx_\alpha \, dx_\beta \tag{39.12}$$

be represented as

$$g_{\alpha\beta} = \sum_{n=1}^{N} e_n \frac{\partial y_n}{\partial x_\alpha} \frac{\partial y_n}{\partial x_\beta} \tag{39.13}$$

where the numbers e_n are ± 1 and the

$$y_n = y_n(x_0, x_1, x_2, x_3) \tag{39.14}$$

are some functions. In the ordinary Theory of Relativity the $g_{\alpha\beta}$ are obtained from the quadratic form (35.09) and can be represented by (35.15); this corresponds to $N = 4$. In the most general case we have ten $g_{\alpha\beta}$ and to represent them in the form (39.13) not more than ten functions y_n are required. (This can be rigorously proved.) It should be noted that since the signature of the quadratic form (39.12) is $(+ - - -)$ there must be at least one positive and at least three negative e_n.

We can formally interpret the y_n as cartesian coordinates in some many-dimensional pseudo-Euclidean space in which the metric is given by

$$d\eta^2 = \sum_{n=1}^{N} e_n \, dy_n^2 \tag{39.15}$$

Space-time is then a certain hypersurface in this many-dimensional space.

To an ordinary contravariant vector A^α in space-time there will correspond in the many-dimensional space a vector tangential to the hypersurface and having the cartesian components

$$Y_n = \frac{\partial y_n}{\partial x_\alpha} A^\alpha \tag{39.16}$$

(Here and in the following summation from 0 to 3 is assumed for Greek indices.) Using (39.13) we thus obtain the following expression for the covariant vector components A_α:

$$A_\alpha = \sum_{n=1}^{N} e_n Y_n \frac{\partial y_n}{\partial x_\alpha} \tag{39.17}$$

In analogy with (39.06) we can define the values of the vector components after parallel transport to an adjacent point by

$$A_\alpha + \delta A_\alpha = \sum_{n=1}^{N} e_n Y_n \left(\frac{\partial y_n}{\partial x_\alpha} + \frac{\partial^2 y_n}{\partial x_\alpha \partial x_\beta} \cdot \delta x_\beta \right) \tag{39.18}$$

whence
$$\delta A_\alpha = \sum_{n=1}^{N} e_n Y_n \frac{\partial^2 y_n}{\partial x_\alpha \partial x_\beta} \delta x_\beta \tag{39.19}$$

and, on insertion of the expressions (39.16) for Y_n,

$$\delta A_\alpha = \sum_{n=1}^{N} e_n \frac{\partial y_n}{\partial x_\gamma} \frac{\partial^2 y_n}{\partial x_\alpha \partial x_\beta} A^\gamma \delta x_\beta \tag{39.20}$$

Now, by analogy with (39.10), it follows from (39.13) that

$$\sum_{n=1}^{N} e_n \frac{\partial y_n}{\partial x_\gamma} \frac{\partial^2 y_n}{\partial x_\alpha \partial x_\beta} = \Gamma_{\gamma, \alpha\beta} \tag{39.21}$$

where the $\Gamma_{\gamma,\alpha\beta}$, are the ordinary Christoffel symbols

$$\Gamma_{\gamma, \alpha\beta} = \frac{1}{2} \left(\frac{\partial g_{\alpha\gamma}}{\partial x_\beta} + \frac{\partial g_{\beta\gamma}}{\partial x_\alpha} - \frac{\partial g_{\alpha\beta}}{\partial x_\gamma} \right) \tag{39.22}$$

Thus the formula for the increment of vector components due to parallel transport has the form

$$\delta A_\alpha = \Gamma_{\gamma, \alpha\beta} A^\gamma \delta x_\beta \tag{39.23}$$

just as for an ordinary surface in Euclidean space.

Equation (39.23) contains both covariant and contravariant vector components, but it is simple to state it entirely in terms of one or the other kind of components. We have

$$A^\gamma = g^{\nu\gamma} A_\nu \tag{39.24}$$

and

$$g^{\nu\gamma} \Gamma_{\gamma,\,\alpha\beta} = \Gamma^\nu_{\alpha\beta} \tag{39.25}$$

so that

$$\delta A_\alpha = \Gamma^\nu_{\alpha\beta} A_\nu \, \delta x_\beta \tag{39.26}$$

Only covariant components enter these equations. On the other hand we have

$$\delta A_\alpha = g_{\alpha\gamma} \, \delta A^\gamma + A^\gamma \frac{\partial g_{\alpha\gamma}}{\partial x_\beta} \, \delta x^\beta = \Gamma_{\gamma,\,\alpha\beta} A^\gamma \, \delta x_\beta \tag{39.27}$$

and it is easily verified that

$$\Gamma_{\gamma,\,\alpha\beta} + \Gamma_{\alpha,\,\beta\gamma} = \frac{\partial g_{\alpha\gamma}}{\partial x_\beta} \tag{39.28}$$

Hence

$$g_{\alpha\gamma} \, \delta A^\gamma = - \Gamma_{\alpha,\,\beta\gamma} A^\gamma \, \delta x_\beta \tag{39.29}$$

and therefore in terms of contravariant components the required equation is

$$\delta A^\nu = - \Gamma^\nu_{\alpha\beta} A^\alpha \, \delta x_\beta \tag{39.30}$$

We now consider the change in the scalar product of two vectors in parallel transport. We have

$$\delta(A^\nu B_\nu) = B_\nu \, \delta A^\nu + A^\alpha \, \delta B_\alpha \tag{39.31}$$

We insert the expression for δA^ν given by (39.30) and write δB_α according to (39.26) as

$$\delta B_\alpha = \Gamma^\nu_{\alpha\beta} B_\nu \, \delta x_\beta \tag{39.32}$$

It is then evident that the two terms on the right-hand side of (39.31) cancel, giving

$$\delta(A^\nu B_\nu) = 0 \tag{39.33}$$

Thus the scalar product of two vectors remains unchanged in parallel transport. In particular, the magnitude of a vector is unaltered.

We have hitherto considered infinitesimal displacements, but by adding up such displacements we can define the parallel transport along any given curve. We assume that the coordinates of a point on a curve are given as functions of some parameter p :

$$x_\beta = x_\beta(p) \tag{39.34}$$

The $\Gamma^\nu_{\alpha\beta}$, being functions of the coordinates, will then also be known functions of p. To obtain the vector A^ν as a function of p we have to solve the differential equations

$$\frac{dA^\nu}{dp} = - \Gamma^\nu_{\alpha\beta} A^\alpha \frac{dx_\beta}{dp} \tag{39.35}$$

If the values of A^ν are given at the initial point of the curve we can integrate (39.35) and so obtain the values of the A^ν at the final point of the curve. In this way we perform the parallel transport of any vector from the initial to the final point of the curve. Evidently the result depends on the nature of the curve along which the parallel transport is made.

We compare the equations (39.35) with the previously given equations for a geodesic

$$\frac{d^2x_\nu}{dp^2} + \Gamma^\nu_{\alpha\beta} \frac{dx_\alpha}{dp} \frac{dx_\beta}{dp} = 0 \tag{38.27}$$

The two sets are the same if we put

$$A^\nu = \frac{dx_\nu}{dp} \tag{39.36}$$

If the geodesic is time-like, so that it describes a point moving with a speed less than that of light, the proper time τ can be used as the parameter p and the vector A^ν will be the four-dimensional velocity. Thus in this case the equation of a geodesic can be interpreted (in four-dimensional terms) as the equation for parallel transport of the velocity vector in the direction given by this vector itself.

The equations for the parallel transport of a tensor of any rank are easily obtained from those for a vector. As an example we consider the case of a covariant second rank tensor $T_{\mu\nu}$. We start from the requirement that the invariant

$$I = T_{\mu\nu} A^\mu B^\nu \tag{39.37}$$

should not change in parallel transport, whatever the vectors A^μ and B^ν. With some relabelling of indices we can write δI as

$$\delta I = A^\mu B^\nu \left(\delta T_{\mu\nu} - T_{\mu\alpha}\Gamma^\alpha_{\nu\beta} \delta x_\beta - T_{\alpha\nu}\Gamma^\alpha_{\mu\beta} \delta x_\beta \right) \tag{39.38}$$

Since this expression must vanish for arbitrary A^μ and B^ν we must have

$$\delta T_{\mu\nu} = T_{\mu\alpha}\Gamma^\alpha_{\nu\beta} \delta x_\beta + T_{\alpha\nu}\Gamma^\alpha_{\mu\beta} \delta x_\beta \tag{39.39}$$

which is the required generalization of the equation of parallel transport.

40. Covariant Differentiation

In the case when the $g_{\mu\nu}$ were constants it was possible to treat the operation of differentiation as a symbolic multiplication by a vector; if, for instance, A_ν is a vector given as a point function in some region then, for constant $g_{\mu\nu}$, the expression $\nabla_\mu A_\nu = \partial A_\nu / \partial x_\mu$ is a tensor with the same transformation properties as the product of the vectors ∇_μ and A_ν. Consequently in this special case tensor analysis and tensor algebra are formally identical.

For variable $g_{\mu\nu}$ this is not so; the derivatives of a vector with respect to the coordinates no longer form a tensor. However, it is still possible to construct certain linear combinations of the derivatives of vector components and of the components themselves which transform as a tensor.

We consider a vector field A_ν defined in some region of space. The vector components are then functions of the coordinates. The change of the vector in going from a point $P(x_\beta)$ to an adjacent point $Q(x_\beta + \delta x_\beta)$ is

$$(A_\nu)_Q - (A_\nu)_P = \delta_1 A_\nu = \frac{\partial A_\nu}{\partial x_\beta} \delta x_\beta \tag{40.01}$$

However, we can also compare the values $(A_\nu)_Q$ of the components A_ν at Q not with their values at P but with the result $(A_\nu)_Q''$ of their parallel transport from P to Q. According to (39.26) the change of a vector in parallel transport is

$$(A_\nu)_Q'' - (A_\nu)_P = \delta_2 A_\nu = \Gamma^\mu_{\nu\beta} A_\mu \delta x_\beta \tag{40.02}$$

K

Subtraction of this expression from the previous one to obtain the difference

$$(A_\nu)_Q - (A_\nu)''_Q = \delta A_\nu = \delta_1 A_\nu - \delta_2 A_\nu \tag{40.03}$$

results in

$$\delta A_\nu = \left(\frac{\partial A_\nu}{\partial x_\beta} - \Gamma^\mu_{\nu\beta} A_\mu\right) \delta x_\beta \tag{40.04}$$

The quantity δA_ν gives the difference between the actual change of the vector and the change it would experience in parallel transport. It is at the same time the difference of two vectors both referring to the same point Q. Therefore the δA_ν form a vector. For arbitrary δx_β this can only be true if the quantities

$$\nabla_\beta A_\alpha \equiv \frac{\partial A_\alpha}{\partial x_\beta} - \Gamma^\nu_{\alpha\beta} A_\nu \tag{40.05}$$

form a covariant tensor of the second rank.† It is called the tensor derivative or covariant derivative of the vector and is the required generalization to variable $g_{\mu\nu}$ of the ordinary derivative of a vector.

By analogous considerations we can derive an expression for the covariant derivative of a contravariant vector. It has the form

$$\nabla_\beta A^\nu \equiv \frac{\partial A^\nu}{\partial x_\beta} + \Gamma^\nu_{\alpha\beta} A^\alpha \tag{40.06}$$

The formulae of covariant differentiation are easily generalized to apply to arbitrary tensors. We consider first the second rank tensor $T_{\mu\nu}$. According to (39.39) parallel transport from P to Q changes its components by

$$\delta_2 T_{\mu\nu} = \left(\Gamma^\alpha_{\mu\beta} T_{\alpha\nu} + \Gamma^\alpha_{\nu\beta} T_{\mu\alpha}\right) \delta x_\beta \tag{40.07}$$

Taking the $T_{\mu\nu}$ to be functions of the coordinates their change in going from P to Q is

$$\delta_1 T_{\mu\nu} = \frac{\partial T_{\mu\nu}}{\partial x_\beta} \delta x_\beta \tag{40.08}$$

The difference

$$\delta T_{\mu\nu} = \delta_1 T_{\mu\nu} - \delta_2 T_{\mu\nu} \tag{40.09}$$

becomes

$$\delta T_{\mu\nu} = \left(\frac{\partial T_{\mu\nu}}{\partial x_\beta} - \Gamma^\rho_{\mu\beta} T_{\rho\nu} - \Gamma^\rho_{\nu\beta} T_{\mu\rho}\right) \delta x_\beta \tag{40.10}$$

and is a tensor for arbitrary displacements δx_β. Therefore, the quantity

$$\nabla_\beta T_{\mu\nu} = \frac{\partial T_{\mu\nu}}{\partial x_\beta} - \Gamma^\rho_{\mu\beta} T_{\rho\nu} - \Gamma^\rho_{\nu\beta} T_{\mu\rho} \tag{40.11}$$

must be a tensor.

Similarly one proves the tensor character of

$$\nabla_\beta T^{\mu\nu} = \frac{\partial T^{\mu\nu}}{\partial x_\beta} + \Gamma^\mu_{\rho\beta} T^{\rho\nu} + \Gamma^\nu_{\rho\beta} T^{\mu\rho} \tag{40.12}$$

where $T^{\mu\nu}$ is a contravariant tensor and of

$$\nabla_\beta T^\mu_\nu = \frac{\partial T^\mu_\nu}{\partial x_\beta} - \Gamma^\rho_{\beta\nu} T^\mu_\rho + \Gamma^\mu_{\rho\beta} T^\rho_\nu \tag{40.13}$$

where T^ν_μ is a mixed tensor.

---

† The tensor character of (40.05) can also be proved without use of the notion of parallel transport. To do this one starts from (37.06) and proves the transformation law (42.04) for Christoffel symbols. One then transforms (40.05) to new variables using the two transformation laws (42.04) and (37.06).

By applying the rules of covariant differentiation to either the covariant or the contravariant components of the metric tensor expressions (40.11) and (40.12) can be shown to vanish. This fact is known as Ricci's lemma. Because of its importance we shall consider its formulation in some detail.

If we put $T_{\mu\nu} = g_{\mu\nu}$ equation (40.11) gives

$$\nabla_\beta g_{\mu\nu} \equiv \frac{\partial g_{\mu\nu}}{\partial x_\beta} - g_{\rho\nu}\Gamma^\rho_{\mu\beta} - g_{\mu\rho}\Gamma^\rho_{\nu\beta} = 0 \qquad (40.14)$$

for, written in the form
$$\frac{\partial g_{\mu\nu}}{\partial x_\beta} = \Gamma_{\nu,\,\mu\beta} + \Gamma_{\mu,\,\nu\beta} \qquad (40.15)$$

this equation is an obvious consequence of the definition (39.22) of the $\Gamma_{\gamma,\alpha\beta}$ and was already stated in (39.28).

If we put $T^{\mu\nu} = g^{\mu\nu}$ in (40.12) we get

$$\nabla_\beta g^{\mu\nu} \equiv \frac{\partial g^{\mu\nu}}{\partial x_\beta} + g^{\rho\nu}\Gamma^\mu_{\rho\beta} + g^{\mu\rho}\Gamma^\nu_{\rho\beta} = 0 \qquad (40.16)$$

This can be verified by using the explicit expressions (38.31) for the $\Gamma^\nu_{\alpha\beta}$. Then (40.16) reduces to

$$\frac{\partial g^{\mu\nu}}{\partial x_\beta} + g^{\mu\rho}g^{\nu\sigma}\frac{\partial g_{\rho\sigma}}{\partial x_\beta} = 0 \qquad (40.17)$$

and this is equivalent to

$$g_{\nu\alpha}\frac{\partial g^{\mu\nu}}{\partial x_\beta} + g^{\mu\nu}\frac{\partial g_{\nu\alpha}}{\partial x_\beta} = \frac{\partial}{\partial x_\beta}(g^{\mu\nu}g_{\nu\alpha}) = 0 \qquad (40.18)$$

Finally, if $T^\mu_\nu = \delta^\mu_\nu$, the expression (40.13) reduces to zero by virtue of the symmetry of the $\Gamma^\mu_{\alpha\beta}$ with respect to their lower indices.

Covariant differentiation of a product of two tensors obeys the same rules as ordinary differentiation. This follows directly from our method of deriving the expression for a covariant derivative, for the rule was obtained from the expression for an infinitesimal increment for which the ordinary rule for differentiating a product is valid.

Let us verify the product rule in the differentiation of the product of two vectors. Inserting

$$T_{\mu\nu} = U_\mu V_\nu \qquad (40.19)$$

into (40.11) we get

$$\nabla_\beta(U_\mu V_\nu) = \left(\frac{\partial U_\mu}{\partial x_\beta} - \Gamma^\rho_{\mu\beta}U_\rho\right)V_\nu + U_\mu\left(\frac{\partial V_\nu}{\partial x_\beta} - \Gamma^\rho_{\nu\beta}V_\rho\right) \qquad (40.20)$$

and, using (40.05),

$$\nabla_\beta(U_\mu V_\nu) = (\nabla_\beta U_\mu)\cdot V_\nu + U_\mu(\nabla_\beta V_\nu) \qquad (40.21)$$

Applying the product rule to the expression

$$U_\mu = g_{\mu\nu}U^\nu \qquad (40.22)$$

and using the fact that the covariant derivatives of the metric tensor vanish, we obtain

$$\nabla_\beta U_\mu = g_{\mu\nu}\nabla_\beta U^\nu \tag{40.23}$$

Thus we see that in covariant differentiation the $g_{\mu\nu}$ behave as constants so that they can be taken outside the differentiation symbol. In other words it is immaterial whether indices are raised (or lowered) before or after covariant differentiation.

We have just stated explicitly the expression for the covariant derivatives of a vector and of a second rank tensor. The covariant derivative of a scalar is the same as the ordinary derivative

$$\nabla_\beta \Phi = \frac{\partial \Phi}{\partial x_\beta} \tag{40.24}$$

This quantity is, as we know, a covariant vector.

For completeness we write down the general expression for the covariant derivative of a tensor of arbitrary rank

$$U_{(\nu)}^{(\mu)} = U_{\nu_1\cdots\nu_k}^{\mu_1\cdots\mu_m} \tag{40.25}$$

which has m contravariant and k covariant indices. We have

$$\nabla_\beta U_{(\nu)}^{(\mu)} = \frac{\partial}{\partial x_\beta}(U_{(\nu)}^{(\mu)}) + \Gamma_{\rho\beta}^{\mu_1} U_{(\nu)}^{\rho\mu_2\cdots\mu_m} + \ldots + \Gamma_{\rho\beta}^{\mu_m} U_{(\nu)}^{\mu_1\cdots\mu_{m-1}\rho}$$
$$- \Gamma_{\beta\nu_1}^{\rho} U_{\rho\nu_2\ldots\nu_k}^{(\mu)} - \ldots - \Gamma_{\beta\nu_k}^{\rho} U_{\nu_1\ldots\nu_{k-1}\rho}^{(\mu)} \tag{40.26}$$

In each term of this sum one index of the tensor being differentiated becomes an index attached in the same position to the Γ-symbol, while in its place the tensor itself carries a summation index which is repeated in the opposite position as one of the indices of the accompanying Γ-symbol. One of the lower indices of Γ is always the label of the coordinate with respect to which one is differentiating. The terms in which a change in a superfix of the tensor is made enter with a plus sign and those in which a suffix is involved have a minus.

Sometimes it is convenient to use a special notation for the operation of covariant differentiation combined with a raising of the suffix. The operation

$$\nabla^\alpha = g^{\alpha\beta}\nabla_\beta \tag{40.27}$$

may be called contravariant differentiation.

41. Examples of Covariant Differentiation

We shall now apply to some special cases the rules of covariant differentiation obtained above.

First we calculate the divergence of a vector. By (40.06) the expression

$$\nabla_\mu A^\nu = \frac{\partial A^\nu}{\partial x_\mu} + \Gamma_{\alpha\mu}^\nu A^\alpha \tag{41.01}$$

is a mixed second rank tensor. Contraction with respect to μ and ν gives the scalar

$$\text{Div } A \equiv \nabla_\nu A^\nu = \frac{\partial A^\nu}{\partial x_\nu} + \Gamma^\nu_{\alpha\nu} A^\alpha \tag{41.02}$$

This is a generalization of the expression (21.24) for the four-dimensional divergence. It can be simplified as follows. We have

$$\Gamma^\nu_{\alpha\nu} = g^{\mu\nu} \cdot \frac{1}{2}\left(\frac{\partial g_{\mu\nu}}{\partial x_\alpha} + \frac{\partial g_{\mu\alpha}}{\partial x_\nu} - \frac{\partial g_{\nu\alpha}}{\partial x_\mu} \right) = \frac{1}{2} g^{\mu\nu} \frac{\partial g_{\mu\nu}}{\partial x_\alpha} \tag{41.03}$$

and if g is the determinant formed from the $g_{\mu\nu}$ and if in it $gg^{\mu\nu}$ is the minor of $g_{\mu\nu}$, then the rule for differentiating a determinant gives

$$dg = gg^{\mu\nu} dg_{\mu\nu} \tag{41.04}$$

whence

$$\frac{1}{g}\frac{\partial g}{\partial x_\alpha} = g^{\mu\nu} \frac{\partial g_{\mu\nu}}{\partial x_\alpha} \tag{41.05}$$

We note that by (40.18) we also have

$$\frac{1}{g}\frac{\partial g}{\partial x_\alpha} = -g_{\mu\nu} \frac{\partial g^{\mu\nu}}{\partial x_\alpha} \tag{41.06}$$

and therefore

$$\Gamma^\alpha_{\alpha\nu} = \frac{1}{2g}\frac{\partial g}{\partial x_\alpha} = \frac{\partial}{\partial x_\alpha} \lg \sqrt{(-g)} \tag{41.07}$$

Insertion into (41.02) gives

$$\nabla_\nu A^\nu = \frac{1}{\sqrt{(-g)}} \frac{\partial}{\partial x_\nu} \{ \sqrt{(-g)} \cdot A^\nu \} \tag{41.08}$$

We see that the divergence of a vector A multiplied by $\sqrt{(-g)}$ is equal to the sum of partial derivatives with respect to the coordinates of $\sqrt{(-g)}$ times the contravariant vector components.

If for our vector we take the gradient of some scalar φ, putting

$$A_\mu = \frac{\partial \varphi}{\partial x_\mu} \tag{41.09}$$

so that

$$A^\nu = g^{\mu\nu} \frac{\partial \varphi}{\partial x_\mu} \tag{41.10}$$

the divergence of this vector is the invariant expression

$$\Box \varphi = \frac{1}{\sqrt{(-g)}} \frac{\partial}{\partial x_\nu} \left(\sqrt{(-g)} \cdot g^{\mu\nu} \frac{\partial \varphi}{\partial x_\mu} \right) \tag{41.11}$$

This is the generalization of the d'Alembertian (21.27).

The same divergence may also be calculated by a different method. We form first the covariant derivative of the gradient of φ. By the general rule (40.05) we get

$$\varphi_{\mu\nu} = \frac{\partial^2 \varphi}{\partial x_\mu \partial x_\nu} - \Gamma^\alpha_{\mu\nu} \frac{\partial \varphi}{\partial x_\alpha} \tag{41.12}$$

and the expression is symmetric in μ and ν. It can be called the covariant second derivative of the scalar φ. If we then form the invariant

$$\Box \varphi = g^{\mu\nu} \varphi_{\mu\nu} \tag{41.13}$$

we obtain

$$\Box \varphi = g^{\mu\nu} \frac{\partial^2 \varphi}{\partial x_\mu \, \partial x_\nu} - \Gamma^\alpha \frac{\partial \varphi}{\partial x_\alpha} \tag{41.14}$$

where we have put for brevity $\quad \Gamma^\alpha = g^{\mu\nu} \Gamma^\alpha_{\mu\nu} \tag{41.15}$

Since both (41.11) and (41.12) give the divergence of one and the same vector they must be equal. It is immediately obvious that the coefficients of the second derivatives of φ are equal, but equating the coefficients of the first derivatives leads to the identity

$$\Gamma^\alpha = -\frac{1}{\sqrt{(-g)}} \frac{\partial}{\partial x_\beta} \{ \sqrt{(-g)} \cdot g^{\alpha\beta} \} \tag{41.16}$$

This identity could also have been verified directly.

We note that in a system of coordinates in which x_0, x_1, x_2 and x_3 are four solutions of the equation $\Box \varphi = 0$, the Γ^α will vanish. Coordinates of this kind, which in addition satisfy certain conditions at infinity to be discussed in a later chapter, are called harmonic. In ordinary Relativity Theory cartesian spatial coordinates together with time are harmonic.

If a vector A_μ is the gradient of some scalar the difference of covariant derivatives $\nabla_\mu A_\nu - \nabla_\nu A_\mu$ vanishes. In general this difference does not vanish and can be considered to be the four-dimensional generalization of the curl or vorticity of the vector field. We put†

$$(\mathrm{Rot}\, A)_{\mu\nu} = \nabla_\mu A_\nu - \nabla_\nu A_\mu \tag{41.17}$$

By its definition this is an antisymmetric covariant tensor of second rank. Using equation (40.05) we can easily see that in the difference (41.17) the terms characteristic of covariant differentiation cancel and we have

$$(\mathrm{Rot}\, A)_{\mu\nu} = \frac{\partial A_\nu}{\partial x_\mu} - \frac{\partial A_\mu}{\partial x_\nu} \tag{41.18}$$

which is the same as the usual expression for vorticity. The latter is thus valid in arbitrary coordinates.

Let us now write $A_{\mu\nu}$ for the symmetric part of the covariant derivative of the vector A_μ. We have

$$A_{\mu\nu} = \frac{1}{2} \left(\nabla_\nu A_\mu + \nabla_\mu A_\nu \right) \tag{41.19}$$

or, using (40.05) $\quad A_{\mu\nu} = \frac{1}{2} \left(\frac{\partial A_\mu}{\partial x_\nu} + \frac{\partial A_\nu}{\partial x_\mu} \right) - \Gamma^\alpha_{\mu\nu} A_\alpha \tag{41.20}$

With the aid of the symmetric tensor $A_{\mu\nu}$ we can define the covariant second derivative of the vector A_μ by

$$\nabla_{\mu\nu} A_\sigma = \nabla_\nu A_{\mu\sigma} + \nabla_\mu A_{\nu\sigma} - \nabla_\sigma A_{\mu\nu} \tag{41.21}$$

† The symbol Rot will be used for the four-dimensional vorticity; the symbol curl is retained for the three-dimensional case.

Using (40.11) to express the derivatives on the right-hand side we get

$$\nabla_{\mu\nu}A_\sigma = \frac{\partial^2 A_\sigma}{\partial x_\mu \, \partial x_\nu} - 2\Gamma^\rho_{\mu\nu}A_{\rho\sigma} + \frac{\partial}{\partial x_\sigma}(\Gamma^\rho_{\mu\nu}A_\rho) - \frac{\partial}{\partial x_\nu}(\Gamma^\rho_{\mu\sigma}A_\rho) - \frac{\partial}{\partial x_\mu}(\Gamma^\rho_{\nu\sigma}A_\rho)$$

(41.22)

Similarly the covariant second derivative of a contravariant vector is given by

$$\nabla_{\mu\nu}A^\rho = \frac{\partial^2 A_\rho}{\partial x_\mu \, \partial x_\nu} + \Gamma^\rho_{\mu\alpha}\frac{\partial A^\alpha}{\partial x_\nu} + \Gamma^\rho_{\nu\alpha}\frac{\partial A^\alpha}{\partial x_\mu} - \Gamma^\alpha_{\mu\nu}\frac{\partial A^\rho}{\partial x_\alpha} + \frac{\partial \Gamma^\rho_{\mu\nu}}{\partial x_\alpha}A^\alpha \qquad (41.23)$$

We now consider the divergence of a second rank tensor, which we shall write in contravariant form. According to (40.12) we have

$$\nabla_\nu T^{\mu\nu} = \frac{\partial T^{\mu\nu}}{\partial x_\nu} + \Gamma^\mu_{\rho\nu}T^{\rho\nu} + \Gamma^\nu_{\rho\nu}T^{\mu\rho} \qquad (41.24)$$

Transforming the third term with the aid of (41.07) we can write

$$\nabla_\nu T^{\mu\nu} = \frac{1}{\sqrt{(-g)}}\frac{\partial}{\partial x_\nu}\{\sqrt{(-g)}\cdot T^{\mu\nu}\} + \Gamma^\mu_{\alpha\beta}T^{\alpha\beta} \qquad (41.25)$$

Putting $T^{\mu\nu} = g^{\mu\nu}$ and remembering that the covariant derivatives of the metric tensor vanish we again get the identity (41.16). If $T^{\mu\nu}$ is antisymmetric the last term in (41.25) vanishes, so that the divergence of an antisymmetric tensor is like the divergence of a vector in being a sum of derivative terms. For a general tensor, on the other hand, such a representation does not exist.

We now write down the expression for a covariant derivative of a covariant second rank tensor together with two expressions obtained from the first one by cyclic permutation of suffixes :

$$\nabla_\sigma F_{\mu\nu} = \frac{\partial F_{\mu\nu}}{\partial x_\sigma} - \Gamma^\rho_{\mu\sigma}F_{\rho\nu} - \Gamma^\rho_{\nu\sigma}F_{\mu\rho}$$

$$\nabla_\mu F_{\nu\sigma} = \frac{\partial F_{\nu\sigma}}{\partial x_\mu} - \Gamma^\rho_{\nu\mu}F_{\rho\sigma} - \Gamma^\rho_{\sigma\mu}F_{\nu\rho} \qquad (41.26)$$

$$\nabla_\nu F_{\sigma\mu} = \frac{\partial F_{\sigma\mu}}{\partial x_\nu} - \Gamma^\rho_{\sigma\nu}F_{\rho\mu} - \Gamma^\rho_{\mu\nu}F_{\sigma\rho}$$

Assuming that $F_{\mu\nu}$ is antisymmetric, i.e.

$$F_{\mu\nu} = - F_{\nu\mu} \qquad (41.27)$$

we find that $\quad \nabla_\sigma F_{\mu\nu} + \nabla_\mu F_{\nu\sigma} + \nabla_\nu F_{\sigma\mu} = \dfrac{\partial F_{\mu\nu}}{\partial x_\sigma} + \dfrac{\partial F_{\nu\sigma}}{\partial x_\mu} + \dfrac{\partial F_{\sigma\mu}}{\partial x_\nu} \qquad (41.28)$

because the terms not involving derivatives cancel in pairs. The expression

$$F_{\mu\nu\sigma} = \frac{\partial F_{\mu\nu}}{\partial x_\sigma} + \frac{\partial F_{\nu\sigma}}{\partial x_\mu} + \frac{\partial F_{\sigma\mu}}{\partial x_\nu} \qquad (41.29)$$

which is antisymmetric in all three suffixes is therefore a tensor of third rank which may be called the *cyclic derivative* of the antisymmetric tensor $F_{\mu\nu}$. We have previously encountered such an expression in Section 24.

The cyclic derivative of any antisymmetric tensor is related to the divergence of the antisymmetric pseudo-tensor dual to it. As in (37.67) we introduce the dual pseudo-tensor by the relation

$$\overset{*}{F}{}^{\alpha\beta} = \frac{1}{2} E^{\alpha\beta\gamma\delta} F_{\gamma\delta} \tag{41.30}$$

so that

$$\sqrt{(-g)} \cdot \overset{*}{F}{}^{10} = F_{23}; \quad \sqrt{(-g)} \cdot \overset{*}{F}{}^{20} = F_{31}; \quad \sqrt{(-g)} \cdot \overset{*}{F}{}^{30} = F_{12}$$
$$\sqrt{(-g)} \cdot \overset{*}{F}{}^{23} = F_{10}; \quad \sqrt{(-g)} \cdot \overset{*}{F}{}^{31} = F_{20}; \quad \sqrt{(-g)} \cdot \overset{*}{F}{}^{12} = F_{30} \tag{41.31}$$

We also introduce the pseudo-vector dual to $F_{\mu\nu\sigma}$ as in (37.68):

$$\overset{*}{F}{}^{\rho} = \frac{1}{6} E^{\rho\mu\nu\sigma} F_{\mu\nu\sigma} \tag{41.32}$$

so that

$$\sqrt{(-g)} \cdot \overset{*}{F}{}^{0} = -F_{123};$$
$$\sqrt{(-g)} \cdot \overset{*}{F}{}^{1} = F_{230}; \quad \sqrt{(-g)} \cdot \overset{*}{F}{}^{2} = F_{310}; \quad \sqrt{(-g)} \cdot \overset{*}{F}{}^{3} = \overset{*}{F}{}_{120} \tag{41.33}$$

If $F_{\mu\nu\sigma}$ is the cyclic derivative of $F_{\mu\nu}$ we have

$$\frac{1}{\sqrt{(-g)}} \frac{\partial \{\sqrt{(-g)} \cdot \overset{*}{F}{}^{\alpha\beta}\}}{\partial x_\beta} = \overset{*}{F}{}^{\alpha} \tag{41.34}$$

i.e. the pseudo-vector $\overset{*}{F}{}^{\alpha}$ is the divergence of the pseudo-tensor $\overset{*}{F}{}^{\alpha\beta}$.

The same result is easily obtained without considering individual components by using the fact that the covariant derivatives of $E^{\alpha\beta\gamma\delta}$ and also of $E_{\alpha\beta\gamma\delta}$, calculated by the general rule, vanish identically.

42. The Transformation Law for Christoffel Symbols and the Locally Geodesic Coordinate System. Conditions for transforming ds^2 to a Form with Constant Coefficients

Covariant, or tensorial, derivatives differ from ordinary derivatives by terms involving the Christoffel symbols

$$\Gamma^{\nu}_{\alpha\beta} = \frac{1}{2} g^{\mu\nu} \left(\frac{\partial g_{\alpha\mu}}{\partial x_\beta} + \frac{\partial g_{\beta\mu}}{\partial x_\alpha} - \frac{\partial g_{\alpha\beta}}{\partial x_\mu} \right) \tag{42.01}$$

If at some point $x_\rho = x_\rho^0$ all the Christoffel symbols vanish, the expressions for tensorial and ordinary derivatives are the same. We shall show that in the neighbourhood of any point it is possible to introduce a system of coordinates such that all the $\Gamma^{\nu}_{\alpha\beta}$ vanish at the point. Then, by (40.14) and (40.16) all derivatives of the metric tensor with respect to coordinates will vanish at the point in question.

We first establish the law according to which the Christoffel symbols transform when one passes from the original system of coordinates (x_0, x_1, x_2, x_3) to some new system (x_0', x_1', x_2', x_3'). This law could be derived directly from the definition (42.01) of the $\Gamma^{\nu}_{\alpha\beta}$ using also the transformation law for the metric tensor. It is, however, simpler to argue as follows. We know that the quantities

$$\varphi_{\mu\nu} = \frac{\partial^2 \varphi}{\partial x_\mu \, \partial x_\nu} - \Gamma^{\alpha}_{\mu\nu} \frac{\partial \varphi}{\partial x_\alpha} \tag{42.02}$$

represent a tensor. This means that for any function φ and any coordinate transformation the equations

$$\frac{\partial^2\varphi}{\partial x_\mu\,\partial x_\nu} - \Gamma^\rho_{\mu\nu}\frac{\partial\varphi}{\partial x_\rho} = \left(\frac{\partial^2\varphi}{\partial x'_\alpha\,\partial x'_\beta} - (\Gamma^\sigma_{\alpha\beta})'\frac{\partial\varphi}{\partial x'_\sigma}\right)\frac{\partial x'_\alpha}{\partial x_\mu}\frac{\partial x'_\beta}{\partial x_\nu} \tag{42.03}$$

are valid where the $(\Gamma^\sigma_{\alpha\beta})'$ are Christoffel symbols in the primed coordinate system. Putting $\varphi = x'_\sigma$ we get

$$\frac{\partial^2 x'_\sigma}{\partial x_\mu\,\partial x_\nu} - \Gamma^\rho_{\mu\nu}\frac{\partial x'_\sigma}{\partial x_\rho} = -(\Gamma^\sigma_{\alpha\beta})'\frac{\partial x'_\alpha}{\partial x_\mu}\frac{\partial x'_\beta}{\partial x_\nu} \tag{42.04}$$

This is the required transformation law. The presence of the term involving the second derivative shows that $\Gamma^\sigma_{\alpha\beta}$ is not a tensor. If the transformation under consideration is linear the term mentioned is absent and, therefore, for linear transformations the $\Gamma^\rho_{\mu\nu}$ behave like a tensor.

Let the values of the $\Gamma^\rho_{\mu\nu}$ at the given point be $(\Gamma^\rho_{\mu\nu})_0$. The primed quantities $(\Gamma^\sigma_{\alpha\beta})'$ will vanish at the point if the transformation of coordinates satisfies the relations

$$\left(\frac{\partial^2 x'_\sigma}{\partial x_\mu\,\partial x_\nu}\right)_0 - (\Gamma^\rho_{\mu\nu})_0\left(\frac{\partial x'_\sigma}{\partial x_\rho}\right)_0 = 0 \tag{42.05}$$

These relations will be satisfied if we put

$$x'_\sigma = x_\sigma - x^0_\sigma + \frac{1}{2}(\Gamma^\sigma_{\mu\nu})_0\,(x_\mu - x^0_\mu)\,(x_\nu - x^0_\nu) \tag{42.06}$$

For this transformation

$$\left(\frac{\partial x'_\sigma}{\partial x_\rho}\right)_0 = \delta^\sigma_\rho \tag{42.07}$$

and, therefore, the values at the point of the components of any tensor will be the same in the primed and the unprimed system. In particular there is no change in the components of the metric tensor ; the derivatives of this tensor on the other hand all transform to zero. This fact may be utilized to simplify calculations involving tensors, for it follows that if some quantity is known to be a tensor and also known to vanish if $\partial g_{\mu\nu}/\partial x_\alpha = 0$ the quantity must also vanish without that condition.

It can be proved that with a suitable choice of coordinate system the derivatives of the $g_{\mu\nu}$ may be made to vanish not only at one point, but even along any given line [14].

A coordinate system in which the derivatives of the $g_{\mu\nu}$ vanish at a given point is called locally geodesic. This name is justified by the fact that in such a system the equations of a geodesic reduce at the point in question to the statement that the second derivatives of the coordinates with respect to the parameter p vanish. (In the vicinity of the point these derivatives will be first order infinitesimals.) Hence the coordinates there will be linear functions of p up to terms of third order.

We now ask the question : What is the condition for the existence of a co-ordinate system (x'_0, x'_1, x'_2, x'_3) in which the Christoffel symbols vanish not only at the given point or along some line, but even in some finite region?

If such a coordinate system exists the equations

$$\frac{\partial^2\varphi}{\partial x_\mu\,\partial x_\nu} - \Gamma^\rho_{\mu\nu}\frac{\partial\varphi}{\partial x_\rho} = 0 \tag{42.08}$$

must have a solution, because they are satisfied by the functions

$$\varphi = x_0' ; \qquad \varphi = x_1' ; \qquad \varphi = x_2' ; \qquad \varphi = x_3' \tag{42.09}$$

For all the equations (42.08) to be compatible it is obviously necessary that expressions for the same third derivative calculated from one or other of the equations must coincide. We have

$$\frac{\partial}{\partial x_\alpha}\left(\frac{\partial^2\varphi}{\partial x_\mu \, \partial x_\nu}\right) = \frac{\partial}{\partial x_\alpha}\left(\Gamma^\rho_{\mu\nu}\frac{\partial\varphi}{\partial x_\rho}\right)$$
$$\frac{\partial}{\partial x_\nu}\left(\frac{\partial^2\varphi}{\partial x_\mu \, \partial x_\alpha}\right) = \frac{\partial}{\partial x_\nu}\left(\Gamma^\rho_{\mu\alpha}\frac{\partial\varphi}{\partial x_\rho}\right) \tag{42.10}$$

Here the left-hand sides are equal, therefore also the right-hand sides. We equate the latter, perform the differentiations and express the second derivatives in terms of the first, getting

$$\left(\frac{\partial\Gamma^\rho_{\mu\nu}}{\partial x_\alpha} - \frac{\partial\Gamma^\rho_{\mu\alpha}}{\partial x_\nu} + \Gamma^\sigma_{\mu\nu}\Gamma^\rho_{\sigma\alpha} - \Gamma^\sigma_{\mu\alpha}\Gamma^\rho_{\sigma\nu}\right)\frac{\partial\varphi}{\partial x_\rho} = 0 \tag{42.11}$$

These equations must be valid for $\varphi = x_0'$, $\varphi = x_1'$, $\varphi = x_2'$ and $\varphi = x_3'$. Since the determinant

$$D = \frac{D\,(x_0',\, x_1',\, x_2',\, x_3')}{D\,(x_0,\, x_1,\, x_2,\, x_3)} \tag{42.12}$$

is not zero all the coefficients of the $\partial\varphi/\partial x_\rho$ in (42.11) must vanish. These coefficients are

$$R^\rho_{\mu,\,\nu\alpha} = \frac{\partial\Gamma^\rho_{\mu\nu}}{\partial x_\alpha} - \frac{\partial\Gamma^\rho_{\mu\alpha}}{\partial x_\nu} + \Gamma^\sigma_{\mu\nu}\Gamma^\rho_{\sigma\alpha} - \Gamma^\sigma_{\mu\alpha}\Gamma^\rho_{\sigma\nu} \tag{42.13}$$

We now prove that the conditions

$$R^\rho_{\mu,\,\nu\alpha} = 0 \tag{42.14}$$

are not only necessary but also sufficient to ensure that the system of equations (42.08) has a solution. To do this we put

$$\varphi_\nu = \frac{\partial\varphi}{\partial x_\nu} \tag{42.15}$$

and write (42.08) as

$$\frac{\partial\varphi_\nu}{\partial x_\mu} = \Gamma^\rho_{\mu\nu}\varphi_\rho \tag{42.16}$$

Let the values of the φ_ν be given at some point which has the coordinates x_α^0. To get the values for an arbitrary point x_α we join the two points by some curve

$$x_\alpha = \xi^\alpha\,(p) \tag{42.17}$$

where p is a parameter, and we consider φ_ν, and also $\Gamma^\rho_{\mu\nu}$ as functions of p. The φ_ν are then determined by the system of ordinary differential equations

$$\frac{d\varphi_\nu}{dp} = \Gamma^\rho_{\mu\nu}\dot{\xi}^\mu\varphi_\rho \tag{42.18}$$

where the dot denotes differentiation with respect to the parameter p.

This system uniquely determines the values of φ_ν at the end point of the curve. It remains to show that the values of φ_ν so found do not depend on the shape of the curve joining the initial and final points. To do this we consider an infinitesimally differing curve joining the two points :

$$x_\alpha = \xi^\alpha(p) + \delta\xi^\alpha(p) \tag{42.19}$$

Here $\delta\xi^\alpha$ is an infinitesimal vector which becomes zero at the initial and final points. We denote the values of φ_ν on the varied curve by $\varphi_\nu + \delta\varphi_\nu$.

The equations for $\varphi_\nu + \delta\varphi_\nu$ will evidently be of the form

$$\frac{d}{dp}(\varphi_\nu + \delta\varphi_\nu) = \left(\Gamma^\rho_{\mu\nu} + \frac{\partial\Gamma^\rho_{\mu\nu}}{\partial x_\alpha}\,\delta\xi^\alpha\right)(\dot\xi^\mu + \delta\dot\xi^\mu)(\varphi_\rho + \delta\varphi_\rho) \tag{42.20}$$

Subtracting (42.18) from this and neglecting higher order infinitesimals, we get

$$\frac{d}{dp}(\delta\varphi_\nu) = \frac{\partial\Gamma^\rho_{\mu\nu}}{\partial x_\alpha}\,\dot\xi^\mu\varphi_\rho\delta\xi^\alpha + \Gamma^\rho_{\mu\nu}\dot\xi^\mu\delta\varphi_\rho + \Gamma^\rho_{\mu\nu}\varphi_\rho\delta\dot\xi^\mu \tag{42.21}$$

Using (42.18) once again and introducing the notation of (42.13) we can put this into the form

$$\frac{d}{dp}(\delta\varphi_\nu - \Gamma^\rho_{\alpha\nu}\varphi_\rho\delta\xi^\alpha) = R^\rho_{\nu,\,\mu\alpha}\dot\xi^\mu\delta\xi^\alpha + \Gamma^\rho_{\mu\nu}\dot\xi^\mu(\delta\varphi_\rho - \Gamma^\sigma_{\alpha\rho}\varphi_\sigma\delta\xi^\alpha) \tag{42.22}$$

For brevity we write

$$\eta_\nu = \delta\varphi_\nu - \Gamma^\rho_{\alpha\nu}\varphi_\rho\delta\xi^\alpha \tag{42.23}$$

Then, if (42.14) holds, (42.22) takes the form

$$\frac{d\eta_\nu}{dp} = \Gamma^\rho_{\mu\nu}\dot\xi^\mu\eta_\rho \tag{42.24}$$

Thus the equations for η_ν have the same appearance as those for φ_ν ; both represent equations of parallel transport of a vector along the chosen curve. The η_ν, just as the φ_ν, are uniquely determined by the initial conditions. But the initial conditions for the η_ν are simply that they vanish. For the coordinates of the initial point are fixed, so that there $\delta\xi^\alpha = 0$, and the value of φ_ν at this point is also fixed, giving $\delta\varphi_\nu = 0$. Hence $\eta_\nu = 0$ at the initial point ; with this condition it follows that along the whole curve

$$\eta_\nu = 0 \tag{42.25}$$

and therefore

$$\delta\varphi_\nu = \Gamma^\rho_{\alpha\nu}\varphi_\rho\delta\xi^\alpha \tag{42.26}$$

We now consider the final point of the curve. Its coordinates are also fixed, giving $\delta\xi^\alpha = 0$, consequently, by (42.26) we must also have $\delta\varphi_\nu = 0$. This means that the function takes on the same value at the final point whether it is calculated using the initial curve or the infinitesimally varied one. Deforming the curve continuously we shall then also obtain the same result for any two curves joining the same two points, not only for curves differing infinitesimally. It follows that in any simply connected region the φ_ν are single valued point functions determined by their values at an arbitrary initial point.

By virtue of the differential equations (42.16) we have

$$\frac{\partial\varphi_\nu}{\partial x_\mu} = \frac{\partial\varphi_\mu}{\partial x_\nu} \tag{42.27}$$

because the $\Gamma^\rho_{\mu\nu}$ are symmetric in their lower indices. It follows that the expression

$$d\varphi = \varphi_\nu\,dx_\nu \tag{42.28}$$

is a total differential. Integrating and fixing the constant by the value of φ at the initial point completes the determination of φ.

We have proved that the necessary and sufficient condition for a solution of equation (42.08) to exist is the vanishing of (42.13), and that φ is determined apart from an additive constant by the values at one point of its partial derivatives with respect to the coordinates.

If two, not necessarily different, solutions φ and ψ of equations (42.08) are given, the expression

$$\varphi_{,\nu}\psi^{\nu} = g^{\mu\nu} \frac{\partial\varphi}{\partial x_{\nu}} \frac{\partial\psi}{\partial x_{\mu}} \tag{42.29}$$

remains constant as a consequence of these equations. To prove this it is sufficient to form the covariant derivative of the scalar (42.29) and to verify that it vanishes. (As we saw, (42.16) is just an expression of the fact that the covariant derivatives of the φ_{ν} vanish.)

We denote by x'_0, x'_1, x'_2 and x'_3 four solutions of (42.08) which are so chosen that at the initial point one has

$$g^{\mu\nu} \frac{\partial x'_{\alpha}}{\partial x_{\mu}} \frac{\partial x'_{\beta}}{\partial x_{\nu}} = e_{\alpha}\delta_{\alpha\beta} \tag{42.30}$$

(no summation over α). Then (42.30) will also be true for all values of the coordinates. Hence it follows by purely algebraic reasoning that

$$g_{\alpha\beta} = \sum_{k=0}^{3} e_k \frac{\partial x'_k}{\partial x_{\alpha}} \frac{\partial x'_k}{\partial x_{\beta}} \tag{42.31}$$

i.e. that $g_{\alpha\beta}$ can be represented in the form (35.15) and that therefore ds^2 can be brought to the form (35.09).

Thus the necessary and sufficient condition for the quadratic form

$$ds^2 = g_{\alpha\beta}\, dx_{\alpha}\, dx_{\beta} \tag{42.32}$$

to be reducible to

$$ds^2 = (dx'_0)^2 - (dx'_1)^2 - (dx'_2)^2 - (dx'_3)^2 \tag{42.33}$$

is the vanishing of the expression

$$R^{\rho}_{\mu,\,\nu\alpha} = \frac{\partial\Gamma^{\rho}_{\mu\nu}}{\partial x_{\alpha}} - \frac{\partial\Gamma^{\rho}_{\mu\alpha}}{\partial x_{\nu}} + \Gamma^{\sigma}_{\mu\nu}\Gamma^{\rho}_{\mu\alpha} - \Gamma^{\sigma}_{\mu\alpha}\Gamma^{\rho}_{\sigma\nu} \tag{42.13}$$

formed out of the Christoffel symbols belonging to the quadratic form (42.32).

43. The Curvature Tensor

In the foregoing section we introduced the quantity

$$R^{\rho}_{\mu,\,\nu\alpha} = \frac{\partial\Gamma^{\rho}_{\mu\nu}}{\partial x_{\alpha}} - \frac{\partial\Gamma^{\rho}_{\mu\alpha}}{\partial x_{\nu}} + \Gamma^{\sigma}_{\mu\nu}\Gamma^{\rho}_{\sigma\alpha} - \Gamma^{\sigma}_{\mu\alpha}\Gamma^{\rho}_{\sigma\nu} \tag{43.01}$$

This quantity plays an important role in general tensor analysis and in the theory of gravitation. It is thus necessary to investigate its properties in detail. We first prove that it is a tensor. This can be done in different ways. The most direct method of proof consists in differentiating the equations

$$\frac{\partial^2 x'_{\sigma}}{\partial x_{\mu}\, \partial x_{\nu}} - \Gamma^{\rho}_{\mu\nu} \frac{\partial x'_{\sigma}}{\partial x_{\rho}} = -(\Gamma^{\sigma}_{\alpha\beta})' \frac{\partial x'_{\alpha}}{\partial x_{\mu}} \frac{\partial x_{\beta}}{\partial x_{\nu}} \tag{43.02}$$

which state the transformation law for Christoffel symbols as it was given in (42.04). The result of differentiating (43.02) with respect to x_λ can be written as

$$\frac{\partial^3 x'_\sigma}{\partial x_\lambda\, \partial x_\mu\, \partial x_\nu} + (\Gamma^\sigma_{\alpha\beta})' \left(\frac{\partial x'_\alpha}{\partial x_\lambda} \frac{\partial^2 x'_\beta}{\partial x_\mu\, \partial x_\nu} + \frac{\partial x'_\alpha}{\partial x_\mu} \frac{\partial^2 x'_\beta}{\partial x_\nu\, \partial x_\lambda} + \frac{\partial x'_\alpha}{\partial x_\nu} \frac{\partial^2 x'_\beta}{\partial x_\lambda\, \partial x_\mu} \right)$$

$$= \left(\frac{\partial \Gamma^\rho_{\mu\nu}}{\partial x_\lambda} + \Gamma^\tau_{\mu\nu} \Gamma^\rho_{\tau\lambda} \right) \frac{\partial x'_\sigma}{\partial x_\rho} - \left(\frac{\partial (\Gamma^\sigma_{\beta\gamma})'}{\partial x'_\alpha} + (\Gamma^\tau_{\beta\gamma})'\,(\Gamma^\sigma_{\tau\alpha})' \right) \frac{\partial x'_\alpha}{\partial x_\lambda} \frac{\partial x'_\beta}{\partial x_\mu} \frac{\partial x'_\gamma}{\partial x_\nu} \quad (43.03)$$

Here the left-hand side is symmetric in λ, μ and ν and therefore the right-hand side must also have this symmetry. Interchanging λ and ν on the right and equating the expression obtained to the original right-hand side, we get an equation which, in terms of (43.01), can be written as

$$R^\rho_{\mu,\,\nu\lambda} \frac{\partial x'_\sigma}{\partial x_\rho} = (R^\sigma_{\beta,\,\gamma\alpha})' \frac{\partial x'_\alpha}{\partial x_\lambda} \frac{\partial x'_\beta}{\partial x_\mu} \frac{\partial x'_\gamma}{\partial x_\nu} \quad (43.04)$$

This equation indeed expresses the fact that $R^\rho_{\mu,\,\nu\lambda}$ is a fourth rank tensor which is covariant in μ, ν and λ and contravariant in ρ. This tensor is called the curvature tensor.

With the aid of the curvature tensor one can give an expression for the change of a vector in parallel transport around an infinitesimal closed contour. Let the value of the vector A_ρ at the starting point x^0_α be $(A_\rho)_0$. If it is transported to an adjacent point its components will take on the values

$$A_\rho = (A_\rho)_0 + (\Gamma^\sigma_{\alpha\rho})_0\,(A_\sigma)_0\,(x_\alpha - x^0_\alpha) \quad (43.05)$$

apart from quantities of second order of smallness† in the $x_\alpha - x^0_\alpha$. It is thus obvious that the changes ΔA_μ undergone by the vector components A_μ when going round an infinitesimal closed contour will be at least of second order in the greatest displacements occurring. These changes can be expressed as the line integral

$$\Delta A_\mu = \int \Gamma^\rho_{\mu\nu} A_\rho\, dx_\nu \quad (43.06)$$

taken around the contour in question. For an infinitesimal contour the A_ρ under the integral may be replaced by (43.05) and the $\Gamma^\rho_{\mu\nu}$ by

$$\Gamma^\rho_{\mu\nu} = (\Gamma^\rho_{\mu\nu})_0 + \left(\frac{\partial \Gamma^\rho_{\mu\nu}}{\partial x_\alpha} \right)_0 (x_\alpha - x^0_\alpha) \quad (43.07)$$

Inserting (43.05) and (43.07) into (43.06) and using the fact that the integral of a total differential around a closed contour vanishes. we get

$$\Delta A_\mu = \left(\frac{\partial \Gamma^\rho_{\mu\nu}}{\partial x_\alpha} + \Gamma^\sigma_{\mu\nu} \Gamma^\rho_{\sigma\alpha} \right)_0 (A_\rho)_0 \int (x_\alpha - x^0_\alpha)\, dx_\nu \quad (43.08)$$

The quantities

$$Q^{\nu\alpha} = \int (x_\alpha - x^0_\alpha)\, dx_\nu = \frac{1}{2} \int [(x_\alpha - x^0_\alpha)\, dx_\nu - (x_\nu - x^0_\nu)\, dx_\alpha] \quad (43.09)$$

---

† Such second order quantities will depend on the nature of the curve along which the displacement is made, because the vector A_ρ is not considered as point function.

can be interpreted as the projections of the surface enclosed by the contour on the coordinate " planes ". It is easy to verify that they form a contravariant antisymmetric tensor. Owing to this antisymmetry equation (43.08) can be written as

$$\Delta A_\mu = \frac{1}{2} R^\rho_{\mu,\,\nu\alpha} A_\rho Q^{\nu\alpha} \tag{43.10}$$

Here we have suppressed the suffix 0 which characterizes the initial point.

By similar arguments the change in the contravariant components of a vector can be shown to be given by

$$\Delta A^\sigma = -\frac{1}{2} R^\sigma_{\rho,\,\nu\alpha} A^\rho Q^{\nu\alpha} \tag{43.11}$$

We already know that $R^\rho_{\mu,\nu\alpha}$ is a tensor ; this can also be seen from (43.10) and (43.11), for ΔA_μ is the difference of two vectors referring to the same point and is thus itself a vector. On the other hand, if an arbitrary symmetric part is added to the antisymmetric tensor $Q^{\nu\alpha}$ equation (43.10) does not change. Therefore the right-hand side of (43.10) is a vector for any tensor $Q^{\nu\alpha}$ and any vector A_ρ. This is possible only if $R^\rho_{\mu,\nu\alpha}$ is a tensor.

In Section 40 we introduced the operation of covariant differentiation. In general, covariant differentiations do not commute, the second covariant derivative of a vector or a tensor taken first with respect to x_β and then to x_α is not equal to the second derivative with respect to x_α and then x_β. We now consider the difference of these two derivatives for the case of a vector. According to (40.05) we have

$$\nabla_\beta A_\mu = \frac{\partial A_\mu}{\partial x_\beta} - \Gamma^\nu_{\mu\beta} A_\nu \tag{43.12}$$

We calculate $\nabla_\alpha \nabla_\beta A_\mu$ in a locally geodesic coordinate system, which is one in which the first derivatives of the $g_{\mu\nu}$ vanish at the point considered. We have

$$\nabla_\alpha \nabla_\beta A_\mu = \frac{\partial^2 A_\mu}{\partial x_\alpha \, \partial x_\beta} - \frac{\partial \Gamma^\nu_{\mu\beta}}{\partial x_\alpha} A_\nu \tag{43.13}$$

whence $\qquad \nabla_\alpha \nabla_\beta A_\mu - \nabla_\beta \nabla_\alpha A_\nu = \left(\frac{\partial \Gamma^\nu_{\mu\alpha}}{\partial x_\beta} - \frac{\partial \Gamma^\nu_{\mu\beta}}{\partial x_\alpha} \right) A_\nu \tag{43.14}$

In the locally geodesic system the factor of A_ν on the right-hand side coincides with the expression for the curvature tensor

$$R^\nu_{\mu,\,\alpha\beta} = \frac{\partial \Gamma^\nu_{\mu\alpha}}{\partial x_\beta} - \frac{\partial \Gamma^\nu_{\mu\beta}}{\partial x_\alpha} + \Gamma^\sigma_{\mu\alpha} \Gamma^\nu_{\sigma\beta} - \Gamma^\sigma_{\mu\beta} \Gamma^\nu_{\sigma\alpha} \tag{43.15}$$

Therefore, in a locally geodesic system the equation

$$(\nabla_\alpha \nabla_\beta - \nabla_\beta \nabla_\alpha) A_\mu = R^\nu_{\mu,\,\alpha\beta} A_\nu \tag{43.16}$$

is valid. Now, both sides of this equation are tensors and therefore (43.16) must also be true in an arbitrary system of coordinates. The expression (43.16) for the difference of second derivatives of a vector is thus of general validity.

The corresponding equations for a contravariant vector

$$(\nabla_\alpha \nabla_\beta - \nabla_\beta \nabla_\alpha) A^\nu = -R^\nu_{\mu,\,\alpha\beta} A^\mu \tag{43.17}$$

can be derived similarly.

The technique used here of first stating an equation between tensors in a locally geodesic system and then concluding that it is generally valid is very useful for abbreviating the derivation of results. The equations (43.16) and (43.17) are so simple that they can also be obtained quite easily without using this technique, but there are other cases where the simplification is more substantial.

Let us, for instance, consider the expression for the difference of second covariant derivatives of a tensor of arbitrary rank.

$$U^{(\mu)}_{(\nu)} = U^{\mu_1 \cdots, \mu_m}_{\nu_1 \cdots, \nu_k} \tag{43.18}$$

Equation (40.26) for the first derivative can be written in the form

$$\nabla_\beta U^{(\mu)}_{(\nu)} = \frac{\partial}{\partial x_\beta}(U^{(\mu)}_{(\nu)}) + \sum_{i=1}^{m} \Gamma^{\mu_i}_{\rho\beta} U^{\mu_1 \cdots \mu_{i-1}\rho\mu_{i+1} \cdots \mu_m}_{(\nu)}$$
$$- \sum_{j=1}^{k} \Gamma^{\rho}_{\beta\nu_j} U^{(\mu)}_{\nu_1 \cdots \nu_{j-1}\rho\nu_{j+1} \cdots \nu_k} \tag{43.19}$$

Forming the second derivative in a geodesic system gives

$$\nabla_\alpha \nabla_\beta U^{(\mu)}_{(\nu)} = \frac{\partial^2}{\partial x_\alpha \partial x_\beta}(U^{(\mu)}_{(\nu)}) + \sum_{i=1}^{m} \frac{\partial \Gamma^{\mu_i}_{\rho\beta}}{\partial x_\alpha} U^{\mu_1 \cdots \mu_{i-1}\rho\mu_{i+1} \cdots \mu_m}_{(\nu)}$$
$$- \sum_{j=1}^{k} \frac{\partial \Gamma^{\rho}_{\beta\nu_j}}{\partial x_\alpha} U^{(\mu)}_{\nu_1 \cdots \nu_{j-1}\rho\nu_{j+1} \cdots \nu_k} \tag{43.20}$$

Therefore, the difference of second derivatives in a geodesic system coincides with the expression

$$(\nabla_\alpha \nabla_\beta - \nabla_\beta \nabla_\alpha)U^{(\mu)}_{(\nu)} = -\sum_{i=1}^{m} R^{\mu_i}_{\rho,\,\alpha\beta} U^{\mu_1 \cdots \mu_{i-1}\rho\mu_{i+1} \cdots \mu_m}_{(\nu)}$$
$$+ \sum_{j=1}^{k} R^{\rho}_{\nu_j,\,\alpha\beta} U^{(\mu)}_{\nu_1 \cdots \nu_{j-1}\rho\nu_{j+1} \cdots \nu_k} \tag{43.21}$$

But since both sides of this equation are tensors, (43.21) must be correct in all coordinate systems.

44. The Basic Properties of the Curvature Tensor

Side by side with the mixed curvature tensor

$$R^{\sigma}_{\mu,\,\alpha\beta} = \frac{\partial \Gamma^{\sigma}_{\mu\alpha}}{\partial x_\beta} - \frac{\partial \Gamma^{\sigma}_{\mu\beta}}{\partial x_\alpha} + \Gamma^{\rho}_{\mu\alpha}\Gamma^{\sigma}_{\rho\beta} - \Gamma^{\rho}_{\mu\beta}\Gamma^{\sigma}_{\rho\alpha} \tag{44.01}$$

we shall consider the covariant tensor

$$R_{\mu\nu,\,\alpha\beta} = g_{\nu\sigma}R^{\sigma}_{\mu,\,\alpha\beta} \tag{44.02}$$

According to this definition the mixed tensor $R^{\sigma}_{\mu,\alpha\beta}$ is obtained from $R_{\mu\nu,\alpha\beta}$ by raising the *second* covariant suffix. Therefore, a more precise notation for it would be

$$R^{\sigma}_{\mu,\,\alpha\beta} = R^{\;\;\sigma}_{\mu,\;\alpha\beta} = g^{\sigma\nu}R_{\mu\nu,\,\alpha\beta} \tag{44.03}$$

We note that in older literature the covariant and the mixed tensors used to be denoted by the symbols

$$R_{\mu\nu,\,\alpha\beta} = (\mu\nu,\,\alpha\beta) \tag{44.04}$$

and
$$R^{\sigma}_{\mu,\,\alpha\beta} = \{\mu\sigma,\,\alpha\beta\}, \tag{44.05}$$

which were known as Riemann's four-index symbols of the first and second kind.

Evaluating the covariant curvature tensor by (44.02) we get

$$R_{\mu\nu,\,\alpha\beta} = \frac{\partial}{\partial x_\beta}[\mu\alpha,\,\nu] - \frac{\partial}{\partial x_\alpha}[\mu\beta,\,\nu] + \Gamma^\rho_{\mu\alpha}\left([\rho\beta,\,\nu] - \frac{\partial g_{\nu\rho}}{\partial x_\beta}\right) - \Gamma^\rho_{\mu\beta}\left([\rho\alpha,\,\nu] - \frac{\partial g_{\nu\rho}}{\partial x_\alpha}\right)$$

(44.06)

or finally

$$R_{\mu\nu,\,\alpha\beta} = \frac{1}{2}\left(\frac{\partial^2 g_{\nu\alpha}}{\partial x_\mu\,\partial x_\beta} + \frac{\partial^2 g_{\mu\beta}}{\partial x_\nu\,\partial x_\alpha} - \frac{\partial^2 g_{\nu\beta}}{\partial x_\mu\,\partial x_\alpha} - \frac{\partial^2 g_{\mu\alpha}}{\partial x_\nu\,\partial x_\beta}\right) - \Gamma^\rho_{\mu\alpha}[\nu\beta,\,\rho] + \Gamma^\rho_{\mu\beta}[\nu\alpha,\,\rho]$$

(44.07)

Here the last two terms can be expressed in terms of the $\Gamma^\rho_{\mu\nu}$, giving

$$R_{\mu\nu,\,\alpha\beta} = \frac{1}{2}\left(\frac{\partial^2 g_{\nu\alpha}}{\partial x_\mu\,\partial x_\beta} + \frac{\partial^2 g_{\mu\beta}}{\partial x_\nu\,\partial x_\alpha} - \frac{\partial^2 g_{\nu\beta}}{\partial x_\mu\,\partial x_\alpha} - \frac{\partial^2 g_{\mu\alpha}}{\partial x_\nu\,\partial x_\beta}\right) - g_{\rho\sigma}\Gamma^\rho_{\mu\alpha}\Gamma^\sigma_{\nu\beta} + g_{\rho\sigma}\Gamma^\rho_{\mu\beta}\Gamma^\sigma_{\nu\alpha}$$

(44.08)

From this expression the following symmetry properties of the tensor can be deduced :

1. Antisymmetry in its first two suffixes

$$R_{\nu\mu,\,\alpha\beta} = -R_{\mu\nu,\,\alpha\beta}$$

(44.09)

2. Antisymmetry in its last two suffixes

$$R_{\mu\nu,\,\beta\alpha} = -R_{\mu\nu,\,\alpha\beta}$$

(44.10)

3. Cyclic symmetry

$$R_{\mu\nu,\,\alpha\beta} + R_{\mu\alpha,\,\beta\nu} + R_{\mu\beta,\,\nu\alpha} = 0$$

(44.11)

The first two properties are obvious. To verify the last it is sufficient to write the left-hand side of (44.11) in a locally geodesic system and to verify that the twelve second derivatives that occur cancel in pairs.

From the three stated properties it follows further that we can interchange the first pair of suffixes with the second, without any change of order within either pair :

$$R_{\alpha\beta,\,\mu\nu} = R_{\mu\nu,\,\alpha\beta}$$

(44.12)

This last property also follows directly from the definition (44.08); to show that it is not independent, but a consequence of the other three, we can add together equation (44.11) and three other equations obtained from (44.11) by cyclic permutation of the four suffixes (μ, ν, α, β). If the antisymmetry properties 1. and 2. are used eight of the twelve terms in the sum cancel in pairs, the remaining four giving

$$-2R_{\mu\alpha,\,\nu\beta} + 2R_{\nu\beta,\,\mu\alpha} = 0$$

(44.13)

This differs from (44.12) only in the naming of suffixes.

We now count how many independent components the curvature tensor possesses ; we do this on the assumption that each suffix may take on n values so that actually $n = 4$. Evidently all four suffixes cannot be equal. All non-vanishing components having only two distinct suffixes reduce to the type $R_{\alpha\beta,\,\alpha\beta}$. Their number is the number of pairs of unequal suffixes, i.e. $\frac{1}{2}n(n-1)$

Further, if a triplet of different numbers, α, β, γ is given—and there are $\frac{1}{6}n(n-1)(n-2)$ such triplets—the non-vanishing tensor components that may be formed from it are $R_{\alpha\beta,\alpha\gamma}$; $R_{\beta\alpha,\beta\gamma}$; $R_{\gamma\alpha,\gamma\beta}$ which respectively have the first, second or third of the numbers α, β and γ repeated. The number of such components will be three times the number of triplets, i.e. $\frac{1}{2}n(n-1)(n-2)$. Finally, there exist $\frac{1}{24}n(n-1)(n-2)(n-3)$ combinations of four different numbers, α, β, γ and δ. With each such combination one can form components $R_{\alpha\beta,\gamma\delta}$, $R_{\alpha\delta,\beta\gamma}$ and $R_{\alpha\gamma,\delta\beta}$, while all other combinations of suffixes reduce to these three. However, these three components are not independent because they are linked by the cyclic symmetry condition, leaving only two independent quantities. Therefore, the number of independent tensor components having four distinct suffixes is twice that of quartets of numbers, i.e. is equal to $\frac{1}{12}n(n-1)(n-2)(n-3)$. The total number of independent components is

$$\frac{1}{2}n(n-1) + \frac{1}{2}n(n-1)(n-2) + \frac{1}{12}n(n-1)(n-2)(n-3) = \frac{1}{12}n^2(n^2-1)$$

(44.14)

In the case of interest $n = 4$ so that the number is

$$6 + 12 + 2 = 20 \tag{44.15}$$

One might note that in three-dimensional space ($n = 3$) the number of independent components of the curvature tensor is 6, which is also the number of components of a symmetric second rank tensor. In fact, for $n = 3$, the curvature tensor can be expressed in terms of a second rank symmetric tensor, as shown in Appendix E. Finally, the curvature tensor of a two-dimensional surface ($n = 2$) has only one component—the Gaussian curvature.

We note that in Section 31 we have already encountered quantities with the same symmetry properties as the covariant curvature tensor and we observed there the connection of such quantities with Krutkov's symmetric tensor.

We have studied the properties of the covariant curvature tensor. The mixed curvature tensor has analogous properties

$$R^\sigma_{\mu,\,\beta\alpha} = -R^\sigma_{\mu,\,\alpha\beta} \tag{44.16}$$

and
$$R^\sigma_{\mu,\,\alpha\beta} + R^\sigma_{\alpha,\,\beta\mu} + R^\sigma_{\beta,\,\mu\alpha} = 0 \tag{44.17}$$

corresponding to (44.12) and (44.11). As regards the property corresponding to (44.19) it takes on a somewhat more complicated form, namely

$$g_{\sigma\nu}g^{\rho\mu}R^\sigma_{\mu,\,\alpha\beta} = -R^\rho_{\nu,\,\alpha\beta} \tag{44.18}$$

(It means that the raising of the first suffix and the lowering of the superfix results in a change of sign of the component.) This property can easily be derived independently of (44.09) by comparing (43.10) and (43.11) or (43.16) and (43.17) or alternatively by use of the equation

$$(\nabla_\alpha\nabla_\beta - \nabla_\beta\nabla_\alpha)g_{\mu\nu} = R^\rho_{\mu,\,\alpha\beta}g_{\rho\nu} + R^\rho_{\nu,\,\alpha\beta}g_{\rho\mu} = 0 \tag{44.19}$$

which follows from the general rule (43.21).

In addition to the algebraic identities just discussed the curvature tensor satisfies some differential relations which can be written as

$$\nabla_\lambda R_{\mu\nu,\,\alpha\beta} + \nabla_\mu R_{\nu\lambda,\,\alpha\beta} + \nabla_\nu R_{\lambda\mu,\,\alpha\beta} = 0 \tag{44.20}$$

and are called the Bianchi identities. To verify them we introduce a locally geodesic coordinate system, in which covariant and ordinary derivatives can be identified. The calculations are simplified by the fact that in the expression (44.08) for $R_{\mu\nu,\alpha\beta}$ the terms not containing second derivatives are quadratic in the $\Gamma^{\rho}_{\mu\nu}$, so that not only these terms themselves, but also their first derivatives become zero in a locally geodesic system. In such a system the left-hand side of (44.20) is equal to

$$
\frac{\partial}{\partial x_\lambda} R_{\mu\nu,\,\alpha\beta} + \frac{\partial}{\partial x_\mu} R_{\nu\lambda,\,\alpha\beta} + \frac{\partial}{\partial x_\nu} R_{\lambda\mu,\,\alpha\beta}
$$
$$
= \frac{1}{2}\left(\frac{\partial^3 g_{\nu\alpha}}{\partial x_\lambda\,\partial x_\mu\,\partial x_\beta} + \frac{\partial^3 g_{\mu\beta}}{\partial x_\nu\,\partial x_\lambda\,\partial x_\alpha} + \frac{\partial^3 g_{\lambda\alpha}}{\partial x_\mu\,\partial x_\nu\,\partial x_\beta} + \frac{\partial^3 g_{\nu\beta}}{\partial x_\lambda\,\partial x_\mu\,\partial x_\alpha} \right.
$$
$$
\left. + \frac{\partial^3 g_{\mu\alpha}}{\partial x_\nu\,\partial x_\lambda\,\partial x_\beta} + \frac{\partial^3 g_{\lambda\beta}}{\partial x_\mu\,\partial x_\nu\,\partial x_\alpha} \right) - \frac{1}{2}(\ldots) \qquad (44.21)
$$

where the dots denote terms of the same structure as those given but with α and β interchanged. Now, the expression in the bracket is itself symmetric in α and β so that the two brackets are equal and their difference vanishes. This proves that (44.20) is valid in a locally geodesic system and thus, being a tensor equation, it must be valid generally.

By contracting with respect to two indices one can construct a second rank tensor out of the fourth rank curvature tensor. Contraction with respect to the first two, or the last two suffixes evidently gives zero, all other contractions give one and the same result, apart from a sign. In this way we get the tensor

$$
R_{\mu\nu} = g^{\alpha\beta} R_{\mu\alpha,\,\beta\nu} = R^{\beta}_{\mu,\,\beta\nu} \qquad (44.22)
$$

which is called the second rank curvature tensor or the Riemann tensor. It is easy to see that the Riemann tensor is symmetric. For, using (44.09), (44.10) and (44.12) we get

$$
g^{\alpha\beta} R_{\mu\alpha,\,\beta\nu} = g^{\alpha\beta} R_{\beta\nu,\,\mu\alpha} = g^{\alpha\beta} R_{\nu\beta,\,\alpha\mu} = g^{\alpha\beta} R_{\nu\alpha,\,\beta\mu} \qquad (44.23)
$$

or
$$
R_{\mu\nu} = R_{\nu\mu} \qquad (44.24)
$$

Side by side with the covariant Riemann tensor one considers also the mixed tensor

$$
R^{\mu}_{\nu} = g^{\mu\rho} R_{\rho\nu} \qquad (44.25)
$$

and the contravariant tensor

$$
R^{\mu\nu} = g^{\mu\rho} g^{\nu\sigma} R_{\rho\sigma} \qquad (44.26)
$$

Further contraction, with respect to μ and ν leads to the scalar

$$
R = R^{\nu}_{\nu} = g^{\mu\nu} R_{\mu\nu} = g^{\mu\nu} g^{\alpha\beta} R_{\mu\alpha,\,\beta\nu} \qquad (44.27)
$$

which is called the scalar curvature.

We now calculate the divergence of the Riemann tensor,

$$
Y_{\nu} = \nabla_{\lambda} R^{\lambda}_{\nu} = g^{\mu\lambda} \nabla_{\lambda} R_{\mu\nu} \qquad (44.28)
$$

Introducing (44.22) for $R_{\mu\nu}$ we get

$$
Y_{\nu} = g^{\mu\lambda} g^{\alpha\beta} \nabla_{\lambda} R_{\mu\alpha,\,\beta\nu} \qquad (44.29)
$$

To the covariant derivative in the above we apply the Bianchi identities written in the form

$$\nabla_\lambda R_{\mu\alpha,\,\beta\nu} + \nabla_\beta R_{\mu\alpha,\,\nu\lambda} + \nabla_\nu R_{\mu\alpha,\,\lambda\beta} = 0 \tag{44.30}$$

which is obtained from (44.20) with the aid of (44.12). This gives

$$Y_\nu = -\,g^{\mu\lambda}g^{\alpha\beta}\nabla_\beta R_{\mu\alpha,\,\nu\lambda} - g^{\mu\lambda}g^{\alpha\beta}\nabla_\nu R_{\mu\alpha,\,\lambda\beta} \tag{44.31}$$

This relation can be rewritten as

$$Y_\nu = -Y_\nu + \nabla_\nu R \tag{44.32}$$

for if the summation indices in the first term on the right of (44.31) are renamed so as to exchange λ with β and μ with α it becomes the same as (44.29). In the last term of (44.31) the summation may be performed before the covariant differentiation, reducing that term to $\nabla_\nu R$. Thus we find

$$Y_\nu = \frac{1}{2}\nabla_\nu R = \frac{1}{2}\frac{\partial R}{\partial x_\nu} \tag{44.33}$$

in view of the fact that for a scalar the covariant and the ordinary derivative coincide. Comparing (44.28) and (44.33) we see that the divergence of the tensor

$$G_{\mu\nu} = R_{\mu\nu} - \frac{1}{2}g_{\mu\nu}R \tag{44.34}$$

vanishes identically. For this reason the tensor $G_{\mu\nu}$ is called the conservative tensor. As it plays an important part in Einstein's Theory of Gravitation it is also called the Einstein tensor.

Further transformations of the curvature tensor will be postponed until Chapter V, which deals with the theory of gravitation.

CHAPTER IV

A FORMULATION OF RELATIVITY THEORY IN ARBITRARY COORDINATES

45. Properties of Space-Time and Choice of Coordinates

The form of the equations that describe the course of a physical process in space and time depends not only on the specific nature of the particular process but also on two further circumstances : the properties of space-time and the coordinates chosen. The properties of space-time are objective, they are determined by Nature and do not depend on our choice. In contrast, the use of one system of coordinates or another is to a very high degree a matter of our choice. It is true that there is a certain limitation to arbitrariness, in so far as the existence of certain preferential coordinate systems, namely the Galilean ones, is only assured by reason of the objective properties of space-time ; such coordinate systems would not exist if these properties were different. However, it is always possible, by a mathematical transformation, to pass from a preferential coordinate system to any other arbitrary one. We have studied the rules for doing this in the preceding chapter.

To detach oneself from the specific characteristics of any particular process one must consider those equations which are of greatest generality and which characterize most directly the properties of space-time. The equation that states the law of propagation of a wave front travelling with the limiting velocity is of this kind. In the first place, this law is obeyed by light, i.e. electromagnetic waves in free space, but we have already pointed out that it should not be regarded as referring specifically to light, but as a general law to which any disturbance travelling with limiting velocity is subject. The equation for the propagation of a wave front in free space characterizes not only the properties of the kind of matter being propagated (e.g. of the electromagnetic field) but also the properties of space-time itself. (We have repeatedly pointed out that the practical measurement of great distances is based on triangulation and on radar, i.e. also on the use of the laws of electromagnetic wave propagation.) Consequently, the concepts of geometry and the notion of time are very closely connected with the law of wave front propagation in free space.

In Galilean coordinates

$$x_0' = ct ; \quad x_1' = x ; \quad x_2' = y ; \quad x_3' = z \tag{45.01}$$

this law is expressed by the equation

$$\left(\frac{\partial\omega}{\partial x_0'}\right)^2 - \left(\frac{\partial\omega}{\partial x_1'}\right)^2 - \left(\frac{\partial\omega}{\partial x_2'}\right)^2 - \left(\frac{\partial\omega}{\partial x_3'}\right)^2 = 0 \tag{45.02}$$

where $\omega = $ const. is the equation of the moving surface forming the wave front. Equation (45.02) is a mathematical statement of the fact that the wave surface moves in the direction of its own normal and with the speed of

158

light. If we identify the normal to a wave surface with a light ray and consider the point of intersection of ray and front, equation (45.02) permits us to assert that in Galilean coordinates this front moves along the ray in a straight line and uniformly with the speed of light.

Side by side with the propagation of a wave front we can consider the simplest process in which a motion with a speed less than that of light is realized. This is the free motion of a mass point. In the form due to Hamilton and Jacobi its equations of motion take on a form similar to (45.02), namely

$$\left(\frac{\partial \omega}{\partial x_0'}\right)^2 - \left(\frac{\partial \omega}{\partial x_1'}\right)^2 - \left(\frac{\partial \omega}{\partial x_2'}\right)^2 - \left(\frac{\partial \omega}{\partial x_3'}\right)^2 = 1 \tag{45.03}$$

where ω is proportional to the action function. Indeed, equation (45.03) has a complete integral of the form

$$\omega = a_1 x_1' + a_2 x_2' + a_3 x_3' - \sqrt{(1 + a_1^2 + a_2^2 + a_3^2)} \cdot x_0' \tag{45.04}$$

If the derivatives of ω with respect to a_1, a_2, a_3 are equated to constants the resulting equations describe uniform rectilinear motion with less than light velocity. Thus we can take (45.02) and (45.03) to be the equations which reflect most directly the properties of space-time.

The differential expression

$$(\nabla \omega)^2 = \left(\frac{\partial \omega}{\partial x_0'}\right)^2 - \left(\frac{\partial \omega}{\partial x_1'}\right)^2 - \left(\frac{\partial \omega}{\partial x_2'}\right)^2 - \left(\frac{\partial \omega}{\partial x_3'}\right)^2 \tag{45.05}$$

which enters these equations characterizes both the properties of space-time and the physical significance of the coordinates.

If we did not know the significance of the variables (x_0', x_1', x_2', x_3') and knew only that they were in some way related to space and time (or, mathematically expressed, that they served to arithmeticize space and time) we would be able to obtain their physical interpretation by considering processes described by the equations (45.02) and (45.03). In fact this is how we proceeded in constructing the Theory of Relativity. We established the physical meaning of the variables (45.01) in two stages. First we made use of those not completely accurate concepts of space coordinates and of time which were accepted in classical pre-relativistic physics. The provisional definition of time linked the variable t with the motion of a clock or the course of any other periodic process and the definition of the space coordinates related the variables x, y and z to distances measured with the aid of solid bodies on the basis of Euclidean geometry, i.e. to a coordinate mesh. But we stressed from the start that these definitions needed to be made more precise.

Indeed, the use of clocks at different points in space requires a solution of the problem of their synchronization and the use of rigid rods for measuring large distances is not only impossible in practice but also open to objections of principle.

The definition of physical quantities is never arbitrary; it always reflects Nature with greater or lesser accuracy. Therefore it is possible to make definitions more precise only on the basis of a deeper knowledge of Nature. The particular definitions we are here concerned with, those of the space and time coordinates, are supported not only by the law of the uniform rectilinear motion of a free body, already invoked by Newton—but also by the firmly established law for the front of a light wave, i.e. by (45.02) and (45.03). These were just the lines we followed in developing the Theory of Relativity which is essentially a theory of space and time. (The designation " Relativity " has historic reasons and gives only a one-sided idea of the content of the theory.) The Lorentz transformations, so fundamental for the Theory of Relativity as the expressions of the nature of space and time and of the precise meaning of the variables x, y, z and t, are indeed derived *from* the law of wavefront propagation, together with the requirement of conservation for uniform rectilinear motion ; they are not given *a priori, before* this law is established.

Thus both the properties of space-time and the significance of the Galilean coordinates (45.01) are derived from equations (45.02) and (45.03).

Both the wave front equation and the Hamilton-Jacobi equations for a free mass point may, however, be written in more general form :

$$g^{\mu\nu}\frac{\partial x}{\partial x_\mu}\frac{\partial \omega}{\partial x_\nu} = 0 \qquad (45.06)$$

and

$$g^{\mu\nu}\frac{\partial \omega}{\partial x_\mu}\frac{\partial \omega}{\partial x_\nu} = 1 \qquad (45.07)$$

and the statement just made remains true : both the nature of space-time and the significance of the coordinates (x_0, x_1, x_2, x_3) may be determined from these equations.

Let us assume that the $g^{\mu\nu}$ are given functions of their variables. Which properties of these functions reflect properties of space-time itself and which are determined merely by the particular choice of coordinates?

If we admit that the objective properties of space-time are correctly described by the usual Theory of Relativity, these properties may be expressed by the statement that there exist Galilean coordinate systems in which equations (45.06) and (45.07) assume the forms (45.02) and (45.03).

This assertion means that there exists a substitution

$$x'_\alpha = f_\alpha(x_0, x_1, x_2, x_3) \qquad (\alpha = 0, 1, 2, 3) \qquad (45.08)$$

which reduces the expression

$$(\nabla\omega)^2 = g^{\mu\nu}\frac{\partial \omega}{\partial x_\mu}\frac{\partial \omega}{\partial x_\nu} \qquad (45.09)$$

to the form

$$(\nabla\omega)^2 = \sum_{k=0}^{3} e_k\left(\frac{\partial \omega}{\partial x'_k}\right)^2 \qquad (45.10)$$

We know from general tensor analysis that a necessary and sufficient condition for the possibility of reducing the quadratic form (45.09) to one with constant coefficients is the vanishing of the fourth rank tensor of curvature formed from the $g^{\mu\nu}$ and the related $g_{\mu\nu}$. In order that the transformed quadratic form should have one plus sign and three minus signs attached to the squared partial derivatives, it is necessary, in addition, that the inequalities stated in Section 35 be satisfied.

Thus, the equations that must be satisfied by the $g^{\mu\nu}$ are

$$R_{\mu\nu,\,\alpha\beta} = 0 \qquad (45.11)$$

and

$$g^{00} > 0 ; \quad \sum_{i,\,k=1}^{3} g^{ik}\xi_i\xi_k < 0 \qquad (45.12)$$

where ξ_1, ξ_2 and ξ_3 are arbitrary numbers. These, then, are the equations which express, independently of any choice of coordinates, the properties of space-time in the approximation in which the ordinary Theory of Relativity is valid.

If these equations are satisfied, the form of the required transformation (45.08) is determined uniquely except for a Lorentz transformation. The quantities $x'_\alpha = f_\alpha$ must therefore be interpreted as Galilean coordinates, and this also gives the interpretation of the variables (x_0, x_1, x_2, x_3), in which the equations were originally stated.

In the foregoing discussion we assumed that the $g^{\mu\nu}$ are given functions of the coordinates, but we can also adopt a different point of view and consider them as unknown functions subject only to the conditions (45.11) and (45.12) which express the nature of space-time.

Solving these equations one finds for the covariant components of the metric tensor expressions of the form

$$g_{\alpha\beta} = \sum_{k=1}^{3} e_k \frac{\partial f_k}{\partial x_\alpha} \frac{\partial f_k}{\partial x_\beta} \tag{45.13}$$

involving four arbitrary functions f_k. (The appearance of arbitrary functions in the solution is connected with the fact that the equations for the $g_{\alpha\beta}$ are covariant with respect to arbitrary coordinate transformations.) One or other choice of the arbitrary functions f_k can in no way influence the physical consequences of the theory, for it corresponds to a purely mathematical transformation of the equations from one set of independent variables to another. It is, however, appropriate to limit the choice of arbitrary functions in such a way that the permitted transformations form as restricted a group as possible and that the basic equations appear in the simplest possible form. If such a limitation is possible—and this does depend on the objective properties of space-time—the preferred coordinate systems obtained in this way will have a more direct physical interpretation. In the case here considered a Galilean system is so preferred; it is obtained if in the general solution of (45.13) we put $f_k = x_k$.

It is, nevertheless, also possible to leave the functions f_k indeterminate and to formulate the equations for physical processes without presupposing a solution of the problem of choosing independent variables. Then, for instance, the law of wave front propagation will be expressed by the system of equations (45.06), (45.11) and (45.12) for the unknown functions ω and $g^{\mu\nu}$. The law of motion of a free mass point is expressible similarly. Other examples of such a generally covariant formulation follow in the next section.

46. The Equations of Mathematical Physics in Arbitrary Coordinates

If for some system of differential equations of mathematical physics the tensor form in Galilean coordinates is known, the corresponding equations in arbitrary coordinates are obtained simply by replacing ordinary by covariant derivatives. This rule is even applicable to equations involving second or higher derivatives because, if $R_{\mu\nu,\alpha\beta} = 0$, covariant differentiations applied to any vector or tensor are commutative by the general rule (43.21).

We consider first the equations of electrodynamics.

Since the linear differential form (24.04)

$$\delta\varphi = A_\nu \, dx_\nu \tag{46.01}$$

is an invariant the components of potential occurring in it form a covariant vector even for general coordinate transformations. The differential relation (24.05) which is imposed on the components of potential can be written as

$$\nabla_{\nu} A^{\nu} = 0 \tag{46.02}$$

where the A^{ν} are the contravariant components

$$A^{\nu} = g^{\mu\nu} A_{\mu} \tag{46.03}$$

According to (41.08) an explicit form of (46.02) is

$$\frac{1}{\sqrt{(-g)}} \frac{\partial}{\partial x_{\nu}} \{\sqrt{(-g)} \cdot A^{\nu}\} = 0 \tag{46.04}$$

The connection between fields and potentials is given by

$$F_{\mu\nu} = \nabla_{\mu} A_{\nu} - \nabla_{\nu} A_{\mu} \tag{46.05}$$

but, as was already noted in Section 41, the terms in which covariant and ordinary differentiations differ, cancel when the difference in (46.05) is taken, so that for the antisymmetric field tensor we have the expression

$$F_{\mu\nu} = \frac{\partial A_{\nu}}{\partial x_{\mu}} - \frac{\partial A_{\mu}}{\partial x_{\nu}} \tag{46.06}$$

which is the same as (24.10). The first set of Maxwell-Lorentz equations, which in the usual notation has the appearance

$$\operatorname{curl} \mathbf{E} + \frac{1}{c} \frac{\partial \mathbf{H}}{\partial t} = 0 ; \qquad \operatorname{div} \mathbf{H} = 0 \tag{46.07}$$

can now be written as

$$F_{\mu\nu\sigma} = 0 \tag{46.08}$$

in agreement with (24.17), $F_{\mu\nu\sigma}$ being the totally antisymmetric† third rank tensor which is expressible in terms of $F_{\mu\nu}$ as

$$F_{\mu\nu\sigma} = \nabla_{\sigma} F_{\mu\nu} + \nabla_{\mu} F_{\nu\sigma} + \nabla_{\nu} F_{\sigma\mu} \tag{46.09}$$

in generalization of (24.12). According to (41.28) this expression is equal to

$$F_{\mu\nu\sigma} = \frac{\partial F_{\mu\nu}}{\partial x_{\sigma}} + \frac{\partial F_{\nu\sigma}}{\partial x_{\mu}} + \frac{\partial F_{\sigma\mu}}{\partial x_{\nu}} \tag{46.10}$$

because $F_{\mu\nu}$ is antisymmetric.

Thus equation (24.12) remains unchanged. We now write down the second set of Maxwell-Lorentz equations in arbitrary coordinates. In the usual notation this set appears as

$$\operatorname{div} \mathbf{E} = 4\pi\rho ; \qquad \operatorname{curl} \mathbf{H} - \frac{1}{c} \frac{\partial \mathbf{E}}{\partial t} = \frac{4\pi}{c} \mathbf{j} \tag{46.11}$$

According to (24.20) the left-hand side of (46.11) represents the contravariant divergence of the field tensor and, according to (41.25), it may be expressed in general coordinates as

$$\nabla_{\nu} F^{\mu\nu} = \frac{1}{\sqrt{(-g)}} \frac{\partial}{\partial x_{\nu}} \{\sqrt{(-g)} \cdot F^{\mu\nu}\} \tag{46.12}$$

---

† i.e. antisymmetric in all its indices.

since the field tensor is antisymmetric. On the right-hand sides of (46.11) we have $4\pi/c$ times the contravariant current vector, i.e. the vector

$$s^\mu = \frac{4\pi}{c}\rho^* u^\mu \tag{46.13}$$

where ρ^* is the invariant density and u^μ the contravariant velocity of the charge. Therefore, in general coordinates the equations (46.11) will appear as

$$\frac{1}{\sqrt{(-g)}}\frac{\partial}{\partial x_\nu}\{\sqrt{(-g)}\cdot F^{\mu\nu}\} = s^\mu = \frac{4\pi}{c}\rho^* u^\mu \tag{46.14}$$

and the law of charge conservation follows from them in the form

$$\nabla_\mu s^\mu = \frac{1}{\sqrt{(-g)}}\frac{\partial}{\partial x_\mu}\{\sqrt{(-g)}\cdot s^\mu\} = 0 \tag{46.15}$$

In order to write the generally covariant equations of motion of a charged mass point in an external field it is sufficient to find an expression for the vector of acceleration. If τ is the proper time, the four-dimensional velocity is

$$u^\nu = \frac{dx_\nu}{d\tau} \tag{46.16}$$

where
$$g_{\mu\nu}u^\mu u^\nu = c^2 \tag{46.17}$$

The acceleration vector w^ν will be given by the left-hand side of (38.34) so that

$$w^\nu = \frac{d^2 x_\nu}{d\tau^2} + \Gamma^\nu_{\alpha\beta}\frac{dx_\alpha}{d\tau}\frac{dx_\beta}{d\tau} \tag{46.18}$$

This quantity is indeed a vector and in Galilean coordinates it goes over into the ordinary expression for acceleration. As for the expression for the Lorentz force, we have already stated it in a covariant form in Section 25. Therefore the equations of motion will be

$$w_\mu = -\frac{e}{mc}u^\nu F_{\mu\nu} \tag{46.19}$$

where the w_μ are the covariant components of acceleration given by

$$w_\mu = g_{\mu\nu}w^\nu \tag{46.20}$$

In Section 33 we considered the energy tensor of the electromagnetic field and represented the density of Lorentz force as its (negative) divergence. The corresponding generally covariant equations are easy to state.

The generalizations of the expressions for the energy tensor of the electro-magnetic field are

$$U_{\mu\nu} = -\frac{1}{4\pi}g^{\alpha\beta}F_{\mu\alpha}F_{\nu\beta} + \frac{1}{16\pi}g_{\mu\nu}F_{\alpha\beta}F^{\alpha\beta} \tag{46.21}$$

and
$$U^{\mu\nu} = -\frac{1}{4\pi}g_{\alpha\beta}F^{\mu\alpha}F^{\nu\beta} + \frac{1}{16\pi}g^{\mu\nu}F_{\alpha\beta}F^{\alpha\beta} \tag{46.22}$$

Using the Maxwell-Lorentz equations (46.08) and (46.14) we get, after some calculation :

$$\nabla_\nu U^{\mu\nu} = \frac{1}{4\pi}g^{\mu\nu}F_{\nu\alpha}s^\alpha \tag{46.23}$$

On the right-hand side we have here the negative of the Lorentz force density. The generally covariant equations of motion for a continuous distribution of charge can be written as in (33.09) in the form

$$\mu^* w^\rho = -\frac{1}{4\pi} g^{\rho\sigma} F_{\sigma\alpha} s^\alpha \tag{46.24}$$

where μ^* is the invariant rest-mass density which satisfies the equation

$$\nabla_\sigma(\mu^* u^\sigma) \equiv \frac{1}{\sqrt{(-g)}} \frac{\partial}{\partial x_\sigma} \{\sqrt{(-g)} \cdot \mu^* u_\sigma\} = 0 \tag{46.25}$$

As for the acceleration w^ρ, according to (46.18), it can be written as

$$w^\rho = \frac{du^\rho}{d\tau} + \Gamma^\rho_{\sigma\alpha} u^\sigma u^\alpha \tag{46.26}$$

or

$$w^\rho = u^\sigma \frac{\partial u^\rho}{\partial x_\sigma} + \Gamma^\rho_{\sigma\alpha} u^\sigma u^\alpha \tag{46.27}$$

The last expression is equal to

$$w^\rho = u^\sigma \nabla_\sigma u^\rho \tag{46.28}$$

where $\nabla_\sigma u^\rho$ is a covariant derivative.

If in analogy to (37.01) we introduce a mass tensor for the charged particles, namely

$$\Theta^{\rho\sigma} = \frac{1}{c^2} \mu^* u^\rho u^\sigma \tag{46.29}$$

and if we use the law of rest-mass conservation (46.25) we can write

$$\mu^* w^\rho = c^2 \nabla_\sigma \Theta^{\rho\sigma} \tag{46.30}$$

In the equations of motion (46.24) we can express the left-hand side in the form (46.30) and we can use (46.23) on the right. Then we get

$$\nabla_\sigma T^{\rho\sigma} = 0 \tag{46.31}$$

where

$$c^2 T^{\rho\sigma} = \mu^* u^\rho u^\sigma + U^{\rho\sigma} \tag{46.32}$$

which is c^2 times the mass tensor of the system of particles and field.

In a similar way we can write down the generally covariant equation of motion of a continuous medium of the type of an ideal fluid. Denoting by μ^* the invariant rest-mass density, including that part of it which changes as a result of changes in energy of compression, we get, as in (32.17), for the complete energy tensor, i.e. for c^2 times the mass tensor :

$$c^2 T^{\rho\sigma} = \left(\mu^* + \frac{p}{c^2}\right) u^\rho u^\sigma - p g^{\rho\sigma} \tag{46.33}$$

This also satisfies the conservation law (46.31). We note that equation (46.25) will now no longer be satisfied but only a similar equation for a quantity ρ^* related to μ^* by (32.25) and representing the invariant density of that part of the rest-mass which is conserved.

In Section 31 we established a general rule according to which the mass tensor must be a function of the state of the system and cannot depend explicitly on the coordinates. This rule referred to Galilean coordinates, in which the $g^{\mu\nu}$ have given constant values. We can retain this rule for arbitrary coordinates if we agree to include among our functions of state the $g^{\mu\nu}$. (The identities (40.14) and (40.16), which express Ricci's lemma, will formally play the part of field equations for the $g^{\mu\nu}$.)

In all examples here considered, the mass tensor obeys this generalized rule. For instance, in (46.33) the functions of state involved are the velocity components u^ρ, the pressure p, the invariant density μ^* and the components of the metric tensor $g^{\rho\sigma}$. (Not all these functions are independent.) In the energy tensor of the electromagnetic field the functions of state are the field components $F_{\alpha\beta}$ and the $g^{\mu\nu}$.

47. A Variational Principle for the Maxwell-Lorentz System of Equations

Many equations of mathematical physics can be formulated as conditions that a certain integral, called the action integral, take on an extremal value. One of the simplest examples of such a formulation is given by the equation of a geodesic considered in Section 38. We shall now investigate the rather more complicated example of the Maxwell-Lorentz system of equations which describe the motion of a continuous charged medium, the elements of which interact by means of the electromagnetic field.

The Maxwell-Lorentz system of equations involves the field components $F_{\mu\nu}$, the components u^ν of four-dimensional velocity, the invariant rest-mass density μ^* and the invariant charge density ρ^*. They have the form

$$\frac{\partial F_{\mu\nu}}{\partial x_\lambda} + \frac{\partial F_{\lambda\mu}}{\partial x_\nu} + \frac{\partial F_{\nu\lambda}}{\partial x_\mu} = 0 \qquad (47.01)$$

$$\nabla_\nu F^{\mu\nu} = \frac{4\pi}{c} \rho^* u^\mu \qquad (47.02)$$

and

$$\mu^* w_\alpha + \frac{\rho^*}{c} F_{\alpha\beta} u^\beta = 0 \qquad (47.03)$$

Here w_α is the covariant component of the acceleration vector of which the contravariant components are

$$w^\alpha = u^\nu \nabla_\nu u^\alpha \qquad (47.04)$$

The invariant densities μ^* and ρ^* satisfy the equations

$$\nabla_\alpha (\mu^* u^\alpha) = 0 \qquad (47.05)$$

and

$$\nabla_\alpha (\rho^* u^\alpha) = 0 \qquad (47.06)$$

the second of which is a consequence of (47.02)

We must seek to construct an action integral in such a way that variations with respect to the functions involved will give rise to the equations stated.

We can simplify the task by the introduction of auxiliary functions chosen in such a way as to satisfy some of the equations identically; the variation must then give the remaining equations.

With this aim we introduce the potentials and the positions of the particles of the medium, and express the remaining functions in terms of these.

Putting

$$F_{\mu\nu} = \frac{\partial A_\nu}{\partial x_\mu} - \frac{\partial A_\mu}{\partial x_\nu} \qquad (47.07)$$

we satisfy (47.01) identically and we shall regard the potentials A_ν as functions to be varied.

For the description of the motion of the medium we introduce Lagrange variables a_1, a_2, a_3 and $a_0 = p$, where a_1, a_2 and a_3 are, for instance, the initial coordinates of a particle of the medium and p is a parameter of the nature of a time. The functions to be subjected to variation will be

$$x_\alpha = f_\alpha(p, a_1, a_2, a_3) \tag{47.08}$$

For constant a_1, a_2 and a_3 and varying p they give the motion of a particular particle of the fluid. A variation of these functions, i.e. a variation of the positions, will be called a displacement and denoted by ξ^α :

$$\xi^\alpha = \delta x_\alpha = \delta f_\alpha(p, a_1, a_2, a_3) \tag{47.09}$$

This notation is justified because such variations represent an infinitesimal contravariant vector. We shall, in general, think of the ξ^α as functions not of the Lagrange variables (p, a_1, a_2, a_3) but of the coordinates (x_0, x_1, x_2, x_3) which are related to the Lagrange variables by (47.08).

The components of the four-dimensional velocity can be expressed in terms of the Lagrange variables as

$$u^\alpha = \frac{c(\partial f_\alpha/\partial p)}{\sqrt{\{g_{\mu\nu}(\partial f_\mu/\partial p)(\partial f_\nu/\partial p)\}}} \tag{47.10}$$

so that the relation $\qquad u_\alpha u^\alpha = c^2 \tag{47.11}$

is identically satisfied. In (47.10) the $g_{\mu\nu}$ have as their arguments the $x_\alpha = f_\alpha$, so that when f_α is varied the change in the $g_{\mu\nu}$ must be taken into account.

The introduction of Lagrange variables causes the equation of continuity (47.07) to be identically satisfied in terms of the expressions (47.10) for the velocity and the expression for the invariant density determined from the relation

$$\mu^* \sqrt{(-g)} \cdot I = F(a_1, a_2, a_3) \cdot \sqrt{\left(g_{\mu\nu} \frac{\partial f_\mu}{\partial p} \frac{\partial f_\nu}{\partial p} \right)} \tag{47.12}$$

Here I is the absolute value of the Jacobian

$$I = \frac{D(x_0, x_1, x_2, x_3)}{D(p, a_1, a_2, a_3)} \tag{47.13}$$

We denote by $\delta_1 u^\alpha$ and $\delta_1 \mu^*$ the variations due to the change in the form of the functions f_α. The quantity $u^\alpha + \delta_1 u^\alpha$ is the velocity of the varied motion at the point $x_\alpha + \xi^\alpha$. On the other hand, the velocity of the varied motion at the point x_α is

$$u^\alpha + \delta u^\alpha = u^\alpha - \frac{\partial u^\alpha}{\partial x_\sigma}\xi^\sigma + \delta_1 u^\alpha \tag{47.14}$$

Thus the variation δu^α which describes the change of the velocity field is

$$\delta u^\alpha = \delta_1 u^\alpha - \frac{\partial u^\alpha}{\partial x_\sigma}\xi^\sigma \tag{47.15}$$

We note that the variation $\delta_1 u^\alpha$ is the difference of the values of two vectors taken at different points and is, therefore, not a vector. In contrast δu^α is the difference of the values of two vectors at one and the same point and is, therefore, a vector. Similarly we can introduce variations $\delta_1 \mu^*$ and $\delta \mu^*$ for the invariant density. They are related by

$$\delta \mu^* = \delta_1 \mu^* - \frac{\partial \mu^*}{\partial x^\sigma} \xi^\sigma \tag{47.16}$$

For the calculation of $\delta_1 \mu^*$ we must find the variations of both sides of (47.12). We have

$$\delta_1 \left\{ \sqrt{\left(g_{\mu\nu} \frac{\partial f_\mu}{\partial p} \frac{\partial f_\nu}{\partial p} \right)} \right\} = \frac{1}{\sqrt{\{g_{\alpha\beta}(\partial f_\alpha / \partial p)(\partial f_\beta / \partial p)\}}} \left(\frac{1}{2} \frac{\partial g_{\mu\nu}}{\partial x_\sigma} \xi^\sigma \frac{\partial f_\mu}{\partial p} \frac{\partial f_\nu}{\partial p} + g_{\mu\sigma} \frac{\partial f_\mu}{\partial p} \frac{\partial \xi^\sigma}{\partial p} \right) \tag{47.17}$$

Inserting

$$\frac{\partial \xi^\sigma}{\partial p} = \frac{\partial \xi^\sigma}{\partial x_\nu} \frac{\partial f_\nu}{\partial p} \tag{47.18}$$

and using the expression (47.10) for the velocities, we get

$$\delta_1 \left\{ \sqrt{\left(g_{\mu\nu} \frac{\partial f_\mu}{\partial p} \frac{\partial f_\nu}{\partial p} \right)} \right\} = \sqrt{\left(g_{\alpha\beta} \frac{\partial f_\alpha}{\partial p} \frac{\partial f_\beta}{\partial p} \right)} \cdot \frac{1}{c^2} u^\mu u^\nu \left(\frac{1}{2} \frac{\partial g_{\mu\nu}}{\partial x_\sigma} \xi^\sigma + g_{\mu\sigma} \frac{\partial \xi^\sigma}{\partial x_\nu} \right) \tag{47.19}$$

Using the relation

$$\nabla_\nu \xi^\sigma = \frac{\partial \xi^\sigma}{\partial x_\nu} + \Gamma^\sigma_{\nu\rho} \xi^\rho \tag{47.20}$$

for the covariant derivative we can write the foregoing equation in the form

$$\delta_1 \left\{ \sqrt{\left(g_{\mu\nu} \frac{\partial f_\mu}{\partial p} \frac{\partial f_\nu}{\partial p} \right)} \right\} = \sqrt{\left(g_{\alpha\beta} \frac{\partial f_\alpha}{\partial p} \frac{\partial f_\beta}{\partial p} \right)} \cdot \frac{1}{c^2} u_\sigma u^\nu \nabla_\nu \xi^\sigma \tag{47.21}$$

The variation of the right-hand side of (47.12) will be proportional to this expression. Further, the varied value of the Jacobian I will be

$$I + \delta_1 I = \frac{D(x_0 + \xi^0, x_1 + \xi^1, x_2 + \xi^2, x_3 + \xi^3)}{D(p, a_1, a_2, a_3)}$$

$$= \frac{D(x_0 + \xi^0, \ldots)}{D(x_0 \ldots)} I = \left(1 + \frac{\partial \xi^\alpha}{\partial x_\alpha} \right) I \tag{47.22}$$

whence

$$\delta_1 I = \frac{\partial \xi^\alpha}{\partial x_\alpha} I \tag{47.23}$$

We also have

$$\delta_1 \{ \sqrt{(-g)} \} = \frac{\partial \sqrt{(-g)}}{\partial x_\alpha} \cdot \xi^\alpha \tag{47.24}$$

and, therefore,

$$\delta_1 \{ \sqrt{(-g)} \cdot I \} = \frac{\{ \partial \sqrt{(-g)} \cdot \xi^\alpha \}}{\partial x_\alpha} \tag{47.25}$$

or

$$\delta_1 \{ \sqrt{(-g)} \cdot I \} = \nabla_\alpha \xi^\alpha \cdot \sqrt{(-g)} \cdot I \tag{47.26}$$

Using (47.21) and (47.26) we can write the variation δ_1 of the logarithms of both sides in the form

$$\frac{\delta_1\mu^*}{\mu^*} + \nabla_\sigma\xi^\sigma = \frac{1}{c^2}\,u_\sigma u^\nu\nabla_\nu\xi^\sigma \tag{47.27}$$

whence

$$\delta_1\mu^* = -\mu^*\nabla_\sigma\xi^\sigma + \frac{\mu^*}{c^2}\,u_\sigma u^\nu\nabla_\nu\xi^\sigma \tag{47.28}$$

and by (47.16)

$$\delta\mu^* = -\nabla_\sigma(\mu^*\xi^\sigma) + \frac{\mu^*}{c^2}\,u_\sigma u^\nu\nabla_\nu\xi^\sigma \tag{47.29}$$

In calculating the variation δ_1 of the expression (47.10) for u^α we can use the result (47.21). The calculation gives

$$\delta_1 u^\alpha = u^\nu\frac{\partial\xi^\alpha}{\partial x_\nu} - u^\alpha\frac{1}{c^2}\,u_\sigma u^\nu\nabla_\nu\xi^\sigma \tag{47.30}$$

and, from (47.15),

$$\delta u^\alpha = u^\sigma\frac{\partial\xi^\alpha}{\partial x_\sigma} - \frac{\partial u^\alpha}{\partial x_\sigma}\xi^\sigma - \frac{1}{c^2}\,u^\alpha u_\sigma u^\nu\nabla_\nu\xi^\sigma \tag{47.31}$$

The last expression can be written in the form

$$\delta u^\alpha = u^\sigma\nabla_\sigma\xi^\alpha - \xi^\sigma\nabla_\sigma u^\alpha - \frac{1}{c^2}\,u^\alpha u_\sigma u^\nu\nabla_\nu\xi^\sigma \tag{47.32}$$

whence it is evident that δu^α is a vector. We also have

$$u_\alpha\delta u^\alpha = 0 \tag{47.33}$$

in agreement with (47.11).

As the charge density ρ^* satisfies the same form of continuity equation (47.06) as the mass-density μ^* its variation will have the same form as (47.29), namely

$$\delta\rho^* = -\nabla_\sigma(\rho^*\xi^\sigma) + \frac{\rho^*}{c^2}\,u_\sigma u^\nu\nabla_\nu\xi^\sigma \tag{47.34}$$

Combining (47.32) and (47.34) and using (47.06) we get

$$\delta(\rho^*u^\alpha) = \nabla_\sigma(\rho^*u^\sigma\xi^\alpha - \rho^*u^\alpha\xi^\sigma) \tag{47.35}$$

or

$$\delta(\rho^*u^\alpha) = \frac{1}{\sqrt{(-g)}}\frac{\partial}{\partial x_\sigma}[\sqrt{(-g)}\cdot\rho^*(u^\sigma\xi^\alpha - u^\alpha\xi^\sigma)] \tag{47.36}$$

whence it follows that the varied current vector also satisfies an equation of continuity, as was to be expected.

We note that if the displacements ξ^σ are proportional to the velocity, so that $\xi^\sigma = \tau u^\sigma$ where τ is an arbitrary function of the coordinates, the varied velocity field and also the varied density do not differ from the non-varied ones. This can be verified by a direct calculation; putting $\xi^\sigma = \tau u^\sigma$ into our equations gives $\delta u^\alpha = 0$, $\delta\mu^* = 0$ and $\delta\rho^* = 0$.

Having calculated the variations suffered by all quantities as a result of displacements ξ^σ it is easy to verify that the field equations (47.02) and the equations of motion (47.03) represent the conditions that the integral

$$S = \int\left(c^2\mu^* - \frac{\rho^*}{c}\,u^\alpha A_\alpha + \frac{1}{16\pi}\,F_{\alpha\beta}F^{\sigma\beta}\right)\sqrt{(-g)}\cdot(dx) \tag{47.37}$$

should have an extreme value. For brevity we have written

$$(dx) = dx_0\,dx_1\,dx_2\,dx_3 \tag{47.38}$$

The integral (47.37) is to be taken over some four-dimensional region on the boundaries of which the variations ξ^σ and δA_α vanish.

We calculate first the variation of the last term in (47.37). As is readily verified

$$\delta(F_{\alpha\beta}F^{\alpha\beta}) = 2F^{\alpha\beta}\delta F_{\alpha\beta} \tag{47.39}$$

Therefore

$$\frac{1}{16\pi}\delta\int F_{\alpha\beta}F^{\alpha\beta}\sqrt{(-g)}\cdot(dx) = \frac{1}{8\pi}\int F^{\alpha\beta}\,\delta F_{\alpha\beta}\sqrt{(-g)}\cdot(dx)$$

$$= \frac{1}{8\pi}\int F^{\alpha\beta}\left(\frac{\partial\delta A_\beta}{\partial x_\alpha} - \frac{\partial\delta A_\alpha}{\partial x_\beta}\right)\sqrt{(-g)}\cdot(dx) \tag{47.40}$$

Since the tensor $F^{\alpha\beta}$ is antisymmetric the contributions of both terms in the bracket are equal, therefore we have

$$\frac{1}{16\pi}\delta\int F_{\alpha\beta}F^{\alpha\beta}\sqrt{(-g)}\cdot(dx) = -\frac{1}{4\pi}\int F^{\alpha\beta}\frac{\partial\delta A_\alpha}{\partial x_\beta}\sqrt{(-g)}\cdot(dx)$$

$$= \frac{1}{4\pi}\int\frac{\partial}{\partial x_\beta}\{\sqrt{(-g)}\cdot F^{\alpha\beta}\}\cdot\delta A_\alpha(dx) \tag{47.41}$$

after an integration by parts.

The variation of the second term in (47.37) is, by (47.36), equal to

$$-\frac{1}{c}\delta\int\rho^* u^\alpha A_\alpha\sqrt{(-g)}\cdot(dx)$$

$$= -\frac{1}{c}\int\rho^* u^\alpha\delta A_\alpha\sqrt{(-g)}\cdot(dx) - \frac{1}{c}\int A_\alpha\frac{\partial}{\partial x_\sigma}[\sqrt{(-g)}\cdot\rho^*(u^\sigma\xi^\alpha - u^\alpha\xi^\sigma)](dx) \tag{47.42}$$

Performing an integration by parts we obtain from the last integral in (47.42)

$$\frac{1}{c}\int\rho^*(u^\sigma\xi^\alpha - u^\alpha\xi^\sigma)\frac{\partial A_\alpha}{\partial x_\sigma}\sqrt{(-g)}\cdot(dx)$$

$$= -\frac{1}{c}\int\rho^* u^\alpha\xi^\sigma\left(\frac{\partial A_\alpha}{\partial x_\sigma} - \frac{\partial A_\sigma}{\partial x_\alpha}\right)\sqrt{(-g)}\cdot(dx)$$

$$= -\frac{1}{c}\int\rho^* u^\alpha F_{\sigma\alpha}\xi^\sigma\sqrt{(-g)}\cdot(dx) \tag{47.43}$$

Thus the second term gives

$$-\frac{1}{c}\delta\int\rho^* u^\alpha A_\alpha\sqrt{(-g)}\cdot(dx) = -\frac{1}{c}\int\rho^* u^\alpha(\delta A_\alpha + F_{\sigma\alpha}\xi^\sigma)\sqrt{(-g)}\cdot(dx) \tag{47.44}$$

Finally, the variation of the first term in (47.37) is, by (47.29),

$$\delta\int c^2\mu^*\sqrt{(-g)}\cdot(dx) = \int[-c^2\nabla_\sigma(\mu^*\xi^\sigma) + \mu^* u_\sigma u^\nu\nabla_\nu\xi^\sigma]\sqrt{(-g)}\cdot(dx) \tag{47.45}$$

After integration by parts the term on the right proportional to c^2 vanishes and the remaining term gives

$$\delta\int c^2\mu^*\sqrt{(-g)}\cdot(dx) = -\int\mu^*(u^\nu\nabla_\nu u_\sigma)\xi^\sigma\sqrt{(-g)}\cdot(dx) \tag{47.46}$$

For, as a result of the equation of continuity (47.05), we have

$$\mu^* u_\sigma u^\nu\nabla_\nu\xi^\sigma = \nabla_\nu(\mu^* u_\sigma u^\nu\xi^\sigma) - \mu^*(u^\nu\nabla_\nu u_\sigma)\xi^\sigma \tag{47.47}$$

and the integral of the first term is zero.

Following (47.04) we introduce the notation

$$w_\sigma = u^\nu \nabla_\nu u_\sigma \tag{47.48}$$

for the acceleration and get

$$\delta \int c^2 \mu^* \sqrt{(-g)} \cdot (dx) = - \int \mu^* w_\sigma \xi^\sigma \sqrt{(-g)} \cdot (dx) \tag{47.49}$$

Combining equations (47.41), (47.44) and (47.49) we obtain the following final expression for the variation of the action integral (47.37):

$$\delta S = - \int \left(\mu^* w_\sigma + \frac{\rho^*}{c} F_{\sigma\alpha} u^\alpha \right) \xi^\sigma \sqrt{(-g)} \cdot (dx)$$
$$+ \int \left(- \frac{\rho^*}{c} u^\alpha + \frac{1}{4\pi} \nabla_\beta F^{\alpha\beta} \right) \delta A_\alpha \sqrt{(-g)} \cdot (dx) \tag{47.50}$$

Here the coefficients of ξ^σ and of δA_α are zero by the equations of motion (47.03) and the field equations (47.02). Thus we have proved that

$$\delta S = 0 \tag{47.51}$$

Conversely, from the condition that the action integral

$$S = \int \left(c^2 \mu^* - \frac{\rho^*}{c} u^\alpha A_\alpha + \frac{1}{16\pi} F_{\alpha\beta} F^{\alpha\beta} \right) \sqrt{(-g)} \cdot (dx) \tag{47.37}$$

be an extremum and, using the fact that the variations ξ^σ and δA_α are arbitrary, we can conclude that the equations of motion and the field equations are satisfied.

The circumstance that a variation of the form $\xi^\sigma = \tau u^\sigma$ does not change the velocity field, gives rise to the relation

$$u^\sigma \left(\mu^* w_\sigma + \frac{\rho^*}{c} F_{\sigma\alpha} u^\alpha \right) = 0 \tag{47.52}$$

which is valid identically, i.e. independently of the equations of motion being satisfied. This relation shows that of the four equations of motion only three are independent. The fact that a variation of the form $\delta A_\alpha = \delta \, \partial\varphi/\partial x_\alpha$ does not change the electromagnetic field gives rise to the relation

$$\nabla_\alpha \left(- \frac{\rho^*}{c} u^\alpha + \frac{1}{4\pi} \nabla_\beta F^{\alpha\beta} \right) = 0 \tag{47.53}$$

which is also identically fulfilled, i.e. independently of the field equations. This relation shows that the four field equations are not independent but are related by (47.53).

48. The Variational Principle and the Energy Tensor

In Section 45 we pointed out that in the formulation of the Theory of Relativity in arbitrary coordinates two points of view are possible. From the first point of view the $g_{\mu\nu}$ are considered as given functions of the coordinates which are obtained by the usual tensor rule from their Galilean values. From the other the $g_{\mu\nu}$ are thought of as unknown functions subject to the equation

$$R_{\mu\nu, \alpha\beta} = 0 \tag{48.01}$$

and also to some inequalities which we have stated repeatedly.

When calculating the variation of the action integral we adopted the first point of view and, accordingly, the form of the functions $g_{\mu\nu}$ was not varied. We can, however, adopt the second point of view and vary the $g_{\mu\nu}$ also. This will lead to the appearance of a third term in the expression (47.50) for δS in addition to the two terms corresponding to the variations ξ^σ and δA_α, a term arising from the variation of the $g_{\mu\nu}$. We shall now calculate this term.

We shall denote the variations of quantities due to the variation of the $g_{\mu\nu}$ by the symbol δ_g. In (47.12) neither the Jacobian I nor the function F contains the $g_{\mu\nu}$, therefore

$$\frac{\delta_g\{\mu^*\sqrt{(-g)}\}}{\mu^*\sqrt{(-g)}} = \frac{\partial f_\mu/\partial p \;\partial f_\nu/\partial p \;\delta g_{\mu\nu}}{2g_{\alpha\beta}(\partial f_\alpha/\partial p)(\partial f_\beta/\partial p)} = \frac{1}{2c^2}\, u^\mu u^\nu\, \delta g_{\mu\nu} \qquad (48.02)$$

and consequently

$$\delta_g\{\mu^*\sqrt{(-g)}\} = \frac{\mu^*\sqrt{(-g)}}{2c^2}\, u^\mu u^\nu\, \delta g_{\mu\nu} \qquad (48.03)$$

Further, if we multiply (47.10) by (47.12) we obtain an expression that does not contain the $g_{\mu\nu}$; the variation of this expression with respect to $g_{\mu\nu}$ will be zero. Since the charge density ρ^* satisfies the same continuity equation as the mass density μ^*, the variation of the corresponding expression with μ^* replaced by ρ^* is also zero. Thus

$$\delta_g\{\rho^*u^\alpha\sqrt{(-g)}\} = 0 \qquad (48.04)$$

and also

$$\delta_g\{\rho^*u^\alpha A_\alpha\sqrt{(-g)}\} = 0 \qquad (48.05)$$

as the A_α are now not varied.

Further,

$$\delta_g(F_{\alpha\beta}F^{\alpha\beta}) = F_{\alpha\beta}\,\delta_g F^{\alpha\beta} \qquad (48.06)$$

since the $F_{\alpha\beta}$ are not varied, but only the $F^{\alpha\beta}$, for they are connected with the $F_{\alpha\beta}$ by the relations

$$F^{\alpha\beta} = g^{\alpha\mu}g^{\beta\nu}F_{\mu\nu} \qquad (48.07)$$

which contain the $g_{\mu\nu}$. The calculation gives

$$F_{\alpha\beta}\,\delta_g F^{\alpha\beta} = 2F_{\alpha\beta}F^{\alpha\mu}g_{\mu\nu}\,\delta g^{\beta\nu} = -2F_{\alpha\beta}F^{\alpha\mu}g^{\beta\nu}\,\delta g_{\mu\nu} \qquad (48.08)$$

Since

$$\frac{1}{\sqrt{(-g)}}\,\delta_g\sqrt{(-g)} = \frac{1}{2}\,g^{\mu\nu}\,\delta g_{\mu\nu} \qquad (48.09)$$

we get

$$\frac{1}{\sqrt{(-g)}}\,\delta\{F_{\alpha\beta}F^{\alpha\beta}\sqrt{(-g)}\} = \left(-2F_{\alpha\beta}F^{\alpha\mu}g^{\beta\nu} + \frac{1}{2}F_{\alpha\beta}F^{\alpha\beta}g^{\mu\nu}\right)\delta g_{\mu\nu} = 8\pi U^{\mu\nu}\,\delta g_{\mu\nu} \qquad (48.10)$$

where $U^{\mu\nu}$ is the expression (46.22) for the electromagnetic energy tensor.

Equations (48.03), (48.05) and (48.10) result in the following additional term in the variation of the action integral

$$\delta_g S = \frac{1}{2}\int (\mu^* u^\mu u^\nu + U^{\mu\nu})\,\delta g_{\mu\nu}\,\sqrt{(-g)}\cdot(dx) \qquad (48.11)$$

But according to (46.32) the expression in brackets under the integral is c^2 times the mass tensor of the system of particles and field:

$$c^2 T^{\mu\nu} = \mu^* u^\mu u^\nu + U^{\mu\nu} \qquad (48.12)$$

Thus, the expression for the mass tensor appears automatically when the action integral is varied with respect to the components of the metric tensor.

The complete variation of the action integral with respect to all functions involved in it is

$$\delta S = \frac{1}{2} \int (\mu^* u^\mu u^\nu + U^{\mu\nu}) \delta g_{\mu\nu} \sqrt{(-g)} \cdot (dx)$$

$$- \int \left(\mu^* w_\sigma + \frac{\rho^*}{c} F_{\sigma\alpha} u^\alpha \right) \xi^\sigma \sqrt{(-g)} \cdot (dx)$$

$$+ \int \left(-\frac{\rho^*}{c} u^\alpha + \frac{1}{4\pi} \nabla_\beta F^{\alpha\beta} \right) \delta A_\alpha \sqrt{(-g)} \cdot (dx) \qquad (48.13)$$

The variations ξ^σ and δA_α were completely arbitrary; equating their coefficients to zero gave us the equation of motion and the field equations. The variations $\delta g_{\mu\nu}$, however, are not arbitrary because the functions $g_{\mu\nu}$ are subject to the condition

$$R_{\mu\nu,\,\alpha\beta} = 0 \qquad (48.01)$$

We shall now express the variations $\delta g_{\mu\nu}$ in terms of independent arbitrary quantities.

The most general form of functions $g_{\mu\nu}$ which satisfy (48.01) can be obtained by coordinate transformation starting from the Galilean values of these quantities, therefore all possible forms of the $g_{\mu\nu}$ compatible with (48.01) can also be obtained one from the other by coordinate transformations. Thus the permissible infinitesimal variations of these functions must correspond to infinitesimal coordinate transformations.

Let an infinitesimal coordinate transformation be written in the form

$$x'_\alpha = x_\alpha + \eta^\alpha \qquad (48.14)$$

where η^α is an arbitrary infinitesimal vector whose components are functions of x_0, x_1, x_2 and x_3. According to the general transformation formula for tensors we have

$$g'^{\mu\nu}(x') = g^{\alpha\beta}(x) \frac{\partial x'_\mu}{\partial x_\alpha} \frac{\partial x'_\nu}{\partial x_\beta} \qquad (48.15)$$

and, ignoring higher order infinitesimals,

$$g'^{\mu\nu}(x') = g^{\mu\nu}(x) + g^{\mu\alpha} \frac{\partial \eta^\nu}{\partial x_\alpha} + g^{\nu\alpha} \frac{\partial \eta^\mu}{\partial x_\alpha} \qquad (48.16)$$

To obtain the variation, i.e. the change of the form of the functions $g^{\mu\nu}$, one must compare $g'^{\mu\nu}$ and $g^{\mu\nu}$ for the same values of the arguments.

As we have

$$g'^{\mu\nu}(x') = g'^{\mu\nu}(x) + \frac{\partial g^{\mu\nu}}{\partial x_\sigma} \eta^\sigma \qquad (48.17)$$

(having replaced $g'^{\mu\nu}$ by $g^{\mu\nu}$ in the correction term), it follows that

$$g'^{\mu\nu}(x) - g^{\mu\nu}(x) = \delta g^{\mu\nu}(x) = g^{\mu\alpha} \frac{\partial \eta^\nu}{\partial x_\alpha} + g^{\nu\alpha} \frac{\partial \eta^\mu}{\partial x_\alpha} - \frac{\partial g^{\mu\nu}}{\partial x_\sigma} \eta^\sigma \qquad (48.18)$$

This equation can be written as

$$\delta g^{\mu\nu} = g^{\mu\alpha} \nabla_\alpha \eta^\nu + g^{\nu\alpha} \nabla_\alpha \eta^\mu \qquad (48.19)$$

or, more briefly, as

$$\delta g^{\mu\nu} = \nabla^\mu \eta^\nu + \nabla^\nu \eta^\mu \qquad (48.20)$$

In the case of the Maxwell-Lorentz equation we verified this by direct calculation (see equation (48.12)).

Let us illustrate the above reasoning with another example, namely, the equations of hydrodynamics. In this case the action integral will be of the form

$$S = \int (\rho^* c^2 + \rho^* \Pi) \sqrt{(-g)} \cdot (dx) \tag{48.28}$$

Here ρ^* is the invariant density of that part of the rest mass which does not change in the motion and which satisfies the conservation law

$$\nabla_\nu(\rho^* u^\nu) = 0 \tag{48.29}$$

(see Section 32) and Π is the potential energy per unit mass of elastic compression of the fluid

$$\Pi = \int\limits_0^p \frac{dp}{\rho^*} - \frac{p}{\rho^*} \; ; \qquad d\Pi = \frac{p \, d\rho^*}{\rho^{*2}} \tag{48.30}$$

p being the pressure.

It is simple to calculate the variation of the integral S, from the expressions for the variation of density derived above. Using equations (47.29), (48.03) and (48.09), in which we now write ρ^* instead of μ^* the total variation becomes

$$\delta\rho^* = -\nabla_\sigma(\rho^* \xi^\sigma) + \frac{\rho^*}{c^2} u_\sigma u^\nu \nabla_\nu \xi^\sigma + \frac{\rho^*}{2}\left(\frac{u^\mu u^\nu}{c^2} - g^{\mu\nu}\right)\delta g_{\mu\nu} \tag{48.31}$$

and, as before,

$$\frac{\delta\sqrt{(-g)}}{\sqrt{(-g)}} = \frac{1}{2} g^{\mu\nu} \delta g_{\mu\nu} \tag{48.32}$$

Putting

$$F(\rho^*) = \rho^* c^2 + \rho^* \Pi \tag{48.33}$$

we have

$$\delta S = \delta \int F(\rho^*) \sqrt{(-g)} \cdot (dx) = \int \left[F'(\rho^*) \delta\rho^* + F(\rho^*) \frac{\delta\{\sqrt{(-g)}\}}{\sqrt{(-g)}} \right] \sqrt{(-g)} \cdot (dx) \tag{48.34}$$

Inserting (48.31) and (48.32) and integrating by parts we get

$$\delta S = \frac{1}{2} \int \left[(F - \rho^* F') g^{\mu\nu} + \rho^* F' \frac{u^\mu u^\nu}{c^2} \right] \delta g_{\mu\nu} \sqrt{(-g)} \cdot (dx)$$

$$+ \int \left[\rho F'' \left(\frac{\partial\rho^*}{\partial x_\sigma} - \frac{u_\sigma u^\nu}{c^2} \frac{\partial\rho^*}{\partial x_\nu} \right) - \frac{1}{c^2} \rho^* F' w_\sigma \right] \xi^\sigma \sqrt{(-g)} \cdot (dx) \tag{48.35}$$

where w_σ is the acceleration (47.48). Using the relations

$$\rho^* F' - F = p \; ; \qquad \rho^* F'' d\rho^* = dp \tag{48.36}$$

which follow from (48.30) and (48.33) we can replace (48.35) by

$$\delta S = \frac{1}{2} \int \left\{ -pg^{\mu\nu} + \left[\rho^* + \frac{1}{c^2}(\rho^* \Pi + p) \right] u^\mu u^\nu \right\} \delta g_{\mu\nu} \sqrt{(-g)} \cdot (dx)$$

$$+ \int \left\{ \frac{\partial p}{\partial x_\sigma} - \frac{u_\sigma u^\nu}{c^2} \frac{\partial p}{\partial x_\nu} - \left[\rho^* + \frac{1}{c^2}(\rho^* \Pi + p) \right] w_\sigma \right\} \xi^\sigma \sqrt{(-g)} \cdot (dx) \tag{48.37}$$

The analogous equation

$$\delta g_{\mu\nu} = -\nabla_\mu \eta_\nu - \nabla_\nu \eta_\mu \qquad (48.21)$$

can be obtained either independently by the same method or by use of the relation $g_{\mu\alpha} g^{\mu\nu} = \delta_\alpha^\nu$.

Rewriting (48.11) as

$$\delta_g S = \frac{c^2}{2} \int T^{\mu\nu} \delta g_{\mu\nu} \sqrt{(-g)} \cdot (dx) \qquad (48.22)$$

and inserting (48.21) we get

$$\delta_g S = -\frac{c^2}{2} \int T^{\mu\nu}(\nabla_\mu \eta_\nu + \nabla_\nu \eta_\mu) \sqrt{(-g)} \cdot (dx) = -c^2 \int T^{\mu\nu} \nabla_\nu \eta_\mu \sqrt{(-g)} \cdot (dx) \qquad (48.23)$$

since the tensor $T_{\mu\nu}$ is symmetric. After integration by parts we get

$$\delta_g S = c^2 \int (\nabla_\nu T^{\mu\nu}) \eta_\mu \sqrt{(-g)} \cdot (dx) \qquad (48.24)$$

If it is assumed that the divergence of the mass tensor vanishes, it can be concluded from (48.24) that the action integral also has an extremal value for permissible variations of the $g_{\mu\nu}$. However, a reversal of the argument is also possible and the equation

$$\nabla_\nu T^{\mu\nu} = 0 \qquad (48.25)$$

can be deduced from the properties of the action integral, $T^{\mu\nu}$ being the tensor that appears as the coefficient of $\delta g_{\mu\nu}$ in the expression for the complete variation of S. For the action integral is a scalar, or invariant, and therefore does not change for an infinitesimal or any other coordinate transformation. The expression for its complete variation

$$\delta S = c^2 \int (\nabla_\nu T^{\mu\nu}) \eta_\mu \sqrt{(-g)} \cdot (dx)$$
$$- \int \left(\mu^* w_\sigma + \frac{\rho^*}{c} F_{\sigma\alpha} u^\alpha \right) \xi^\sigma \sqrt{(-g)} \cdot (dx)$$
$$+ \int \left(-\frac{\rho^*}{c} u^\alpha + \frac{1}{4\pi} \nabla_\beta F^{\alpha\beta} \right) \delta A_\alpha \sqrt{(-g)} \cdot (dx) \qquad (48.26)$$

must necessarily vanish, if the variations ξ^σ and δA_α occur as a result of the infinitesimal transformation η_μ. This conclusion follows from the invariance property alone and is not dependent on whether S is the action integral or any other invariant integral. But, if S is the action integral, the coefficients of ξ^σ and δA_α are separately equal to zero. Therefore, the remaining terms in S must also be zero and we have

$$\delta_g S = c^2 \int (\nabla_\nu T^{\mu\nu}) \eta_\mu \sqrt{(-g)} \cdot (dx) = 0 \qquad (48.27)$$

for arbitrary η_μ. Hence (48.25) follows.

The fact that the tensor $T^{\mu\nu}$, defined as the coefficient of $\delta g_{\mu\nu}$, is the mass tensor or proportional to it, follows from the uniqueness of the mass tensor established in Section 31, under the condition that its components are functions of the state of the system ; here the $g_{\mu\nu}$ are to be included among such functions.

Hence we conclude that the equations of motion have the form

$$\left[\rho^* + \frac{1}{c^2}\left(\rho^*\Pi + p\right)\right]w_\sigma = \frac{\partial p}{\partial x_\sigma} - \frac{u_\sigma u^\nu}{c^2}\frac{\partial p}{\partial x_\nu} \qquad (48.38)$$

and that the energy tensor is

$$c^2 T^{\mu\nu} = \left[\rho^* + \frac{1}{c^2}\left(\rho^*\Pi + p\right)\right]u^\mu u^\nu - pg^{\mu\nu} \qquad (48.39)$$

We know also that the divergence of this tensor vanishes.

These expressions are a generalization of (32.29) and (32.28) and reduce to them in Galilean coordinates.

In conclusion, we remark that, mathematically speaking, by no means every system of equations can be derived from a variational principle. The fact that the basic equations of mathematical physics can be so derived reveals a remarkable property possessed by them.

49. The Integral Form of the Conservation Laws in Arbitrary Coordinates

As we know, the mass tensor $T^{\mu\nu}$ satisfies the equation

$$\nabla_\nu T^{\mu\nu} = 0 \qquad (49.01)$$

which, for a closed conservative system, must express the conservation laws for energy and momentum and also the conservation law for angular momentum and the law of mass centre motion.

In explicit form (49.01) can be written as (see (41.24)) :

$$\frac{\partial T^{\mu\nu}}{\partial x_\nu} + \Gamma^\mu_{\rho\nu} T^{\rho\nu} + \Gamma^\nu_{\rho\nu} T^{\mu\rho} = 0 \qquad (49.02)$$

or, if the first and last terms are combined,

$$\frac{1}{\sqrt{(-g)}}\frac{\partial\{\sqrt{(-g)}\cdot T^{\mu\nu}\}}{\partial x_\nu} + \Gamma^\mu_{\rho\nu} T^{\rho\nu} = 0 \qquad (49.03)$$

Owing to the fact that in (49.03) there is a term remaining outside the sign of differentiation the passage from the differential to the integral form of the conservation laws is not quite as obvious in general as in Galilean coordinates (see Section 31). Therefore, we shall discuss in more detail the question of the existence of integral forms of the conservation laws.

We introduce a vector φ_μ and integrate the equation

$$\nabla_\nu(T^{\mu\nu}\varphi_\mu) = \frac{1}{\sqrt{(-g)}}\frac{\partial}{\partial x_\nu}\{\sqrt{(-g)}\cdot T^{\mu\nu}\varphi_\mu\} \qquad (49.04)$$

over a three-dimensional volume on the boundaries of which $T^{\mu\nu}$ vanishes. We get

$$\int \nabla_\nu\left(T^{\mu\nu}\varphi_\mu\right)\sqrt{(-g)}\cdot dx_1\,dx_2\,dx_3 = \frac{d}{dx_0}\int T^{\mu 0}\varphi_\mu\sqrt{(-g)}\cdot dx_1\,dx_2\,dx_3 \qquad (49.05)$$

If $T^{\mu\nu}$ is the mass tensor it is symmetric and of vanishing divergence. For such a tensor the previous equation can be written as

$$\frac{d}{dx_0} \int T^{\mu 0}\varphi_\mu \sqrt{(-g)} \cdot dx_1\,dx_2\,dx_3$$

$$= \frac{1}{2} \int T^{\mu\nu}(\nabla_\nu\varphi_\mu + \nabla_\mu\varphi_\nu) \sqrt{(-g)} \cdot dx_1\,dx_2\,dx_3 \quad (49.06)$$

The quantity $\qquad\qquad I = \int T^{\mu 0}\varphi_\mu\sqrt{(-g)} \cdot dx_1\,dx_2\,dx_3 \qquad\qquad (49.07)$

will be constant, i.e. will be independent of x_0, the coordinate that has the character of time, if the vector φ_μ satisfies the equations

$$\nabla_\nu\varphi_\mu + \nabla_\mu\varphi_\nu = 0 \qquad\qquad (49.08)$$

We first discuss these equations in the general case that the fourth order curvature term is not necessarily zero.

We put

$$\nabla_\nu\varphi_\mu = \varphi_{\mu\nu} \qquad\qquad (49.09)$$

By (49.08) the $\varphi_{\mu\nu}$ form an antisymmetric tensor; we calculate its covariant derivative. By (49.08) we can write

$$\nabla_\sigma\varphi_{\mu\nu} = \frac{1}{2}(\nabla_\mu\nabla_\nu - \nabla_\nu\nabla_\mu)\varphi_\sigma + \frac{1}{2}(\nabla_\sigma\nabla_\nu - \nabla_\nu\nabla_\sigma)\varphi_\mu - \frac{1}{2}(\nabla_\sigma\nabla_\mu - \nabla_\mu\nabla_\sigma)\varphi_\nu$$

$$(49.10)$$

Using the relation (43.16) for the difference of covariant derivatives and the symmetry properties of the tensor $R_{\mu\nu,\alpha\beta}$ we get

$$\nabla_\sigma\varphi_{\mu\nu} = R^\rho_{\sigma,\mu\nu}\varphi_\rho \qquad\qquad (49.11)$$

Thus the equation (49.08) can be replaced by the system (49.09) and (49.11) which is equivalent to a system of total differential equations.† It can be shown that this system will be completely integrable in the case that

$$R_{\mu\nu,\,\alpha\beta} = K\,(g_{\nu\alpha}g_{\mu\beta} - g_{\mu\alpha}g_{\nu\beta}) \qquad\qquad (49.12)$$

where K is a constant. A space in which the curvature tensor has the form (49.12) is called a space of constant curvature; it is a four-dimensional generalization of Lobachevsky space. The constant K is called the constant of curvature.

If the conditions of complete integrability are fulfilled, the values of the ten functions φ_μ and $\varphi_{\mu\nu}$ are determined throughout space by their values at one point, so that the general solution of the system (49.09) and (49.11) involves ten constants.

We are interested in the case

$$R_{\mu\nu,\,\alpha\beta} = 0 \qquad\qquad (49.13)$$

which is obtained from (49.12) by taking $K = 0$. (For this reason a space for which $R_{\mu\nu,\alpha\beta} = 0$ is called a space of zero curvature, or a flat space.)

In flat space-time, with which we are concerned in the Theory of Relativity, we can immediately indicate ten integrals of the system (49.08). Let x'_0, x'_1, x'_2 and x'_3 be Galilean coordinates. We can then introduce the four vectors

$$\varphi^{(0)}_\mu = \frac{\partial x'_0}{\partial x_\mu}; \qquad \varphi^{(1)}_\mu = \frac{\partial x'_1}{\partial x_\mu}; \qquad \varphi^{(2)}_\mu = \frac{\partial x'_2}{\partial x_\mu}; \qquad \varphi^{(3)}_\mu = \frac{\partial x'_3}{\partial x_\mu} \qquad (49.14)$$

† An exposition of the theory of such systems can be found in Reference [14].

(These quantities are vectors with respect to the unprimed coordinates x_0, x_1, x_2, x_3; the Galilean coordinates are to be considered as scalars.) By virtue of (42.16) each of the four vectors (49.14) satisfies

$$\nabla_\nu \varphi_\mu^{(\alpha)} = 0 ; \qquad (\alpha = 0, 1, 2, 3) \tag{49.15}$$

and, therefore, also equation (49.08).

Further, we can introduce the six vectors

$$\varphi_\mu^{(\alpha\beta)} = x_\alpha' \frac{\partial x_\beta'}{\partial x_\mu} - x_\beta' \frac{\partial x_\alpha'}{\partial x_\mu} \tag{49.16}$$

each of which satisfies

$$\nabla_\nu \varphi_\mu^{(\alpha\beta)} + \nabla_\mu \varphi_\nu^{(\alpha\beta)} = 0 \tag{49.17}$$

which is the same as (49.08).

Insertion of the vectors (49.14) into (49.07) and multiplication by c gives the constant integrals

$$P'^\alpha = c \int T^{\mu 0} \frac{\partial x_\alpha'}{\partial x_\mu} \sqrt{(-g)} \cdot dx_1 \, dx_2 \, dx_3 \tag{49.18}$$

and insertion of the vectors (49.16) into the same expression gives the further constant integrals

$$M'^{\alpha\beta} = c \int T^{\mu 0} \left(x_\alpha' \frac{\partial x_\beta'}{\partial x_\mu} - x_\beta' \frac{\partial x_\alpha'}{\partial x_\mu} \right) \sqrt{(-g)} \cdot dx_1 \, dx_2 \, dx_3 \tag{49.19}$$

Comparing these expressions with their counterparts in Galilean coordinates (equations (31.02), (31.03) and (31.08), (31.09)) it is simple to see their physical meaning. The quantity P'^0 is the energy divided by c, or the mass multiplied by c, the P'^i ($i = 1, 2, 3$) are the components of momentum. Further, the M'^{i0} are the integrals of mass centre motion and the M'^{ik} the integrals of angular momentum.

The P'^α are components of a constant vector and the $M'^{\alpha\beta}$ the components of a constant antisymmetric tensor with respect to a Galilean coordinate system. But to a constant vector or tensor in a Galilean system there corresponds in an arbitrary coordinate system a *free* vector or tensor, i.e. one all of whose covariant derivatives vanish. Therefore, in an arbitrary coordinate system we can relate to the integrals of motion the free vector

$$P_\nu = \sum_{\alpha=0}^3 e_\alpha P'^\alpha \frac{\partial x_\alpha'}{\partial x_\nu} \tag{49.20}$$

and the free antisymmetric tensor

$$M_{\mu\nu} = \sum_{\alpha,\beta=0}^3 e_\alpha e_\beta M'^{\alpha\beta} \frac{\partial x_\alpha'}{\partial x_\mu} \frac{\partial x_\beta'}{\partial x_\nu} \tag{49.21}$$

These quantities will be functions of the space and time coordinates satisfying

$$\nabla_\sigma P_\nu = 0 ; \qquad \nabla_\sigma M_{\mu\nu} = 0 \tag{49.22}$$

The values of these functions at all points are determined by their values at any one point. Therefore, the number of constants on which the P_ν and $M_{\mu\nu}$ depend will be equal to the number of these quantities, namely, ten. The constants of motion P'^α and $M'^{\alpha\beta}$ are just these constants.

In the above discussion the role of the Galilean coordinates was purely auxiliary, they were simply used as variables in which to express the various vectors corresponding to the different integrals of equation (49.08). It is, of course, much simpler to conduct the whole argument in terms of Galilean coordinates, as was done in Chapter II. However, the very aim of the more complicated discussion was to show that even the integral form of the conservation laws can be derived directly from equations written in arbitrary coordinates.

The formulae given in the last two sections of this chapter enable us to formulate the condition for the space-time to be uniform. This can be done in the following way.

As stated in the Introduction, space-time is of maximum uniformity if a ten-parametric transformation group exists that leaves the functional form of the $g_{\mu\nu}$ invariant. (This means that the $g_{\mu\nu}$ transformed according to the tensor rule are the same functions of the new variables as the original $g_{\mu\nu}$ were of the old.) For an infinitesimal transformation (48.14) belonging to this group we have $\delta g_{\mu\nu} = 0$, where $\delta g_{\mu\nu}$ is given by (48.21). But if in the equations $\delta g_{\mu\nu} = 0$ we replace the η_ν by the φ_ν the equations will take on the same form as that of the equations (49.08), which are related to the conservation laws. For these latter equations the condition for total integrability is (49.12). Thus this equation will also be the condition for integrability of the equations $\delta g_{\mu\nu} = 0$.

We see that the necessary and sufficient conditions for space-time to be uniform coincide with the conditions for the existence of an integral form of the conservation laws for the mass tensor. Therefore the conservation laws for those forms of energy which are included in the mass tensor are directly connected with the uniformity of space-time.

49*. Remark on the Relativity Principle and the Covariance of Equations

At the beginning of this book (Section 6) we gave a formulation of the principle of relativity, which together with the postulate that the velocity of light has a limiting character, may be made the basis of relativity theory. We shall now investigate in more detail the question of the connection of the physical principle of relativity with the requirement that the equations be covariant. We have already touched on this problem in the Introduction.

In the first place, we shall attempt to give a generally covariant formulation of the principle of relativity, without as yet making this concept more precise. In its most general form the principle of relativity states the equivalence of the coordinate systems (or frames of reference) that belong to a certain class and are related by transformations of the form

$$x'_\alpha = f_\alpha(x_0, x_1, x_2, x_3) \tag{49*.01}$$

which may be stated more briefly as

$$x' = f(x) \tag{49*.02}$$

It is essential to remember that, in addition to the group of permissible transformations, the class of coordinate systems must be characterized by certain supplementary conditions.

Thus, for instance, if we consider Lorentz transformations, it is self-evident that these linear transformations must connect not any arbitrary coordinates, but only the Galilean coordinates in two inertial reference frames. To consider linear transformations between any other (non-Galilean) coordinates has no sense, because the Galilean principle of relativity has no validity in relation to such artificial linear transformations. On the other hand, if one introduces any other variables in place of the Galilean coordinates, a Lorentz transformation can evidently be expressed in terms of these variables, but then the transformation formulae will have a more complicated form.

Let us now state more precisely what is meant in the formulation of the principle of relativity by equivalence of reference frames. Two reference frames (x) and (x') may be called *physically equivalent* if *phenomena proceed in the same way in them*. This means that if a possible process is described in the coordinates (x) by the functions

$$\varphi_1(x), \ \varphi_2(x), \ \ldots, \ \varphi_n(x) \tag{49*.03}$$

then there is another possible process which is describable by *the same* functions

$$\varphi_1(x'), \ \varphi_2(x'), \ \ldots, \ \varphi_n(x') \tag{49*.04}$$

in the coordinates (x'). Conversely any process of the form (49.04) in the second system corresponds to a possible process of the form (49*.03) in the first system. Such a definition of corresponding processes agrees fully with that given in Section 6. Thus *a relativity principle is a statement concerning the existence of corresponding processes in a set of reference frames of a certain class*; the systems of this class are then accepted as *equivalent*. It is clear from this definition that both the principle of relativity itself and the equivalence of two reference frames are physical concepts, and the statement that the one or the other is valid involves a definite physical hypothesis and is not just conventional. In addition, it follows that the very notion of a " principle of relativity " becomes well defined only when a definite class of frames of reference has been singled out. In the usual theory of relativity this class is that of inertial systems.

The functions (49*.03) or (49*.04) describing a physical process will be called field functions or functions of state. We have already indicated in Section 46 that in a generally covariant formulation of the equations describing physical processes the components $g_{\mu\nu}$ of the metric tensor must be included among the functions of state. In the example there discussed we then get the following collection of field functions:

$$F_{\mu\nu}(x), \qquad j_\nu(x), \qquad g_{\mu\nu}(x) \tag{49*.05}$$

i.e. the electromagnetic field, the current vector and the metric tensor. The requirement entering the formulation of a principle of relativity that in two equivalent reference frames corresponding phenomena should proceed in the same way applies equally to the metric tensor. Thus if we compare two corresponding phenomena in two physically equivalent reference frames, then for the first phenomenon, described in the old coordinates, not only the components of electro-magnetic field and of current density, but also the components of the metric tensor must have the same mathematical form as for the second phenomenon described in the new coordinates.

What can be concluded further will depend on whether we assume that the metric is fixed or whether we take into consideration phenomena which themselves influence the metric. In the usual theory of relativity described in the previous chapters it is assumed that the metric is given once and for all and does not depend on any physical processes. The generally covariant formulation of the theory of relativity given in the present chapter does not change anything in this. As long as the assumption remains in force that the character of space-time is Galilean and the $g_{\mu\nu}$ are introduced only to achieve general covariance, these quantities will depend only on the choice of coordinate system, not on the nature of the physical process discussed; they are functions of state only in a formal sense. In the theory of gravitation on the other hand, to the description of which we turn in the following chapter, a different assumption is made concerning the nature of space-time. There the $g_{\mu\nu}$ are functions of state, not only in a formal sense, but in fact: they describe a certain physical field, namely the field of gravitation. However, when discussing small-scale processes which do not influence the motion of heavy masses one can also assume that the metric is fixed (though not Galilean).

To give a definite meaning to the principle of relativity in such circumstances, it is essential to specify more closely not only the class of coordinate systems, but also the nature of the physical processes for which the principle is being formulated.

We shall first start from the assumption that the metric is fixed ("rigid"), or else that it may be considered as fixed for a certain class of physical processes. We return to the above definition of corresponding phenomena in two physically equivalent coordinate systems, according to which all field functions, including the components of the metric tensor, must have the same mathematical form for the first process described in the old coordinates as for the second process described in the new coordinates. If the $g_{\mu\nu}$ are independent of the nature of the physical phenomenon, then in relation to these quantities we need not make a distinction between the first and second process, and need consider only transformations of the coordinates. But then the quantities

$$g_{\mu\nu}(x) \qquad \text{and} \qquad g'_{\mu\nu}(x') \qquad\qquad (49^*.06)$$

will be connected by the tensor transformation rule; the requirement of the relativity principle that they should have one and the same mathematical form reduces (for infinitesimal coordinate transformations) to the equations $\delta g_{\mu\nu} = 0$ discussed in Sections 48 and 49.

We know that the most general class of transformations that satisfies these equations contains 10 parameters and is possible only in uniform space-time, where the relation

$$R_{\mu\nu,\ \alpha\beta} = K \cdot (g_{\nu\alpha} g_{\mu\beta} - g_{\mu\alpha} g_{\nu\beta}) \qquad\qquad (49^*.07)$$

(see equation (49.12)) is valid. If in these relations K is zero, the space-time is Galilean and the transformations in question are Lorentz transformations, except that possibly they may be written down in other (non-Galilean) coordinates.

Thus *with the rigidity assumption for the metric, the principle of relativity implies the uniformity of space-time*, and if the additional condition $K = 0$ holds, we obtain a Galilean metric in appropriate coordinates. The relativity principle in general form then reduces to the Galilean relativity principle. As for the condition $K = 0$, it results in an additional uniformity of space-time; if the scale of the Galilean coordinates is changed, then the scale of the elementary interval changes in the same proportion.† This property implies in turn that there is no absolute scale for space-time, unlike the absolute scale that exists for velocities in terms of the velocity of light; the absence of an absolute scale for space-time leads conversely to the equation $K = 0$.

If we now go over to discuss phenomena which may themselves influence the metric, we must reckon with the possibility that under certain conditions the principle of relativity will be valid in non-uniform space also. For this to be so, it is necessary that the motion of the masses producing the non-uniformity be included in the description of the phenomena.

Indeed, at the end of this book it will ·be shown that *under the assumption that space-time is uniform at infinity* (where it must be Galilean) one can single out a class of coordinate systems that are analogous to inertial systems and defined up to a Lorentz transformation. In relation to this class of coordinate systems a principle of relativity will hold in the same form as in the usual theory of relativity, in spite of the fact that at a finite distance from the masses the space is non-uniform. Here however one must bear in mind the essential role played by the boundary conditions that require uniformity at infinity. Thus in the last analysis the relativity principle is here also a result of uniformity.

Since the greatest possible uniformity is expressed by Lorentz transformations there cannot be a more general principle of relativity than that discussed in ordinary relativity theory. All the more, there cannot be a general principle of relativity, as a physical principle, which would hold with respect to arbitrary frames of reference.

In order to make this fact clear, it is essential to distinguish sharply between a physical principle that postulates the existence of corresponding phenomena in different frames of reference and the simple requirement that equations should be covariant in the passage from one frame of reference to another. It is clear that a principle of relativity implies a covariance of equations, but the converse is not true: covariance of differential equations is possible also when no principle of relativity is satisfied. Quite apart from the fact that not all laws of nature reduce to differential equations, even fields described by differential equations require for their definitions not only these equations, but also all kinds of initial, boundary and other conditions. These conditions are not covariant. Therefore the preservation of their physical content requires a change in their mathematical form and, conversely, preservation of their mathematical form implies a change of their physical content. But the realiz-ability of a process with a new physical content is an independent question which cannot be solved *a priori*. If within a given class of reference systems " corresponding " physical processes are possible, then a principle of relativity holds. In the opposite case it does not. It is clear, however, that such a model representation of physical processes, and in particular such a model representa-tion of the metric, is possible at most for a narrow class of reference systems, and certainly cannot be unlimited. This argument shows once again (without in-voking the concept of uniformity) that *a general principle of relativity, as a physical principle, holding in relation to arbitrary frames of reference, is impossible.*

† It should be remembered that in the general case the expression for ds^2, though always a homogeneous function of the coordinate *differentials*, may also depend in a non-homogeneous way on the coordinates themselves.

But as a motivation of the requirement of covariance of the equations a general principle of relativity is also *unnecessary*. The covariance requirement can be justified independently. It is a self-evident, purely logical requirement that in all cases in which the coordinate system is not fixed in advance, equations written down in different coordinate systems should be mathematically equivalent. The class of transformations with respect to which the equations must be covariant must correspond to the class of coordinate systems considered. Thus if one deals with inertial systems related by Lorentz transformations and if Galilean coordinates are used, it is sufficient to require covariance with respect to Lorentz transformations (as was done in Chapters I and II of this book). If, however, arbitrary coordinates are employed, it is necessary to demand general covariance (Chapter IV).

It should be noted that covariance of coordinate systems acquires a definite physical meaning if, and only if, a principle of relativity exists for the class of reference frames used. Such is the covariance with respect to Lorentz transformations. This concept was so fruitful in the formulation of physical laws because it contains concrete chrono-geometric elements (rectilinearity and uniformity of motion) and also dynamic elements (the concept of inertia in the mechanical and the electromagnetic senses; Section 5). Because of this, it is related to the physical principle of relativity and itself becomes concrete and physical. If, however, in place of the Lorentz transformations one discusses arbitrary transformations, one ceases to single out that class of coordinate systems relative to which the principle of relativity exists, and by doing this one destroys the connection between physics and the concept of covariance. There remains a purely logical side to the concept of covariance as a consistency requirement on equations written in different coordinate systems. Naturally this requirement is necessary, but it is always satisfiable.

In dealing with classes of reference frames that are more general than that relative to which a principle of relativity holds, the necessity arises of replacing the explicit formulation of the principle by some other statement. The explicit formulation consists in indicating a class of physically equivalent frames of reference; the new formulation must express those properties of space and time by virtue of which the principle of relativity is possible. With the assumption of a rigid metric this is achieved by introducing an additional equation (49*.07). We saw in this chapter that with the additional assumption of the absence of a universal scale ($K = 0$) these equations lead to a generally covariant formulation of the theory of relativity, without any alteration of its physical content. The Galileo–Lorentz principle of relativity is then maintained to its full extent.

The very possibility of formulating the ordinary theory of relativity in a generally covariant form shows particularly clearly the difference between the principle of relativity as a physical principle and the covariance of the equations as a logical requirement. In addition, such a formulation opens the way to generalizations based on a relaxation of the assumption of a rigid metric. This relaxation provides the possibility of replacing the supplementary conditions (49*.07) by others which reflect better the properties of space and time. This leads us to Einstein's theory of gravitation, which will be discussed in the following chapters.

CHAPTER V

THE PRINCIPLES OF THE THEORY OF GRAVITATION

50. The Generalization of Galileo's Law

The most essential characteristic of the gravitational field by which it differs from all other fields known to physics reveals itself in the effect of the field on the motion of a freely moving body or mass point. In a gravitational field all otherwise free bodies move in the same manner, provided the initial conditions of their motion, i.e. their initial positions and velocities, are the same. This fundamental law may be thought of as a generalization of Galileo's law that in the absence of resistance all bodies fall equally fast.

It is appropriate to recall at this point the definitions of inertial mass and of gravitational mass. Inertial mass is the measure of the ability of a body to resist acceleration; for a given force the acceleration is inversely proportional to the inertial mass. Gravitational mass is the measure of the ability of a body to produce a gravitational field and to suffer the action of such a field; in a given field the force experienced by a body is proportional to the gravitational mass.

Using these definitions the aforementioned generalization of Galileo's law can be formulated as a statement that the inertial and the gravitational masses of any body are equal.

According to Newton the gravitational field can be characterized by the gravitational potential $U(x, y, z)$. The gravitational potential produced by an isolated spherically symmetric mass M at points exterior to itself is

$$U = \frac{\gamma M}{r} \tag{50.01}$$

where r is the distance from the centre of the mass. The quantity γ is the Newtonian constant of gravitation—in c.g.s. units it has the value

$$\gamma = \frac{1}{15\,000\,000} \frac{\text{cm}^3}{\text{g.sec}^2} \tag{50.02}$$

Thus U has the dimensions of the square of a velocity. We note immediately that in all cases encountered in Nature, even on the surface of the Sun or of super-dense stars, the quantity U is very small compared to the square of the speed of light

$$U \ll c^2 \tag{50.03}$$

In the general case of an arbitrary mass distribution the Newtonian potential U it produces satisfies Poisson's equation

$$\Delta U = -4\pi\gamma\rho \tag{50.04}$$

where ρ is the mass density. The Newtonian potential is fully determined by Poisson's equation together with continuity and boundary conditions which

183

are as follows : the function U and its first derivatives must be finite, single-valued and continuous throughout space and must tend to zero at infinity.

Let us assume that the Newtonian potential U is given. The force experienced by a body (mass point) of gravitational mass $(m)_{gr}$ in a gravitational field of potential U is

$$\mathbf{F} = (m)_{gr} \operatorname{grad} U \tag{50.05}$$

On the other hand, by Newton's laws of motion, we have

$$(m)_{in}\mathbf{w} = \mathbf{F} \tag{50.06}$$

Therefore

$$(m)_{in}\mathbf{w} = (m)_{gr}\operatorname{grad} U \tag{50.07}$$

By the generalization of Galileo's law the motion of the body in a given gravitational field cannot depend on its mass. Therefore, the ratio of inertial mass $(m)_{in}$ to gravitational mass $(m)_{gr}$ must be the same for all bodies ; it is thus a universal constant whose value can only depend on the choice of units for the two masses. In the units quite generally accepted one has simply

$$(m)_{in} = (m)_{gr} = m \tag{50.08}$$

so that inertial and gravitational masses are equal.

The equality of inertial and gravitational mass is such a familiar fact that it is usually accepted as something obvious. However, the matter is not so simple : their equality is a separate and very important law of Nature, closely connected with the generalization of Galileo's law.

As a result of the equality of inertial and gravitational mass the equation of motion

$$\mathbf{w} = \operatorname{grad} U \tag{50.09}$$

has universal character, and thus formally expresses the generalization of Galileo's law.

We note that the equations of motion (50.09) can be obtained from the variational principle

$$\delta \int (\tfrac{1}{2}v^2 + U)dt = 0 \tag{50.10}$$

This fact will be a guide to us in constructing the theory of gravitation.

51. The Square of the Interval in Newtonian Approximation

The phenomenon of universal gravitation forces us to widen the framework of the theory of space and time which was the subject of the foregoing chapters. The necessity of this widening becomes clear from the following considerations.

It follows from the equation of wave front propagation, which can be stated in the form

$$\frac{1}{c^2}\left(\frac{\partial\omega}{\partial t}\right)^2 - \left[\left(\frac{\partial\omega}{\partial x}\right)^2 + \left(\frac{\partial\omega}{\partial y}\right)^2 + \left(\frac{\partial\omega}{\partial z}\right)^2\right] =, 0 \tag{51.01}$$

that light is propagated in straight lines. But light possesses energy and by the law of proportionality of mass and energy all energy is indissolubly connected with mass. Therefore light must possess mass. On the other hand, by the law of universal gravitation, any mass located in a gravitational field must experience the action of that field and in general its motion will therefore not be rectilinear.† Hence it follows that in a gravitational field the law of wave front propagation must have a form somewhat different from the one given above. But the equation of wave front propagation is a basic character-istic of the properties of space and time. Hence it follows that the presence of the gravitational field must affect the properties of space and time and their metric is then not a rigid one. This is indeed the conclusion reached in the theory of gravitation which we now begin to construct.

As was shown in Chapter I, the equation of wave front propagation (51.01), with some additional assumptions, leads to the following expression for the square of the interval :

$$ds^2 = c^2\,dt^2 - (dx^2 + dy^2 + dz^2) \qquad (51.02)$$

The influence of the gravitational field on the properties of space and time must have the consequence that the coefficients in the equation of wave front propagation and in the expression for the square of the interval will differ from the constant values appearing in (51.01) and (51.02). We must now find an approximate form for the square of the interval in a gravitational field of Newtonian potential U, relying on the generalization of Galileo's law to guide us. The fundamental fact that the law of motion for a body moving freely in a gravitational field is a universal one which does not depend on the nature of the body permits us to find the relation between the law of motion and the metric of space-time.

The equations of a geodesic in a space-time with given metric were studied in Section 38. We shall now try to find a metric such that these equations coincide approximately with the Newtonian equations of motion for a free body in a given gravitational field. If this attempt is successful it will enable us to introduce the hypothesis that in a space-time with given metric a free body (mass point) moves along a geodesic ; in this way the connection between the law of motion and the metric will be established.

As we know, the equation of a geodesic may be derived from the variational principle

$$\delta \int ds = 0 \qquad (51.03)$$

If the squared interval is of the form (51.02) we have

$$ds = \sqrt{(c^2 - v^2)}\,dt \qquad (51.04)$$

or, for small velocities, $\qquad ds = \left(c - \dfrac{v^2}{2c}\right)dt \qquad (51.05)$

Inserting (51.04) or (51.05) into (51.03) gives equations that describe motion with constant velocity, which indeed is free motion in the absence of a gravita-tional field. We can now assume that for small velocities and weak gravitational fields ($U \ll c^2$) the expression for the interval takes the form

$$ds = \sqrt{(c^2 - 2U - v^2)}\,dt \qquad (51.06)$$

or $\qquad ds = \left[c - \dfrac{1}{c}\left(\tfrac{1}{2}v^2 + U\right)\right]dt \qquad (51.07)$

† The theory of the deflection of light in a gravitational field is given in Section 59 below.

in place of (51.04) or (51.05). Since neither an additive constant nor a constant multiplier are of any importance in a Lagrangian the variational principle (51.03), with ds taken from (51.07), gives the same result as the variational principle

$$\delta \int (\tfrac{1}{2}v^2 + U)dt = 0 \tag{51.08}$$

which was formulated at the end of Section 50, but this did indeed describe free motion of a body in a gravitational field.

It is true that just because additive constants and multiplicative factors in a Lagrangian are immaterial equation (51.08) could be obtained from (51.03) and (51.06) with any sufficiently large value of the constant c; but we must require that in the absence of gravitation, when $U = 0$, the expression (51.06) for the interval shall go over into the Galilean form (51.04) whatever the value of v^2. This requirement fixes the constant c in (51.06) to be equal to the speed of light.

These arguments give us good reason to assume that under the conditions

$$U \ll c^2$$
$$\left(\frac{dx}{dt}\right)^2 + \left(\frac{dy}{dt}\right)^2 + \left(\frac{dz}{dt}\right)^2 = v^2 \ll c^2 \tag{51.09}$$

the square of the interval differs little from the form

$$ds^2 = (c^2 - 2U)dt^2 - (dx^2 + dy^2 + dz^2) \tag{51.10}$$

Here the relative error in the coefficient of dt^2 will certainly be of higher order than the term $2U/c^2$ which is included. As regards the coefficient of the purely spatial part of the interval, it may differ from unity by a quantity of the same order as $2U/c^2$. Indeed, the theory of gravitation to be developed in the following sections gives the more exact expression

$$ds^2 = (c^2 - 2U)dt^2 - \left(1 + \frac{2U}{c^2}\right)(dx^2 + dy^2 + dz^2) \tag{51.11}$$

Under the conditions (51.09) the difference between (51.10) and (51.11) is negligible, as it should be.

In principle the value found for the coefficient of dt^2 is capable of experimental verification.

Let us assume that at some point (x_1, y_1, z_1) at which the gravitational potential is U_1, there is some emitter of radiation of proper period T_0. The wave radiated by it will have a time dependence of the form

$$\exp\left(i2\pi \frac{t}{T_1}\right) \tag{51.12}$$

where T_1 is not equal to T_0 but is related to it in the same way as dt is related to $d\tau$, the differential of the proper time of the emitter. If, for simplicity, the emitter is assumed to be at rest in the frame of reference chosen, we have approximately

$$d\tau = \frac{1}{c} ds = \left(1 - \frac{U_1}{c^2}\right)dt \tag{51.13}$$

and therefore
$$T_0 = \left(1 - \frac{U_1}{c^2}\right)T_1 \tag{51.14}$$

In this problem the dependence of gravitational potential on time may be ignored, so that the gravitational field can be treated as static. Then the wave being propagated from the emitter will retain its time dependence (51.12) throughout space.

Let us now assume further that at some other point (x_2, y_2, z_2), where the gravitational potential has a different value U_2, there is a second identical emitter, e.g. another atom of the same element. The wave emitted by it will have a time dependence throughout space of the form

$$\exp\left(i2\pi\,\frac{t}{T_2}\right) \tag{51.15}$$

where
$$T_0 = \left(1 - \frac{U_2}{c^2}\right)T_2 \tag{51.16}$$

Thus the two waves emitted by identical sources but originating from places of different gravitational potential have periods differing by

$$T_2 - T_1 = \frac{U_2 - U_1}{c^2}\,T_0 \tag{51.17}$$

If U_2 is the potential on the Sun and U_1 the potential on the Earth we have $U_2 > U_1$ and the numerical value of the factor of T_0 in (51.17) is approximately equal to

$$\frac{U_2 - U_1}{c^2} = 2 \times 10^{-6} \tag{51.18}$$

Thus the wave lengths of spectral lines originating on the Sun must be displaced relative to the corresponding lines produced on the Earth by two parts in a million towards the red end of the spectrum.

However, one must note that the emission of spectral lines on the Sun takes place in physical conditions different from those on Earth and that the change of period due to the difference of gravitational potentials is to a great extent masked by other corrections.

There are, however, certain super-dense stars, such as the companion of Sirius, which have a density tens of thousands of times greater than that of water. On their surfaces the value of gravitational potential is significantly greater than on the surface of the Sun—twenty times greater in the case of the companion of Sirius—for such stars the correction due to the difference in gravitational potential becomes very appreciable and can be detected experimentally.

Recently (1959) the influence of the gravitational potential on the frequency of emitted light was successfully revealed in terrestrial conditions by making use of the extremely sharp lines corresponding to nuclear levels. These sharp lines are obtained in the emission of gamma-quanta by atoms in crystals in those emission processes which are not accompanied by emission or absorption of phonons. In such radiation the recoil momentum is transferred to the whole crystal, as a result of which the energy transfer to the crystal proves to be negligibly small and the emitted gamma-quantum possesses practically the same frequency as it would have had without recoil. This phenomenon was discovered by Mössbauer in 1958[46]. We shall not discuss the relevant theory here, but will mention that the crystal temperature has a decisive influence on the probability of " phononless " radiation, but not on its frequency or line breadth. Conversely, in radiation accompanied by phonons (which also occurs) a considerable line broadening takes place as a result of the Doppler effect, connected with the thermal motion of the atoms in the crystal.

The frequency of the gamma-radiation in the phononless process is in resonance with the absorption frequency of the same line in the absorber crystal, and this resonance is so sharp that a relative change of one of the frequencies by a quantity of order 10^{-16} is sufficient to destroy the resonance. With such a sensitivity the change in the potential of terrestrial gravitation in a rise of, say, 10 m above the surface of the Earth becomes detectable; for, putting $g = 9.8$ m/sec^2 and $h = 10$ m we get

$$\frac{U_2 - U_1}{c^2} = \frac{gh}{c^2} = 11 \times 10^{-16} \tag{51.19}$$

Thus, if the absorber atom is above the emitting atom its resonance frequency will be greater than the frequency of the gamma-quantum reaching it from below (as it rises, the gamma-quantum, so to speak, loses energy); at a height of 10 m the relative frequency difference is given by (51.19). This difference can be compensated, and therefore measured, by using the Doppler effect produced by moving the crystal as a whole. Here one has to use the transverse (quadratic) Doppler effect, because the longitudinal (linear) effect would be too coarse a means of compensating the frequency shift in such precision experiments.

The theory of the Doppler effect is given in Section 13; the formula for the transverse effect is found from (13.16) for $v_r = 0$. As is clear from the discussion of Section 13, the frequency shift in the transverse Doppler effect occurs as a result of the relation between proper time τ and coordinate time t, while there is no correction due to the need to express the instant t of emission in terms of the instant t^* of signal reception, provided the radial velocity is zero. Therefore equation (15.07) may be used directly to derive the condition that the gravitational effect be compensated by the transverse Doppler effect. This formula can be written as a relation between the frequencies; we put ν_0 for the proper frequency of the quantum and ν for the local frequency that corresponds to coordinate time. We then get

$$\frac{1}{\nu_0} = \left[1 - \frac{1}{c^2}\left(\frac{1}{2}v^2 + U\right)\right] \cdot \frac{1}{\nu} \tag{51.20}$$

If the lower point is the position of the stationary crystal and has the potential U_2, while the potential at the upper point is U_1 and the crystal there is moving with the transverse velocity v, then the atoms in both crystals will be in resonance ($\nu_2 = \nu_1$) if the condition

$$\tfrac{1}{2}v^2 + U_1 = U_2 \tag{51.21}$$

is satisfied. Since we have $U_2 - U_1 = gh$, this gives

$$v^2 = 2gh \tag{51.22}$$

We see that the experimentally established presence of a frequency shift in the gravitational field and the possibility of compensating it by a transverse

Doppler effect provide a direct verification of equation (51.07), and by the same token, of equation (51.10) for the squared interval.

Thus, one can consider that the value we have found for the coefficient dt^2 in the metric form is in agreement with experimental findings.

52. Einstein's Gravitational Equations

Einstein's theory of gravitation in its restricted, non-cosmological, form has the following basic idea.

The geometrical properties of real physical space and time correspond not to Euclidean but to Riemannian geometry. In Chapter III we discussed the basic postulates of this geometry. Any deviation of geometrical properties from their Euclidean, or to be precise, pseudo-Euclidean form appears in Nature as a gravitational field. The geometrical properties are indissolubly linked with the distribution and motion of ponderable matter. This relationship is mutual. On the one hand the deviations of geometrical properties from the Euclidean are determined by the presence of gravitating masses, on the other, the motion of masses in the gravitational field is determined by these deviations. In short, masses determine the geometrical properties of space and time, and these properties determine the movement of the masses.

We shall now attempt to formulate these ideas mathematically.

In the previous section we saw that in a certain coordinate system, which for practical purposes coincides with an inertial frame of Newtonian mechanics, the Newtonian potential of gravitation U enters the coefficient of dt^2 in the expression for the square of the interval, i.e. the coefficient g_{00} of the general expression

$$ds^2 = g_{\mu\nu} \, dx_\mu \, dx_\nu \tag{52.01}$$

On the other hand, in Newtonian approximation the gravitational potential U satisfies Poisson's equation

$$\Delta U = - 4\pi\gamma\rho \tag{52.02}$$

The required generalization of Newton's theory of gravitation must be covariant with respect to arbitrary coordinate transformations. Therefore it is impossible to regard as a generalization of the Newtonian potential a term in the coefficient g_{00} or this whole coefficient; instead the whole set of coefficients $g_{\mu\nu}$ must be taken into consideration and must appear as the generalization of Newton's potential. The fundamental metric tensor must satisfy a set of equations that are generally covariant and in the Newtonian approximation one of them must go over into Poisson's equation for the potential U. The total number of equations must, generally speaking, be equal to the number of unknown functions, i.e. to the number of components of the tensor $g_{\mu\nu}$, which is ten.

On the left-hand side of Poisson's equation there is a second order differential operator, the Laplace operator, acting on U. Therefore, the simplest generally covariant generalization of this left-hand side will be a tensor which involves linearly the second derivatives of the metric tensor $g_{\mu\nu}$.

Such tensors are the curvature tensors (either of second or fourth rank). The fourth rank curvature tensor $R_{\mu\nu,\alpha\beta}$ is unsuitable because its components do not contain expressions which could be generalizations of the Laplace operator acting on U. Also, it has too many components, the number being twenty, twice as many as there are unknown functions.† Therefore, there remains the second rank curvature tensor which has just the right number of components.

On the right-hand side of Poisson's equation the mass density ρ appears. A generalization of the mass density which has the required tensor character is the mass tensor $T^{\mu\nu}$ whose invariant is equal to the invariant mass density.

We are thus led to the conclusion that the required generalization of Poisson's equation must be a relation between the second rank curvature tensor $R^{\mu\nu}$ and the mass tensor $T^{\mu\nu}$.

In the previous chapters we saw that in the absence of gravitational fields the divergence of the tensor $T^{\mu\nu}$ must vanish

$$\nabla_\nu T^{\mu\nu} = 0 \tag{52.03}$$

We shall retain this equation for the general case, postponing the discussion of questions connected with it (questions of the energy of a gravitational field, of the integral form of conservation laws, etc.) until Chapter VII.

But we established at the end of Chapter III that the tensor

$$G^{\mu\nu} = R^{\mu\nu} - \tfrac{1}{2}g^{\mu\nu}R \tag{52.04}$$

which is known as Einstein's tensor, or the conservative tensor, has the remarkable property that its divergence is identically zero.

$$\nabla_\nu G^{\mu\nu} \equiv 0 \tag{52.05}$$

Therefore, if we put

$$R^{\mu\nu} - \tfrac{1}{2}g^{\mu\nu}R = -\varkappa T^{\mu\nu} \tag{52.06}$$

where $\varkappa$ is a constant, equations (52.03) for the mass tensor will be a consequence of (52.06).

As we know, the metric tensor $g^{\mu\nu}$ itself also satisfies (52.05), therefore we could add to the conservative tensor on the left-hand side of (52.06) a tensor of the form $\lambda g^{\mu\nu}$ where λ is a constant, without violating (52.03).

We saw in Section 31* that if one imposes purely local conditions on the mass tensor (the condition that it should depend on the field components or other functions of state, but not on the coordinates; the vanishing of its divergence by virtue of the field equations) it is only determined apart from two constants. To be more precise, if the tensor $T^{\mu\nu}$ satisfies the conditions stated, these are also satisfied by

$$T'^{\mu\nu} = \alpha T^{\mu\nu} + \beta g^{\mu\nu} \tag{52.07}$$

Here the constant α depends on the choice of energy unit, the constant β also on the conditions at infinity. If in supplementation of the local conditions one demands that at infinity, where the field vanishes, the mass tensor should also be zero, then β will be zero and the mass tensor is determined uniquely.

† It is true that even an excessive number of equations for the tensor $R_{\mu\nu,\alpha\beta}$ might prove to be compatible as is the case for a space of constant curvature (equation (49.12)) but in that case the equations permit the metric to be determined purely locally, i.e. without using boundary conditions. They therefore have a character different from that of Poisson's equation for which boundary conditions are essential.

These results were established for the case of a Euclidean metric, but one may expect that they will be true also for the general case, which differs from that discussed in Section 31* in two respects. In the first place, the ordinary derivatives with respect to the coordinates in the field equations will be replaced by tensor derivatives. In the second place, the quantities $g^{\mu\nu}$ will be added to the functions of state (with the statements that their tensor derivatives vanish taken, formally, to be their field equations). However neither of these facts can essentially change our conclusion on the degree of uniqueness of the mass tensor determined from local conditions. The possibility of introducing two constants α and β is directly evident in the general case too; one may thus expect that our conclusion on the uniqueness of the mass tensor also remains valid (of course, it would be desirable to have a formal proof).†

Replacement of the tensor $T^{\mu\nu}$ by the linear function (52.07) of itself corresponds to replacing the gravitational equations (52.06) by

$$R^{\mu\nu} - \tfrac{1}{2}g^{\mu\nu}R = -\varkappa T^{\mu\nu} - \lambda g^{\mu\nu} \tag{52.08}$$

The constant λ is called the cosmological constant. It is clear from these remarks that the question of the value of λ acquires a definite meaning only after the conditions are formulated by which the tensor $T^{\mu\nu}$ is to be defined uniquely. Such conditions will necessarily be of non-local character; they can therefore only be formulated starting from definite assumptions about the character of space-time as a whole.

At the beginning of this section we stated the basic assumptions of Einstein's theory of gravitation in its limited (non-cosmological) formulation. According to these the concept of spatial infinity retains its meaning, space-time at infinity being pseudo-Euclidean (Galilean). Deviations from Euclidean character are observed only at a finite distance from massive bodies. But in this case the mass tensor may continue to be subjected to the requirement stated for the case when the whole of space-time was assumed pseudo-Euclidean. We can demand that at infinity, where the field vanishes, the mass tensor should also become zero. It then has a uniquely defined meaning to inquire after the value of the cosmological constant and the answer can be based on the following consideration. According to our basic postulates, the absence of a gravitational field signifies the absence of deviations of the geometry of space-time from the Euclidean, and therefore also the vanishing of the curvature tensor $R^{\mu\nu}$ and of its invariant R. On the other hand, the gravitational field will be absent if the mass tensor $T^{\mu\nu}$ is zero everywhere. Therefore the equations $T^{\mu\nu} = 0$ and $R^{\mu\nu} = 0$ must certainly be compatible and this is only possible if the equations relating $G^{\mu\nu}$ to $T^{\mu\nu}$ do not contain the term $\lambda g^{\mu\nu}$ (i.e. if $\lambda = 0$).

Thus, given the assumptions formulated at the beginning of this section and given our definition of the mass tensor, the appropriate generalization of Poisson's equation for the potential will just be equations (52.06).

As for equations (52.08), they should be used if the problem is stated cosmologically, in which case the concept of spatial infinity is inapplicable and the tensor $T^{\mu\nu}$ contains an unknown constant β, even after units have been fixed. According to the value of this constant the value of the so-called cosmological

† A proof of uniqueness for the electrodynamic and the electromagnetic cases is given in the papers by C. Jankiewicz [47].

constant λ must be selected; it is evidently related to β. The choice of some particular value of λ for a given normalization of $T^{\mu\nu}$ represents a special hypothesis, which must be introduced explicitly; this is true also for the value $\lambda = 0$.

Returning to the non-cosmological case and to equations (52.05) we may assert that under the conditions stated (correspondence with Poisson's equation, general covariance, linearity in the second derivatives of the $g^{\mu\nu}$, identical vanishing of the left-hand side of (52.05) and Euclidean character in the absence of masses) these equations are unique.

The equations (52.06) are called Einstein's gravitational equations ; they play a fundamental part in the theory of gravitation. They will be examined in the following sections.

53. The Characteristics of Einstein's Equations. The Speed of Propagation of Gravitation

We begin our discussion of Einstein's gravitational equations

$$R^{\mu\nu} - \tfrac{1}{2}g^{\mu\nu}R = -\varkappa T^{\mu\nu} \tag{53.01}$$

with the derivation of the first order equation for their characteristics. From a physical point of view the equation of the characteristics represents the propagation law for the wave front of a gravitational wave.

Multiplying (53.01) by $g_{\mu\nu}$ and summing we obtain the relation

$$R = \varkappa T \tag{53.02}$$

connecting the invariants of the curvature tensor and of the mass tensor. This relation enables us to write the gravitational equations in the form

$$R^{\mu\nu} = -\varkappa(T^{\mu\nu} - \tfrac{1}{2}g^{\mu\nu}T) \tag{53.03}$$

In Appendix B the contravariant curvature tensor $R^{\mu\nu}$ is shown to be expressible as

$$R^{\mu\nu} = -\tfrac{1}{2}g^{\alpha\beta}\frac{\partial^2 g^{\mu\nu}}{\partial x_\alpha\,\partial x_\beta} - \Gamma^{\mu\nu} + \Gamma^{\mu,\alpha\beta}\Gamma^\nu_{\alpha\beta} \tag{53.04}$$

where $\Gamma^{\mu,\alpha\beta}$ is the quantity obtained from $\Gamma^\mu_{\alpha\beta}$ by raising suffixes

$$\Gamma^{\mu,\alpha\beta} = g^{\alpha\rho}g^{\beta\sigma}\Gamma^\mu_{\rho\sigma} \tag{53.05}$$

Therefore, the last term in (53.04) does not involve second derivatives but is a homogeneous quadratic form in the $\Gamma^\nu_{\alpha\beta}$ and hence also in the first derivatives of the metric tensor.

Second derivatives appear in the first term and also in the $\Gamma^{\mu\nu}$, but the latter dependence is only through first derivatives of the quantities

$$\Gamma^\nu = g^{\alpha\beta}\Gamma^\nu_{\alpha\beta} \tag{53.06}$$

which were introduced in Section 41. We recall that the d'Alembertian of any function ψ may be written in the form

$$\Box\psi = g^{\alpha\beta}\frac{\partial^2\psi}{\partial x_\alpha\,\partial x_\beta} - \Gamma^\nu\frac{\partial\psi}{\partial x_\nu} \tag{53.07}$$

or, alternatively, as

$$\Box\psi = \frac{1}{\sqrt{(-g)}}\ \frac{\partial}{\partial x_\beta}\left\{\sqrt{(-g)}\ g^{\alpha\beta}\ \frac{\partial\psi}{\partial x_\alpha}\right\} \tag{53.08}$$

whence

$$\Gamma^\alpha = -\frac{1}{\sqrt{(-g)}}\ \frac{\partial}{\partial x_\beta}\{\sqrt{(-g)}\ g^{\alpha\beta}\} \tag{53.09}$$

and also

$$\Gamma^\alpha = -\Box x_\alpha \tag{53.10}$$

The $\Gamma^{\mu\nu}$ are obtained from the Γ^ν by a rule which is formally identical with the rule for forming the symmetrical contravariant derivative of a vector :

$$\Gamma^{\mu\nu} = \tfrac{1}{2}(\nabla^\mu\Gamma^\nu + \nabla^\nu\Gamma^\mu) \tag{53.11}$$

or in detail

$$\Gamma^{\mu\nu} = \frac{1}{2}\left(g^{\mu\alpha}\frac{\partial\Gamma^\nu}{\partial x_\alpha} + g^{\nu\alpha}\frac{\partial\Gamma^\mu}{\partial x_\alpha} - \frac{\partial g^{\mu\nu}}{\partial x_\alpha}\Gamma^\alpha\right) \tag{53.12}$$

Of course, since Γ^ν is not a vector the $\Gamma^{\mu\nu}$ are not a tensor. This circumstance proves very useful in simplifying Einstein's equations.

Einstein's equations are generally covariant and therefore permit coordinate transformations involving four arbitrary functions. Suppose the equations are solved in some arbitrary system of coordinates. We can then go over to other coordinates by taking as independent variables four solutions of the equation $\Box\psi = 0$. These solutions may be chosen in such a way as to satisfy the inequalities to which the $g^{\mu\nu}$ must be subject, according to Section 35, and they may also be subjected to some additional conditions. But as long as each of the coordinates x_0, x_1, x_2 and x_3 satisfies the equation $\Box x_\alpha = 0$ we shall have in that system

$$\Gamma^\alpha = 0 \tag{53.13}$$

and therefore also

$$\Gamma^{\mu\nu} = 0 \tag{53.14}$$

We shall call such a coordinate system harmonic. At the moment we are not interested in the question of the uniqueness of the harmonic coordinate system or rather in the additional conditions which could guarantee uniqueness. This question will be considered in Section 93. Here it is only important to note that the equations (53.13) are compatible with Einstein's equations and that they do not impose any essential limitation on the solutions of the latter, serving only to narrow down the class of permissible coordinate systems.†

Under the conditions (53.13) the expression for the $R^{\mu\nu}$ simplifies, becoming

$$R^{\mu\nu} = -\tfrac{1}{2}g^{\alpha\beta}\frac{\partial^2 g^{\mu\nu}}{\partial x_\alpha\ \partial x_\beta} + \Gamma^{\mu,\,\alpha\beta}\Gamma^\nu_{\alpha\beta} \tag{53.15}$$

Hence second derivatives only appear combined in the d'Alembert operator acting on the single quantity $g^{\mu\nu}$ which has the same indices as the particular $R^{\mu\nu}$ on the left-hand side.

The form of the equation of the characteristics for any given system of equations depends only on the terms containing the highest occurring order

† The conditions $\Gamma^\alpha = 0$ were first introduced by de Donder [16] and by Lanczos [17].

of derivatives. In the case of the system (53.01) and (53.13) these terms are just those involving the d'Alembertian.

Therefore the system of equations of gravitation will have the same characteristics as d'Alembert's equation,

$$\Box \psi = 0 \tag{53.16}$$

and these are easily found. As shown in Appendix C they have the form

$$g^{\mu\nu} \frac{\partial \omega}{\partial x_\mu} \frac{\partial \omega}{\partial x_\nu} = 0 \tag{53.17}$$

where

$$\omega(x_0, x_1, x_2, x_3) = \text{const.} \tag{53.18}$$

is the equation of a wave front, i.e. the equation of a moving surface on which any discontinuities of the gravitational field must lie.

The equation (53.17) for the propagation of a gravitational wave-front is the same as the corresponding equation for the front of a light wave in empty space on which the whole theory of space and time was based.[†] Briefly one can say that gravitation is propagated with the speed of light.

That in Einstein's theory gravitation is propagated with the speed of light is a fact of fundamental significance. It shows that the assumed form of the gravitational equations is in agreement with the general postulate of the Theory of Relativity according to which there exists a limiting velocity for the propagation of all types of action, namely the velocity of light in free space. The existence of a finite propagation velocity for gravity removes the contradiction inherent in Newton's theory of gravitation with its admission of instantaneous action at a distance.

54. A Comparison with the Statement of the Problem in Newtonian Theory. Boundary Conditions

In Newton's theory of gravitation the gravitational potential satisfies the equation

$$\Delta U = - 4\pi\gamma\rho \tag{54.01}$$

and tends to zero at infinity in such a way that

$$\lim_{r \to \infty} rU = \gamma M \tag{54.02}$$

where M is the total mass of all the bodies of the system in question and is equal to

$$M = \int \rho \, dx \, dy \, dz \tag{54.03}$$

Einstein's theory, which is based on the gravitational equations

$$R^{\mu\nu} - \tfrac{1}{2}g^{\mu\nu}R = - \varkappa T^{\mu\nu} \tag{54.04}$$

must, in first approximation, give the same result as Newton's theory. Newtonian theory is applicable to such mass distributions for which the total mass,

---

[†] When we derived that law from Maxwell's equations in Section 3, we assumed space-time to be Euclidean. But, according to a remark at the end of Appendix E, the same result can be obtained without this assumption, starting from the generally covariant form of Maxwell's equations given in Section 46.

given by the integral (54.03) taken over all space, remains finite. This condition is in particular satisfied by any mass distribution of insular character. We use this term to describe the case that all the masses of the system studied are concentrated within some finite volume which is separated by very great distances from all other masses not forming part of the system. When these other masses are sufficiently far away one can neglect their influence on the given system of masses, which then may be treated as isolated.

In formulating Einstein's theory we shall likewise start from the assumption that the mass distribution is insular. This assumption makes it possible to impose definite limiting conditions at infinity as for Newtonian theory, and so makes the mathematical problem a determined one.

Theoretically, other assumptions are also admissible. For instance, one can assume a mass distribution which on the average is uniform throughout space. Such a point of view is appropriate to the study of distances so enormous that in comparison even the distances between galaxies are taken to be very small. Very little is known of the mass distribution over such great distances and therefore a theory dealing with them will necessarily be less reliable and less capable of experimental verification than the theory of smaller scale astronomical phenomena.

The bulk of this book will be devoted to the case of insular distributions of masses. The assumption of uniform distribution will be considered only in Sections 94 and 95, where we give the theory of Friedmann-Lobachevsky space to which this assumption leads.

We shall thus now assume that space-time is in the main Euclidean, or rather pseudo-Euclidean, and that any deviation of space-time geometry from Euclidean geometry is a result of the presence of a gravitational field. Wherever there is no gravitational field, geometry must be Euclidean. For an insular distribution of masses the gravitational field must tend to zero at infinity and therefore we have to assume that at points far removed from the masses the geometry of space-time becomes Euclidean. However, when geometry is Euclidean there exist Galilean coordinates x, y, z and t, in terms of which the square of the interval has the form

$$ds^2 = c^2\, dt^2 - (dx^2 + dy^2 + dz^2) \tag{54.05}$$

Since experiment shows that the geometry of space-time nowhere deviates greatly from Euclidean geometry one may expect that there should exist in the whole of space variables in terms of which the square of the interval deviates but little from (54.05). In the following we shall give a more precise definition of these quasi-Galilean coordinates.

We note that Newton's theory is simplest to formulate in just these Galilean coordinates, i.e. in an inertial frame of reference. Consequently Einstein's theory, which is its generalization, should be compared with it in terms of coordinates with as similar properties as possible.

Newtonian theory is non-relativistic and in passing from a relativistic theory to a non-relativistic one, it is essential to single out the speed of light as a large parameter. Therefore we shall no longer introduce the quantity c into the definition of the time-coordinate ; instead of (35.03) we shall now write

$$x_0 = t\,; \qquad x_1 = x\,; \qquad x_2 = y\,; \qquad x_3 = z \tag{54.06}$$

Thus henceforth the variable x_0 will mean simply the time t and not ct as previously.

The expression (54.05) for the square of the interval now appears as

$$ds^2 = c^2 dx_0^2 - (dx_1^2 + dx_2^2 + dx_3^2) \tag{54.07}$$

This must be valid at sufficiently large distance from the masses, where the geometry is Euclidean.

Comparing with the general expression

$$ds^2 = g_{\mu\nu} dx_\mu dx_\nu \tag{54.08}$$

we find that the $g_{\mu\nu}$ must have the following limiting values at infinity

$$\begin{aligned}(g_{00})_\infty &= c^2; & (g_{0i})_\infty &= 0 \\ (g_{ik})_\infty &= -\delta_{ik} & (i, k &= 1, 2, 3)\end{aligned} \tag{54.09}$$

The corresponding limiting values of the contravariant components of the metric tensor will be

$$(g^{00})_\infty = \frac{1}{c^2}; \qquad (g^{0i})_\infty = 0; \qquad (g^{ik})_\infty = -\delta_{ik} \tag{54.10}$$

These are then to be considered as the boundary conditions on the metric tensor.

However, the number of boundary conditions so far stated is insufficient; some additional ones must be added which characterize the asymptotic behaviour of the differences $g_{\mu\nu} - (g_{\mu\nu})_\infty$ at large distances from the masses.

In the previous section we saw that, at least if $\Gamma^\nu = 0$, Einstein's equations are of the type of the wave equation, because their main terms involve the d'Alembert operator. Outside the mass distribution the tensor $T^{\mu\nu}$ vanishes and the equations take on the form

$$R^{\mu\nu} = 0 \tag{54.11}$$

where, provided $\Gamma^\nu = 0$, the tensor $R^{\mu\nu}$ has the form

$$R^{\mu\nu} = -\tfrac{1}{2} g^{\alpha\beta} \frac{\partial^2 g^{\mu\nu}}{\partial x_\alpha \partial x_\beta} + \Gamma^{\mu, \alpha\beta} \Gamma^\nu_{\alpha\beta} \tag{54.12}$$

We assume that at large distances the differences $g^{\mu\nu} - (g^{\mu\nu})_\infty$ and their first and second derivatives tend to zero as $1/r$, where $r = \sqrt{(x_1^2 + x_2^2 + x_3^2)}$. (This assumption will be justified in the following.) Then at large distances the second term of (54.12), being a homogeneous quadratic form in the first derivatives, will tend to zero as $1/r^2$. As for the term involving the d'Alembertian, the coefficients in it can be replaced by their limiting values to the same approximation. After these simplifications we get

$$R^{\mu\nu} \cong -\frac{1}{2c^2} \frac{\partial^2 g^{\mu\nu}}{\partial x_0^2} + \frac{1}{2}\left(\frac{\partial^2 g^{\mu\nu}}{\partial x_1^2} + \frac{\partial^2 g^{\mu\nu}}{\partial x_2^2} + \frac{\partial^2 g^{\mu\nu}}{\partial x_3^2}\right) \tag{54.13}$$

A more complete investigation of the asymptotic behaviour of the $g^{\mu\nu}$ will be given in Section 87. It shows that the asymptotic form of $g^{\mu\nu}$ is influenced by the terms of order $1/r^2$ omitted from (54.13) but that qualitatively the behaviour of the difference $g^{\mu\nu} - (g^{\mu\nu})_\infty$ will be the same as the behaviour of a function ψ satisfying the wave equation

$$\frac{1}{c^2}\frac{\partial^2\psi}{\partial t^2} - \Delta\psi = 0 \tag{54.14}$$

where Δ is the usual, Euclidean Laplace operator.

We are interested in solutions of the wave equation (54.14) which correspond to outgoing waves dying off at infinity. They have the asymptotic form

$$\psi = \frac{1}{r}f\left(t - \frac{r}{c}, \mathbf{n}\right) \tag{54.15}$$

where $\mathbf{n}$ is a unit vector with the components

$$n_x = \frac{x}{r}; \qquad n_y = \frac{y}{r}; \qquad n_z = \frac{z}{r} \tag{54.16}$$

and f is an arbitrary function. The function f and its derivatives with respect to all its arguments are assumed finite. The argument $\mathbf{n}$ gives the dependence of f on the direction along which a point recedes to infinity.

Other possible solutions of the wave equations must be discarded for physical reasons, for in our statement of the problem the system is considered to be isolated. This means that no waves impinge on it from outside, all waves have bodies of the system as their sources and, since in a system of insular type all bodies are concentrated in a finite region, all waves originate in this region and so have the asymptotic form (54.15) at large distances from the region.

The conditions that a solution of the wave equations should at large distances have the form indicated can be stated in the differential form

$$\lim \left(\frac{\partial(r\psi)}{\partial r} + \frac{1}{c}\frac{\partial(r\psi)}{\partial t}\right) = 0 \tag{54.17}$$

This condition must hold for $r \to \infty$ and all values of $t_0 = t + r/c$ in an arbitrary fixed interval. It can be called the condition of outward radiation. It ensures the uniqueness of the solution provided it is associated with the requirement that the function ψ and its first derivatives with respect to x, y, z and t should be everywhere bounded and should die off at infinity as $1/r$ (see Section 92).

We note that the above considerations refer strictly speaking to the ordinary wave equation (54.14) and not to Einstein's equations. Therefore the asymptotic form of the difference

$$g^{\mu\nu} - (g^{\mu\nu})_\infty = \psi \tag{54.18}$$

will, in fact, differ somewhat from (54.15). However, a slightly modified condition of outward radiation written in the differential form (54.17) will still be valid for (54.18).

Summing up, we can say that in our statement of the problem the metric tensor must satisfy the condition of being Euclidean at infinity and also the condition of outward radiation.

55. Solution of Einstein's Gravitational Equations in First Approximation and Determination of the Constant

To compare the gravitational theories of Einstein and of Newton we must first of all determine the constant $\varkappa$ which enters Einstein's gravitational equations

$$R^{\mu\nu} - \tfrac{1}{2}g^{\mu\nu}R = -\varkappa T^{\mu\nu} \tag{55.01}$$

The value of this constant can be found by comparing the expression for the square of the interval derived in Newtonian approximation in Section 51 with that obtainable by approximately solving Einstein's equations.

For the mass tensor on the right-hand side of (55.01) we may take the approximate expression corresponding to a Euclidean metric that was discussed in Section 32. There the mass term was given explicitly for the case of an elastic body. In taking over the equations of that section we must remember that we now understand x_0 to mean simply the time t and not ct as previously. Therefore the previous T^{00} will in the new notation be equal to $c^2 T^{00}$ and the previous T^{0i} to the new cT^{0i}, the meaning of T^{ik} being unaltered. Thus if $x_0 = t$ the equations (32.34) become

$$c^2 T^{00} = \rho + \frac{1}{c^2}\left(\tfrac{1}{2}\rho v^2 + \rho \Pi\right)$$

$$c^2 T^{0i} = \rho v_i + \frac{1}{c^2}\left\{v_i\left(\tfrac{1}{2}\rho v^2 + \rho\Pi\right) - \sum_{k=1}^{3} p_{ik}v_k\right\} \tag{55.02}$$

$$c^2 T^{ik} = \rho v_i v_k - p_{ik}$$

In the present approximation we must disregard the terms corresponding to the density and current of energy—Umov's scalar and vector—and we write simply

$$c^2 T^{00} = \rho \; ; \qquad c^2 T^{0i} = \rho v_i \tag{55.03}$$

To the same accuracy to which this is valid we may replace the invariant of the mass tensor by the value

$$T = \rho \tag{55.04}$$

Equations (55.03) and (55.04) enable us to calculate the approximate values of the tensor components entering the right-hand side of Einstein's equations written in the form

$$R^{\mu\nu} = -\varkappa(T^{\mu\nu} - \tfrac{1}{2}g^{\mu\nu}T) \tag{55.05}$$

which was given in (53.03). Using the Galilean values of the $g^{\mu\nu}$ we get

$$T^{00} - \tfrac{1}{2}g^{00}T = \frac{1}{2c^2}\rho$$

$$T^{0i} - \tfrac{1}{2}g^{0i}T = \frac{1}{c^2}\rho v_i \tag{55.06}$$

$$T^{ik} - \tfrac{1}{2}g^{ik}T = \tfrac{1}{2}\rho\delta_{ik}$$

On the other hand, according to (54.13), if we use harmonic coordinates we have approximately,

$$R^{\mu\nu} = \tfrac{1}{2}\Delta g^{\mu\nu} - \frac{1}{2c^2}\frac{\partial^2 g^{\mu\nu}}{\partial t^2} \tag{55.07}$$

where Δ is the usual Euclidean Laplace operator. As we shall be interested in a quasi-static solution we can discard the term involving the second time derivative. Inserting (55.07) and (55.06) into (55.05) we have

$$\Delta g^{00} = -\frac{\varkappa}{c^2}\rho$$

$$\Delta g^{0i} = -\frac{2\varkappa}{c^2}\rho v_i \qquad (55.08)$$

$$\Delta g^{ik} = -\varkappa\rho\delta_{ik}$$

We now refer back to the expression for the squared interval in Newtonian approximation. According to (51.10) we have then

$$g_{00} = c^2 - 2U \qquad (55.09)$$

where U is the Newtonian potential. In this approximation the remaining components of the metric tensor are to be replaced by their Galilean values. Using the relation

$$g_{00}g^{00} + \sum_{i=1}^{3} g_{0i}g^{i0} = 1 \qquad (55.10)$$

and the fact that the products $g_{0i}g^{i0}$ are very small compared to unity† we can take

$$g_{00}g^{00} = 1 \qquad (55.11)$$

and therefore

$$g^{00} = \frac{1}{c^2} + \frac{2U}{c^4} \qquad (55.12)$$

But Newton's potential satisfies the equation

$$\Delta U = -4\pi\gamma\rho \qquad (55.13)$$

hence

$$\Delta g^{00} = -\frac{8\pi\gamma}{c^4}\rho \qquad (55.14)$$

Comparing this with the first equation in (55.08) we see that the two are coincident, if Einstein's gravitational constant $\varkappa$ is related to Newton's constant γ by the relation

$$\varkappa = \frac{8\pi\gamma}{c^2} \qquad (55.15)$$

The Newtonian potential U is that solution of (55.13) which satisfies the appropriate boundary conditions at infinity. As is well-known that solution can be written in the form of a volume integral :

$$U = \gamma \int \frac{\rho'}{|\mathbf{r} - \mathbf{r}'|}\, dx'\, dy'\, dz' \qquad (55.16)$$

Side by side with this Newtonian potential we introduce the functions

$$U_i = \gamma \int \frac{(\rho v_i)'}{|\mathbf{r} - \mathbf{r}'|}\, dx'\, dy'\, dz' \qquad (55.17)$$

which satisfy

$$\Delta U_i = -4\pi\gamma\rho v_i \qquad (55.18)$$

† An estimate of these terms will be given later.

and also the conditions at infinity. In analogy with the corresponding electromagnetic quantities these functions may be called gravitational vector potentials. Now the solution of (55.08) can be written as

$$g^{00} = \frac{1}{c^2}\left(1 + \frac{2U}{c^2}\right)$$

$$g^{0i} = \frac{4}{c^4}U_i \tag{55.19}$$

$$g^{ik} = -\left(1 - \frac{2U}{c^2}\right)\delta_{ik}$$

We have used (55.15) to eliminate $\varkappa$.

We note that U has the dimensions of a velocity squared and the U_i the dimensions of a velocity cubed. In estimating the orders of magnitude of quantities we can take U to be of the order q^2 and the U_i of the order q^3, where q is some speed much smaller than the speed of light.

It is now purely a matter of algebra to obtain from the contravariant components of the metric tensor its covariant components, its determinant, etc.

To simplify the algebraic manipulations we introduce a system of quantities

$$a_{ik} = -g_{ik} + \frac{g_{0i}g_{0k}}{g_{00}}; \qquad a^{ik} = -g^{ik} \tag{55.20}$$

where $i, k = 1, 2, 3$. It is easy to verify that

$$\sum_{m=1}^{3} a_{im}a^{mk} = \delta_{ik} \tag{55.21}$$

The set of quantities a_{ik} may be interpreted as a three-dimensional spatial metric tensor, but only its algebraic properties are of importance to us here.

If we put

$$a = \text{Det } a_{ik} \tag{55.22}$$

and therefore

$$\frac{1}{a} = \text{Det } a^{ik} \tag{55.23}$$

we get

$$g = -ag_{00} \tag{55.24}$$

It follows directly from the definitions (55.20) that

$$g_{00}g^{0k} = \sum_{m=1}^{3} a^{mk}g_{m0} \tag{55.25}$$

and also

$$g_{i0} = g_{00}\sum_{k=1}^{3} a_{ik}g^{0k} \tag{55.26}$$

If the $g^{\mu\nu}$ have the values (55.19) it follows that

$$a^{ik} = \left(1 - \frac{2U}{c^2}\right)\delta_{ik} \tag{55.27}$$

and therefore

$$a_{ik} = \left(1 + \frac{2U}{c^2}\right)\delta_{ik} \tag{55.28}$$

Noting the form of g_{00} we get

$$g_{00}a_{ik} = c^2\delta_{ik} \tag{55.29}$$

with an error of order higher than U/c^2.

Hence, with the same relative error, we have

$$g_{i0} = c^2 g^{i0} \tag{55.30}$$

Using these results we obtain for the covariant components of the metric tensor

$$g_{00} = c^2 - 2U$$

$$g_{0i} = \frac{4}{c^2}U_i \tag{55.31}$$

$$g_{ik} = -\left(1 + \frac{2U}{c^2}\right)\delta_{ik}$$

Knowing the approximate values of the g_{0i} and the g^{0i} we can now verify the accuracy to which the use of (55.11) was justified. We have, approximately

$$g_{00}g^{00} = 1 - \frac{16}{c^6}\sum_{i=1}^{3} U_i^2 \tag{55.32}$$

If the U_i are of order q^3 the above expression differs from unity by quantities of order q^6/c^6. Therefore (55.11) may be used not only in this but also in the next higher approximation in U/c^2 or v^2/c^2. We note that (52.26) leads to

$$g_{00}g^{00} = 1 - g_{00}\sum_{i,k=1}^{3} a_{ik}g^{0i}g^{0k} \tag{55.33}$$

Here g_{00} is positive and the double sum is a positive definite quadratic form, therefore we shall always have, quite rigorously

$$g_{00}g^{00} \leqslant 1 \tag{55.34}$$

though, as we have seen, the deviation from unity of the left-hand side is exceedingly small.

We now state the value of the determinant g and of $\sqrt{(-g)}$ times the contravariant components of the metric tensor. We shall write

$$\mathfrak{g}^{\mu\nu} = \sqrt{(-g)} \cdot g^{\mu\nu} \tag{55.35}$$

We then have

$$-g = c^2 + 4U \tag{55.36}$$

and therefore

$$\sqrt{(-g)} = c + \frac{2U}{c} \tag{55.37}$$

Hence, using (55.35)

$$\mathfrak{g}^{00} = \frac{1}{c} + \frac{4U}{c^3}$$

$$\mathfrak{g}^{0i} = \frac{4}{c^3}U_i \tag{55.38}$$

$$\mathfrak{g}^{ik} = -c\delta_{ik}$$

We must now estimate the magnitude of the neglected terms in $R^{\mu\nu}$ which are quadratic in the first derivatives.

These terms are of the form $\Gamma^{\mu,\alpha\beta}\Gamma^{\nu}_{\alpha\beta}$. To calculate approximate values of the Christoffel symbols we could use the approximate form of the metric tensor that has just been derived. However, we shall not perform these calculations here as the quadratic terms will be determined in detail in Chapter VI where we shall solve the gravitational equations in the next approximation. Here we only need the order of magnitude of the quadratic terms. It turns out that the terms in R^{00} and R^{0i} will be of sixth and those in R^{ik} of fourth order in $1/c$. In our present approximation these terms have no influence.

It remains to verify whether the conditions which ensure that the coordinates are harmonic,

$$\Gamma^{\nu} \equiv -\frac{1}{(\sqrt{-g})}\cdot\frac{\partial}{\partial x_{\mu}}\{\sqrt{(-g)}\cdot g^{\mu\nu}\} = 0 \qquad (55.39)$$

are satisfied to the approximation required. Let us first make it clear to what accuracy we require them to hold. If we do not omit the terms in $\Gamma^{\mu\nu}$ in the expression (53.04) for $R^{\mu\nu}$ but instead retain them to the accuracy corresponding to the approximation (55.07) for the other terms, we obtain in place of (55.07)

$$R^{00} = \tfrac{1}{2}\Delta g^{00} - \frac{1}{2c^2}\frac{\partial^2 g^{00}}{\partial t^2} - \frac{1}{c^2}\frac{\partial\Gamma^0}{\partial t}$$

$$R^{0i} = \tfrac{1}{2}\Delta g^{0i} - \frac{1}{2c^2}\frac{\partial^2 g^{0i}}{\partial t^2} + \frac{1}{2}\left(\frac{\partial\Gamma^0}{\partial x_i} - \frac{1}{c^2}\frac{\partial\Gamma^i}{\partial t}\right) \qquad (55.40)$$

$$R^{ik} = \tfrac{1}{2}\Delta g^{ik} - \frac{1}{2c^2}\frac{\partial^2 g^{ik}}{\partial t^2} + \frac{1}{2}\left(\frac{\partial\Gamma^i}{\partial x_k} + \frac{\partial\Gamma^k}{\partial x_i}\right)$$

In order that the previously neglected terms in Γ^{ν} should really be small compared to terms of the type $\Delta g^{\mu\nu}$ which were retained, it is necessary that Γ^0 should be of a higher order of smallness in c than $1/c^4$ and Γ^i of a higher order than $1/c^2$. These conditions are indeed satisfied. For it is directly evident from (55.38) that the Γ^i will be of fourth order in $1/c$. As for Γ^0, the terms of fourth order in it are

$$\Gamma^0 = -\frac{4}{c^4}\left(\frac{\partial U}{\partial t} + \sum_{i=1}^{3}\frac{\partial U_i}{\partial x_i}\right) \qquad (55.41)$$

These must vanish. Therefore the equation

$$\frac{\partial U}{\partial t} + \sum_{i=1}^{3}\frac{\partial U_i}{\partial x_i} = 0 \qquad (55.42)$$

must hold. As is evident from the definition of U and the U_i (either by means of differential equations with boundary conditions or in terms of volume integrals) this equation is indeed satisfied as a consequence of the relation

$$\frac{\partial\rho}{\partial t} + \sum_{i=1}^{3}\frac{\partial(\rho v_i)}{\partial x_i} = 0 \qquad (55.43)$$

which expresses the law of mass conservation in Newtonian approximation.

Thus the expressions just derived for the metric tensor satisfy to first approximation not only the gravitational equations but also the "harmonic conditions". In addition they obviously satisfy the boundary conditions at infinity. The expression for the square of the elementary interval corresponding to the expressions derived is

$$ds^2 = (c^2 - 2U)\, dt^2 - \left(1 + \frac{2U}{c^2}\right)(dx_1^2 + dx_2^2 + dx_3^2)$$

$$+ \frac{8}{c^2}\, (U_1 dx_1 + U_2 dx_2 + U_3 dx_3)\, dt \qquad (55.44)$$

Usually the terms involving the products $dx_i\, dt$ are of no importance. Omitting them we get the expression

$$ds^2 = (c^2 - 2U)\, dt^2 - \left(1 + \frac{2U}{c^2}\right)(dx_1^2 + dx_2^2 + dx_3^2) \qquad (55.45)$$

which involves only the Newtonian potential. This expression has already been quoted without proof in Section 51, equation (51.11).

56. The Gravitational Equations in the Static Case and Conformal Space

The metric tensor is called static if its components do not depend on the time coordinate $x_0 = t$, so that

$$\frac{\partial g_{\mu\nu}}{\partial t} = 0 \qquad (56.01)$$

and if, in addition,

$$g_{0i} = 0 \qquad (i = 1, 2, 3) \qquad (56.02)$$

It is evident from physical considerations that if several masses are present they must be in motion†. Therefore a static metric tensor can only occur in the case of a single mass. In spite of limited applicability, the static case is of some physical interest, first of all because it permits a deeper insight into the analogy with the Newtonian theory of gravitation (which is also a static theory) and also because in the static case it is easy to discuss the question of the uniqueness of the solution. Also, rigouros solutions of Einstein's equations can be found in this case.

Under the conditions (56.01) and (56.02) the time coordinate is determined uniquely, while the space coordinates permit a group of transformations among themselves. Therefore it is natural, in this problem, to use the apparatus of three-dimensional tensor analysis and to write the gravitational equations accordingly. Three-dimensional tensor analysis can be applied either directly to the spatial part of ds^2, or else to this spatial part multiplied by some factor. Remembering the approximate form of (55.29) obtained from Einstein's equations, we introduce into the spatial part a factor inversely proportional to the factor in the time part, putting

$$ds^2 = c^2 V^2\, dt^2 - \frac{1}{V^2}\, h_{ik}\, dx_i\, dx_k \qquad (56.03)$$

We shall consider the quantity V^2 to be a three-dimensional scalar and the quadratic form

$$d\sigma^2 = h_{ik}\, dx_i\, dx_k \qquad (56.04)$$

---

† The problem of the motion of a system of masses is considered in detail in Chapter VI.

to be the squared length of arc in a certain auxiliary space, which we shall call *conformal* space. Three-dimensional tensor analysis will be applied to this conformal space. As may be seen by comparing (56.03) with (55.45), in the approximation in which the latter holds we can assume the conformal space to be Euclidean and the quantity V^2 to be related to the Newtonian potential U.

Thus we shall have

$$\left. \begin{array}{ll} g_{00} = c^2 V^2, \qquad g_{0i} = 0, \\[2mm] \qquad g_{ik} = -\dfrac{h_{ik}}{V^2}, \end{array} \right\} \tag{56.05}$$

and also

$$\left. \begin{array}{ll} g^{00} = \dfrac{1}{c^2 V^2}, \qquad g^{0i} = 0, \\[2mm] \qquad g^{ik} = -V^2 h^{ik} \end{array} \right\} \tag{56.06}$$

Here the quantities h_{ik} and h^{ik} are connected by

$$h_{ij} h^{kj} = h_i^k \qquad (h_i^k = \delta_i^k) \tag{56.07}$$

this relation being analogous to (37.18) for the $g_{\mu\nu}$. Denoting by h the determinant of the h_{ik} we easily obtain

$$\sqrt{(-g)} = \frac{c}{V^2}\sqrt{h} \tag{56.08}$$

Therefore we have

$$\left. \begin{array}{l} \sqrt{(-g)} \cdot g^{00} = \dfrac{1}{cV^4}\sqrt{h}, \\[3mm] \sqrt{(-g)} \cdot g^{ik} = -c\sqrt{h}\cdot h^{ik} \end{array} \right\} \tag{56.09}$$

and the d'Alembert operator (41.11) applied to a function ψ may be written as

$$\Box\psi = \frac{1}{c^2 V^2}\frac{\partial^2 \psi}{\partial t^2} - V^2(\Delta\psi)_h \tag{56.10}$$

where $(\Delta\psi)_h$ denotes the Laplace operator in the conformal space:

$$(\Delta\psi)_h = \frac{1}{\sqrt{h}}\frac{\partial}{\partial x_i}\left(\sqrt{h}\cdot h^{ik}\frac{\partial\psi}{\partial x_k}\right) \tag{56.11}$$

Hence we see that spatial coordinates that are harmonic in the four-dimensional sense will also be harmonic in the three-dimensional conformal space.

We denote the four-dimensional Christoffel symbols (formed from the metric tensor $g_{\mu\nu}$) by $(\Gamma^\rho_{\mu\nu})_g$ and the three-dimensional Christoffel symbols (formed from the metric tensor h_{ik}) by $(\Gamma_{ik})_h$. Similarly we shall attach suffixes g and h respectively to quantities that are tensors in relation to the metrics $(g_{\mu\nu})$ and (h_{ik}).

The four-dimensional Christoffel symbols and the curvature tensor can be expressed in terms of the corresponding three-dimensional quantities. These expressions will involve derivatives of the three-dimensional scalar V, which we will denote by

$$V_k = \frac{\partial V}{\partial x_k}, \qquad (V^i)_h = h^{ik} V_k \qquad (56.12)$$

The suffix h attached to the V^i will sometimes be omitted for brevity. The Christoffel symbols with purely spatial indices will be

$$(\Gamma^l_{ik})_g = (\Gamma^l_{ik})_h + h_{ik} \frac{(V^l)_h}{V} - h^l_k \frac{V_i}{V} - h^l_i \frac{V_k}{V} \qquad (56.13)$$

If one or all three indices are zero, the Christoffel symbols become zero:

$$(\Gamma^0_{00})_g = 0, \qquad (\Gamma^0_{ik})_g = 0, \qquad (\Gamma^k_{i0})_g = 0 \qquad (56.14)$$

Finally, if two of the indices are zero we get

$$(\Gamma^i_{00})_g = c^2 V^3 (V^i)_h; \qquad (\Gamma^0_{0i})_g = \frac{V_i}{V} \qquad (56.15)$$

Using the general formula

$$R^\rho_{\sigma,\,\mu\nu} = \frac{\partial \Gamma^\rho_{\sigma\mu}}{\partial x_\nu} - \frac{\partial \Gamma^\rho_{\sigma\nu}}{\partial x_\mu} + \Gamma^\alpha_{\sigma\mu} \Gamma^\rho_{\alpha\nu} - \Gamma^\alpha_{\sigma\nu} \Gamma^\rho_{\alpha\mu} \qquad (56.16)$$

we can express the four-dimensional curvature tensor in terms of a three-dimensional tensor and the covariant derivatives of the three-dimensional scalar V. Leaving out elementary, though rather tedious, calculations we obtain for the components with four spatial indices

$$(R^l_{i,mk})_g = (R^l_{i,mk})_h + h_{im} \frac{1}{V} (V^l_k)_h - h_{ik} \frac{1}{V} (V^l_m)_h$$

$$+ h^l_k \frac{1}{V} (V_{im})_h - h^l_m \frac{1}{V} (V_{ik})_h - (h_{im} h^l_k - h_{ik} h^l_m) \frac{1}{V^2} (V_j V^j)_h, \qquad (56.17)$$

where $(V_{ik})_h$ is the second covariant derivative of V with respect to the metric (h):

$$(V_{ik})_h = \frac{\partial^2 V}{\partial x_i \partial x_k} - (\Gamma^j_{ik})_h \frac{\partial V}{\partial x_j} \qquad (56.18)$$

and $(V^l_k)_h$ is the same derivative with a suffix raised:

$$(V^l_k)_h = h^{il} (V_{ik})_h \qquad (56.19)$$

If only one index is zero, we have

$$(R^0_{i,mk})_g = 0, \qquad (R^l_{0,mk})_g = 0, \qquad (R^l_{i,0k})_g = 0 \qquad (56.20)$$

If two indices are zero we get

$$(R^0_{0,mk})_g = 0 \qquad (56.21)$$

and also

$$(R^0_{i,0k})_g = \frac{1}{V} (V_{ik})_h + \frac{2}{V^2} V_i V_k - h_{ik} \cdot \frac{1}{V^2} (V_j V^j)_h \qquad (56.22)$$

and finally

$$(R^l_{0,0k})_g = c^2 V^2 \{ V V^l_k + 2 V^l V_k - h^l_k (V_j V^j) \}_h \qquad (56.23)$$

It is now simple to form the contracted curvature tensor which enters Einstein's gravitational equations.

Using the formula

$$(R_{ik})_g = (R_{i,\,mk}^m)_g + (R_{i,\,0k}^0)_g \tag{56.24}$$

we obtain from (56.17) and (56.22)

$$(R_{ik})_g = (R_{ik})_h - h_{ik} \cdot \frac{1}{V}(\Delta V)_h + \frac{2}{V^2} V_i V_k + h_{ik} \cdot \frac{1}{V}(V_j V^j)_h \tag{56.25}$$

where $(\Delta V)_h$ is the Laplace operator applied to V:

$$(\Delta V)_h = (V_i^k)_h = \frac{1}{\sqrt{h}}\frac{\partial}{\partial x_i}\left(\sqrt{h} \cdot h^{ik}\frac{\partial V}{\partial x_k}\right) \tag{56.26}$$

On the other hand the formula

$$(R_{00})_g = (R_{0,\,k0}^k)_g = -(R_{0,\,0k}^k)_g \tag{56.27}$$

gives, using (56.23),

$$(R_{00})_g = -c^2 V^2 \{V \cdot (\Delta V)_h - (V_j V^j)_h\} \tag{56.28}$$

As for the mixed components of $R_{\mu\nu}$, they vanish as a consequence of (56.20):

$$(R_{0i})_g = 0 \tag{56.29}$$

By virtue of the relations (56.06) between the four- and three-dimensional metric tensors, equations (56.25), (56.28) and (56.29) lead to the following expression for the invariant $(R)_g$:

$$(R)_g = -V^2(R)_h + 2V(\Delta V)_h - 4(V_j V^j)_h \tag{56.30}$$

We denote by $G_{\mu\nu}$ the conservative Einstein tensor

$$G_{\mu\nu} = (R_{\mu\nu})_g - \tfrac{1}{2}g_{\mu\nu}(R)_g \tag{56.31}$$

and by H_{ik} the conservative tensor in the conformal space

$$H_{ik} = (R_{ik})_h - \tfrac{1}{2}h_{ik}(R)_h \tag{56.32}$$

The invariant of the latter is

$$H = h^{ik}H_{ik} = -\tfrac{1}{2}(R)_h \tag{56.33}$$

as a result of which we have

$$(R_{ik})_h = H_{ik} - h_{ik}H \tag{56.34}$$

For the spatial part of the conservative Einstein tensor we obtain the simple expression

$$G_{ik} = H_{ik} + \frac{2}{V^2} V_i V_k - h_{ik}\frac{1}{V^2}(V_j V^j)_h \tag{56.35}$$

which is remarkable for the fact that it does not contain second derivatives of the three-dimensional scalar V.

The mixed components of the conservative tensor vanish,

$$G_{i0} = 0 \tag{56.36}$$

while the component G_{00} is given by

$$G_{00} = c^2 V^2 \{ -V^2 H - 2V(\Delta V)_h + 3(V_j V^j)_h \} \tag{56.37}$$

We go over to the formulation of the gravitational equations. We have just noted that the quantities G_{ik} do not contain second derivatives of V. On the other hand, (56.28) shows that R_{00} does not involve second derivatives of the h_{ik}. Therefore, if we write down the gravitational equations in a form solved with respect to R_{00} and G_{ik} the second derivatives of V and of h_{ik} will be separated from each other. By virtue of the general equations

$$R_{\mu\nu} = -\varkappa(T_{\mu\nu} - \tfrac{1}{2}g_{\mu\nu}T) \tag{56.38}$$

which are the covariant form of (53.03), we have

$$R_{00} = -\varkappa(T_{00} - \tfrac{1}{2}g_{00}T) \tag{56.39}$$

where T is the invariant

$$T = (T)_g = (T_0^0 + T_1^1 + T_2^2 + T_3^3)_g \tag{56.40}$$

Hence by virtue of (56.05) we get

$$R_{00} = -\tfrac{1}{2}\varkappa c^2 V^2 (T_0^0 - T_1^1 - T_2^2 - T_3^3)_g \tag{56.41}$$

and, by using the value (56.28) of R_{00}:

$$V \cdot (\Delta V)_h - (V_j V^j)_h = \tfrac{1}{2}\varkappa(T_0^0 - T_1^1 - T_2^2 - T_3^3)_g \tag{56.42}$$

The equations for the spatial components are

$$H_{ik} + \frac{2}{V^2} V_i V_k - h_{ik} \cdot \frac{1}{V^2} (V_j V^j)_h = -\varkappa T_{ik} \tag{56.43}$$

As regards the equations for the mixed components,

$$G_{i0} = -\varkappa T_{i0} \tag{56.44}$$

they are satisfied identically, because here the left-hand side is zero by virtue of (56.36) and the right-hand side is also zero, because the mass current is zero.

The equations so obtained acquire a more pictorial form if one introduces some new symbols.

We put

$$\mu = \frac{1}{V^2} (T_0^0 - T_1^1 - T_2^2 - T_3^3)_g \tag{56.45}$$

The quantity μ can also be written in the form

$$\mu = c^2 T^{00} + h^{ik} T_{ik} \tag{56.45'}$$

As may be seen by comparing this with the approximate expression (55.02) the quantity μ represents a certain mass density; we shall see that it can be interpreted as the mass density in the conformal space.

Further, we replace V by the quantity ϕ, according to the formula

$$V = e^{-\phi} \tag{56.46}$$

so that the relation between the space-time metric and the metric in the conformal space takes on the form

$$ds^2 = c^2 e^{-2\phi} dt^2 - e^{2\phi} d\sigma^2 \tag{56.47}$$

we have

$$\frac{\partial \phi}{\partial x_i} \equiv \phi_i = -\frac{V_i}{V}$$

$$\Delta\phi = -\frac{\Delta V}{V} + \frac{V_j V^j}{V^2} \tag{56.48}$$

Therefore, the gravitational equations (56.42) and (56.43) may be written as

$$(\Delta\phi)_h = -\tfrac{1}{2}\varkappa\mu \tag{56.49}$$

$$H_{ik} = -2\phi_i\phi_k + h_{ik}(\phi_j\phi^j)_h - \varkappa T_{ik} \tag{56.50}$$

The first of these equations is essentially Poisson's equation for the Newtonian potential U. Indeed, the symbol Δ is a generalization of the Laplace operator, μ is the mass density and, by (55.15), the constant $\varkappa$ is given by

$$\varkappa = \frac{8\pi\gamma}{c^2} \tag{56.51}$$

Therefore if we put

$$\phi = \frac{U}{c^2} \tag{56.52}$$

the quantity U will satisfy the equation

$$(\Delta U)_h = -4\pi\gamma\mu \tag{56.53}$$

which differs but slightly from equation (55.13) for the Newtonian potential. We can also put

$$\phi_i = \frac{g_i}{c^2} \tag{56.54}$$

where g_i is a component of the gravitational acceleration.

Let us now clarify the physical meaning of (56.50). Apart from a factor the terms involving the ϕ_i can be interpreted as gravitational stresses. If we put

$$2\phi_i\phi_k - h_{ik}(\phi_j\phi^j)_h = \varkappa T_{ik}^* \tag{56.55}$$

we can replace (56.50) by

$$H_{ik} = -\varkappa(T_{ik}^* + T_{ik}) \tag{56.56}$$

The three-dimensional divergence of the tensor T_{ik}, understood as referring to the metric (h_{ik}) is

$$(\nabla^k T_{ik}^*)_h = \frac{2}{\varkappa}\phi_i(\Delta\phi)_h \tag{56.57}$$

and by (56.49) we have

$$(\nabla^k T_{ik}^*)_h - \mu\phi_i \tag{56.58}$$

On the other hand, since H_{ik} is a *conservative* tensor in the conformal space, its divergence is zero. Therefore, apart from its sign, the divergence of the gravitational stress tensor is equal to the divergence of the tensor of elastic and other static stresses T_{ik}. Thus we have

$$(\nabla^k T_{ik})_h = \mu \phi_i \qquad (56.59)$$

These equations represent a generalization of the usual equations in the statics of elastic bodies in a gravitational field.

The equations for the statics in conformal space, written in the form (56.56) stand in analogy to Einstein's equations in space-time. In both sets of equations the left-hand side involves a conservative tensor, while on the right there is a stress tensor or its four-dimensional generalization. Here the gravitational stresses appear in explicit form only after space has been split off from time and after passage to the conformal space.

The conformal space will be almost Euclidean. Indeed, as is seen from (56.54) and from the estimates (55.02) for the tensor T_{ik} the right-hand side of (56.56) will be of the order g_i^2/c^2. This leads to the result that the deviation of the h_{ik} from their Euclidean values will be of the order U^2/c^4. This result is in agreement with the approximate formula (55.45), which was just the basis for introducing the conformal space.

For empty space, when $T_{\alpha\beta} = 0$ and $\mu = 0$, equation (56.49) is a consequence of (56.50). It is easy to see this by equating the divergence of H_{ik} to zero and using (56.57).

If the mass tensor $T_{\alpha\beta}$ is zero in the whole of space, the only static solution of Einstein's equations which has no singular points and which satisfies the boundary conditions will be the solution corresponding to Euclidean space and pseudo-Euclidean space-time. This can be shown in the following manner. In the case of empty space, equation (56.49) gives $(\Delta\phi)_h = 0$. This is an equation of the elliptic type for ϕ, which represents a generalization of Laplace's equation. The function ϕ and its derivatives ϕ_i must be everywhere finite and continuous and at spatial infinity they must tend to zero. But the only solution of Laplace's equation that satisfies these conditions is the solution $\phi = 0$. But then the derivatives ϕ_i will also vanish and therefore also expression (56.55). Since in addition $T_{ik} = 0$ we also have $H_{ik} = 0$. Hence it follows that the curvature tensor of the conformal space is zero, and the space itself Euclidean (see Appendix G).

57. Rigorous Solution of the Gravitational Equations for a Single Concentrated Mass

In the case of a concentrated mass a rigorous spherically symmetric solution of the gravitational equations can be found. As we are dealing with a static case we can use the results of the foregoing section, and write ds^2 as

$$ds^2 = c^2 V^2 \, dt^2 - \frac{1}{V^2} \, d\sigma^2 \qquad (57.01)$$

$$d\sigma^2 = h_{ik} \, dx_i \, dx_k \qquad (57.02)$$

If x_1, x_2 and x_3 are harmonic coordinates we can introduce spherical coordinates related to them by putting

$$x_1 = r^* \sin \vartheta \cos \varphi$$
$$x_2 = r^* \sin \vartheta \sin \varphi \qquad (57.03)$$
$$x_3 = r^* \cos \vartheta$$

The assumption of spherical symmetry implies that the expression for $d\sigma^2$ is of the form

$$d\sigma^2 = F^2 \, dr^{*2} + \rho^2(d\vartheta^2 + \sin^2\vartheta \, d\varphi^2) \qquad (57.04)$$

where F and ρ are functions of r^* only. The coefficient V must also be taken to depend only on r^*.

We note first of all that if we put

$$F \, dr^* = dr \qquad (57.05)$$

we can reduce the general expression (57.04) to the case $F = 1$, so that

$$d\sigma^2 = dr^2 + \rho^2(d\vartheta^2 + \sin^2 \vartheta \, d\varphi^2) \qquad (57.06)$$

It is true that in doing this it may happen that the radius-vector r will be " non-harmonic ", in the sense that it is not related to the harmonic coordinates, x_1, x_2 and x_3 by equations of the form (57.03). But having formed Laplace's equation for the quantities (57.03) with r^* replaced by r one can always go over afterwards to a " harmonic " radius vector r^*.

For the metric (57.06) we get

$$\left. \begin{array}{llll} h_{rr} = 1, & h_{\vartheta\vartheta} = \rho^2, & h_{\varphi\varphi} = \rho^2 \sin^2 \vartheta, \\[2mm] h_{\vartheta\varphi} = 0, & h_{\varphi r} = 0, & h_{r\vartheta} = 0 \end{array} \right\} \qquad (57.07)$$

and therefore

$$\left. \begin{array}{llll} h^{rr} = 1, & h^{\vartheta\vartheta} = \dfrac{1}{\rho^2}, & h^{\varphi\varphi} = \dfrac{1}{\rho^2 \sin^2 \vartheta}, \\[3mm] h^{\vartheta\varphi} = 0, & h^{\varphi r} = 0, & h^{r\vartheta} = 0 \end{array} \right\} \qquad (57.08)$$

Hence

$$\sqrt{h} = \rho^2 \sin \vartheta \qquad (57.09)$$

and the Laplace operator in the conformal space may be written as

$$\Delta\psi = \frac{1}{\rho^2} \frac{\partial}{\partial r} \left(\rho^2 \frac{\partial\psi}{\partial r} \right) + \frac{1}{\rho^2} \Delta^* \psi \qquad (57.10)$$

where $\Delta^*\psi$ is the Laplace operator on a sphere:

$$\Delta^*\psi = \frac{1}{\sin \vartheta} \frac{\partial}{\partial \vartheta} \left(\sin \vartheta \frac{\partial\psi}{\partial \vartheta} \right) + \frac{1}{\sin^2 \vartheta} \frac{\partial^2\psi}{\partial \varphi^2} \qquad (57.11)$$

As a consequence of (56.10) the harmonic coordinates must satisfy Laplace's equation in conformal space. For the quantities (57.03) we have

$$\Delta^* x_i = -2x_i \qquad (57.12)$$

Therefore the condition for harmonic coordinates

$$\Delta x_i = 0 \qquad (57.13)$$

reduces to the form

$$\frac{d}{dr}\left(\rho^2\frac{dr^*}{dr}\right) - 2r^* = 0 \tag{57.14}$$

This is the equation to be used in passing from the initial radius vector r to the harmonic one, r^*.

By applying the general formulae to the metric tensor (57.07) and (57.08) the following expressions for the 18 Christoffel symbols can be derived:

$$\left.\begin{array}{lll}
\Gamma^r_{rr} = 0, & \Gamma^\vartheta_{rr} = 0, & \Gamma^\varphi_{rr} = 0, \\[2mm]
\Gamma^r_{\vartheta\vartheta} = -\rho\rho', & \Gamma^\vartheta_{\vartheta\vartheta} = 0, & \Gamma^\varphi_{\vartheta\vartheta} = 0, \\[2mm]
\Gamma^r_{\varphi\varphi} = -\rho\rho'\sin^2\vartheta, & \Gamma^\vartheta_{\varphi\varphi} = -\sin\vartheta\cos\vartheta, & \Gamma^\varphi_{\varphi\varphi} = 0, \\[2mm]
\Gamma^r_{r\vartheta} = 0, & \Gamma^\vartheta_{r\vartheta} = \dfrac{\rho'}{\rho}, & \Gamma^\varphi_{r\vartheta} = 0, \\[3mm]
\Gamma^r_{r\varphi} = 0, & \Gamma^\vartheta_{r\varphi} = 0, & \Gamma^\varphi_{r\varphi} = \dfrac{\rho'}{\rho}, \\[3mm]
\Gamma^r_{\vartheta\varphi} = 0, & \Gamma^\vartheta_{\vartheta\varphi} = 0, & \Gamma^\varphi_{\vartheta\varphi} = \cot\vartheta
\end{array}\right\} \tag{57.15}$$

Here the prime denotes differentiation with respect to r. The Christoffel symbols and all tensor quantities used in this section refer only to the conformal space; therefore there is no necessity to attach a suffix, as was done in Section 56.

Using the Christoffel symbols tabulated in (57.15) we form the three-dimensional fourth rank curvature tensor and then, using the equations

$$\left.\begin{array}{ll}
R_{rr} = R^\vartheta_{r,\,\vartheta r} + R^\varphi_{r,\,\varphi r}; & R_{r\vartheta} = R^\varphi_{r,\,\varphi\vartheta}; \\[2mm]
R_{\vartheta\vartheta} = R^r_{\vartheta,\,r\vartheta} + R^\varphi_{\vartheta,\,\varphi\vartheta}; & R_{r\varphi} = R^\vartheta_{r,\,\vartheta\varphi}; \\[2mm]
R_{\varphi\varphi} = R^r_{\varphi,\,r\varphi} + R^\vartheta_{\varphi,\,\vartheta\varphi}; & R_{\vartheta\varphi} = R^r_{\vartheta,\,r\varphi}
\end{array}\right\} \tag{57.16}$$

the second rank curvature tensor in the conformal space. In the equations for the non-diagonal components we have omitted terms in which the first lower index is equal to the upper index: owing to the symmetry properties of the fourth rank curvature tensor these terms vanish if the coordinate system is orthogonal. In the general formula (56.16) we leave only those terms which are different from zero and so obtain

$$R^\vartheta_{r,\,\vartheta r} = \frac{\partial\Gamma^\vartheta_{r\vartheta}}{\partial r} + \Gamma^\vartheta_{r\vartheta}\Gamma^\vartheta_{\vartheta r} \tag{57.17}$$

and after inserting the values of the Christoffel symbols from (57.15)

$$R^\vartheta_{r,\,\vartheta r} = \frac{\rho''}{\rho} \tag{57.18}$$

The calculation shows that $R^\varphi_{r,\varphi r}$ has the same value:

$$R^\varphi_{r,\,\varphi r} = \frac{\rho''}{\rho} \tag{57.19}$$

Therefore

$$R_{rr} = 2\frac{\rho''}{\rho} \tag{57.20}$$

Further, we have

$$R^r_{\vartheta,\, r\vartheta} = -\frac{\partial \Gamma^r_{\vartheta r}}{\partial r} + \Gamma^\vartheta_{\vartheta r}\Gamma^r_{\vartheta\vartheta} \tag{57.21}$$

whence

$$R^r_{\vartheta,\, r\vartheta} = \rho\rho'' \tag{57.22}$$

Continuing the calculation, we get

$$R^\varphi_{\vartheta,\, \varphi\vartheta} = \frac{\partial \Gamma^\varphi_{\vartheta\varphi}}{\partial \vartheta} + \Gamma^\varphi_{\vartheta\varphi}\Gamma^\varphi_{\vartheta\varphi} - \Gamma^r_{\vartheta\vartheta}\Gamma^\varphi_{r\varphi} \tag{57.23}$$

whence

$$R^\varphi_{\vartheta,\, \varphi\vartheta} = -1 + \rho'^2 \tag{57.24}$$

Inserting (57.22) and (57.24) into (57.16) we find for $R_{\vartheta\vartheta}$ the expression

$$R_{\vartheta\vartheta} = \rho\rho'' + \rho'^2 - 1 \tag{57.25}$$

Similar calculations give

$$R_{\varphi\varphi} = \sin^2\vartheta R_{\vartheta\vartheta} \tag{57.26}$$

as was to be expected for reasons of spherical symmetry. The non-diagonal elements of the second rank curvature tensor prove to be zero:

$$R_{r\vartheta} = 0, \qquad R_{r\varphi} = 0, \qquad R_{\vartheta\varphi} = 0 \tag{57.27}$$

The invariant of the three-dimensional curvature tensor can be calculated from the formula

$$R = R_{rr} + \frac{2}{\rho^2} R_{\vartheta\vartheta} \tag{57.28}$$

and will be given by

$$R = \frac{2}{\rho^2} (2\rho\rho'' + \rho'^2 - 1) \tag{57.29}$$

Applying equation (56.32) we get the following simple expression for the conservative tensor of the conformal space

$$\left. \begin{array}{lll} H_{rr} = \dfrac{1 - \rho'^2}{\rho^2}, & H_{\vartheta\vartheta} = -\rho\rho'', & H_{\varphi\varphi} = -\rho\rho'' \sin^2\vartheta, \\[2mm] H_{r\vartheta} = 0, & H_{r\varphi} = 0, & H_{\vartheta\varphi} = 0 \end{array} \right\} \tag{57.30}$$

We could have obtained these expressions by a somewhat simpler method using the relation which, in three-dimensional space, connects the covariant fourth rank tensor and the conservative tensor. This relation is discussed in Appendix G. In the notation of this section equations (G.13) of the Appendix may be written in the form

$$\left. \begin{array}{lll} hH^{rr} = R_{\vartheta\varphi,\, \vartheta\varphi}; & hH^{\vartheta\vartheta} = R_{r\varphi,\, r\varphi}; & hH^{\varphi\varphi} = R_{r\vartheta,\, r\vartheta}; \\[2mm] hH^{\vartheta\varphi} = R_{\varphi r,\, r\vartheta}; & hH^{\varphi r} = R_{r\vartheta,\, \vartheta\varphi}; & hH^{r\vartheta} = R_{\vartheta\varphi,\, \varphi r} \end{array} \right\} \tag{57.31}$$

It is easy to see that these formulae lead to expressions (57.30) as previously found.

The formulae we have derived allow us to write down Einstein's gravitational equations in explicit form. In the previous section we saw that if one writes ds^2 in the form

$$ds^2 = c^2 e^{-2\phi} dt^2 - e^{2\phi} d\sigma^2 \tag{57.32}$$

where $d\sigma^2$ has the value (57.04), the gravitational equations appear as

$$\Delta\phi = -\tfrac{1}{2}\varkappa\mu \tag{57.33}$$

$$H_{ik} = -2\phi_i\phi_k + h_{ik}(\phi_j\phi^j) - \varkappa T_{ik} \tag{57.34}$$

where the "mass density" μ is given by (56.44) and (56.45). Going over to the present case of a mass concentrated at a point and using spherical coordinates, in which the Laplace operator has the form (57.10) while the quantities H_{ik} are given by (57.30), we obtain

$$\Delta\phi = \frac{1}{\rho^2}\frac{d}{dr}(\rho^2\phi') = 0 \tag{57.35}$$

$$\left.\begin{aligned} H_{rr} &= \frac{1 - \rho'^2}{\rho^2} = -\phi'^2, \\[1mm] H_{\vartheta\vartheta} &= -\rho\rho'' = \rho^2\phi'^2 \end{aligned}\right\} \tag{57.36}$$

The equation for $H_{\varphi\varphi}$ differs from that for $H_{\vartheta\vartheta}$ only by the factor $\sin^2\vartheta$, while the remaining equations of (57.34) are satisfied identically.

Integrating (57.35) we get

$$\rho^2\phi' = -\alpha \tag{57.37}$$

where α is a constant. Since equation (57.35) is a limiting case of (57.33) with positive μ, the constant α should be taken positive. Indeed, considering first (57.33) and putting

$$4\pi\int\mu\rho^2\,dr = M \tag{57.38}$$

where the integral is extended over the whole region in which μ differs from zero, we see that (57.37) holds everywhere outside this region, with α given by

$$\alpha = \frac{\gamma M}{c^2} \tag{57.39}$$

Here γ is the Newtonian gravitational constant, related to $\varkappa$ by (56.51). Evidently M is the mass of the gravitating body; in going over to the case of a concentrated mass this quantity, and with it α, remain finite and positive. The dimensions of α are those of a length, which is why it is called the gravitational radius of the mass.

Inserting the value of ϕ' from (57.37) into the first equation of (57.36) we obtain

$$\rho'^2 = 1 + \frac{\alpha^2}{\rho^2} \tag{57.40}$$

and taking the square root so as to satisfy the requirement that we have $\rho' \to +1$ at infinity, we get

$$\rho\rho' = \sqrt{(\rho^2 + \alpha^2)} \tag{57.41}$$

Differentiating this expression with respect to r we obtain

$$\rho\rho'' + \rho'^2 = 1 \tag{57.42}$$

which shows that the second equation of (57.36) is also satisfied.

The differential equation (57.41) is easy to solve by quadrature; after setting the additive constant zero, we get

$$r = \sqrt{(\rho^2 + \alpha^2)} \tag{57.43}$$

whence

$$\rho = \sqrt{(r^2 - \alpha^2)} \tag{57.44}$$

Thus finally

$$d\sigma^2 = dr^2 + (r^2 - \alpha^2)(d\vartheta^2 + \sin^2\vartheta \, d\varphi^2) \tag{57.45}$$

By its physical nature ρ must be positive and therefore the range of variation of r is

$$r \geqslant \alpha \tag{57.46}$$

We must now discuss the harmonic condition. Inserting the value of ρ from (57.44) into (57.14) we see that the harmonic radius vector r^* satisfies the equation

$$\frac{d}{dr}(r^2 - \alpha^2)\frac{dr^*}{dr} - 2r^* = 0 \tag{57.47}$$

Evidently this equation has the solution

$$r^* = r \tag{57.48}$$

It is easy to show that this is uniquely the solution which for finite r remains finite in the whole region (57.46) and which at infinity differs from r by not more than a finite quantity. Therefore the variable r which enters our formulae is itself the harmonic radius vector and in place of (57.03) we can simply write

$$\left.\begin{array}{l} x_1 = r \sin\vartheta \cos\varphi, \\ x_2 = r \sin\vartheta \sin\varphi, \\ x_3 = r \cos\vartheta. \end{array}\right\} \tag{57.49}$$

It remains to find the quantity ϕ. Integrating (57.37) and taking into account the boundary conditions we get from (57.44)

$$\phi = \int_r^\infty \frac{\alpha \, dr}{r^2 - \alpha^2} \tag{57.50}$$

or

$$\phi = \frac{1}{2}\ln\frac{r + \alpha}{r - \alpha} \tag{57.51}$$

Hence

$$V^2 = \frac{r - \alpha}{r + \alpha} \tag{57.52}$$

The expression (57.01) or (57.32) for ds^2 takes on the form

$$ds^2 = c^2 \frac{r - \alpha}{r + \alpha} dt^2 - \frac{r + \alpha}{r - \alpha} d\sigma^2 \qquad (57.53)$$

and, after inserting the value of $d\sigma^2$ from equation (57.45) we get

$$ds^2 = c^2 \left(\frac{r - \alpha}{r + \alpha}\right) dt^2 - \left(\frac{r + \alpha}{r - \alpha}\right) dr^2 - (r + \alpha)^2 (d\vartheta^2 + \sin^2 \vartheta \, d\varphi^2) \quad (57.54)$$

The rigorous solution so obtained confirms our conclusion that the conformal space is almost Euclidean and that ϕ is approximately equal to U/c^2, where U is the Newtonian potential for which we can put

$$U = \frac{\gamma M}{r} \qquad (57.55)$$

Indeed, equation (57.45) shows that the components of the metric tensor of $d\sigma^2$ have relative deviations from their Euclidean values of the order

$$\frac{\alpha^2}{r^2} = \frac{U^2}{c^4} \qquad (57.56)$$

and that the error of replacing ϕ by U/c^2 will be of the same order. As the estimate given in the following section will show, the quantity (57.56) is extremely small. One should note that such close agreement with Newton's theory is obtained only if harmonic coordinates are used.

The solution of the problem of a concentrated mass in a form equivalent to (57.54), but in arbitrary non-harmonic coordinates, was first derived by Schwarzschild [18] and is often named after him.

58. The Motion of the Perihelion of a Planet

We have found a rigorous solution of the gravitational equations which may now be applied to the investigation of the gravitational fields of the Sun and the planets.

We have

$$ds^2 = c^2 \left(\frac{r - \alpha}{r + \alpha}\right) dt^2 - \left(\frac{r + \alpha}{r - \alpha}\right) dr^2 - (r + \alpha)^2 (d\vartheta^2 + \sin^2 \vartheta \, d\varphi^2)$$

$$(58.01)$$

where

$$\alpha = \frac{\gamma M}{c^2} \qquad (58.02)$$

is the gravitational radius of the mass M. For the Sun, and even more so for the planets, the gravitational radius α is much smaller than the geometric radius L, which may be defined as the radius of a sphere of volume equal to that of the body. We can set up the following table:

	Sun	Earth	Moon
α	1·48 km	0·443 cm	0·0053 cm
L	696,000 km	6,370 km	1,738 km
$\alpha : L$	2×10^{-6}	7×10^{-10}	3×10^{-11}

For super-dense stars α is of the same order as for the Sun while L, though smaller than for the Sun is not more than a hundred times smaller. Because of the smallness of $\alpha : L$ the metric of space-time is not very far from Euclidean even near and inside the mass. This is all the more true in the conformal space, where by equation (57.56) the deviations from Euclidean values will be of the order $(\alpha/L)^2$. In comparing ds^2 with its Galilean value one must remember that the coefficient of dt^2 has the large factor c^2, while there is no such factor in the spatial part. Therefore, when the speeds involved are low, as in planetary motion, the deviation of g_{00} from a constant value shows up much more sensitively than do comparable relative deviations in the spatial part of the interval. Even in Newtonian approximation the Galilean value $g_{00} = c^2$ must be replaced by the more accurate expression $g_{00} = c^2 - 2U$.

We shall now compare our rigorous solution of the gravitational equations with the approximate solution discussed in Section 55. To do this we must transform (58.01) from spherical to rectangular coordinates which must be harmonic. We can write the spatial part of (58.01)

$$dl^2 = \frac{r+\alpha}{r-\alpha} dr^2 + (r+\alpha)^2(d\vartheta^2 + \sin^2\vartheta \, d\varphi^2) \tag{58.03}$$

in the form

$$dl^2 = \frac{r+\alpha}{r-\alpha} \cdot \frac{\alpha^2}{r^2} dr^2 + \left(1 + \frac{\alpha}{r}\right)^2 (dr^2 + r^2 \, d\vartheta^2 + r^2 \sin^2\vartheta \, d\varphi^2) \tag{58.04}$$

In this last form it is simple to pass to rectangular coordinates. We get

$$ds^2 = c^2 \frac{r-\alpha}{r+\alpha} dt^2 - \left(1 + \frac{\alpha}{r}\right)^2 (dx_1^2 + dx_2^2 + dx_3^2)$$

$$- \frac{r+\alpha}{r-\alpha} \frac{\alpha^2}{r^4} (x_1 \, dx_1 + x_2 \, dx_2 + x_3 \, dx_3)^2 \tag{58.05}$$

whence

$$g_{ik} = -\left(1 + \frac{\alpha}{r}\right)^2 \delta_{ik} - \frac{r+\alpha}{r-\alpha} \cdot \frac{\alpha^2}{r^4} x_i x_k \tag{58.06}$$

and also

$$g_{00} = c^2 \frac{r-\alpha}{r+\alpha}; \qquad g_{0i} = 0 \tag{58.07}$$

If in (58.05) we neglect the square of the ratio α/r we obtain the approximate expression (55.45) with the Newtonian potential

$$U = c^2 \frac{\alpha}{r} = \frac{\gamma M}{r} \tag{58.08}$$

Equations (58.06) and (58.07) lead to the following value of the determinant g in harmonic coordinates

$$g = -c^2 \left(1 + \frac{\alpha}{r}\right)^4 \tag{58.09}$$

We note that the quantity

$$\sqrt[4]{\left(-\frac{g}{c^2}\right)} = 1 + \frac{\alpha}{r} \tag{58.10}$$

satisfies a Laplace equation with Euclidean coefficients. In the next chapter (Section 68) we shall see that quite generally the fourth root of $(-g/c^2)$ approximately satisfies a d'Alembert equation with Euclidean coefficients.

Using (58.06) and (58.07) again, or else transforming directly the equation

$$g^{\mu\nu}\frac{\partial\psi}{\partial x_\mu}\frac{\partial\psi}{\partial x_\nu} = \frac{r+\alpha}{r-\alpha}\cdot\frac{1}{c^2}\left(\frac{\partial\psi}{\partial t}\right)^2 - \left(\frac{r-\alpha}{r+\dot\alpha}\right)\left(\frac{\partial\psi}{\partial r}\right)^2$$
$$-\frac{1}{(r+\alpha)^2}\left[\left(\frac{\partial\psi}{\partial\vartheta}\right)^2 + \frac{1}{\sin^2\vartheta}\left(\frac{\partial\psi}{\partial\varphi}\right)^2\right] \quad (58.11)$$

to rectangular coordinates, we obtain the values of the contravariant components of the metric tensor. We give the expressions for these components multiplied by $\sqrt{(-g)}$. They are

$$\mathfrak{g}^{ik} = \sqrt{(-g)}\cdot g^{ik} = -c\delta_{ik} + c\alpha^2\frac{x_i x_k}{r^4} \quad (58.12)$$

and
$$\mathfrak{g}^{00} = \frac{1}{c}\frac{(1+\alpha/r)^3}{1-\alpha/r}; \qquad \mathfrak{g}^{0i} = 0 \quad (58.13)$$

These relations allow one to verify readily that our coordinates are really harmonic and that

$$\frac{\partial\mathfrak{g}^{ik}}{\partial x_k} = 0 \quad (58.14)$$

Having found the gravitational potentials for the field of a concentrated mass we can determine the motion of a particle in the field with the aid of the assumption that it will move along a geodesic. We saw in Section 51 that this assumption is in agreement with Newtonian mechanics. A fuller justification of this law of the motion of a mass point will be given in Section 63, where it will be deduced from the gravitational equations.

As we know the equations of a geodesic are obtainable from the variational principle

$$\delta\int ds = 0 \quad (58.15)$$

which may also be written in the form

$$\delta\int L\,dt = 0 \quad (58.16)$$

Here L is the Lagrangian and in our case it is equal to the square root of the expression

$$L^2 = c^2\frac{r-\alpha}{r+\alpha} - \left(1+\frac{\alpha}{r}\right)^2(\dot x_1^2 + \dot x_2^2 + \dot x_3^2) - \frac{r+\alpha}{r-\alpha}\frac{\alpha^2}{r^4}(x_1\dot x_1 + x_2\dot x_2 + x_3\dot x_3)^2$$
$$(58.17)$$

in which the dots denote differentiation with respect to time. We thus have before us a simple problem in point mechanics.

In order to solve this problem we note first that the Lagrangian is spherically symmetric. This means that it does not change when the sets of quantities (x_1, x_2, x_3) and $(\dot x_1, \dot x_2, \dot x_3)$ undergo the same linear orthogonal transformation. A consequence of this, as always in mechanics (and see also Section 27), is that there exist the integrals of the motion

$$x_2 \frac{\partial L}{\partial \dot{x}_3} - x_3 \frac{\partial L}{\partial \dot{x}_2} = c_1$$

$$x_3 \frac{\partial L}{\partial \dot{x}_1} - x_1 \frac{\partial L}{\partial \dot{x}_3} = c_2 \qquad (58.18)$$

$$x_1 \frac{\partial L}{\partial \dot{x}_2} - x_2 \frac{\partial L}{\partial \dot{x}_1} = c_3$$

Consequently the trajectory of the particle lies in the plane

$$c_1 x_1 + c_2 x_2 + c_3 x_3 = 0 \qquad (58.19)$$

It does not restrict the generality of the problem to choose this plane as one of the coordinate planes, so that

$$x_3 = 0 ; \qquad \dot{x}_3 = 0 \qquad (58.20)$$

We then have to deal only with motions in the plane, and plane polar coordinates are most convenient for this. Our previous spherical coordinates reduce to these if we put

$$\vartheta = \tfrac{1}{2}\pi ; \qquad \dot{\vartheta} = 0 \qquad (58.21)$$

Rewriting the square of the Lagrangian in these polar coordinates we get

$$L^2 = c^2 \frac{r - \alpha}{r + \alpha} - \frac{r + \alpha}{r - \alpha} \dot{r}^2 - (r + \alpha)^2 \dot{\varphi}^2 \qquad (58.22)$$

The Lagrangian is independent of the time t and also independent of the angle φ. This immediately gives us two integrals :

$$\dot{r} \frac{\partial L}{\partial \dot{r}} + \dot{\varphi} \frac{\partial L}{\partial \dot{\varphi}} - L = \text{const.} \qquad (58.23)$$

and
$$\frac{\partial L}{\partial \dot{\varphi}} = \text{const.} \qquad (58.24)$$

which correspond to the usual integrals of energy and of angular momentum. Remembering that

$$L \, dt = ds = c \, d\tau \qquad (58.25)$$

where τ is the proper time, we can rewrite the integrals (58.23) and (58.24) as

$$\frac{r - \alpha}{r + \alpha} \frac{dt}{d\tau} = \varepsilon \qquad (58.26)$$

and
$$(r + \alpha)^2 \frac{d\varphi}{d\tau} = \mu \qquad (58.27)$$

Here ε and μ are constants. The quantity μ can be interpreted as the angular momentum of a unit mass. If we put

$$\varepsilon = 1 + \frac{E_0}{c^2} \qquad (58.28)$$

where E_0 is a new constant, our equations show that in non-relativistic approximation

$$E_0 = \tfrac{1}{2} v^2 - \frac{\gamma M}{r} \qquad (58.29)$$

so that E_0 is the total energy of a particle of unit mass.

An algebraic consequence of (58.26) and (58.27) is the relation

$$\left(\frac{dr}{d\tau}\right)^2 = c^2\varepsilon^2 - c^2\frac{r-\alpha}{r+\alpha} - \frac{\mu^2(r-\alpha)}{(r+\alpha)^3} \tag{58.30}$$

It is derived by inserting (58.26) and (58.27) into the identity

$$c^2\left(\frac{r-\alpha}{r+\alpha}\right)\left(\frac{dt}{d\tau}\right)^2 - \left(\frac{r+\alpha}{r-\alpha}\right)\left(\frac{dr}{d\tau}\right)^2 - (r+\alpha)^2\left(\frac{d\varphi}{d\tau}\right)^2 = c^2 \tag{58.31}$$

The foregoing equations give us three first order differential equations for the quantities r, φ and t as functions of τ. The solution of these equations evidently reduces to quadratures. We shall not give the integrals explicitly but will confine ourselves to the discussion of the trajectory of the particle, i.e. of the dependence of r on φ.

Eliminating $d\tau$ from (58.27) and (58.30) we obtain

$$\left(\frac{dr}{d\varphi}\right)^2 = \frac{c^2\varepsilon^2}{\mu^2}(r+\alpha)^4 - \frac{c^2}{\mu^2}(r+\alpha)^3(r-\alpha) - (r+\alpha)(r-\alpha) \tag{58.32}$$

We have here on the right-hand side a polynomial of the fourth degree in r. Therefore φ will be expressible in terms of r as an elliptic integral of the first kind and conversely r will be an elliptic function of φ. The real period of this elliptic function will differ somewhat from 2π and therefore the orbit will not be a closed one. The polynomial on the right-hand side of (58.32) obviously has the one negative root $r = -\alpha$; it also has a small positive root

$$r_0 \sim \alpha + \frac{8\alpha^3c^2\varepsilon^2}{\mu^2} \tag{58.33}$$

and two further roots r_1 and r_2. If $\varepsilon^2 < 1$ both these roots are positive and we shall always have $r_1 < r < r_2$, i.e. the orbital motion is a finite one. If, on the other hand, $\varepsilon^2 > 1$, one of the roots, say r_2, becomes negative; we then have $r_1 < r$, and the orbit extends to infinity. If $\varepsilon^2 = 1$ we have $r_2 = \infty$.

If we introduce the variable

$$u = \frac{1}{r} \tag{58.34}$$

in place of r and write the polynomial in an expanded form, we get

$$\left(\frac{du}{d\varphi}\right)^2 = \frac{c^2(\varepsilon^2-1)}{\mu^2} + \frac{2\alpha c^2}{\mu^2}(2\varepsilon^2-1)u + \left(\frac{6\alpha^2c^2\varepsilon^2}{\mu^2}-1\right)u^2$$
$$+ \frac{2\alpha^3c^2(2\varepsilon^2+1)}{\mu^2}u^3 + \alpha^2\left(1+\frac{\alpha^2c^2(\varepsilon^2+1)}{\mu^2}\right)u^4 \tag{58.35}$$

We now estimate the orders of magnitude of the various terms in this expression. As in Section 55 we introduce a characteristic velocity q and a characteristic length l. Then we have, in orders of magnitude

$$\varepsilon^2 - 1 \sim \frac{q^2}{c^2}; \qquad \mu^2 \sim l^2 q^2$$

$$\alpha \sim \frac{q^2}{c^2} l; \qquad u \sim \frac{1}{l}$$

From these estimates we can easily see that on the right-hand of (58.35) the terms involving the zero, first and second powers of a u are of the order of $1/l^2$ whereas the terms containing the third and fourth powers of u are of order $(q^4/c^4) \cdot 1/l^2$. If, therefore, we merely neglect some very small terms, namely those of order q^4/c^4 (or α^2/l^2) compared to unity, we can drop the last two terms in (58.35) leaving the equation

$$\left(\frac{du}{d\varphi}\right)^2 = \frac{c^2(\varepsilon^2 - 1)}{\mu^2} + \frac{2\alpha c^2}{\mu^2}(2\varepsilon^2 - 1)u + \left(\frac{6\alpha^2 c^2 \varepsilon^2}{\mu^2} - 1\right)u^2 \qquad (58.36)$$

The roots of this quadratic polynomial will correspond to the two roots referred to above as r_1, and r_2. We put

$$u_1 = \frac{1}{r_1} = \frac{1 + e}{p}; \qquad u_2 = \frac{1}{r_2} = \frac{1 - e}{p} \qquad (58.37)$$

where p and e are new constants related to our original constants ε and μ. Approximately we have

$$1 - \varepsilon^2 = \frac{\alpha}{p}(1 - e^2) \qquad (58.38)$$

$$\mu^2 = \alpha c^2 p = \gamma M p$$

We also put

$$\nu^2 = 1 - \frac{6\alpha}{p} \qquad (58.39)$$

so that, approximately

$$\nu = 1 - \frac{3\alpha}{p} \qquad (58.40)$$

In this notation we can restate equation (58.36) as

$$\frac{1}{\nu^2}\left(\frac{du}{d\varphi}\right)^2 = \frac{e^2 - 1}{p^2} + \frac{2}{p}u - u^2 \qquad (58.41)$$

The solution of this equation is

$$u = \frac{1 + e \cos \nu\varphi}{p} \qquad (58.42)$$

Here the constant of integration has been so chosen that the largest value of u or the smallest value of the distance r corresponds to the value $\varphi = 0$. The expression (58.42) describes well the general nature of the motion. If ν were equal to 1 we would have an ellipse, a parabola or a hyperbola of semi-latus rectum p and eccentricity e. We shall discuss the case of an ellipse, $e < 1$. The radius vector r returns to its original value when the angle φ increases not by 2π but by the somewhat greater value $2\pi/\nu$. The difference

$$\Delta\varphi = \frac{2\pi}{\nu} - 2\pi = \frac{6\pi\alpha}{p} \qquad (58.43)$$

gives the displacement of perihelion after one period of revolution of the planet.

The orbit of the planet may therefore be described as a precessing ellipse.

One may note that Einstein's equations of motion of a planet reduce to the form of the classical equations of motion of a spherical pendulum ; therefore the trajectory of the planet has the same form as the trajectory of the bob of a pendulum.†

For all planets the numerical value of φ' is exceedingly small. For the Earth, for instance, we can take $p = 1.5 \times 10^8$ km and, using the value $\alpha = 1.5$ km, we get

$$\Delta\varphi = 6\pi \times 10^{-8} = 0.038''$$

in one revolution, i.e. one year, or in other words $3.8''$ per century. For Mercury the advance of perihelion per century is much greater, namely $43''$, because in the first place it is considerably closer to the sun, having an orbit of a radius 0.39 times that of the Earth, and also because its period of revolutions is shorter—420 revolutions per century.

In comparing this theory with experiment it is important to remember that a motion of the perihelion is caused not only by the Einstein effect but also by the perturbing influence of other planets, by their deviation from spherical shape and so on. Such corrections are many times greater than those arising from Einstein's theory. One must also bear in mind that the observation of the position of the perihelion is the more difficult the smaller the eccentricity e, i.e. the closer the orbit is to circular shape. For $e = 0$ the position of perihelion is indeterminate. Nevertheless, astronomical methods of observation are so accurate and computational possibilities in celestial mechanics so great that in the case of Mercury a residual advance of the perihelion, unexplained by Newtonian theory, is known to an accuracy of one second per century. It is $42.6''$ per century, in excellent agreement with the theory. For the Earth this residual advance of the perihelion is known with rather less accuracy to be about $4''$; this is also in full agreement with the Einstein value.

59. The Deflection of a Light Ray Passing Near the Sun

We now consider another observable consequence of Einstein's theory of gravitation, the deflection of a ray of light passing close to the Sun.

Before integrating the equation for a light ray let us first form a general picture of the propagation of light in the gravitational field of the Sun.

We shall write the law for the propagation of the front of a light wave in the form

$$g^{\mu\nu} \frac{\partial\omega}{\partial x_\mu} \frac{\partial\omega}{\partial x_\nu} = 0 \tag{59.01}$$

where we have multiplied our previous equation by $\sqrt{(-g)}$. Using equations (58.10) and (58.11) we have, in spherical coordinates

$$\frac{(1+\alpha/r)^3}{(1-\alpha/r)} \cdot \frac{1}{c^2} \left(\frac{\partial\omega}{\partial t}\right)^2 - \left(1 - \frac{\alpha^2}{r^2}\right)\left(\frac{\partial\omega}{\partial r}\right)^2 - \frac{1}{r^2}\left[\left(\frac{\partial\omega}{\partial\vartheta}\right)^2 + \frac{1}{\sin^2\vartheta}\left(\frac{\partial\omega}{\partial\varphi}\right)^2\right] = 0 \tag{59.02}$$

If we neglect terms of the order α^2/r^2 in comparison with unity the equation

---

† See the diagram in A. N. Krylov's book [19].

for ω reduces to

$$\frac{n^2}{c^2}\left(\frac{\partial\omega}{\partial t}\right)^2 - (\text{grad }\omega)^2 = 0 \qquad (59.03)$$

where
$$n^2 = 1 + \frac{4\alpha}{r}; \qquad n = 1 + \frac{2\alpha}{r} \qquad (59.04)$$

This equation can be formally interpreted as the law of propagation of light in Euclidean space, but in a medium of refractive index n.

We note that (59.03) could also have been obtained from the approximate expression

$$ds^2 = (c^2 - 2U)dt^2 - \left(1 + \frac{2U}{c^2}\right)(dx_1^2 + dx_2^2 + dx_3^2) \qquad (59.05)$$

(see (55.45)) the effective refractive index then being

$$n = 1 + \frac{2U}{c^2} \qquad (59.06)$$

On the other hand, the approximate form (51.10) for ds^2 which was applicable for slow motions would lead to a form for the effective refractive index in which the coefficient of U is half the above. As we shall see below experiment confirms the expression (59.06) derived from the quadratic form (59.05).

The fictitious medium of refractive index (59.06) is optically more dense in the vicinity of the Sun than it is far away from it. Therefore, light waves will bend around the Sun and light rays passing near the Sun will not be straight. We shall see that they will be describable as branches of hyperbolae with the Sun at one focus. The angle between the asymptotes of such a hyperbola will determine the observed deflection of the ray.

As we know from Section 38, a light ray represents a nul geodesic and its Hamilton-Jacobi equation is the equation of wave front propagation. (See also Appendix F.) Since in the previous section we have already solved the problem of a geodesic of finite length we can obtain the equation of a ray from the results of Section 58 by means of a limiting process. Let us recall these results. We found the integrals of motion

$$\frac{r - \alpha}{r + \alpha}\frac{dt}{d\tau} = \varepsilon \qquad (58.26)$$

and
$$(r + \alpha)^2 \frac{d\varphi}{d\tau} = \mu \qquad (58.27)$$

and also the equation for the trajectory

$$\left(\frac{dr}{d\varphi}\right)^2 = \frac{c^2\varepsilon^2}{\mu^2}(r + \alpha)^4 - \frac{c^2}{\mu^2}(r + \alpha)^3(r - \alpha) - (r + \alpha)(r - \alpha) \qquad (58.32)$$

Since for a light ray $d\tau = 0$ the constants in (58.26) and (58.27) will be infinite, but their ratio

$$\frac{(r + \alpha)^3}{r - \alpha}\cdot\frac{d\varphi}{dt} = \frac{\mu}{\varepsilon} = \mu_1 \qquad (59.07)$$

will be finite. Consequently, equation (58.32) will have the form

$$\left(\frac{dr}{d\varphi}\right)^2 = \frac{c^2}{\mu_1^2}(r+\alpha)^4 - (r+\alpha)(r-\alpha) \tag{59.08}$$

In place of the constant μ_1 it is convenient to introduce another constant b, of the dimensions of a length, by the relation

$$\lim \frac{\mu}{\varepsilon} = \mu_1 = cb \tag{59.09}$$

Then (59.08) becomes

$$\left(\frac{dr}{d\varphi}\right)^2 = \frac{1}{b^2}(r+\alpha)^4 - (r+\alpha)(r-\alpha) \tag{59.10}$$

and the corresponding relation for $u = 1/r$ is then

$$\left(\frac{du}{d\varphi}\right)^2 = \frac{1}{b^2}(1+\alpha u)^4 - u^2 + \alpha^2 u^4 \tag{59.11}$$

If r and φ are interpreted as polar coordinates in a Euclidean plane the constant b just introduced will be the "impact parameter" i.e. the length of the perpendicular from the origin to the asymptote of the trajectory. Indeed, elementary relations in plane Euclidean geometry give the following expression in polar coordinates for the perpendicular distance from the origin to the tangent to a curve

$$d = \frac{r}{\sqrt{\{1 + (dr/d\varphi)^2/r^2\}}} = \frac{1}{\sqrt{\{u^2 + (du/d\varphi)^2\}}} \tag{59.12}$$

The asymptote is the tangent at infinity ($u = 0$) and, therefore, the impact parameter is the value of d for $u = 0$. By (59.11) and (59.12) this is equal to b.

Let us return to the equation for the path of the ray in the form (59.11). If u is taken to be of order $1/b$ the terms involving u^3 and u^4 in this equation will be at least of order α^2/b^2 in comparison with the main terms. Dropping these small terms we obtain an equation which can be solved by elementary means. The solution has the form

$$u = \frac{2\alpha}{b^2} + \frac{1}{b}\cos\varphi \tag{59.13}$$

The constant of integration has been chosen so that the greatest value of u, and therefore the least of r, corresponds to $\varphi = 0$. We find approximately

$$r_{\min} = b - 2\alpha \tag{59.14}$$

In the Euclidean (r, φ) plane equation (59.13) describes a hyperbola. The directions of the asymptotes of this hyperbola are determined from the condition $u = 0$ which gives

$$\cos\varphi = -\frac{2\alpha}{b} \tag{59.15}$$

Here the right-hand side is a small negative quantity, so that the limiting values of the angle will be

$$\varphi = \tfrac{1}{2}\pi + \delta; \qquad \varphi = -\tfrac{1}{2}\pi - \delta \tag{59.16}$$

where the small positive quantity δ can be put equal to

$$\delta = \frac{2\alpha}{b} \tag{59.17}$$

The angle by which the ray is deflected is the angle between the asymptotes of the hyperbola, which is

$$2\delta = \frac{4\alpha}{b} \tag{59.18}$$

The displacement of the observed position of a star whose light passes close to the Sun can be observed during a total eclipse of the Sun. If b is put equal to the Sun's radius the angle of deflection 2δ takes on the value

$$2\delta = 1 \cdot 75'' \tag{59.19}$$

which is in good agreement with observed values. An evaluation of the results of observations during the eclipse of 1952 gives a value of $1 \cdot 70''$. This result allows one to assert quite definitely that the observations agree with the expression (59.05) for ds^2 and not with (51.10) which predicts $0 \cdot 87''$, half of the observed value.

In conclusion we make a remark concerning the definition of a straight line in the theory of gravitation. How should a straight line be defined : as a light ray or as a straight line in that Euclidean space in which the harmonic co-ordinates x_1, x_2 and x_3 serve as cartesian coordinates? It seems to us that the only correct definition is the latter. We have, in fact, used it when we said that a light ray near the Sun has the form of the hyperbola (59.13). In the cases here considered the harmonic coordinates are deeply related to the nature of space and time and the definition of a straight line should be based on them. The consideration that a straight line defined as a light ray is more immediately observable, is of no significance. What is decisive in a definition is not immediate observability but a correspondence with Nature, even if this correspondence has to be established by indirect reasoning.

60. A Variational Principle for the Equations of Gravitation

In the equations of gravitation

$$R^{\mu\nu} - \tfrac{1}{2}g^{\mu\nu}R = -\frac{8\pi\gamma}{c^2}\,T^{\mu\nu} \tag{60.01}$$

we have on the left-hand side the conservative tensor and on the right the mass tensor. In Section 48 we saw that the expression for the mass tensor can be obtained by varying the action integral with respect to the components of the metric tensor. Thus in the case of the equations of hydrodynamics the action integral could be written in the form

$$S = \int (\rho^* c^2 + \rho^* \Pi)\sqrt{(-g)} \cdot (dx) \tag{60.02}$$

Here ρ^* is the invariant density of that part of the rest-mass which does not change in the motion and which satisfies the equation of continuity (48.29), and Π is the elastic potential energy of the fluid per unit mass as defined by (48.30). If the integral S is varied with respect to the components of the metric tensor the result is

$$\delta_g S = \frac{c^2}{2} \int T^{\mu\nu} \delta g_{\mu\nu} \sqrt{(-g)} \cdot (dx) \tag{60.03}$$

where $T^{\mu\nu}$ is the hydrodynamical mass tensor defined by (48.39). In the case of electrodynamics the action integral has the form (47.37) ; its main term is a function of the rest-mass and is the same as in the hydrodynamical case. The variation of the electrodynamic action integral with respect to the $g_{\mu\nu}$ again has the form (60.03) where now $T^{\mu\nu}$ is the electrodynamic mass tensor as given by (46.22) and (46.32). As regards variations of the action integral with respect to other quantities entering it, such as displacements and field components, we saw that they give the equations of motion of the material system in question.

We shall assume that we have a system such that for it equation (60.03) is valid with a suitably chosen S. Then the mass tensor which enters the right-hand side of the gravitational equations can be represented as the coefficient of $\delta g_{\mu\nu}$ in the expression for the variation of a certain integral. We shall now attempt to represent the left-hand side of the gravitational equations, i.e. the conservative tensor, in a similar manner.

To do this we consider the expression

$$I = \int R \sqrt{(-g)} \cdot (dx) \tag{60.04}$$

where R is the curvature scalar and we perform the variation of this integral.

In evaluating the variation of the integral we use the fact that the variations of the Christoffel symbols form a tensor, although the Christoffel symbols themselves do not. This can be proved as follows. According to (42.04) the transformation law for Christoffel symbols has the form

$$\frac{\partial^2 x'_\sigma}{\partial x_\mu \partial x_\nu} - \Gamma^\rho_{\mu\nu} \frac{\partial x'_\sigma}{\partial x_\rho} = -(\Gamma^\sigma_{\alpha\beta})' \frac{\partial x'_\alpha}{\partial x_\mu} \frac{\partial x'_\beta}{\partial x_\nu} \tag{60.05}$$

This relation is valid for the quantities $\Gamma^\rho_{\mu\nu}$ related to the given metric $(g_{\alpha\beta})$. We perform a variation of the metric while retaining the connection between old and new coordinates. To the metric $(g_{\alpha\beta} + \delta g_{\alpha\beta})$ there will correspond the quantities $\Gamma^\rho_{\mu\nu} + \delta\Gamma^\rho_{\mu\nu}$ where

$$\delta\Gamma^\rho_{\mu\nu} \frac{\partial x'_\sigma}{\partial x_\rho} = (\delta\Gamma^\sigma_{\alpha\beta})' \frac{\partial x'_\alpha}{\partial x_\mu} \frac{\partial x'_\beta}{\partial x_\nu} \tag{60.06}$$

This proves that the variations $\delta\Gamma^\rho_{\mu\nu}$ form a mixed third rank tensor.

In forming the variation of the scalar R we start from the expressions

$$R^\alpha_{\mu,\,\beta\nu} = \frac{\partial \Gamma^\alpha_{\mu\beta}}{\partial x_\nu} - \frac{\partial \Gamma^\alpha_{\mu\nu}}{\partial x_\beta} + \Gamma^\rho_{\mu\beta} \Gamma^\alpha_{\rho\nu} - \Gamma^\rho_{\mu\nu} \Gamma^\alpha_{\rho\beta} \tag{60.07}$$

and

$$R_{\mu\nu} = \frac{\partial \Gamma^\alpha_{\mu\alpha}}{\partial x_\nu} - \frac{\partial \Gamma^\alpha_{\mu\nu}}{\partial x_\alpha} + \Gamma^\rho_{\mu\alpha} \Gamma^\alpha_{\rho\nu} - \Gamma^\rho_{\mu\nu} \Gamma^\alpha_{\rho\alpha} \tag{60.08}$$

which give the mixed components of the fourth rank curvature tensor and the second rank curvature tensor. In a coordinate system that is geodesic at a given point the variation of $R_{\mu\nu}$ is

$$\delta R_{\mu\nu} = \frac{\partial}{\partial x_\nu}(\delta\Gamma^\alpha_{\mu\alpha}) - \frac{\partial}{\partial x_\alpha}(\delta\Gamma^\alpha_{\mu\nu}) \tag{60.09}$$

because at this point all the Christoffel symbols vanish. Hence with a change of indices in the first term on the right

$$g^{\mu\nu}\delta R_{\mu\nu} = g^{\nu\alpha}\frac{\partial}{\partial x_\alpha}(\delta\Gamma^\mu_{\mu\nu}) - g^{\mu\nu}\frac{\partial}{\partial x_\alpha}(\delta\Gamma^\alpha_{\mu\nu}) \tag{60.10}$$

We now introduce the vector

$$w^\alpha = g^{\mu\nu}\delta\Gamma^\alpha_{\mu\nu} - g^{\alpha\nu}\delta\Gamma^\mu_{\mu\nu} \tag{60.11}$$

It is easy to see that (60.10) is equivalent to the equation

$$g^{\mu\nu}\delta R_{\mu\nu} = -\frac{1}{\sqrt{(-g)}}\frac{\partial}{\partial x_\alpha}\{\sqrt{(-g)}\cdot w^\alpha\} \tag{60.12}$$

since in a geodesic system one can take the quantities $\mathfrak{g}^{\mu\nu} = \sqrt{(-g)}\cdot g^{\mu\nu}$ outside the sign of differentiation; but both sides of the equation (60.12) are scalars so that if it holds in a geodesic system it must hold generally.

We assume that not only the $\delta g_{\mu\nu}$ but also their derivatives and therefore the $\delta\Gamma^\alpha_{\mu\nu}$ vanish on the boundaries of the region of integration and that the vector w^α also vanishes. Then, writing the integral I as

$$I = \int R_{\mu\nu}g^{\mu\nu}\sqrt{(-g)}\cdot(dx) = \int R_{\mu\nu}\mathfrak{g}^{\mu\nu}(dx) \tag{60.13}$$

we obtain for its variation the expression

$$\delta I = \int R_{\mu\nu}\delta\mathfrak{g}^{\mu\nu}(dx) \tag{60.14}$$

since by (60.12) we have

$$\int \delta R_{\mu\nu}\cdot g^{\mu\nu}\sqrt{(-g)}\cdot(dx) = 0 \tag{60.15}$$

Using the relations

$$\delta\sqrt{(-g)} = \tfrac{1}{2}\sqrt{(-g)}\cdot g^{\alpha\beta}\,\delta g_{\alpha\beta} \tag{60.16}$$

and

$$\delta g^{\mu\nu} = -g^{\mu\alpha}g^{\nu\beta}\,\delta g_{\alpha\beta} \tag{60.17}$$

we get

$$\delta\mathfrak{g}^{\mu\nu} = \delta\{\sqrt{(-g)}\cdot g^{\mu\nu}\} = \sqrt{(-g)}\cdot(\tfrac{1}{2}g^{\mu\nu}g^{\alpha\beta} - g^{\mu\alpha}g^{\nu\beta}) \tag{60.18}$$

Inserting this expression into (60.14) and performing the summations over μ and ν we obtain

$$\delta I = \int (\tfrac{1}{2}g^{\alpha\beta}R - R^{\alpha\beta})\delta g_{\alpha\beta}\sqrt{(-g)}\cdot(dx) \tag{60.19}$$

Our immediate object has been achieved; we have represented the conservative tensor as the coefficient of the variation with respect to the metric tensor.

Combining the equations (60.03) and (60.19) we can conclude that the variation of the expression

$$W = S - \frac{c^4}{16\pi\gamma}I \tag{60.20}$$

with respect to the components of the metric tensor is

$$\delta_g W = \frac{c^2}{2} \int \left\{ T^{\mu\nu} + \frac{c^2}{8\pi\gamma} (R^{\mu\nu} - \tfrac{1}{2} g^{\mu\nu} R) \right\} \delta g_{\mu\nu} \sqrt{(-g)} \cdot (dx) \qquad (60.21)$$

This variation vanishes by virtue of the gravitational equations (60.01) and these equations in turn may be obtained from the variational principle $\delta W = 0$, if the variation is with respect to the components of the metric tensor considered as independent. (We recall that we have already discussed the variation of the action integral with respect to the $g_{\mu\nu}$ in Section 48, but that there the $\delta g_{\mu\nu}$ were not completely arbitrary because they corresponded to an infinitesimal change of the coordinates and were expressible in terms of four functions η_ν.)

If W is varied with respect to the other functions that enter the action integral S we obtain the equations of motion and field equations for these functions.

Thus the equations (60.01), the field equations of gravitation, are now unified with the other field equations (for the velocity field of matter, the electromagnetic field, etc.) in one general variational principle.

The variational principle may be given a somewhat different form by taking, in place of the invariant integral

$$I = \int R \sqrt{(-g)} \cdot (dx) \qquad (60.04)$$

another integral which is not invariant, but which does not contain any second derivatives.

In Appendix D we derive the relation

$$R = \square y - \Gamma - L \qquad (60.22)$$

where $\square$ is the d'Alembert operator acting on $y = \log \ (-g)$, see (D.51), Γ is given by (D.43) and the quantity L may, according to (D.54), be written as

$$L = g^{\mu\nu} (\Gamma^\beta_{\mu\alpha} \Gamma^\alpha_{\nu\beta} - \Gamma^\alpha_{\mu\nu} \Gamma^\beta_{\alpha\beta}) \qquad (60.23)$$

as well as in many other forms given in Appendix D.

Using the definitions (D.59) and (D.61) one can also replace (60.22) by

$$R = \frac{1}{\sqrt{(-g)}} \frac{\partial}{\partial x_\nu} \{ \sqrt{(-g)} \cdot (y^\nu - \Gamma^\nu) \} - L \qquad (60.24)$$

The integral I will differ from the expression

$$I^* = - \int L \sqrt{(-g)} \cdot (dx) \qquad (60.25)$$

by the quantity

$$I' = \int \frac{\partial}{\partial x_\nu} \{ \sqrt{(-g)} \cdot (y^\nu - \Gamma^\nu) \} (dx) \qquad (60.26)$$

which reduces to a surface integral and has a vanishing variation. Therefore the variations of I and I^* are equal :

$$\delta I = \delta \int R \sqrt{(-g)} \cdot (dx) = - \delta \int L \sqrt{(-g)} \cdot (dx) = \delta I^* \qquad (60.27)$$

Since in a variational principle only the variations of the integrals, not the integrals themselves, are of importance, we can replace I by I^* in (60.20).

The quantity δI^* (which is equal to δI) is independent of the coordinate system in spite of the fact that I^* itself may depend on the coordinate system. The purpose of replacing I by I^* is the removal of second derivatives from the integrand. The relation

$$\delta \int L \sqrt{(-g)} \cdot (dx) = \int (R^{\alpha\beta} - \tfrac{1}{2} g^{\alpha\beta} R) \, \delta g_{\alpha\beta} \sqrt{(-g)} \cdot (dx) \qquad (60.28)$$

which follows from (60.19) and (60.27) can naturally also be derived directly, though the necessary calculations are somewhat involved.

61. On the Local Equivalence of Fields of Acceleration and of Gravitation

As we have seen, the law of equality of inertial and gravitational mass, which is a rational dynamic generalization of Galileo's law (Section 50), forms an intuitively satisfactory basis for the theory of gravitation. We therefore used it as the foundation of our argument which, after some generalizing assumptions, led us to Einstein's gravitational equations (Sections 51 and 52). When Einstein himself derived his gravitational equations, he argued rather differently. In contrast to our treatment based on the dynamic formulation of Galileo's law Einstein took as his basis a certain kinematical consequence of that law, which he called the " Principle of Equivalence ".

In the theory of gravitation the Principle of Equivalence is understood to be the statement that in some sense a field of acceleration is equivalent to a gravitational field. The equivalence amounts to the following. By introducing a suitable system of coordinates (which is usually interpreted as an accelerated frame of reference) one can so transform the equations of motion of a mass point in a gravitational field that in this new system they will have the appearance of equations of motion of a *free* mass point. Thus a gravitational field can, so to speak, be replaced, or rather imitated, by a field of acceleration. Owing to the equality of inertial and gravitational mass such a transformation is the same for any value of the mass of the particle. But it will succeed in its purpose only in an infinitesimal region of space, i.e. it will be strictly local.

In the general case the transformation described corresponds mathematically to passing to a locally geodesic system of coordinates (see Section 42). As was shown by Fermi, it is possible to introduce coordinate systems which are locally geodesic not only at one point but also along a time-like world line (see [14]).

Thus the principle of equivalence is related to the law of equality of inertial and gravitational mass, but is not identical with it. The latter is of a general, non-local character while the equivalence of a field of acceleration and a field of gravitation exists only locally, i.e. it refers only to a single point in space (more precisely to a spatial neighbourhood of the points on a world line, which is of the nature of a time axis).

The Principle of Equivalence played an important role during the period before Einstein created his theory of gravitation. We shall now describe and analyse an argument given by Einstein at that time.

Einstein illustrated his " equivalence hypothesis " with the example of a laboratory inside a falling lift. All objects within such a lift appear bereft of their weight, they all fall together with the lift, with the same acceleration, so that their relative accelerations vanish even when they are not fixed to the walls of the lift. We have, according to Einstein, two frames of reference, one inertial, or almost inertial, fixed to the Earth and another accelerated, fixed to the lift. In the first, inertial frame, there exists a gravitational field—in the second, accelerated frame, it is absent. Thus, according to Einstein, an acceleration can replace gravitation or at least a uniform field of gravitation. Einstein develops this idea further. He proposes to consider both the accelerated and the unaccelerated frames to be physically completely equivalent and points out that from such a point of view the concepts of inertial frame and absolute acceleration cease to have any meaning.

Let us analyse this view of Einstein's in more detail. First of all the question arises : What is an accelerated frame of reference and how can it be realized physically? In the lift example the " frame of reference " was, so to speak, identified with a certain box, the lift cage. But we have learnt in Section 32 that even when gravitation is not taken into account the abstraction of an absolutely rigid body is not acceptable ; when accelerated all bodies will experience deformations which will be different for different bodies. Therefore a box or a rigid scaffolding of the kind we discussed in Section 11 when dealing with inertial frames are of no use as models for an accelerated frame of reference. Thus in Einstein's reasoning the basic concept of a frame of reference in accelerated motion remains undefined. This difficulty could be avoided only by imposing limitations on the magnitude of the acceleration and on the size of the region of space to be considered. For instance, one could demand the following : the accelerations allowed are to be so small that in the region of space considered the deformations resulting from them may be neglected and the notion of a rigid body may be used. In that case the approximate nature of Einstein's argument becomes obvious.

Further, Einstein himself stresses that not every gravitational field can be replaced by acceleration ; for this to be possible the gravitational field must be uniform. This also imposes limitations on the spatial dimensions of the region in which gravitational and accelerated fields may be approximately equivalent. It is, for instance, impossible to " remove " the gravitational field around the terrestrial globe ; to do it one would have to introduce some absurdity such as a frame of reference in " accelerated contraction ".

Einstein also used his Principle of Equivalence in a non-local manner but his attempt, in a paper published in 1911, to investigate in this way the propagation of light near a heavy body gave a deflection of a light ray of only half the amount resulting from his theory of gravitation (see Section 59). This is connected with the fact that the Principle of Equivalence cannot possibly lead to the correct form (51.11) for ds^2 but at best only the expression (51.10) which is valid for slow motion. Thus, in a non-local interpretation, the approximate equivalence of fields of gravitation and of acceleration is also limited. As already mentioned this equivalence exists only for weak uniform fields and slow motions.

Einstein gave to his principle of equivalence a widened interpretation by taking it to imply the indistinguishability of fields of gravitation and acceleration and asserting that from the point of view of this principle it is as impermissible to speak of absolute acceleration as it is to speak of absolute velocity. To this Einstein related his " General Principle of Relativity " which we discussed in Section 49*; he used the latter to justify the demand that his equations should be generally covariant. However, to us such an extended interpretation seems inconsistent. The essence of the principle of equivalence may be seen in the fact that it allows the introduction of an appropriate locally geodesic (" freely falling ") frame of reference, by use of which a uniform Galilean space can be defined in the infinitesimal. However this in no way justifies conclusions about the equivalence or indistinguishability of fields of acceleration and of gravitation in finite regions of space. To illustrate the nature of the error committed in drawing such conclusions let us examine a mathematical example, which incidentally has a direct bearing on the essence of the present question. All functions that have bounded second derivatives behave as linear functions in the infinitesimal. However, this by no means allows one to conclude that all such functions are indistinguishable in a finite region. But an analogous conclusion, namely that fields of acceleration and of gravitation are completely indistinguishable, was drawn by Einstein, on the basis of their local equivalence alone.

Such a conclusion even contradicts Einstein's theory of gravitation itself. Indeed, if full equivalence between fields of acceleration and of gravitation did exist, a theory built on the idea of equivalence would be purely kinematical, which is by no means the case for Einstein's theory of gravitation. As regards the " General Principle of Relativity ", we have already pointed out in Section 49* that such a physical principle is impossible, and also unnecessary as a basis for the requirement of general covariance, which is the purely logical requirement of consistency for a theory in which the coordinate system is not fixed.

Thus, although the principle of equivalence holds in a narrow sense (approximately and locally) it does not hold in a wider sense. Although the effects of acceleration and of gravitation may be indistinguishable " in the small ", i.e. locally, they are undoubtedly distinguishable " in the large ", i.e. when the boundary conditions to be imposed on gravitational fields, are taken into account. The gravitational potential that is obtained if a uniformly accelerated frame of reference is introduced is a linear function of the coordinates and therefore does not satisfy the conditions at infinity, where it should tend to zero. In a rotating frame of reference the potential of the centrifugal force increases with the square of the distance from the axis of rotation, and in addition there are Coriolis forces. By these characteristics it is possible to detect immediately that the " gravitational field " in such frames of reference is fictitious.

We shall now discuss the example of a uniformly accelerated frame of reference in somewhat greater detail, taking the theory of relativity into account. In doing this we set aside the question of how an accelerated frame might be realized and interpret the term " frame of reference " more formally in the sense of " coordinate system ". In this sense passing to a frame moving with acceleration will mean subjecting the coordinates to a transformation which contains time non-linearly.

We assume that a true gravitational field is not present so that the square of the infinitesimal interval has the form

$$ds^2 = c^2\,dt'^2 - (dx'^2 + dy'^2 + dz'^2) \qquad (61.01)$$

where x', y' and z' are cartesian coordinates and t' the time in some inertial frame of reference. We perform the coordinate transformation†

$$x' = x \cosh \frac{gt}{c} + \frac{c^2}{g}\left(\cosh \frac{gt}{c} - 1\right)$$

$$y' = y ; \qquad z' = z \qquad\qquad (61.02)$$

$$t' = \frac{c}{g} \sinh \frac{gt}{c} + \frac{x}{c} \sinh \frac{gt}{c}$$

where g is a constant of the dimensions of acceleration. Under the condition

$$\frac{gt}{c} \ll 1 \qquad\qquad (61.03)$$

the previous equations may be written as

$$x' = x + \tfrac{1}{2}gt^2 ; \qquad y' = y ; \qquad z' = z ; \qquad t' = t \qquad\qquad (61.04)$$

Inserting (61.02) into (61.01) we obtain

$$ds^2 = \left(c + \frac{gx}{c}\right)^2 dt^2 - (dx^2 + dy^2 + dz^2) \qquad\qquad (61.05)$$

The question arises : can this expression be interpreted as the square of the interval in some *inertial* frame of reference in which there is a gravitational field? The answer to this question is also an answer to the question whether, and to what extent, the Principle of Equivalence is correct.

To find the answer we compare (61.05) with the approximate expression given by the theory of gravitation.

$$ds^2 = (c^2 - 2U)dt^2 - \left(1 + \frac{2U}{c^2}\right)(dx^2 + dy^2 + dz^2) \qquad\qquad (61.06)$$

where U is the Newtonian potential of a true gravitational field.

Under the condition

$$|gx| \ll c^2 \qquad\qquad (61.07)$$

the coefficients of dt^2 are approximately equal if we take a gravitational potential given by

$$U = -gx \qquad\qquad (61.08)$$

As for the coefficient of the spatial part of ds^2, it will not differ significantly from unity for intervals for which the quantity

$$v^2 = \left(\frac{dx}{dt}\right)^2 + \left(\frac{dy}{dt}\right)^2 + \left(\frac{dz}{dt}\right)^2 \qquad\qquad (61.09)$$

satisfies the inequality

$$v^2 \ll c^2 \qquad\qquad (61.10)$$

The value (61.08) for the gravitational potential does indeed lead to uniformly accelerated motion in Newtonian mechanics. For vanishing initial velocity we have constant values of x', y' and z' and approximately

$$x + \tfrac{1}{2}gt^2 = \text{const.} \qquad\qquad (61.11)$$

† This transformation was given by Møller [20].

which describes uniformly accelerated motion in the coordinates (x, t).

We have made a comparison between two expressions for the square of the interval which has shown that a frame of reference in accelerated motion in the absence of gravitation does indeed show an analogy with an inertial frame in the presence of gravitation. However, the same comparison indicates that the analogy is far from complete, so that there can be no question of full equivalence or indistinguishability of inertial and gravitational fields. This becomes particularly clear if one considers the expression (61.05) " in the large ", i.e. throughout the whole of space. In the first place the coefficient of dt^2 does not saitsfy the boundary conditions, since it tends to infinity with x, in the second place that coefficient and with it the speed of light, become zero on the surface $x = - c^2/g$; this is inadmissible.

An even more obvious violation of the boundary conditions for the metric tensor occurs if the transformation (35.47) is used. In Newtonian mechanics it has the significance of introducing a rotating coordinate system. This transformation leads to the expression (35.48) for ds^2. Here the metric tensor not only fails to satisfy the boundary conditions but, at large distances from the axis of rotation, also violates the inequalities established in' Section 35. The impossibility of interpreting the metric tensor in (35.48) as some gravitational field (i.e. in the spirit of the " equivalence hypothesis ") is clear even from a local point of view, owing to the presence of Coriolis forces.

The example just discussed confirms completely the conclusion stated above that the " equivalence " between acceleration and gravitation exists only in a limited region of space, and only for weak and uniform fields and slow motions (equation (61.08) together with the inequalities (61.07) and (61.10)). But if one considers the whole of space, true gravitational fields can be distinguished from fictitious ones caused by acceleration. In Newtonian theory this can be done by using the boundary condition for the Newtonian potential. In Einstein's theory the question of distinguishing true from fictitious gravitational fields is most simply solved if harmonic coordinates are used. Then the components of the metric tensor must satisfy both the harmonic conditions (53.13) and the boundary conditions discussed in Section 54. As will be shown in Section 93, harmonic coordinates can be defined uniquely apart from a Lorentz transformation. Arbitrary coordinate transformations by which fictitious gravitational fields are introduced, violate the harmonic conditions and the boundary conditions. Therefore one can take it that the introduction of harmonic coordinates excludes all fictitious gravitational fields. Thus, if one assumes the quadratic form (61.05) to be given, the passage to harmonic coordinates will consist in the transformation (61.02), accompanied possibly by a Lorentz transformation. As the result of such a transition we come back to the quadratic form (61.01), the form of which indicates the absence of true gravitational fields.

In the discussion of this section we did not use general tensor analysis. Its application to (61.05) would have shown that the fourth rank curvature tensor vanishes and that, therefore, true gravitational fields are indeed absent.

Let us return to the question of utilizing the principle of equivalence to derive the gravitational equations. We have made it clear that it is inconsistent to interpret this principle in a wider sense as a " General Principle of Relativity ". But this does not exclude the use of the principle of equivalence in a more restricted sense, within the limits in which it is valid approximately. In particular the analogy we have discussed between an accelerated frame of reference in the absence of a gravitational field and an inertial frame in the presence of such a field may prove helpful, because the possibility of transforming the expression (61.01) into the form (61.05) gives us an indication of the fact that the Newtonian potential must enter the theory precisely as the coefficient of dt^2. However, an approach based on this idea to the formulation of a gravitational theory seems to us to be unsatisfactory because of its inherent limitations (viz. the local nature of the principle of equivalence and the assumption that the field is uniform). Another disadvantage of this approach is the necessity of using the ill-defined concept of a frame of reference in accelerated motion. Our approach is free from these disadvantages, being based on the direct application of the law of equality of inertial and gravitational masses. It is well to remember that in the derivation of Einstein's gravitational equations we *made no use at all of any frame of reference in accelerated motion* and therefore also *no use of the principle of equivalence*. As for this latter principle, to the extent that it is valid it may be obtained subsequently as a consequence of the other assumptions. Thus it is implied by the hypothesis that space-time has Riemannian character, its mathematical expression being the possibility of introducing a locally geodesic coordinate system along a time-like world line.

We stressed the approximate character of the principle of equivalence. But from the point of view of Einstein's theory of gravitation the law of equality of inertial and gravitational mass also is of approximate character, since the very concepts of inertial and gravitational mass are approximate. These concepts are applicable to the extent to which Newton's laws of motion and law of gravitation are valid and to the extent that it is possible to define any mass as a quantity characterizing a particular body independently of its position and of the motion of other bodies. In Einstein's theory of gravitation this is possible only approximately, because there the law of motion of material bodies is of a more complicated nature. Nevertheless, one can affirm that the law of equality of inertial and gravitational mass agrees fully with Einstein's theory of gravitation, because this law follows from the theory with as much precision as can in general be given to its formulation.

On the other hand Einstein's theory of gravitation does not reduce to a formulation of the law of equality of the masses; it embraces essential new physical principles. There are two such principles. The first is already contained in the ordinary theory of relativity: the unification of space and time into a single four-dimensional manifold with an indefinite metric. This principle is related to the limiting nature of the velocity of light and, closely connected with this, to the more precise specification of what is meant by a sequence of events in time and also by cause and effect (Section 12). The second principle establishes the unity of metric and gravitation; it is the very essence of Einstein's gravitational theory.

It is just these two principles, and not any widening of the concept of relativity, supposedly possible as a result of the local equivalence of acceleration and gravitation, which form the basis of Einstein's theory of gravitation.

62. On the Clock Paradox

To conclude this chapter we consider the so-called clock paradox. We dwell on it not because it is an especially important or abstruse question but because the paradox has been very widely discussed in the literature and some not wholly satisfactory resolutions have been given.

The paradox arises from using incorrectly the concept of relative motion and from ignoring the distinction between inertial and non-inertial frames of reference. It consists of the following.

We imagine a clock A to be at rest in some inertial frame of reference. Let a clock B move past A with a constant velocity v and then, after it has covered a certain distance, let it be subjected to a negative acceleration which reverses its speed so that it again passes A, this time with velocity $-v$. At the two instants at which B is travelling past A the readings of the two clocks can be compared directly without the intermediary of light signals. Such a comparison will show that clock B is running slow compared to A, or at least this is the result of applying the expression for proper time given in Section 14.

Now, motion is relative. Therefore clock B could also be thought of as at rest. Then the other clock, A, must be looked upon as first receding from B with uniform speed and then approaching again so that the same equations of Section 14 appear to predict also that A should be slow compared to B, in contradiction with the previous result.

The difference in the readings of two clocks situated at the same point in space is an absolute and objective fact. It depends neither on the frame of reference nor on the method of description. Therefore, as long as they are correct, all methods of description must lead to the same result. The contradiction obtained shows that an error was made somewhere in the discussion.

It is not difficult to see that the error consists in failing to take into consideration the fact that in the imagined experiment the clocks A and B were subjected to different physical conditions. Clock A did not receive acceleration and experienced no impulses whereas clock B was accelerated; it experienced an impulse which reversed the direction of its velocity. In other words the error consisted in assuming that the two frames of references connected with clock A and clock B respectively were to be treated as equivalent, which they are not; only the frame of A is inertial.

This is the qualitative resolution of the paradox. It has the significance that the equation for proper time given in Section 14

$$\tau = \int_0^t \sqrt{\left(1 - \frac{v^2}{c^2}\right)} dt \qquad (62.01)$$

is valid only in an inertial frame of reference, but not in an accelerated one.

By what should this equation be replaced in the case of an arbitrary frame of reference? The possibility of such paradoxical results will in any case be excluded if we take as our formula for proper time the invariant expression

$$\tau = \frac{1}{c} \int_0^t \sqrt{(g_{00} + 2g_{0i}\dot{x}_i + g_{ik}\dot{x}_i\dot{x}_k)} \, dt \qquad (62.02)$$

Indeed, now the reading of clock A is obtained by evaluating the integral in (62.02) along the path of clock A just as the reading for B is given by the corresponding evaluation along its path. Both integrals so obtained are invariant with respect to any change of variables of integration, i.e. for any transformation of space and time coordinates. The use of different frames of reference, inertial or non-inertial is equivalent to evaluating one and the same integral with different variables. This fact obviously excludes the possibility of any discrepancy in the results.

There remains, however, the question whether expression (62.01) or its generalization to a generally covariant form (62.02) is or is not valid for arbitrarily accelerated motion of the clock. We have already remarked in Section 14 that the physical interpretation of (62.01) as the proper time follows from the general principles of the theory of relativity only in the case of a constant velocity v. In that case it amounts to measuring a localized process connected with a moving point in its " proper " frame of reference (the indication of a moving clock). If however the velocity v is variable such an interpretation of τ represents a hypothesis, which, though not in contradiction with the theory of relativity, certainly does not follow from it. Indeed, we pointed out at the end of Section 14 that without entering into the details of the clock's construction no theory is capable of predicting how a clock will behave in conditions in which it suffers impacts and acceleration. Therefore one should not expect that a formula exists for the reading of any clock in arbitrary motion, in the way (62.01) gives this reading for uniform motion in a straight line.

In such a situation one can adopt either of the following two hypotheses. One can either introduce the concept of a clock which is ideally strong and insensitive to impact (Section 14) and one can assume that the physical meaning of the proper time determined by equation (62.01) or (62.02) is just that it is the reading of such an idealized clock. Or else one can abandon the idea of a universal formula for the reading of a clock moving with an arbitrary acceleration and introduce instead the weaker hypothesis that *whenever the acceleration is caused by a gravitational field* the reading of a clock in free motion in this field is expressed by (62.02), i.e. by an integral which becomes a maximum just when the equations of free motion are satisfied. This hypothesis has in its favour the fact that the gravitational field, and only it, is capable of penetrating into any material body and of acting on all its parts in proportion to their masses. One should also bear in mind that in the free motion of a body in the gravitational field its four-dimensional acceleration is zero (this quantity will be defined more precisely in Section 63). By virtue of this the second hypothesis amounts to saying that the condition for proper time to be given by (62.02) is vanishing of the four-dimensional acceleration. It is thus formally the same condition as in the absence of a gravitational field.

We now calculate approximately the reading of the accelerated clock B on the basis of the above-mentioned special hypothesis. We use the Newtonian approximation to the expression for ds^2 and perform the calculation in the inertial frame in which clock A is at rest. According to (51.07) we have

$$\tau = \int_0^t \left\{1 - \frac{1}{c^2}(\tfrac{1}{2}v^2 + U)\right\}dt \qquad (62.03)$$

Let U_0 be the constant value of U at the position of A. If B passes A for the first time at $t = 0$ and then, when returning, again at $t = T$ the difference in the readings of A between the passages is

$$\tau_A = \int_0^T \left(1 - \frac{U_0}{c^2}\right) dt = \left(1 - \frac{U_0}{c^2}\right) T \tag{62.04}$$

Here the influence of the gravitational potential on the rate of A is taken into account (see equation (51.14)). For the difference of the two readings of B over the same length of time we get

$$\tau_B = \int_0^T \left\{1 - \frac{1}{c^2}\left(\tfrac{1}{2}v^2 + U\right)\right\} dt \tag{62.05}$$

Therefore B will be slow compared to A by the amount

$$\tau_A - \tau_B = \frac{1}{c^2} \int_0^T \left(\tfrac{1}{2}v^2 + U - U_0\right) dt \tag{62.06}$$

where the integral must be taken along the trajectory of clock B. By the law of conservation of energy we have

$$\tfrac{1}{2}v^2 - U = \tfrac{1}{2}v_0^2 - U_0 \tag{62.07}$$

where v_0 is the value of the speed of B at the point where $U = U_0$. The relation (62.07) enables us to write (62.06) in various different ways, for example, as

$$\tau_A - \tau_B = \frac{1}{c^2} \int_0^T \left(\tfrac{1}{2} v_0^2 + 2U - 2U_0\right) dt \tag{62.08}$$

We now assume for the potential U that in the region considered it has the form

$$\begin{aligned} U &= U_0 & \text{(for } x < x_1) \\ U &= U_0 + g(x_1 - x) & \text{(for } x > x_1) \end{aligned} \tag{62.09}$$

Let clock A always be at the origin of coordinates and let B move along the x-axis. The x coordinate of B will then be

$$x = v_0 t \qquad \text{(for } t < t_1) \tag{62.10}$$

$$x = x_1 + v_0(t - t_1) - \tfrac{1}{2}g(t - t_1)^2 \qquad \text{(for } t_1 < t < t_2) \tag{62.11}$$

and $\qquad x = x_1 - v_0(t - t_2) \qquad \text{(for } t > t_2) \tag{62.12}$

Here t_1 and t_2 are the times at which B passes through the point $x = x_1$ on its motion to and fro. These times are

$$t_1 = \frac{x_1}{v_0}; \qquad t_2 = t_1 + \frac{2v_0}{g} = t_1 + t^* \tag{62.13}$$

where $\qquad t^* = \dfrac{2v_0}{g} \tag{62.14}$

is the duration of the uniformly accelerated motion. The time of return of B to $x = 0$ is, by (62.12)

$$T = t_2 + \frac{x_1}{v_0} = t_2 + t_1 \tag{62.15}$$

In calculating the integral it is most convenient to use (62.08) because in it the quantity $\frac{1}{2}v_0^2$ is constant and the difference $2U - 2U_0$ differs from zero only in the region $t_1 < t < t_2$ where (62.11) is valid. An elementary calculation using (62.14) gives

$$\tau_A - \tau_B = \frac{v_0^2}{c^2} \left(\tfrac{1}{2}T - \tfrac{2}{3}t^* \right) \tag{62.16}$$

On the other hand, if we had unjustifiably used equation (62.01) for the accelerated motion defined by (62.10) and (62.12) we would have obtained (62.16) with a factor $\frac{1}{3}$ (instead of $\frac{2}{3}$) in the t^* term in brackets. Thus in the factor multiplying v_0^2/c^2 there is only the term $\frac{1}{2}T$ if acceleration is neglected; the terms $\frac{1}{2}T - \frac{1}{3}t^*$ give the kinematical effect including acceleration, and the full physical effect (kinematical and gravitational) is given by the terms $\frac{1}{2}T - \frac{2}{3}t^*$, as in formula (62.16).

It follows from (62.16) that if the duration of the accelerated motion is $\frac{3}{4}T$, the clock B is not observed to be slow at all, and for $t^* = T$ it is even fast. It should incidentally not be forgotten that (62.16) is not general but only derived under rather special assumptions concerning the nature of the motion.

We have performed the calculation in the inertial frame of reference. To repeat it in a frame connected with clock B would have no sense for we should only be evaluating the same integrals in terms of different variables.

In conclusion let us note that in clarifying the clock paradox we deliberately avoided using the principle of equivalence. We did so because the approximate nature of that principle might give reason to doubt whether any resolution of the paradox based on it is exhaustive. It was our intention to avoid all such doubts.

CHAPTER VI

THE LAW OF GRAVITATION AND
THE LAWS OF MOTION

63. The Equations of Free Motion for a Mass Point and their Connection with the Gravitational Equations

In the preceding chapter we have already made use of the assumption that in a given gravitational field a mass point moves along a geodesic. However, this assumption does not represent an independent hypothesis but may be considered to be a consequence of the gravitational equations together with an assumption concerning the form of the mass tensor. To obtain this result the gravitational equations are required only in so far as they lead to the relation

$$\nabla_\mu T^{\mu\nu} = 0 \qquad (63.01)$$

which expresses the divergence-free character of the mass tensor. We can obtain the equations of motion for a mass point from those of a continuous medium by going to the limit of a concentrated mass. We can take the mass tensor

$$T^{\mu\nu} = \frac{1}{c^2} \rho^* u^\mu u^\nu \qquad (63.02)$$

where, as in Section 48, ρ^* is the invariant mass density and u^ν the four-dimensional velocity. These quantities are related by the equation of continuity

$$\nabla_\nu(\rho^* u^\nu) = 0 \qquad (63.03)$$

We shall now give two derivations for the equations of motion of a mass point: the first will be based on a variational principle, the second on a direct application of (63.01).

In Section 47 we established a relation according to which the variation of the action integral

$$S = \int c^2 \rho^* \sqrt{(-g)} \cdot (dx) \qquad (63.04)$$

was equal to

$$\delta \int c^2 \rho^* \sqrt{(-g)} \cdot (dx) = - \int \rho^*(u^\nu \nabla_\nu u_\sigma) \xi^\sigma \sqrt{(-g)} \cdot (dx) \qquad (63.05)$$

where ξ^σ was an infinitesimal displacement vector. (Equation (63.04) differs from (47.46) only in its use of the symbol ρ^* for the invariant density.) On the other hand, if the same action integral is varied with respect to the $g_{\mu\nu}$ then, by (48.03), the result is

$$\delta_g \int c^2 \rho^* \sqrt{(-g)} \cdot (dx) = \tfrac{1}{2} \int \rho^* u^\mu u^\nu \delta g_{\mu\nu} \sqrt{(-g)} \cdot (dx) \qquad (63.06)$$

According to the general relation (48.22) this shows that the action integral (63.04) really corresponds to the mass tensor (63.02).

In the action integral (63.04) we can go to the limit in which the invariant mass density ρ^* differs from zero only in the neighbourhood of a single point in space, the volume integral of the density over a volume surrounding that point being finite.

The equation of continuity (63.03) may be written in the form

$$\frac{\partial}{\partial x_\nu}\{\sqrt{(-g)}\cdot \rho^* u^\nu\} = 0 \qquad (63.07)$$

Multiplying this expression by $dx_1\, dx_2\, dx_3$, integrating over the volume described and using the fact that ρ^* vanishes at the boundaries of the volume, we obtain

$$\frac{d}{dt}\int \rho^* u^0 \sqrt{(-g)}\cdot dx_1\, dx_2\, dx_3 = 0 \qquad (63.08)$$

(we have written t for x_0 to emphasize the meaning of this relation). Consequently the value of the integral

$$\int \rho^* u^0 \sqrt{(-g)}\cdot dx_1\, dx_2\, dx_3 = mc \qquad (63.09)$$

is a constant, independent of time. But the quantity ρ^* differs from zero only around one point. Therefore the factor u^0 may be given its value at that point and taken outside the integral. Its value is

$$u^0 = \frac{dt}{d\tau} = \frac{c}{\sqrt{(g_{00} + 2g_{0i}\dot{x}_i + g_{ik}\dot{x}_i\dot{x}_k)}} \qquad (63.10)$$

where the x_i are the spatial coordinates of the mass point and the $\dot{x}_i$ their derivatives with respect to the time. Using this value of u^0 we get

$$\int \rho^*\sqrt{(-g)}\cdot dx_1\, dx_2\, dx_3 = m\sqrt{(g_{00} + 2g_{0i}\dot{x}_i + g_{ik}\dot{x}_i\dot{x}_k)} \qquad (63.11)$$

The action integral can be obtained from this expression by multiplying by $c^2 dt$ and integrating with respect to time. Therefore

$$S = mc^2 \int_{t(0)}^{t} \sqrt{(g_{00} + 2g_{0i}\dot{x}_i + g_{ik}\dot{x}_i\dot{x}_k)}\cdot dt = mc^2 \int d\tau \qquad (63.12)$$

This expression differs only by a constant factor from the integral considered in Section 38, the variation of which gives the equation of the geodesic. Thus the variational principle leads to equations of motion for a mass point

$$\delta S = 0 \qquad (63.13)$$

which coincide with the equations of a geodesic.

We now derive these equations in another way, starting with the fact that the divergence of the mass tensor vanishes.

Equation (63.01) may be stated in more detail as

$$\frac{\partial}{\partial t}\{\sqrt{(-g)}\cdot T^{0\nu}\} + \frac{\partial}{\partial x_i}\{\sqrt{(-g)}\cdot T^{i\nu}\} + \sqrt{(-g)}\cdot \Gamma^\nu_{\alpha\beta}T^{\alpha\beta} = 0 \quad (63.14)$$

Multiplying it by $dx_1\, dx_2\, dx_3$ and integrating over a volume at the boundaries of which the tensor $T^{\mu\nu}$ vanishes, we get

$$\frac{d}{dt}\int \sqrt{(-g)}\cdot T^{0\nu}\, dx_1\, dx_2\, dx_3 + \int \sqrt{(-g)}\cdot \Gamma^\nu_{\alpha\beta}T^{\alpha\beta}\, dx_1\, dx_2\, dx_3 = 0 \quad (63.15)$$

Here we can insert the expressions (63.02) for the components of the mass tensor. If the previous equation is multiplied by c^2 it then assumes the form

$$\frac{d}{dt} \int \rho^* u^0 u^\nu \sqrt{(-g)} \cdot dx_1 \, dx_2 \, dx_3 + \int \Gamma^\nu_{\alpha\beta} \rho^* u^\alpha u^\beta \sqrt{(-g)} \cdot dx_1 \, dx_2 \, dx_3 = 0$$

(63.16)

The integrals involved can be calculated by the same means as the integral in (63.11). Using (63.09) we obtain

$$\int \rho^* u^0 u^\nu \sqrt{(-g)} \cdot dx_1 \, dx_2 \, dx_3 = mcu^\nu$$

(63.17)

and

$$\int \Gamma^\nu_{\alpha\beta} \rho^* u^\alpha u^\beta \sqrt{(-g)} \cdot dx_1 \, dx_2 \, dx_3 = \frac{mc}{u^0} \Gamma^\nu_{\alpha\beta} u^\alpha u^\beta$$

(63.18)

where all quantities are to be taken at the position of the mass point. Replacing dt by $u^0 d\tau$ and dividing by the common factor mc/u^0 we obtain from (63.16)

$$\frac{du^\nu}{d\tau} + \Gamma^\nu_{\alpha\beta} u^\alpha u^\beta = 0$$

(63.19)

or

$$\frac{d^2 x_\nu}{d\tau^2} + \Gamma^\nu_{\alpha\beta} \frac{dx_\alpha}{d\tau} \frac{dx_\beta}{d\tau} = 0; \qquad \frac{dx_\nu}{d\tau} = u^\nu$$

(63.20)

These are the equations of a geodesic in explicit form. We have thus again shown that the equations describing the free motion of a mass point are identical with those of a geodesic. Our derivation shows that these equations can be obtained directly from the equation $\nabla_\mu T^{\mu\nu} = 0$ by integrating over volume and subsequently passing to the limit of a concentrated mass.

Here it is important to note the following. The operation of averaging over the volume is generally speaking not unique: it depends on a weight function. If before integrating over the volume we had introduced a weight function λ we could have obtained a result dependent on λ. However in the present case of a mass tensor of the form (63.02) the factor λ cancels out in the limit of a concentrated mass, and unique equations of motion are obtained.

We note that if the ordinary time $t = x_0$ is taken as the independent variable instead of the proper time τ and if the previous equations are multiplied by $(d\tau/dt)^2$ they appear as

$$\frac{d^2 x_\nu}{dt^2} - \frac{dx_\nu}{dt} \Gamma^0_{\alpha\beta} \frac{dx_\alpha}{dt} \frac{dx_\beta}{dt} + \Gamma^\nu_{\alpha\beta} \frac{dx_\alpha}{dt} \frac{dx_\beta}{dt} = 0$$

(63.21)

The equation for $\nu = 0$ reduces to an identity.

The quantity

$$w^\nu = \frac{du^\nu}{d\tau} + \Gamma^\nu_{\alpha\beta} u^\alpha u^\beta$$

(63.22)

which appears on the left-hand side of the equations of motion is the contravariant acceleration vector of the particle, as it was given by (46.26).

Let us now clarify the precise meaning of this acceleration. If no gravitational field is present the quantity w^ν is the ordinary acceleration; in Galilean coordinates the spatial components of this vector tend in non-relativistic approximation to the second derivatives, with respect to time, of the cartesian coordinates of the particle. When a gravitational field is present this will not be so. To determine the non-relativistic limit of the w^ν in this case one can compute the approximate expressions for the Christoffel symbols $\Gamma^\nu_{\alpha\beta}$ which follow from the expressions for the metric tensor derived in Section 55. It is convenient to postpone these calculations until Section 65, and here we only quote their result. Taking first the $\Gamma^\nu_{\alpha\beta}$ with zero superfix we find that

$$\Gamma^0_{00} = -\frac{1}{c^2}\frac{\partial U}{\partial t}\,; \qquad \Gamma^0_{0i} = -\frac{1}{c^2}\frac{\partial U}{\partial x_i} \tag{63.23}$$

while the others are small. Among the $\Gamma^i_{\alpha\beta}$ with a spatial superfix the most important are

$$\Gamma^i_{00} = -\frac{\partial U}{\partial x_i} \tag{63.24}$$

Further, we require approximate expressions for the four-dimensional velocity. Denoting the ordinary velocity by

$$v_i = \frac{dx_i}{dt} \tag{63.25}$$

we can put, approximately

$$u^i = \frac{dx_i}{d\tau} \cong v_i \tag{63.26}$$

and

$$u^0 = \frac{dt}{d\tau} \cong 1 + \frac{1}{c^2}\left(\tfrac{1}{2}\,v^2 + U\right) \tag{63.27}$$

Insertion of these expressions into (63.22) gives

$$w^i \cong \frac{dv_i}{dt} - \frac{\partial U}{\partial x_i} \tag{63.28}$$

and

$$w^0 \cong \frac{1}{c^2}\,v_k\left(\frac{dv_k}{dt} - \frac{\partial U}{\partial x_k}\right) \tag{63.29}$$

(Here summation over k from 1 to 3 is implied.)

These equations show that the spatial components of the vector w^ν represent the acceleration of the particle *apart from the acceleration due to gravity*, while the zero component is proportional to the work done on the particle in unit time by all forces *except gravity*.

64. General Statement of the Problem of the Motion of a System of Masses

The problem that will now concern us has already been generally characterized in Section 54. We consider a problem of an astronomical type, relating to the motion of celestial bodies in empty space. It is known from astronomical observations that the distribution of mass over the universe is far from uniform: an overwhelmingly large part is concentrated in the form of separate celestial bodies at great distances from each other. We shall assume accordingly that the components of the mass tensor vanish throughout space, except in some separated regions whose dimensions are small compared to their mutual distances ; each such region will correspond to a celestial body.

Within each body the mass tensor must in the first place conform to whatever physical model we accept for the body (that of a gas, a liquid or an elastic solid, etc.), and it must further satisfy the requirement that its divergence vanishes

$$\nabla_\nu T^{\mu\nu} = 0 \tag{64.01}$$

To achieve conformity with some physical model one must express the components of the mass tensor in a definite manner in terms of functions of the state of the physical system that makes up the body. (Such functions of state are density, velocity, pressure, etc., see for instance (55.02).)

The form of the mass tensor will depend not only on the physical properties of the body in question but also on the metric. Therefore its components will involve not only the state functions in the narrower sense but also the metric tensor. The metric tensor and its derivatives will also enter into the divergence expression (64.01).

Thus, if one wishes to write down the mass tensor one must know the metric. But the metric has to be determined from Einstein's equations which have the mass tensor on their right-hand sides. It is therefore evident that only a joint determination of the mass tensor and the metric as functions of the coordinates can be possible.

Let us compare the problem we are considering with those encountered in Newton's theory of gravitation. There the most common problem is to determine the gravitational potential from a mass density that is assumed to be known. But there are other more complicated problems in Newtonian theory in which the potential must be determined simultaneously with the density. A famous problem of this kind is that of the shape of a mass of liquid in rotation. This problem was studied by Liapunov in Russia and by Jeans and Poincaré elsewhere. Its rigorous solution was given in Liapunov's posthumous work [21, 22]. The problem we are concerned with is reminiscent in its general character of Liapunov's problem, but in our case one has to find two tensors, the metric tensor and the mass tensor, instead of two scalars, the Newtonian potential and the density. In addition, we must deal not with equilibrium but with motion. It may be noted that in Section 73 we shall also encounter the basic equations of Liapunov's problem.

Our problem is simplified in the first place by the fact that the metric nowhere deviates greatly from the Euclidean; the table given in Section 58 gives an idea of how small the deviation is. A further simplifying circumstance is that at all significant distances from the bodies, the metric does not depend on the detailed internal structure of the latter, but only on certain overall characteristics. Such characteristics are the total mass of the body, its moments of inertia, the position and velocity of its mass centre and so on. The Newtonian potential of a body depends on these same quantities.

To solve Einstein's equations we shall use a method of approximation which is a development of the method of calculation employed in Section 55. It is based on an expansion of all required functions in inverse powers of the speed of light. An expansion that can formally be so described will, in fact, be an expansion in powers of certain dimensionless quantities, such as U/c^2 and v^2/c^2 where U is the Newtonian potential and v^2 the square of some velocity, say the velocity of one of the bodies. For systems to which the virial theorem applies the two quantities U and v^2 will be of the same order, of order q^2 say, where q is a parameter of the dimensions of a speed. (We have already used this parameter in Sections 55 and 58.) Then the quantity q^2/c^2 can be used as the dimensionless parameter in terms of which the expansion proceeds.

If we solve wave equations by introducing corrections for retardation we imply that the dimensions of the system are small compared to the wavelength of the waves emitted, which in this case are gravitational waves. This assumption is not independent of those made above. For if the angular velocity of the revolution of a planet is denoted by ω and the radius of its orbit by R we can write the condition for the smallness of the system as $R \ll c/\omega$ since c/ω is the wave length of the gravitational wave divided by 2π. On the other hand, the condition that the speed $v = R\omega$ of the planet shall be small compared to the speed of light has the form $R\omega \ll c$, which is the same as the previous inequality.

In astronomical problems we are interested in " quasistationary " states of the gravitational field, i.e. states which are established after many planetary revolutions. The solution of the wave equation obtained by introducing corrections for retardation satisfies the conditions for a quasistationary state.

We have already remarked that in most astronomical problems the distances separating celestial bodies are extremely large compared to their linear dimensions. If R is a length characterizing the order of the separations and L a length characterizing the linear dimensions of the bodies we have the inequality

$$L \ll R \qquad (64.02)$$

The use of this inequality introduces considerable simplifications into the calculations of the gravitational potential and of the metric tensor outside the masses : as was mentioned, these quantities become independent of the detailed internal structure of the bodies. Therefore, we shall also use the inequality (64.02) though it is less essential than the inequalities $v^2 \ll c^2$ and $U \ll c^2$ on which our method of solving Einstein's equations is based.

We note that on the surfaces of the bodies and in their interiors, where the gravitational potential is greatest, we shall have, in orders of magnitude,

$$U/c^2 = \alpha/L \qquad (64.03)$$

where α is the gravitational radius of the body (see the table in Section 58). Therefore the two inequalities to be used can be written as

$$\alpha \ll L \ll R \qquad (64.04)$$

Our problem consists in determining the metric tensor and the mass tensor. If we know the components of the mass tensor as functions of the space and time coordinates we also know the motion of the masses, for the masses are just the regions in which the mass tensor differs from zero. It is essential to note that the motion of these regions cannot be prescribed in advance ; the laws of motion are a consequence of the laws of gravitation.

The solution to our problem gives us, firstly, some approximate expressions for the mass tensor and the metric tensor which involve certain unknown functions ; secondly, it gives us equations for these unknown functions from which they can be determined, given certain initial conditions. These are the equations of motion.

In the course of solving the problem it becomes apparent how to choose these unknown functions. The procedure of solution leads in a natural way to just the quantities that are used in Newtonian mechanics, such as the mass centre coordinates of each body, its total mass, its angular momentum, its moments of inertia and all the other quantities characterizing it.

For all these quantities equations of motion are obtained which, to first approximation, coincide with those of Newtonian theory and to second approximation deviate from them by small corrections. We shall be interested both in obtaining these corrections and in expressing the metric tensor and other quantities of Einstein's theory in terms of Newtonian quantities.

65. The Divergence of the Mass Tensor in Second Approximation

We shall attack the problem of determining the mass tensor and the metric tensor in a series of steps, starting from the discussion of Section 55. We recall that discussion. In the initial approximation the metric is taken to be Euclidean, which corresponds to complete neglect of the forces of gravity. In that approximation it was possible to prescribe only the components T^{00} and T^{0i} of the mass tensor. According to equation (55.03) these components appear in Galilean coordinates as

$$T^{00} = \frac{1}{c^2}\rho; \qquad T^{0i} = \frac{1}{c^2}\rho v_i \tag{65.01}$$

where ρ is the density and v_i the velocity of the ponderable matter at any point, with

$$\frac{\partial \rho}{\partial t} + \sum_{i=1}^{3} \frac{\partial (\rho v_i)}{\partial x_i} = 0 \tag{65.02}$$

The spatial components T^{ik} were not determined in this approximation; it was only assumed that their order of magnitude is the same as in the absence of gravity.

These assumptions concerning the mass tensor proved to be sufficient to determine the first approximation for the metric. According to (55.31) we have

$$g_{00} = c^2 - 2U$$

$$g_{0i} = \frac{4}{c^2} U_i \tag{65.03}$$

$$g_{ik} = -\left(1 + \frac{2U}{c^2}\right)\delta_{ik}$$

where U is the Newtonian potential of gravitation satisfying the equation

$$\Delta U = -4\pi\gamma\rho \tag{65.04}$$

while U_i is the vector potential of gravitation satisfying

$$\Delta U_i = -4\pi\gamma\rho v_i \tag{65.05}$$

It must be remembered that the potentials U and U_i are related to the mass density ρ and the mass current ρv_i in a non-local manner; the value of the potentials within a given body depends on the distribution of density throughout space and not only within the body itself.

In Section 55 we also gave equations for the contravariant components of the metric tensor, namely

$$g^{00} = \frac{1}{c^2}\left(1 + \frac{2U}{c^2}\right)$$

$$g^{0i} = \frac{4}{c^4} U_i \tag{65.06}$$

$$g^{ik} = -\left(1 - \frac{2U}{c^2}\right)\delta_{ik}$$

We had also, according to (55.37),

$$\sqrt{(-g)} = c + \frac{2U}{c} \tag{65.07}$$

Knowing the metric to the approximation of these equations we can take the next step in the construction of the mass tensor. To this end we must first write down more precisely an expression for its divergence. This is the aim of the present section.

According to (41.24) the general expression for the divergence of a symmetric tensor has the form

$$\nabla_\nu T^{\mu\nu} = \frac{\partial T^{\mu\nu}}{\partial x_\nu} + \Gamma^\mu_{\alpha\beta} T^{\alpha\beta} + y_\nu T^{\mu\nu} \tag{65.08}$$

where for brevity we have put

$$y_\nu = \frac{\partial}{\partial x_\nu} [\log \sqrt{(-g)}] = \Gamma^\alpha_{\nu\alpha} \tag{65.09}$$

In any case the order of magnitude of the components of the mass tensor is given correctly by the equations (55.02). We have

$$T^{00} = O\left(\frac{\rho}{c^2}\right); \qquad T^{0i} = O\left(\frac{\rho}{c^2} q\right); \qquad T^{ik} = O\left(\frac{\rho}{c^2} q^2\right) \tag{65.10}$$

where q is the parameter used before which characterizes the order of magnitude of the velocity.

Let us consider the zero component of the divergence of the mass tensor. It is given by (65.08) with $\mu = 0$. In our initial approximation we neglected all but the derivative term in this equation. To take the next step we must know the quantities $\Gamma^0_{\alpha\beta}$ and y up to terms of the order of $1/c^2$ inclusive. As for the spatial components of the divergence, they were neglected completely in the initial approximation. To take them into account in first approximation we must now find the leading term of $\Gamma^i_{\alpha\beta}$, which does not contain a factor $1/c^2$. For the determination of y_ν, $\Gamma^0_{\alpha\beta}$ and $\Gamma^i_{\alpha\beta}$ to the required accuracy the approximation represented by (65.03) to (65.07) is sufficient.

From (65.07) and (65.09) we readily obtain

$$y_0 = \frac{2}{c^2} \frac{\partial U}{\partial t}; \qquad y_i = \frac{2}{c^2} \frac{\partial U}{\partial x_i} \tag{65.11}$$

If we then calculate the Christoffel symbols from the well known relations

$$\Gamma^\mu_{\alpha\beta} = g^{\mu\nu} \Gamma_{\nu,\alpha\beta} \tag{65.12}$$

where

$$\Gamma_{\nu,\alpha\beta} = \tfrac{1}{2}\left(\frac{\partial g_{\nu\alpha}}{\partial x_\beta} + \frac{\partial g_{\nu\beta}}{\partial x_\alpha} - \frac{\partial g_{\alpha\beta}}{\partial x_\nu}\right) \tag{65.13}$$

it is easy to see that in the last equation our approximation allows us to neglect all terms containing the factor $1/c^2$. There then remains

$$\Gamma_{0,00} = -\frac{\partial U}{\partial t}; \qquad \Gamma_{0,0i} = -\frac{\partial U}{\partial x_i} \tag{65.14}$$

and also

$$\Gamma_{i,00} = \frac{\partial U}{\partial x_i} \tag{65.15}$$

Hence we get for $\Gamma^0_{\alpha\beta}$:

$$\Gamma^0_{00} = -\frac{1}{c^2}\frac{\partial U}{\partial t}; \qquad \Gamma^0_{0i} = -\frac{1}{c^2}\frac{\partial U}{\partial x_i} \tag{65.16}$$

whereas the Γ^0_{ik} will be of higher order of smallness, namely

$$\Gamma^0_{ik} = O\left(\frac{1}{c^4}\right) \tag{65.17}$$

Among the Christoffel symbols with a spatial superfix there occurs

$$\Gamma^i_{00} = -\frac{\partial U}{\partial x_i} \tag{65.18}$$

while all the others will be small :

$$\Gamma^i_{0k} = O\left(\frac{1}{c^2}\right); \qquad \Gamma^i_{kl} = O\left(\frac{1}{c^2}\right) \tag{65.19}$$

Having found the values of the Christoffel symbols we can now write down the required expression for the divergence of the mass tensor.

Equation (65.08) with $\mu = 0$ may be stated in more detail as

$$\nabla_\nu T^{0\nu} = \frac{\partial T^{00}}{\partial t} + \frac{\partial T^{0i}}{\partial x_i} + (\Gamma^0_{00} + y_0)\,T^{00} + (2\Gamma^0_{0i} + y_i)\,T^{0i} + \Gamma^0_{ik}\,T^{ik} \tag{65.20}$$

By (65.11) and (65.16) the coefficient of T^{00} in the above is

$$\Gamma^0_{00} + y_0 = \frac{1}{c^2}\frac{\partial U}{\partial t} \tag{65.21}$$

As for the coefficient of T^{0i}, it proves to be negligibly small, namely

$$2\Gamma^0_{0i} + y_i = O\left(\frac{1}{c^4}\right) \tag{65.22}$$

By (65.17) the coefficient of T^{ik} is of the same order.

Thus in our approximation equation (65.20) assumes the form

$$\nabla_\nu T^{0\nu} = \frac{\partial T^{00}}{\partial t} + \frac{\partial T^{0i}}{\partial x_i} + \frac{1}{c^2}\frac{\partial U}{\partial t}\,T^{00} \tag{65.23}$$

For the spatial components of the divergence, equation (65.08) with $\mu = i$ gives

$$\nabla_\nu T^{i\nu} = \frac{\partial T^{i0}}{\partial t} + \frac{\partial T^{ik}}{\partial x_k} + \Gamma^i_{00}T^{00} + 2\Gamma^i_{0k}T^{0k} + y_0 T^{0i} + \Gamma^i_{kl}T^{kl} + y_k T^{ik} \tag{65.24}$$

As may be seen from the estimates discussed above, the coefficients of the last four terms on the right-hand side will all have a factor of $1/c^2$ so that these terms may be discarded. Expressing Γ^i_{00} by (65.18) we therefore get

$$\nabla_\nu T^{i\nu} = \frac{\partial T^{i0}}{\partial t} + \frac{\partial T^{ik}}{\partial x_k} - \frac{\partial U}{\partial x_i}\,T^{00} \tag{65.25}$$

Thus, if the deviation of the metric from the Euclidean, or, in other words the force of gravity, is taken into account, to first order, we must express the condition of vanishing divergence by the equations

$$\frac{\partial T^{00}}{\partial t} + \frac{\partial T^{0k}}{\partial x_k} + \frac{1}{c^2} \frac{\partial U}{\partial t} T^{00} = 0 \tag{65.26}$$

and

$$\frac{\partial T^{i0}}{\partial t} + \frac{\partial T^{ik}}{\partial x_k} - \frac{\partial U}{\partial x_i} T^{00} = 0 \tag{65.27}$$

66. The Approximate Form of the Mass Tensor for an Elastic Solid with Inclusion of the Gravitational Field

In Section 32 we obtained approximate expressions for the mass tensor of an elastic solid or fluid body, neglecting gravitational forces, by studying Umov's scalar and vector of energy density and current. These expressions were then written down in Section 55 in the notation we are now using ($x_0 = t$). According to (55.02) they have the form

$$c^2 T^{00} = \rho \left\{ 1 + \frac{1}{c^2}(\tfrac{1}{2}v^2 + \Pi) \right\}$$

$$c^2 T^{0i} = \rho v_i \left\{ 1 + \frac{1}{c^2}(\tfrac{1}{2}v^2 + \Pi) \right\} - \frac{1}{c^2} p_{ik} v_k \tag{66.01}$$

$$c^2 T^{ik} = \rho v_i v_k - p_{ik}$$

We note that here p_{ik} denotes the three-dimensional elastic stress tensor and Π the elastic energy per unit mass of the body. According to (30.08) these quantities satisfy the relation

$$\rho \frac{d\Pi}{dt} = \tfrac{1}{2} p_{ik} \left(\frac{\partial v_i}{\partial x_k} + \frac{\partial v_k}{\partial x_i} \right) \tag{66.02}$$

We now have to generalize the expression for the mass tensor so as to take the gravitational field into account. According to Newton's theory the negative of the Newtonian potential is also the potential energy of a particle of unit mass placed in a given gravitational field. Therefore one would expect that the required expressions for the energy density and energy current may be obtained by adding the terms $(-\rho U)$ and $(-\rho v_i U)$ respectively to the expressions for Umov's scalar and vector in equations (30.17) and (30.18). This gives

$$S = \tfrac{1}{2}\rho v^2 + \rho(\Pi - U) \tag{66.03}$$

and

$$S_i = v_i \{\tfrac{1}{2}\rho v^2 + \rho(\Pi - U)\} - p_{ik} v_k \tag{66.04}$$

The components of the mass tensor can then be obtained from the relations

$$c^2 T^{00} = \rho + \frac{1}{c^2} S \tag{66.05}$$

and

$$c^2 T^{0i} = \rho v_i + \frac{1}{c^2} S_i \tag{66.06}$$

We shall thus finally have

$$c^2 T^{00} = \rho \left\{ 1 + \frac{1}{c^2}(\tfrac{1}{2}v^2 + \Pi - U) \right\}$$

$$c^2 T^{0i} = \rho v_i \left\{ 1 + \frac{1}{c^2}(\tfrac{1}{2}v^2 + \Pi - U) \right\} - \frac{1}{c^2}\, p_{ik}\, v_k \qquad (66.07)$$

$$c^2 T^{ik} = \rho v_i v_k - p_{ik}$$

If our argument is correct, then to the approximation required these expressions must satisfy the equations derived at the end of the preceding section, namely

$$\frac{\partial T^{00}}{\partial t} + \frac{\partial T^{0k}}{\partial x_k} + \frac{1}{c^2}\frac{\partial U}{\partial t}\, T^{00} = 0$$
$$\frac{\partial T^{i0}}{\partial t} + \frac{\partial T^{ik}}{\partial x_k} - \frac{\partial U}{\partial x_i}\, T^{00} = 0 \qquad (66.08)$$

These equations must be satisfied by virtue of the equations of motion for the quantities involved in the mass tensor. We have, firstly, the equation of continuity

$$\frac{\partial \rho}{\partial t} + \frac{\partial(\rho v_i)}{\partial x_i} = 0 \qquad (66.09)$$

and, secondly, the equations of motion of an elastic body in a gravitational field of acceleration $\partial U/\partial x_i$:

$$\rho\,\frac{dv_i}{dt} - \rho\,\frac{\partial U}{\partial x_i} = \frac{\partial p_{ik}}{\partial x_k} \qquad (66.10)$$

In addition, the relation (66.02) between the stress tensor and the elastic potential energy is valid. Using (66.09), (66.10) and (66.02) we find that Umov's scalar and vector are related by

$$\frac{\partial S}{\partial t} + \frac{\partial S_i}{\partial x_i} = -\,\rho\,\frac{\partial U}{\partial t} \qquad (66.11)$$

whence with the use of (66.09) we obtain

$$\frac{\partial T^{00}}{\partial t} + \frac{\partial T^{0k}}{\partial x_k} = -\frac{1}{c^4}\,\rho\,\frac{\partial U}{\partial t} \qquad (66.12)$$

Since $\rho = c^2 T^{00}$ approximately, equation (66.12) and the first equation of (66.08) coincide in the approximation in question. As for the remaining equations of (66.08), after multiplication by c^2 they coincide approximately with the equation of motion (66.10) written in the form

$$\frac{\partial(\rho v_i)}{\partial t} + \frac{\partial(\rho v_i v_k)}{\partial x_k} - \frac{\partial p_{ik}}{\partial x_k} - \rho\,\frac{\partial U}{\partial x_i} = 0 \qquad (66.13)$$

(here it is sufficient to take the leading terms in the expressions for T^{i0} and T^{00}).

Thus the equations (66.08), which express the fact that the mass tensor has vanishing (non-Euclidean) divergence, are indeed approximately satisfied if the quantities (66.07) are taken to represent the mass tensor.

In the equations (66.07) the density ρ satisfies the equation of continuity

(66.09). The corresponding generally covariant equation has the form

$$\frac{\partial}{\partial x_\alpha}\{\sqrt{(-g)}\cdot\rho^*u^\alpha\} = 0 \tag{66.14}$$

where ρ^* is the invariant density and u^α the four-dimensional velocity. To make (66.09) and (66.14) coincide we can put

$$\rho = \frac{1}{c}\sqrt{(-g)}\cdot\rho^*u^0$$
$$\rho v_i = \frac{1}{c}\sqrt{(-g)}\cdot\rho^*u^i \tag{66.15}$$

(The factor $1/c$ has been included so as to make ρ^* approximately equal to ρ.) Noting that by (65.07) and (63.27)

$$\frac{1}{c}\sqrt{(-g)} = 1 + \frac{2U}{c^2}; \qquad u^0 = 1 + \frac{1}{c^2}(\tfrac{1}{2}v^2 + U) \tag{66.16}$$

we get, approximately

$$\rho^* = \rho\left\{1 - \frac{1}{c^2}(\tfrac{1}{2}v^2 + 3U)\right\} \tag{66.17}$$

The equations (66.07) allow one to write down an expression for the invariant of the mass tensor. Introducing the pressure by the equation

$$p = -\tfrac{1}{3}(p_{11} + p_{22} + p_{33}) \tag{66.18}$$

we get

$$T = \rho\left\{1 + \frac{1}{c^2}(-\tfrac{1}{2}v^2 + \mathrm{II} - 3U)\right\} - \frac{3}{c^2}p \tag{66.19}$$

and using the equation (66.17) for ρ^*

$$T = \rho^*\left(1 + \frac{\mathrm{II}}{c^2}\right) - \frac{3}{c^2}p \tag{66.20}$$

This last expression agrees with (32.30).

67. Approximate Expressions for the Christoffel Symbols and Some Other Quantities

In order to take the next step in the determination of the metric tensor we must extend the calculations of Section 55. As all our calculations will be done in harmonic coordinates it is convenient to use as unknown functions the contravariant components of the metric tensor multiplied by $\sqrt{(-g)}$, i.e. the quantities

$$\mathfrak{g}^{ik} = \sqrt{(-g)}\cdot g^{\mu\nu} \tag{67.01}$$

The advantage of using these quantities comes from the fact that they permit the harmonic condition (55.79) to be stated in the simple form

$$\frac{\partial\mathfrak{g}^{\mu\nu}}{\partial x_\mu} = 0 \tag{67.02}$$

so that it is *linear* in the unknown functions. A further advantage of this choice of unknown functions is that the spatial components $\mathfrak{g}^{ik}$ differ very little from constants. Finally it is also most convenient that the left-hand side of every one of the gravitational equations involves the d'Alembert operator applied to the appropriate component $\mathfrak{g}^{\mu\nu}$, so that approximately each component $g^{\mu\nu}$ is connected only with the single component of the mass tensor having the same indices.

In Section 55 (equations (55.38)) we found approximate expressions for the $g^{\mu\nu}$:

$$g^{00} = \frac{1}{c} + \frac{4U}{c^3}$$

$$g^{0i} = \frac{4}{c^3} U_i \tag{67.03}$$

$$g^{ik} = -c\delta_{ik}$$

Here U is the Newtonian potential and U_i the gravitational vector potential. We now use more accurate expressions obtained by adding the next terms in the expansion in inverse powers of the speed of light. We have then:

$$g^{00} = \frac{1}{c} + \frac{4U}{c^3} + \frac{4S}{c^5}$$

$$g^{0i} = \frac{4U_i}{c^3} + \frac{4S_i}{c^5} \tag{67.04}$$

$$g^{ik} = -c\delta_{ik} + \frac{4S_{ik}}{c^3}$$

Using these expressions we can calculate the Christoffel symbols and the other quantities that enter the gravitational equations.

We begin by calculating the determinant g. As is easily verified (see equation (B.67)) it is equal to the determinant of the $g^{\mu\nu}$. The equations (67.04) give

$$g = -c^2\left(1 + \frac{4U}{c^2} + \frac{4S - 4S_{kk}}{c^4}\right) \tag{67.05}$$

Here we have used the summation convention for spatial indices and have put

$$S_{kk} = \sum_{k=1}^{3} S_{kk} = S_{11} + S_{22} + S_{33} \tag{67.06}$$

Extracting the square root we obtain further

$$\sqrt{(-g)} = c\left(1 + \frac{2U}{c^2} + \frac{2S - 2S_{kk} - 2U^2}{c^4}\right) \tag{67.07}$$

We introduce a special symbol for the fourth root

$$\sqrt[4]{\left(-\frac{g}{c^2}\right)} = f \tag{67.08}$$

By (67.06) this quantity is

$$f = 1 + \frac{U}{c^2} + \frac{1}{c^4}(S - S_{kk} - \tfrac{3}{2}U^2) \tag{67.09}$$

The quantity f will approximately satisfy a linear differential equation which will be derived in the next section.

From (67.04) and (67.07) we obtain for c^2g^{00} the expression

$$c^2g^{00} = 1 + \frac{2U}{c^2} + \frac{2S + 2S_{kk} - 2U^2}{c^4} \tag{67.10}$$

If we put

$$U^* = U + \frac{1}{c^2}(S + S_{kk} - 2U^2) \tag{67.11}$$

we have with the same accuracy

$$c^2 g^{00} = \frac{c^2 + U^*}{c^2 - U^*} \tag{67.12}$$

and also

$$\frac{1}{c^2} g_{00} = \frac{c^2 - U^*}{c^2 + U^*} \tag{67.13}$$

We shall encounter the quantity U^* in the following.

We now pass on to the calculation of the quantities

$$\Pi^{\mu,\,\alpha\beta} = \frac{1}{2g}\left(g^{\alpha\rho}\frac{\partial g^{\mu\beta}}{\partial x_\rho} + g^{\beta\rho}\frac{\partial g^{\mu\alpha}}{\partial x_\rho} - g^{\mu\rho}\frac{\partial g^{\alpha\beta}}{\partial x_\rho}\right) \tag{67.14}$$

These are introduced in Appendix B and are related to the Christoffel symbols. Using (67.04) and (67.05) we obtain the following set of equations

$$\Pi^{0,\,00} = -\frac{2}{c^6}\frac{\partial U}{\partial t}$$

$$\Pi^{0,\,0l} = \frac{2}{c^4}\frac{\partial U}{\partial x_l} \tag{67.15}$$

$$\Pi^{0,\,kl} = \frac{2}{c^4}\left(\frac{\partial U_k}{\partial x_l} + \frac{\partial U_l}{\partial x_k}\right)$$

and

$$\Pi^{i,\,00} = -\frac{2}{c^4}\left\{\frac{\partial U}{\partial x_i} + \frac{1}{c^2}\left(\frac{\partial S}{\partial x_i} - 4U\frac{\partial U}{\partial x_i} + 2\frac{\partial U_i}{\partial t}\right)\right\}$$

$$\Pi^{i,\,k0} = \frac{2}{c^4}\left(\frac{\partial U_i}{\partial x_k} - \frac{\partial U_k}{\partial x_i}\right) \tag{67.16}$$

$$\Pi^{i,\,kl} = O\left(\frac{1}{c^4}\right)$$

If we lower the second and third superfix we obtain the $\Pi^\mu_{\alpha\beta}$. We find

$$\Pi^0_{00} = -\frac{2}{c^2}\frac{\partial U}{\partial t}$$

$$\Pi^0_{0l} = -\frac{2}{c^2}\frac{\partial U}{\partial x_l} \tag{67.17}$$

$$\Pi^0_{kl} = O\left(\frac{1}{c^4}\right)$$

and

$$\Pi^i_{00} = -2\left\{\frac{\partial U}{\partial x_i} + \frac{1}{c^2}\left(\frac{\partial S}{\partial x_i} - 8U\frac{\partial U}{\partial x_i} + 2\frac{\partial U_i}{\partial t}\right)\right\}$$

$$\Pi^i_{k0} = -\frac{2}{c^2}\left(\frac{\partial U_i}{\partial x_k} - \frac{\partial U_k}{\partial x_i}\right) \tag{67.18}$$

$$\Pi^i_{kl} = O\left(\frac{1}{c^4}\right)$$

In calculating Π^i_{00} the value $g_{00} = c^2 - 2U$ is needed, but for the calculation of the other quantities it is sufficient to use the Galilean values of the metric tensor components. In the equations for the $\Pi^\mu_{\alpha\beta}$ we have restricted ourselves to terms of the order $1/c^2$.

In order to evaluate the Christoffel symbols we require not only the $\Pi^\mu_{\alpha\beta}$

$$\Lambda^{\mu}_{\alpha\beta} = \tfrac{1}{2}(y_{\alpha}\delta^{\mu}_{\beta} + y_{\beta}\delta^{\mu}_{\alpha} - y^{\mu}g_{\alpha\beta}) \tag{67.19}$$

where
$$y_{\alpha} = \frac{\partial \log \sqrt{(-g)}}{\partial x_{\alpha}}, \qquad y^{\mu} = g^{\mu\alpha}y_{\alpha} \tag{67.20}$$

(see Appendix D). We state the approximate values of the y_{α}. Differentiating (67.05) we obtain

$$y_i = \frac{2}{c_2}\left\{\frac{\partial U}{\partial x_i} + \frac{1}{c^2}\left(\frac{\partial S}{\partial x_i} - 4U\frac{\partial U}{\partial x_i} - \frac{\partial S_{kk}}{\partial x_i}\right)\right\}$$

$$y_0 = \frac{2}{c^2}\left\{\frac{\partial U}{\partial t} + \frac{1}{c^2}\left(\frac{\partial S}{\partial t} - 4U\frac{\partial U}{\partial t} - \frac{\partial S_{kk}}{\partial t}\right)\right\} \tag{67.21}$$

Retaining terms up to the order of $1/c^4$ we find the following values for the y^{μ} with upper indices

$$y^i = -\frac{2}{c^2}\left\{\frac{\partial U}{\partial x_i} + \frac{1}{c^2}\left(\frac{\partial S}{\partial x_i} - 6U\frac{\partial U}{\partial x_i} - \frac{\partial S_{kk}}{\partial x_i}\right)\right\}$$

$$y^0 = \frac{2}{c^4}\frac{\partial U}{\partial t} \tag{67.22}$$

The Christoffel symbols are expressible in terms of the quantities just derived as

$$\Gamma^{\mu}_{\alpha\beta} = \Pi^{\mu}_{\alpha\beta} + \Lambda^{\mu}_{\alpha\beta} \tag{67.23}$$

If we confine ourselves to terms of order not higher than $1/c^2$ we find for $\mu = 0$ just as in the approximation (65.16) :

$$\Gamma^0_{00} = -\frac{1}{c^2}\frac{\partial U}{\partial t}; \qquad \Gamma^0_{0i} = -\frac{1}{c^2}\frac{\partial U}{\partial x_i}; \qquad \Gamma^0_{ik} = O\left(\frac{1}{c^4}\right) \tag{67.24}$$

whereas for $\mu = i$ we obtain expressions that are more accurate than (65.18) and (65.19) :

$$\Gamma^i_{00} = -\frac{\partial U}{\partial x_i} - \frac{1}{c^2}\left(\frac{\partial S}{\partial x_i} + \frac{\partial S_{kk}}{\partial x_i} - 8U\frac{\partial U}{\partial x_i} + 4\frac{\partial U_i}{\partial t}\right)$$

$$\Gamma^i_{0k} = \frac{1}{c^2}\frac{\partial U}{\partial t}\delta_{ik} - \frac{2}{c^2}\left(\frac{\partial U_i}{\partial x_k} - \frac{\partial U_k}{\partial x_i}\right) \tag{67.25}$$

$$\Gamma^i_{kl} = \frac{1}{c^2}\left(\frac{\partial U}{\partial x_l}\delta_{ik} + \frac{\partial U}{\partial x_k}\delta_{il} - \frac{\partial U}{\partial x_i}\delta_{kl}\right)$$

In approximate calculations it is convenient to use equations arranged in such a form that the $\Pi^{\mu}_{\alpha\beta}$ are involved rather than the $\Gamma^{\mu}_{\alpha\beta}$. The advantage of the former quantities over the latter may be seen by comparing (67.18) with (67.25). These equations show that the Π^i_{kl} may be neglected, but the Γ^i_{kl} may not.

In Appendix D we obtain an equation for the Einstein tensor which has been brought to the form described; this is equation (D.87). It involves the Lagrangian, which by (D.95) is equal to

$$L = -\frac{1}{2\sqrt{(-g)}}\Pi^{\nu}_{\alpha\beta}\frac{\partial g^{\alpha\beta}}{\partial x_{\nu}} + \tfrac{1}{2}y_{\nu}y^{\nu} \tag{67.26}$$

We derive the approximate value of this expression. From (67.21) and (67.22)

we get

$$\sqrt{(-g)} \cdot y_\alpha y^\alpha = \frac{4}{c^5}\left(\frac{\partial U}{\partial t}\right)^2 - \frac{4}{c^3}\left(1 - \frac{8U}{c^2}\right)\left(\frac{\partial U}{\partial x_i} + \frac{1}{c^2}\frac{\partial(S - S_{kk})}{\partial x_i}\right)^2$$

(67.27)

On the other hand, if we use (67.17) and (67.18) in conjunction with the initial expressions (67.04) for the $g^{\mu\nu}$ we find

$$-\frac{1}{2}\Pi^\rho_{\alpha\beta}\frac{\partial g^{\alpha\beta}}{\partial x_\rho} = \frac{4}{c^5}\left(\frac{\partial U}{\partial t}\right)^2 + \frac{16}{c^5}\frac{\partial U}{\partial x_i}\frac{\partial U_i}{\partial t}$$
$$+ \frac{4}{c^3}\left(1 - \frac{8U}{c^2}\right)\left(\frac{\partial U}{\partial x_i} + \frac{1}{c^2}\frac{\partial S}{\partial x_i}\right)^2 - \frac{4}{c^5}\left(\frac{\partial U_i}{\partial x_k} - \frac{\partial U_k}{\partial x_i}\right)^2$$

(67.28)

Adding this to one half of the preceding equation we obtain for $\sqrt{(-g)}$ times the Lagrangian

$$L\sqrt{(-g)} = \frac{2}{c^3}\left(1 - \frac{8U}{c^2}\right)\left[\left(\frac{\partial U}{\partial x_i}\right)^2 + \frac{2}{c^2}\frac{\partial U}{\partial x_i}\left(\frac{\partial S}{\partial x_i} + \frac{\partial S_{kk}}{\partial x_i}\right)\right]$$
$$+ \frac{6}{c^5}\left(\frac{\partial U}{\partial t}\right)^2 + \frac{16}{c^5}\frac{\partial U}{\partial x_i}\frac{\partial U_i}{\partial t} - \frac{4}{c^5}\left(\frac{\partial U_i}{\partial x_k} - \frac{\partial U_k}{\partial x_i}\right)^2$$

(67.29)

Introducing $U*$ from (67.11) this expression may be written as

$$L\sqrt{(-g)} = \frac{2}{c^3}\left(\frac{\partial U*}{\partial x_i}\right)^2 + \frac{6}{c^5}\left(\frac{\partial U*}{\partial t}\right)^2 + \frac{16}{c^5}\frac{\partial U*}{\partial x_i}\frac{\partial U_i}{\partial t} - \frac{4}{c^5}\left(\frac{\partial U_i}{\partial x_k} - \frac{\partial U_k}{\partial x_i}\right)^2$$

(67.30)

Here we have replaced U by $U*$ in the correction terms. The last equation is remarkable in having on its right-hand side a homogeneous quadratic form in the first derivatives of the *four* quantities $U*$ and U_i with *constant* coefficients.

By comparing (67.27) and (67.29) we see that the sum

$$\sqrt{(-g)} \cdot (L + \tfrac{1}{2}y_\alpha y^\alpha)$$
$$= \frac{8}{c^5}\left\{\frac{\partial U}{\partial x_i}\frac{\partial S_{kk}}{\partial x_i} - \frac{1}{2}\left(\frac{\partial U_i}{\partial x_k} - \frac{\partial U_k}{\partial x_i}\right)^2 + \left(\frac{\partial U}{\partial t}\right)^2 + 2\frac{\partial U}{\partial x_i}\frac{\partial U_i}{\partial t}\right\}$$

(67.31)

will be of a higher order of smallness than (67.27) and (67.29) separately. This remark enables one to derive a very simple approximate expression for the curvature scalar R. According to the relation (D.49) we have in harmonic coordinates

$$R = g^{\alpha\beta}\frac{\partial^2 \log \sqrt{(-g)}}{\partial x_\alpha \partial x_\beta} - L$$

(67.32)

Using the definition (67.08) we may write

$$\sqrt{(-g)} = cf^2$$

(67.33)

whence we get

$$R = \frac{2}{f}g^{\alpha\beta}\frac{\partial^2 f}{\partial x_\alpha \partial x_\beta} - \frac{2}{f^2}g^{\alpha\beta}\frac{\partial f}{\partial x_\alpha}\frac{\partial f}{\partial x_\beta} - L$$

(67.34)

But we have

$$y_\alpha = \frac{2}{f}\frac{\partial f}{\partial x_\alpha}$$

(67.35)

Therefore

$$R = \frac{2}{cf^3} \, \mathfrak{g}^{\alpha\beta} \frac{\partial^2 f}{\partial x_\alpha \, \partial x_\beta} - (\tfrac{1}{2} \, y_\alpha y^\alpha + L) \tag{67.36}$$

We now pass to the approximate equations. According to (67.31) the quantity $(\tfrac{1}{2} y_\alpha y^\alpha + L)$ will be of sixth order in $1/c$. Discarding quantities of sixth order we can replace the $\mathfrak{g}^{\alpha\beta}$ by their Galilean values. The curvature scalar R then assumes the very simple approximate form

$$R = \frac{2}{f^3} \left(\frac{1}{c^2} \frac{\partial^2 f}{\partial t^2} - \Delta f \right) \tag{67.37}$$

where Δ is the Laplace operator with Euclidean coefficients.

68. Approximate Form of the Gravitational Equations

The calculations of the preceding section permit us to write the left-hand side of Einstein's gravitational equations

$$R^{\mu\nu} - \tfrac{1}{2} g^{\mu\nu} R = -\frac{8\pi\gamma}{c^2} \, T^{\mu\nu} \tag{68.01}$$

in the approximation corresponding to the required accuracy. Let us first write down the value of the left-hand side without any approximations. According to (D.87) we have

$$R^{\mu\nu} - \tfrac{1}{2} g^{\mu\nu} R = \frac{1}{2g} \, \mathfrak{g}^{\alpha\beta} \frac{\partial^2 \mathfrak{g}^{\mu\nu}}{\partial x_\alpha \, \partial x_\beta} + \Pi^{\mu,\alpha\beta} \Pi^\nu_{\alpha\beta} - \tfrac{1}{2} y^\mu y^\nu$$

$$+ \tfrac{1}{2} g^{\mu\nu} L + \tfrac{1}{2} g^{\mu\nu} B - B^{\mu\nu} \tag{68.02}$$

Here L is the Lagrangian

$$L = -\frac{1}{2\sqrt{(-g)}} \, \Pi^\nu_{\alpha\beta} \frac{\partial \mathfrak{g}^{\alpha\beta}}{\partial x_\nu} + \tfrac{1}{2} y_\nu y^\nu \tag{68.03}$$

which was already encountered in the preceding section. According to (D.85) the quantities $B^{\mu\nu}$ are given by the equations

$$B^{\mu\nu} = \Gamma^{\mu\nu} + \tfrac{1}{2}(y^\mu \Gamma^\nu + y^\nu \Gamma^\mu) = \tfrac{1}{2}(\nabla^\mu + y^\mu) \, \Gamma^\nu + \tfrac{1}{2}(\nabla^\nu + y^\nu) \, \Gamma^\mu \tag{68.04}$$

where the Γ^ν are the quantities introduced in Sections 41 and 53 :

$$\Gamma^\nu = -\frac{1}{\sqrt{(-g)}} \frac{\partial g^{\mu\nu}}{\partial x^\mu} \tag{68.05}$$

The quantity B is the " quasi-invariant " formed from the $B^{\mu\nu}$

$$B = g_{\mu\nu} B^{\mu\nu} = (\nabla_\nu + y_\nu) \Gamma^\nu \tag{68.06}$$

It is not a true invariant because the $B^{\mu\nu}$ do not form a tensor.

In a harmonic system of coordinates the Γ^ν vanish and, therefore, also the $\Gamma^{\mu\nu}$ and so do the $B^{\mu\nu}$ and B.

We note that as long as the left-hand side of Einstein's equations (68.01) contains the complete expression (68.02) for the conservative tensor, the equation

$$\nabla_\mu T^{\mu\nu} = 0 \tag{68.07}$$

is a consequence of the equations themselves. However, if from the start we drop the terms in $B^{\mu\nu}$ and B from the conservative tensor the equation (68.07) will only be true if the conditions $\Gamma^\nu = 0$ are satisfied.

Passing to the approximate form of Einstein's equations we shall first consider the terms involving second derivatives. Using (67.04) we get

$$g^{\alpha\beta}\frac{\partial^2\varphi}{\partial x_\alpha\,\partial x_\beta} = -c\Delta\varphi + \frac{1}{c}\frac{\partial^2\varphi}{\partial t^2} + \frac{4}{c^3}\left(S_{ik}\frac{\partial^2\varphi}{\partial x_i\,\partial x_k} + 2U_i\frac{\partial^2\varphi}{\partial x_i\,\partial t} + U\frac{\partial^2\varphi}{\partial t^2}\right)$$

(68.08)

Here the leading terms combine to give c times the Euclidean d'Alembertian while the terms with variable coefficients represent corrections which may be neglected in the approximation considered. We consider in more detail the order of magnitude of these corrections. The expression (68.02) for the Einstein tensor involves the quantity (68.08) divided by $2g$, if the corresponding component of $g^{\mu\nu}$ is inserted for φ. The derivatives of φ will be of third order and since $g = -c^2$ approximately, the division by $2g$ makes the correction terms in (68.08) of eighth order in $1/c$. Since we intend to neglect terms of this order we must evaluate all other quantities involved in (68.02) to a corresponding accuracy.

To avoid denominators involving g we shall evaluate not the Einstein tensor itself but, instead, that tensor multiplied by a factor which differs little from unity, namely $(-g/c^2)$. Then to the required accuracy the terms involving second derivatives will be

$$-\frac{1}{2c^2}g^{\alpha\beta}\frac{\partial^2 g^{\mu\nu}}{\partial x_\alpha\,\partial x_\beta} = \frac{1}{2c}\Delta g^{\mu\nu} - \frac{1}{2c^3}\frac{\partial^2 g^{\mu\nu}}{\partial t^2}$$

(68.09)

In evaluating the terms involving first derivatives we shall first use the relations (67.15) to (67.18) to obtain the quantities

$$\left(-\frac{g}{c^2}\right)\Pi^{0,\,\alpha\beta}\Pi^0_{\alpha\beta} = -\frac{8}{c^6}\left(\frac{\partial U}{\partial x_s}\right)^2$$

(68.10)

$$\left(-\frac{g}{c^2}\right)\Pi^{0,\,\alpha\beta}\Pi^i_{\alpha\beta} = \frac{4}{c^6}\frac{\partial U}{\partial t}\frac{\partial U}{\partial x_i} - \frac{8}{c^6}\left(\frac{\partial U_i}{\partial x_s} - \frac{\partial U_s}{\partial x_i}\right)\frac{\partial U}{\partial x_s}$$

(68.11)

and

$$\left(-\frac{g}{c^2}\right)\Pi^{i,\,\alpha\beta}\Pi^k_{\alpha\beta}$$

$$= \frac{4}{c^4}\left(1 - \frac{8U}{c^2}\right)\left(\frac{\partial U}{\partial x_i} + \frac{1}{c^2}\frac{\partial S}{\partial x_i} + \frac{2}{c^2}\frac{\partial U_i}{\partial t}\right)\left(\frac{\partial U}{\partial x_k} + \frac{1}{c^2}\frac{\partial S}{\partial x_k} + \frac{2}{c^2}\frac{\partial U_k}{\partial t}\right)$$

$$- \frac{8}{c^6}\left(\frac{\partial U_i}{\partial x_s} - \frac{\partial U_s}{\partial x_i}\right)\left(\frac{\partial U_k}{\partial x_s} - \frac{\partial U_s}{\partial x_k}\right)$$

(68.12)

In the equations (68.10) and (68.11) we need not have included the factor $(-g/c^2)$ because in the present approximation it may be replaced by unity. Further, using the expressions (67.22) for y^α and introducing the notation

$$N^{\mu\nu} = \left(-\frac{g}{c^2}\right)\{\Pi^{\mu,\,\alpha\beta}\Pi^\nu_{\alpha\beta} - \tfrac{1}{2}y^\mu y^\nu + \tfrac{1}{2}g^{\mu\nu}L\}$$

(68.13)

we obtain
$$N^{00} = -\frac{7}{c^6}\left(\frac{\partial U}{\partial x_s}\right)^2 \tag{68.14}$$

$$N^{0i} = \frac{6}{c^6}\frac{\partial U}{\partial t}\frac{\partial U}{\partial x_i} - \frac{8}{c^6}\left(\frac{\partial U_i}{\partial x_s} - \frac{\partial U_s}{\partial x_i}\right)\frac{\partial U}{\partial x_s} \tag{68.15}$$

and
$$N^{ik} = \frac{2}{c^4}\left(\frac{\partial U^*}{\partial x_i} + \frac{4}{c^2}\frac{\partial U_i}{\partial t}\right)\left(\frac{\partial U^*}{\partial x_k} + \frac{4}{c^2}\frac{\partial U_k}{\partial t}\right)$$
$$- \frac{8}{c^6}\left(\frac{\partial U_i}{\partial x_s} - \frac{\partial U_s}{\partial x_i}\right)\left(\frac{\partial U_k}{\partial x_s} - \frac{\partial U_s}{\partial x_k}\right) - \frac{1}{2}\delta_{ik}\frac{\sqrt{(-g)}}{c}L \tag{68.16}$$

where
$$\frac{1}{c}\sqrt{(-g)}\cdot L = \frac{2}{c^4}\left(\frac{\partial U^*}{\partial x_s}\right)^2 + \frac{6}{c^6}\left(\frac{\partial U}{\partial t}\right)^2 + \frac{16}{c^6}\frac{\partial U}{\partial x_s}\frac{\partial U_s}{\partial t}$$
$$- \frac{4}{c^6}\left(\frac{\partial U_s}{\partial x_r} - \frac{\partial U_r}{\partial x_s}\right)^2 \tag{68.17}$$

and U^* is the quantity given by (67.11). Since U enters these equations through terms of sixth order it can be replaced by U^* as was done in (67.30). Then the only first derivatives contained in the $N^{\mu\nu}$ are those of the four quantities U^* and U_s and all the $N^{\mu\nu}$ are homogeneous quadratic functions of these first derivatives, with *constant* coefficients. This represents a very great simplification of the exact equations (68.13).

With the use of the expressions found we can immediately write down the approximate form of Einstein's equations; we have

$$\left(\frac{-g}{c^2}\right)(R^{\mu\nu} - \tfrac{1}{2}g^{\mu\nu}R) = \frac{1}{2c}\Delta\mathfrak{g}^{\mu\nu} - \frac{1}{2c^3}\frac{\partial^2\mathfrak{g}^{\mu\nu}}{\partial t^2} + N^{\mu\nu} = \frac{8\pi\gamma g}{c^4}T^{\mu\nu} \tag{68.18}$$

where the $N^{\mu\nu}$ have the values (68.14) to (68.16).

In order to use equation (68.18) for the determination of the $\mathfrak{g}^{\mu\nu}$ the quantities U^* and U_i appearing in the $N^{\mu\nu}$ must first of all be evaluated to the accuracy required.

As regards the U_i they enter into the expressions (68.14) to (68.16) only through terms of sixth order; it is therefore sufficient to know them to the accuracy reached in Section 55. The relevant equations were also given in Section 65. (These equations can be obtained from the equation (68.18) with $\mu = 0$, $\nu = i$ by neglecting N^{0i} and the second time derivative, replacing g by $-c^2$, retaining only the leading term in T^{0i} and expressing $\mathfrak{g}^{0i}$ in terms of U_i.) We have by (65.05)

$$\Delta U_i = -4\pi\gamma\rho v_i \tag{68.19}$$

On the other hand U^* appears in terms not of sixth, but of fourth, order and it must be known with greater accuracy. By the definition (67.11) we have

$$U^* = U + \frac{1}{c^2}(S + S_{kk} - 2U^2) \tag{68.20}$$

According to (67.04) the derivatives of $U + S/c^2$ are equal to the derivatives of $c^3\mathfrak{g}^{00}/4$. Therefore equation (68.18) for $\mu = \nu = 0$ gives:

$$\left(\Delta - \frac{1}{c^2}\frac{\partial}{\partial t^2}\right)\left(U + \frac{1}{c^2}S\right) = -\frac{c^4}{2}N^{00} + 4\pi\gamma gT^{00} \tag{68.21}$$

Further, the derivatives of S_{kk}/c^2 and of $c\mathfrak{g}^{kk}/4$ are equal. Putting $\mu = \nu = k$

in (68.18) and summing over k we get

$$\left(\Delta - \frac{1}{c^2}\frac{\partial^2}{\partial t^2}\right)\frac{1}{c^2}\,S_{kk} = -\frac{c^2}{2}\,N^{kk} - 4\pi\gamma T^{kk} \tag{68.22}$$

(In the second term on the right we have replaced $(-g/c^2)$ by unity.) Finally we can write

$$\left(\Delta - \frac{1}{c^2}\frac{\partial^2}{\partial t^2}\right)\left(\frac{-2U^2}{c^2}\right) = -\frac{4}{c^2}(\operatorname{grad} U)^2 + 16\pi\gamma U T^{00} \tag{68.23}$$

Here we have neglected the second time derivative in the d'Alembertian and have used the identity

$$\Delta(U^2) = 2(\operatorname{grad} U)^2 + 2U\,\Delta U \tag{68.24}$$

and also the equation

$$\Delta U = -4\pi\gamma\rho = -4\pi\gamma c^2 T^{00} \tag{68.25}$$

The required equation for U^* may be obtained by adding the three equations (68.21) to (68.23). We calculate the sum of the right-hand sides. By (68.14) we have

$$-\frac{c^4}{2}\,N^{00} = \frac{7}{2c^2}(\operatorname{grad} U)^2 \tag{68.26}$$

Calculating to the same accuracy we obtain from (68.16) and (68.17)

$$-\frac{c^2}{2}\,N^{kk} = \frac{1}{2c^2}(\operatorname{grad} U)^2 \tag{68.27}$$

and therefore

$$\frac{c^4}{2}\,N^{00} + \frac{c^2}{2}\,N^{kk} + \frac{4}{c^2}(\operatorname{grad} U)^2 = 0 \tag{68.28}$$

Using this relation as well as the equation

$$4\pi\gamma g + 16\pi\gamma U = -4\pi\gamma c^2 \tag{68.29}$$

we get for U^* the simple equation

$$\Delta U^* - \frac{1}{c^2}\frac{\partial^2 U^*}{\partial t^2} = -4\pi\gamma(c^2 T^{00} + T^{kk}) \tag{68.30}$$

Outside the masses U^* satisfies d'Alembert's equation with Euclidean coefficients. This could be expected in view of the form (68.17) of the Lagrangian.

At the end of Section 67 we found an approximate expression for the scalar of curvature R in terms of the function

$$f = \sqrt[4]{\left(\frac{-g}{c^2}\right)} \tag{68.31}$$

which is proportional to the fourth root of the absolute value of the determinant g. We have, approximately

$$R = \frac{2}{f^3}\left(\frac{1}{c^2}\frac{\partial^2 f}{\partial t^2} - \Delta f\right) \tag{68.32}$$

If this is combined with the relation

$$R = \frac{8\pi\gamma}{c^2} T \tag{68.33}$$

which follows from Einstein's equations, and in which T is the invariant of the mass tensor, the preceding equation gives

$$\Delta f - \frac{1}{c^2} \frac{\partial^2 f}{\partial t^2} = - \frac{4\pi\gamma}{c^2} f^3 T \tag{68.34}$$

Let us compare this relation with the expression (68.30) for U^*. We put

$$f = 1 + \frac{U^{**}}{c^2} \tag{68.35}$$

where

$$U^{**} = U + \frac{1}{c^2}(S - S_{kk} - \tfrac{3}{2}U^2) \tag{68.36}$$

as a comparison with (67.09) shows. Like U^* the quantity U^{**} is equal in first approximation to the Newtonian potential U. Equation (68.34) now assumes the form

$$\Delta U^{**} - \frac{1}{c^2} \frac{\partial^2 U^{**}}{\partial t^2} = - 4\pi\gamma \left(1 + \frac{3U}{c^2}\right) T \tag{68.37}$$

To the same degree of accuracy we can write

$$\Delta U^{**} - \frac{1}{c^2} \frac{\partial^2 U^{**}}{\partial t^2} = - 4\pi\gamma \{(c^2 + U)T^{00} - T^{kk}\} \tag{68.38}$$

This last equation can also be derived directly from (68.21) to (68.23) and from the definition (68.36) for U^{**}.

If the invariant T has the form (66.19) we have

$$\left(1 + \frac{3U}{c^2}\right) T = \rho \left\{1 + \frac{1}{c^2}(-\tfrac{1}{2}v^2 + \Pi)\right\} - \frac{3}{c^2} p \tag{68.39}$$

By use of this equation together with (68.37) it can be shown that in the approximation considered the quantity U^{**} is an additive function of the masses.

It is easy to see that the mean of (68.20) and (68.36)

$$\bar{U} = \tfrac{1}{2}(U^* + U^{**}) \tag{68.40}$$

satisfies the equation

$$\Delta \bar{U} - \frac{1}{c^2} \frac{\partial^2 \bar{U}}{\partial t^2} = - 4\pi\gamma(c^2 + \tfrac{1}{2}U)T^{00} \tag{68.41}$$

This equation has only one component of the mass tensor on its right-hand side; it is related to the Einstein equation involving the same component, while the quantity $\bar{U}$ itself is related to g^{00}. Indeed, by multiplying together the expressio

$$g^{00} = \frac{1}{c^2} \frac{c^2 + U^*}{c^2 - U^*} ; \quad \sqrt{(-g)} = c \left(1 + \frac{U^{**}}{c^2}\right)^2 \tag{68.42}$$

and remembering that U^* and U^{**} differ from one another and from U by terms of order $1/c^2$ we get

$$\sqrt{(-g)} \cdot g^{00} \doteq \mathfrak{g}^{00} = \frac{1}{c} + \frac{4}{c^3} U + \frac{7}{c^5} U^2 \tag{68.43}$$

where $\bar{U}$ is a solution of (68.41).

It is not difficult to verify equation (68.43) for $\mathfrak{g}^{00}$. For if $\mathfrak{g}^{00}$ has this value, then

$$\frac{1}{2c} \Delta \mathfrak{g}^{00} - \frac{1}{2c^3} \frac{\partial^2 \mathfrak{g}^{00}}{\partial t^2} = \frac{2}{c^4}\left(1 + \frac{7\bar{U}}{2c^2}\right)\left(\Delta \bar{U} - \frac{1}{c^2}\frac{\partial^2 \bar{U}}{\partial t^2}\right)$$
$$+ \frac{7}{c^6}\left((\text{grad } \bar{U})^2 - \frac{1}{c^2}\left(\frac{\partial \bar{U}}{\partial t}\right)^2\right) \tag{68.44}$$

Here we can replace $\bar{U}$ by U in the correction terms and we can discard $(\partial U/\partial t)^2$. Using the value of N^{00} given by (68.14) we obtain

$$\frac{1}{2c} \Delta \mathfrak{g}^{00} - \frac{1}{2c^3} \frac{\partial^2 \mathfrak{g}^{00}}{\partial t^2} + N^{00} = \frac{2}{c^4}\left(1 + \frac{7U}{2c^2}\right)\left(\Delta \bar{U} - \frac{1}{c^2}\frac{\partial^2 \bar{U}}{\partial t^2}\right) \tag{68.45}$$

If we compare this relation with Einstein's equation (68.18) for $\mu = \nu = 0$ we arrive at (68.41). We may note that to the same order of approximation to which (68.43) holds we can put

$$\mathfrak{g}^{00} = \frac{1}{c}\left(1 + \frac{\bar{U}}{c^2}\right)^3 \Big/ \left(1 - \frac{\bar{U}}{c^2}\right) \tag{68.46}$$

For the case of a static field of a concentrated mass M we obtained a rigorous solution in Section 57. A comparison with that rigorous solution shows that if one inserts

$$U^* = U^{**} = \bar{U} = \frac{\gamma M}{r} \tag{68.47}$$

into equations (68.42) and (68.46) they reduce to the exact expressions (see (58.10) and (58.13)). The expressions (68.47) agree with d'Alembert's equation, which indeed they must satisfy outside the masses, in the approximate theory considered in this section.

69. The Connection Between the Divergence of the Mass Tensor and the Quantities Γ^ν

We have already mentioned at the beginning of the preceding section that if in Einstein's tensor the terms containing the Γ^ν are omitted at the outset, the divergence of the mass tensor will vanish, i.e.

$$\nabla_\mu T^{\mu\nu} = 0 \tag{69.01}$$

only provided the harmonic condition

$$\frac{\partial \mathfrak{g}^{\mu\nu}}{\partial x_\mu} = 0 \tag{69.02}$$

is satisfied. In order to study the equations of motion it is necessary to examine the connection between the conditions (69.01) and (69.02) or, more precisely, between the left-hand sides of these sets of equations.

If no terms are neglected the left-hand side of (69.01) may be written as a rather complicated differential expression involving the left-hand sides of (69.02). However, we are interested not in these rigorous relations but in approximate ones that are valid to the accuracy to which Einstein's equations were given in the preceding section. We now pass on to the derivation of these approximate relations.

The expression for the divergence of a symmetric tensor was developed in detail in Section 65. According to equation (65.24) the spatial components of the divergence are

$$\nabla_\mu T^{i\mu} = \frac{\partial T^{i0}}{\partial t} + \frac{\partial T^{ik}}{\partial x_k} + \Gamma^i_{00} T^{00} + 2\Gamma^i_{0k} T^{0k} + y_0 T^{0i} + \Gamma^i_{kl} T^{kl} + y_k T^{ik} \quad (69.03)$$

The Christoffel symbols and the quantities y_α appearing here have been given in Section 67 (equations (67.25) and (67.21)). We now transform those equations a little. We introduce the quantity U^* following (67.11) and can then replace the first equation of (67.25) by

$$\Gamma^i_{00} = -\left(1 - \frac{4U}{c^2}\right)\left(\frac{\partial U^*}{\partial x_i} + \frac{4}{c^2}\frac{\partial U_i}{\partial t}\right) \quad (69.04)$$

The remaining equations of (67.25) can be written as

$$\Gamma^i_{0k} = \tfrac{1}{2} y_0 \delta_{ik} - \frac{2}{c^2}\left(\frac{\partial U_i}{\partial x_k} - \frac{\partial U_k}{\partial x_i}\right) \quad (69.05)$$

and

$$\Gamma^i_{kl} = \tfrac{1}{2}(y_l \delta_{ik} + y_k \delta_{il}) - \frac{1}{c^2}\frac{\partial U}{\partial x_i}\delta_{kl} \quad (69.06)$$

Inserting these expressions into (69.03) we obtain

$$\nabla_\mu T^{i\mu} = \frac{\partial T^{i0}}{\partial t} + \frac{\partial T^{ik}}{\partial x_k} + 2y_0 T^{i0} + 2y_k T^{ik}$$

$$-\left(1 - \frac{4U}{c^2}\right)\left(\frac{\partial U^*}{\partial x_i} + \frac{4}{c^2}\frac{\partial U_i}{\partial t}\right)T^{00} - \frac{4}{c^2}\left(\frac{\partial U_i}{\partial x_k} - \frac{\partial U_k}{\partial x_i}\right)T^{0k} - \frac{1}{c^2}\frac{\partial U}{\partial x_i} T^{kk}$$

$$(69.07)$$

We multiply this expression by the determinant g which is approximately given by

$$g = -c^2\left(1 + \frac{4U}{c^2}\right) \quad (69.08)$$

and we use the fact that the coefficients of T^{00} and of T^{kk} are nearly proportional to each other. We get

$$g\nabla_\mu T^{i\mu} = \frac{\partial(gT^{i0})}{\partial t} + \frac{\partial(gT^{ik})}{\partial x_k}$$

$$+ \left(\frac{\partial U^*}{\partial x_i} + \frac{4}{c^2}\frac{\partial U_i}{\partial t}\right)(c^2 T^{00} + T^{kk}) + 4\left(\frac{\partial U_i}{\partial x_k} - \frac{\partial U_k}{\partial x_i}\right)T^{0k} \qquad (69.09)$$

This is an expression for g times the divergence of any symmetric tensor. However, if $T^{\mu\nu}$ is the mass tensor the following equations hold :

$$\Delta U^* - \frac{1}{c^2}\frac{\partial^2 U^*}{\partial t^2} = -4\pi\gamma(c^2 T^{00} + T^{kk}) \qquad (69.10)$$

and

$$\Delta U_k = -4\pi\gamma c^2 T^{0k} \qquad (69.11)$$

They were established above (equations (68.19) and (68.30)). With their use the right-hand side of (69.09) can be transformed further. We consider to this end the quantities $N^{\mu\nu}$ introduced by (68.14)—(68.16) and note that in the gravitational equations these quantities combine with the tensor $T^{\mu\nu}$ in the form

$$A^{\mu\nu} = gT^{\mu\nu} - \frac{c^4}{8\pi\gamma}N^{\mu\nu} \qquad (69.12)$$

We form the sum of derivatives

$$A^i = \frac{\partial A^{i\nu}}{\partial x_\nu} \qquad (69.13)$$

Putting for brevity

$$\frac{\partial U^*}{\partial t} + \frac{\partial U_s}{\partial x_s} = \Psi \qquad (69.14)$$

we get

$$\frac{\partial N^{i0}}{\partial t} + \frac{\partial N^{ik}}{\partial x_k} = \frac{2}{c^4}\left(\frac{\partial U^*}{\partial x_i} + \frac{4}{c^2}\frac{\partial U_i}{\partial t}\right)\left(\Delta U^* - \frac{1}{c^2}\frac{\partial^2 U^*}{\partial t^2} + \frac{4}{c^2}\frac{\partial\Psi}{\partial t}\right)$$

$$+ \frac{8}{c^6}\left(\frac{\partial U_i}{\partial x_s} - \frac{\partial U_s}{\partial x_i}\right)\left(\Delta U_s - \frac{\partial\Psi}{\partial x_s}\right) \qquad (69.15)$$

Since to first approximation the relation

$$\frac{\partial U}{\partial t} + \frac{\partial U_s}{\partial x_s} = 0 \qquad (69.16)$$

is valid (see (55.42)) the quantity Ψ will be at least of order $1/c^2$ so that in (69.15) terms containing derivatives of Ψ may be neglected. Discarding such terms and using (69.10) and (69.11) we obtain from (69.15)

$$-\frac{c^4}{8\pi\gamma}\left(\frac{\partial N^{i0}}{\partial t} + \frac{\partial N^{ik}}{\partial x_k}\right)$$

$$= \left(\frac{\partial U^*}{\partial x_i} + \frac{4}{c^2}\frac{\partial U_i}{\partial t}\right)(c^2 T^{00} + T^{kk}) + 4\left(\frac{\partial U_i}{\partial x_k} - \frac{\partial U_k}{\partial x_i}\right)T^{0k} \qquad (69.17)$$

Now, the right-hand side of this equation coincides with the additional terms on the right of (69.09). Thus the latter are expressible as sums of derivatives.

Therefore, if $T^{\mu\nu}$ is the mass tensor we have

$$g\nabla_\mu T^{i\mu} = \frac{\partial}{\partial t}\left(gT^{i0} - \frac{c^4}{8\pi\gamma}N^{i0}\right) + \frac{\partial}{\partial x_k}\left(gT^{ik} - \frac{c^4}{8\pi\gamma}N^{ik}\right) \qquad (69.18)$$

On the other hand differentiation of the gravitational equations written in the form (68.18) gives

$$\left(\Delta - \frac{1}{c^2}\frac{\partial^2}{\partial t^2}\right)\left(\frac{\partial g^{i0}}{\partial t} + \frac{\partial g^{ik}}{\partial x_k}\right)$$

$$= \frac{16\pi\gamma}{c^3}\left\{\frac{\partial}{\partial t}\left(gT^{i0} - \frac{c^4}{8\pi\gamma}N^{i0}\right) + \frac{\partial}{\partial x_k}\left(gT^{ik} - \frac{c^4}{8\pi\gamma}N^{ik}\right)\right\} \qquad (69.19)$$

Comparing the last two equations we may write

$$\left(\Delta - \frac{1}{c^2}\frac{\partial^2}{\partial t^2}\right)\left(\frac{\partial g^{i0}}{\partial t} + \frac{\partial g^{ik}}{\partial x_k}\right) = \frac{16\pi\gamma g}{c^3}\nabla_\mu T^{i\mu} \qquad (69.20)$$

This approximate relation plays an important role in the derivation of equations of motion.

A similar relation may also be derived for the zero component of the divergence of the mass tensor. Differentiating the approximate Einstein equations (68.18) we find

$$\frac{1}{2c}\left(\Delta - \frac{1}{c^2}\frac{\partial^2}{\partial t^2}\right)\frac{\partial g^{0\mu}}{\partial x_\mu} + \frac{\partial N^{0\mu}}{\partial x_\mu} = \frac{8\pi\gamma}{c^4}\frac{\partial}{\partial x_\mu}(gT^{0\mu}) \qquad (69.21)$$

To evaluate the second term of the left-hand side of (69.21) we differentiate the expressions (68.14) and (68.15) for N^{00} and N^{0i}. Using (69.16) we get

$$\frac{\partial N^{00}}{\partial t} + \frac{\partial N^{0i}}{\partial x_i} = \frac{6}{c^6}\frac{\partial U}{\partial t}\Delta U + \frac{8}{c^6}\frac{\partial U}{\partial x_i}\Delta U_i \qquad (69.22)$$

Here we may express the quantities ΔU and ΔU_i in terms of T^{00} and T^{0i} by use of (68.25) and (69.11). Then we have

$$\frac{\partial N^{0\mu}}{\partial x_\mu} = -\frac{24\pi\gamma}{c^4}\frac{\partial U}{\partial t}T^{00} - \frac{32\pi\gamma}{c^4}\frac{\partial U}{\partial x_i}T^{0i} \qquad (69.23)$$

Inserting this into (69.21) and using the expression (69.08) which gives the determinant g in terms of U, we obtain after multiplication with $2c$

$$\left(\Delta - \frac{1}{c^2}\frac{\partial^2}{\partial t^2}\right)\frac{\partial g^{0\mu}}{\partial x_\mu} = \frac{16\pi\gamma}{c^3}g\left(\frac{\partial T^{0\mu}}{\partial x_\mu} + \frac{1}{c^2}\frac{\partial U}{\partial t}T^{00}\right) \qquad (69.24)$$

Instead we may put

$$\left(\Delta - \frac{1}{c^2}\frac{\partial^2}{\partial t^2}\right)\frac{\partial g^{0\mu}}{\partial x_\mu} = \frac{16\pi\gamma}{c^3}g\nabla_\mu T^{0\mu} \qquad (69.25)$$

for, by (65.23), the zero component of the divergence of the mass tensor is equal to the bracketed expression on the right-hand side of (69.24). Equation (69.25) has a structure completely analogous to that of equation (69.20) for the spatial components of the divergence of the mass tensor.

Both equations may be combined as

$$\left(\Delta - \frac{1}{c^2}\frac{\partial^2}{\partial t^2}\right)\frac{\partial g^{\mu\nu}}{\partial x_\mu} = \frac{16\pi\gamma}{c^3}g\nabla_\mu T^{\mu\nu} \qquad (69.26)$$

As was stressed at the beginning of this section these equations are approximate. They are remarkable because the differential operator on the left-hand side has constant coefficients ; consequently the equations can be very conveniently investigated.

70. The Equations of Motion and the Harmonic Conditions

The problem of the motion of a system of masses has already been formulated generally in Section 64. Now we must investigate the form of the equations of motion.

We know that if each moving body is regarded as a continuous medium then within each body the equations

$$\nabla_\mu T^{\mu\nu} = 0 \tag{70.01}$$

must be satisfied. On the other hand one can consider the motion of each body as a whole and characterize it by a finite number of parameters such as the coordinates of its mass centre, the values of its mass and its moments of inertia and so on.

The problem then arises to find the equations of motion of bodies as a whole, i.e. to find differential equations for the parameters characterizing each body.

We have just enumerated some of the parameters characterizing a body. What is it that determines their choice? In the first place it must be required that the parameters chosen are sufficient to find the forces which are exerted on other bodies and which determine their motions. In our problem the forces in question are those of gravitation. Therefore, the parameters characterizing a body as a whole must be so chosen as to permit a sufficiently accurate determination of the gravitational field produced in the region containing the remaining bodies. Since the bodies are supposed to be at great distances from each other the parameters characterizing the body must then satisfactorily determine the gravitational field at large distances from it. The parameters listed above have this property.

What has just been said applies to Newtonian mechanics just as much as to Einstein's mechanics. Since in Einstein's theory, gravitation is related to the metric and it is the metric that has immediate influence on the motion of bodies, the problem of finding equations of motion for a system of bodies must be solved in conjunction with the study of the metric at large distances from the bodies. Both the choice of parameters and the form of the equations of motion must be subject to the requirement that at large distances from each body the metric should be given correctly.

At the end of Section 69 we derived the approximate relations

$$\left(\Delta - \frac{1}{c^2}\frac{\partial^2}{\partial t^2}\right)\frac{\partial \mathfrak{g}^{\mu\nu}}{\partial x_\mu} = \frac{16\pi\gamma}{c^3}\, g\nabla_\mu T^{\mu\nu} \tag{70.02}$$

They follow from Einstein's equations written in the approximate form (68.18). In the rigorous solution both the right-hand side of (70.02) and the expression acted on by the d'Alembert operator on the left-hand side vanish by virtue of the equations (70.01) and the harmonic conditions

$$\frac{\partial \mathfrak{g}^{\mu\nu}}{\partial x_\mu} = 0 \tag{70.03}$$

If, however, the solution considered is approximate, the conditions (70.02) establish a relation between the order of approximation in which the equations (70.01) are valid and that in which the harmonic conditions (70.03) hold.

We have seen that in seeking the laws of motion of bodies as a whole a basic requirement is that the metric at large distances from each body is given correctly. This requirement means in particular that at large distances from all bodies the harmonic condition (70.03) must be fulfilled with greatest possible accuracy. Let us consider what consequence this has for the right-hand side of (70.02).

These equations have the form of the usual equation for a retarded potential

$$\Delta\psi - \frac{1}{c^2}\frac{\partial^2\psi}{\partial t^2} = -4\pi\sigma \tag{70.04}$$

but it must be remembered that in the very process of establishing the equations approximations were made that are equivalent to an expansion of the functions involved in inverse powers of the speed of light. Therefore it would be sufficient in this case to solve (70.04) approximately.

Nevertheless, we begin by examining the exact solution. We assume that the function σ on the right-hand side of the equation, which we shall term the density, differs from zero only in a limited region of space in the neighbourhood of a point having the coordinates

$$x_i = a_i(t) \qquad (i = 1, 2, 3) \tag{70.05}$$

(This is the region occupied by one of the masses.) We are interested in that solution of the equation which corresponds physically to the potential produced by the moving mass of density σ, i.e. the retarded potential. This solution has the form

$$\psi = \int \frac{[\sigma]\,dV'}{|\mathbf{r}-\mathbf{r}'|} \tag{70.06}$$

where $[\sigma]$ is the retarded value of the density, i.e. :

$$[\sigma] = \sigma(t', \mathbf{r}')\,; \qquad t' = t - \frac{1}{c}|\mathbf{r}-\mathbf{r}'| \tag{70.07}$$

The integration is over the coordinates (x', y', z') and extends over the region occupied by the mass.

We now pass to the approximate equations. Expanding $[\sigma]$ in inverse powers of the speed of light c and retaining only the first few terms, we get

$$\psi = \int \frac{\sigma\,dV'}{|\mathbf{r}-\mathbf{r}'|} - \frac{1}{c}\frac{d}{dt}\int \sigma\,dV' + \frac{1}{2c^2}\frac{d^2}{dt^2}\int |\mathbf{r}-\mathbf{r}'|\sigma\,dV' \tag{70.08}$$

where now

$$\sigma = \sigma(t, \mathbf{r}') \tag{70.09}$$

This expression can be further expanded in inverse powers of the distance from the mass in question.

Using the expansions

$$\frac{1}{|\mathbf{r}-\mathbf{r}'|} = \frac{1}{|\mathbf{r}-\mathbf{a}|} + \frac{(x_i - a_i)(x_i' - a_i)}{|\mathbf{r}-\mathbf{a}|^3} + \dots$$

$$|\mathbf{r}-\mathbf{r}'| = |\mathbf{r}-\mathbf{a}| - \frac{(x_i - a_i)(x_i' - a_i)}{|\mathbf{r}-\mathbf{a}|} + \dots \tag{70.10}$$

and putting

$$\int \sigma(t, \mathbf{r}') \, dV' = \mu$$

$$\int \sigma(t, \mathbf{r}')(x_i' - a_i) \, dV' = \mu_i \tag{70.11}$$

we obtain

$$\psi = \frac{\mu}{|\mathbf{r} - \mathbf{a}|} + \frac{\mu_i(x_i - a_i)}{|\mathbf{r} - \mathbf{a}|^3} + \cdots - \frac{1}{c}\frac{d\mu}{dt}$$

$$+ \frac{1}{2c^2}\frac{d^2}{dt^2}\left\{\mu|\mathbf{r} - \mathbf{a}| - \frac{\mu_i(x_i - a_i)}{|\mathbf{r} - \mathbf{a}|} + \cdots\right\} \tag{70.12}$$

The quantities μ and μ_i may be called the " moments " of- zero and first order. It is easy to see that if one puts $\mu = 0$ the terms not containing c will decrease at least as $1/|\mathbf{r} - \mathbf{a}|^2$, the terms inversely proportional to c will vanish and the terms proportional to $1/c^2$ will remain bounded. If, in addition, it is postulated that the first moments vanish, i.e. $\mu_i = 0$, the terms next in order of importance in the expansion (70.12) will also vanish. If the second moments

$$\int \sigma(x_i - a_i)(x_k - a_k) \, dV = \mu_{ik} \tag{70.13}$$

are also zero, further terms vanish, etc. In general not all these conditions are independent. But we can impose as many independent conditions as we have parameters at our disposal.

We assume now that there are several masses so that the density σ differs from zero in the vicinity of several points, say

$$x_i = a_i(t) ; \qquad x_i = b_i(t) \ldots \tag{70.14}$$

Then the same reasoning will apply to each point. Using the notation

$$\mu^{(a)} = \int_{(a)} \sigma(t, \mathbf{r}) \, dV ; \qquad \mu^{(b)} = \int_{(b)} \sigma(t, \mathbf{r}) \, dV \ldots \tag{70.15}$$

and $$\mu_i^{(a)} = \int_{(a)} \sigma(t, \mathbf{r})(x_i - a_i) \, dV ; \qquad \mu_i^{(b)} = \int_{(b)} \sigma(t, \mathbf{r})(x_i - b_i) \, dV \tag{70.16}$$

for the integrals (70.11) extended over the regions occupied by each of the masses separately we find for ψ the expression

$$\psi = \sum_a \frac{\mu^{(a)}}{|\mathbf{r} - \mathbf{a}|} + \sum_a \frac{\mu_i^{(a)}(x_i - a_i)}{|\mathbf{r} - \mathbf{a}|^3} - \frac{1}{c}\frac{d}{dt}\sum_a \mu^{(a)}$$

$$+ \frac{1}{2c^2}\frac{d^2}{dt^2}\sum_a\left\{\mu^{(a)}|\mathbf{r} - \mathbf{a}| - \frac{\mu_i^{(a)}(x_i - a_i)}{|\mathbf{r} - \mathbf{a}|} + \cdots\right\} \tag{70.17}$$

In order that ψ should be small at any point between masses and also at a large distance from all masses we may now require that a series of equations

$$\mu^{(a)} = 0, \qquad \mu_i^{(a)} = 0, \quad \ldots, \tag{70.18}$$

should hold, each of which refers to a single mass.

After this general discussion we return to the study of equation (70.02).

We shall try to satisfy the condition that at any point between masses, and also at a large distance from all masses, the harmonic condition (70.03) be satisfied with the greatest possible accuracy.

When equations of motion are stated in four-dimensional form the equation expressing energy balance usually appears as a consequence of the remaining equations of motion. Therefore we shall first deal with the spatial components in the relation (70.02), corresponding to $\nu = 1, 2, 3$, and shall later verify that the conditions involving the temporal component $\nu = 0$ are also satisfied.

Comparing (70.02) with (70.04) we may put

$$\sigma = \sigma_i = -\, g\nabla_\alpha T^{\alpha i} \tag{70.19}$$

and

$$\psi = \psi_i = \frac{c^3}{4\gamma}\frac{\partial \mathfrak{g}^{\alpha i}}{\partial x_\alpha} \tag{70.20}$$

To make the quantities (70.20) small outside the masses it is necessary to satisfy a set of conditions of the form (70.18). In the first place we require the following integrals over the volumes of the separate masses to vanish

$$\mu_i^{(a)} \equiv -\int\limits_{(a)} g\nabla_\alpha T^{\alpha i}dx_1 dx_2 dx_3 = 0 \tag{70.21}$$

But, by (69.09)

$$g\nabla_\alpha T^{\alpha i} = \frac{\partial}{\partial t}(gT^{i0}) + \frac{\partial}{\partial x_k}(gT^{ik}) + \left(\frac{\partial U^*}{\partial x_i} + \frac{4}{c^2}\frac{\partial U_i}{\partial t}\right)(c^2 T^{00} + T^{kk})$$

$$+ 4\left(\frac{\partial U_i}{\partial x_k} - \frac{\partial U_k}{\partial x_i}\right)T^{0k} \tag{70.22}$$

Therefore the equations (70.21) may be written as

$$-\frac{d}{dt}\int\limits_{(a)} gT^{i0}(dx)^3 = \int\limits_{(a)} \left(\frac{\partial U^*}{\partial x_i} + \frac{4}{c^2}\frac{\partial U_i}{\partial t}\right)(c^2 T^{00} + T^{kk})(dx)^3$$

$$+ 4\int\limits_{(a)} \left(\frac{\partial U_i}{\partial x_k} - \frac{\partial U_k}{\partial x_i}\right)T^{0k}(dx)^3 \tag{70.23}$$

where we have put for brevity

$$(dx)^3 = dx_1\, dx_2\, dx_3 \tag{70.24}$$

We should also remember that

$$g = -\, c^2 - 4U \tag{70.25}$$

Expressions for the components of the mass tensor of an elastic body were obtained in Section 66. According to (66.07) they have the form

$$c^2 T^{00} = \rho\left\{1 + \frac{1}{c^2}(\tfrac{1}{2}v^2 + \Pi - U)\right\}$$

$$c^2 T^{0i} = \rho v_i\left\{1 + \frac{1}{c^2}(\tfrac{1}{2}v^2 + \Pi - U)\right\} - \frac{1}{c^2}p_{ik}v_k \tag{70.26}$$

$$c^2 T^{ik} = \rho v_i v_k - p_{ik}$$

If we confine ourselves to leading terms the result of inserting (70.26) into (70.23) has the form

$$\frac{d}{dt}\int\limits_{(a)} \rho v_i(dx)^3 = \int\limits_{(a)} \rho\frac{\partial U}{\partial x_i}(dx)^3 \tag{70.27}$$

Hence it is clear that the relations (70.21) represent the equations of motion of the mass centres of the various masses. If the number of masses is n there will be $3n$ such equations. This will be the number of degrees of freedom of our mechanical system if the masses are treated as point-like.

Passing on to the discussion of further conditions of the form (70.18) we can postulate that the following combinations of first moments vanish

$$\mu_{ik}^{(a)} \equiv - \int g(x_i \nabla_\alpha T^{\alpha k} - x_k \nabla_\alpha T^{\alpha i})(dx)^3 = 0 \tag{70.28}$$

If here also we confine ourselves to the main terms, equations (70.28) assume the form

$$\frac{d}{dt} \int_{(a)} \rho(x_i v_k - x_k v_i)(dx)^3 = \int_{(a)} \rho\left(x_i \frac{\partial U}{\partial x_k} - x_k \frac{\partial U}{\partial x_i}\right)(dx)^3 \tag{70.29}$$

Evidently they represent the law of the variation of angular momentum for each body. Here the angular momentum includes both the orbital moment arising from the motion of the mass in its orbit and the intrinsic moment arising from its rotation. The orbital moment can be separated out by suitably combining equations (70.27) and (70.29). The number of equations of the form (70.28) is also $3n$, therefore if it is assumed that the masses rotate as rigid bodies the number of equations is equal to the number of rotational degrees of freedom.

71. The Internal and the External Problems in the Mechanics of Systems of Bodies. Newton's Equations for Translational Motion

In the following we shall distinguish between the internal and the external problem of mechanics. We shall relate the equations of motion within a body to the internal and the equations of the motion of a body as a whole to the external problem.

We shall consider in various approximations the influence of the internal structure of a body on its motion as a whole.

We saw that, in order to derive the integral forms (70.27) and (70.29) of the Newtonian equations of motion, it was sufficient to use the equations of the internal problem to the extent of the equation of continuity

$$\frac{\partial \rho}{\partial t} + \frac{\partial(\rho v_i)}{\partial x_i} = 0 \tag{71.01}$$

which determines the zero approximation for some of the components of the mass tensor, namely

$$c^2 T^{00} = \rho ; \qquad c^2 T^{0i} = \rho v_i \tag{71.02}$$

Thus, in the approximation in question it was hardly necessary to make any assumptions concerning the internal structure of the body. Incidentally, a more detailed discussion of the internal structure of a body is itself impossible without knowledge of the metric to a corresponding accuracy. If one calls the Euclidean metric the zero approximation, then the first approximation beyond it already requires the introduction of the Newtonian gravitational potential U and also of the vector potential U_i. This is what was done in Section 55 on the basis of the expressions (71.02) for the mass tensor used there. Physically, the first approximation to the metric corresponds to taking account of the force of gravity in the study of the internal structure.

In Section 66, when we derived the mass tensor (as given above in (70.26)) we required not only the first approximation to the metric but also some definite assumptions as to the internal structure of the body. In fact we took the body to be elastic. In addition to the equation of continuity (71.01) we had to assume that the Newtonian equations of motion were satisfied within the body :

$$\rho\left(\frac{\partial v_i}{\partial t} + v_k\frac{\partial v_i}{\partial x_k}\right) - \rho\frac{\partial U}{\partial x_i} = \frac{\partial p_{ik}}{\partial x_k} \tag{71.03}$$

The equation of continuity for the internal problem enables one to derive the Newtonian equations of motion (70.27) for the external problem. On the other hand the non-relativistic equations (71.03) of the internal problem and the mass tensor (70.26) based on them ensure that in the external problem one can obtain the second (relativistic) approximation to the equations of motion of the body as a whole. This is quite natural, since the non-relativistic equations give the distribution of energy and of related quantities within the body, and energy possesses mass which influences the gravitational field in relativistic approximation.

Our next problem is to obtain in an explicit form the equations of motion that follow from the integral relations established at the end of the preceding section.

To construct these equations it is first of all necessary to state what degrees of freedom it is intended to study, or in other words by what parameters the mechanical system is to be characterized. The considerations that determine the choice of parameters have already been stated at the beginning of the preceding section. Based on these considerations we shall discuss those degrees of freedom which correspond to, first, the translational motion of each body separately and, second, the rotation of each body about its mass centre. In doing this *we shall assume that the bodies rotate as if they were rigid.* (Of course, this does not mean that the bodies are assumed to be rigid ; fluids can also perform such a motion.)†

By virtue of the equation of continuity the mass of a body

$$M_a = \int_{(a)} \rho(dx)^3 \tag{71.04}$$

is. a constant ; therefore it is not to be numbered among the variable parameters. The translational motion of a body is determined by the change in the coordinates a_i of its mass centre. These quantities may be introduced by the relations

$$M_a a_i = \int_{(a)} \rho x_i(dx)^3 \tag{71.05}$$

which may also be written as

$$\int_{(a)} \rho(x_i - a_i)(dx)^3 = 0 \tag{71.06}$$

---

† We note that our calculation is of an approximate nature. The difficulties connected with defining the concept of a rigid body in the Theory of Relativity do not yet arise in the approximation considered.

Differentiating the integral (71.05) with respect to time and using the equation of continuity, we obtain

$$\frac{d}{dt} \int \rho x_i (dx)^3 = \int \frac{\partial \rho}{\partial t} x_i (dx)^3 = - \int \frac{\partial (\rho v_j)}{\partial x_j} x_i (dx)^3 = \int \rho v_i (dx)^3 \quad (71.07)$$

whence

$$\int_{(a)} \rho v_i (dx)^3 = M_a \dot{a}_i \quad (71.08)$$

It follows from (71.08) that regardless of the distribution of velocities within the body the left-hand side of equation (70.27) is equal to the product of the mass of the body and the acceleration of the mass centre.

$$\frac{d}{dt} \int_{(a)} \rho v_i (dx)^3 = M_a \ddot{a}_i \quad (71.09)$$

Let us calculate the integral on the right-hand side of (70.27). The Newtonian potential U may be split into two terms

$$U(\mathbf{r}) = u_a(\mathbf{r}) + U^{(a)}(\mathbf{r}) \quad (71.10)$$

Here u_a is due to the mass M_a while $U^{(a)}$ is due to all the other masses. In accordance with this splitting we get

$$\int_{(a)} \rho \frac{\partial U}{\partial x_i} (dx)^3 = \int_{(a)} \rho \frac{\partial u_a}{\partial x_i} (dx)^3 + \int_{(a)} \rho \frac{\partial U^{(a)}}{\partial x_i} (dx)^3 \quad (71.11)$$

Within the mass M_a the potential u_a satisfies the equation

$$\Delta u_a = - 4\pi\gamma\rho_a \quad (71.12)$$

where ρ_a is the density associated with that mass. The potential may be written as the integral

$$u_a = \gamma \int_{(a)} \frac{\rho'(dx')^3}{|\mathbf{r} - \mathbf{r}'|} \quad (71.13)$$

On the other hand the potential $U^{(a)}$ which originates in the other masses will be a slowly varying function of the coordinates within the mass under consideration and it may be expanded in a Taylor series in powers of $(x_j - a_j)$. This makes it possible to evaluate approximately the second integral in (71.11). Inserting the expression (71.13) for u_a into the first of the integrals we get

$$\int_{(a)} \rho \frac{\partial u_a}{\partial x_i} (dx)^3 = -\gamma \int_{(a)} \int_{(a)} \frac{\rho\rho'}{|\mathbf{r} - \mathbf{r}'|^3} (x_i - x_i')(dx)^3 (dx')^3 \quad (71.14)$$

but the double integral on the right is zero because the integrand is anti-symmetric in the coordinates of the two points. Thus

$$\int_{(a)} \rho \frac{\partial u_a}{\partial x_i} (dx)^3 = 0 \quad (71.15)$$

This relation can be interpreted as the statement that the resultant of the internal gravitational forces vanishes.

We give another proof of this relation. We put

$$q_{ik}^{(a)} = \tfrac{1}{2}\delta_{ik}(\text{grad } u_a)^2 - \frac{\partial u_a}{\partial x_i} \frac{\partial u_a}{\partial x_k} \quad (71.16)$$

Then

$$\frac{\partial q_{ik}^{(a)}}{\partial x_k} = -\frac{\partial u_a}{\partial x_i} \Delta u_a \tag{71.17}$$

or

$$\frac{1}{4\pi\gamma} \frac{\partial q_{ik}^{(a)}}{\partial x_k} = \rho_a \frac{\partial u_a}{\partial x_i} \tag{71.18}$$

as a result of (71.12). If in the integral (71.15) we take the density ρ to be ρ_a, the density of the particular mass under consideration, we can extend the integral over the whole volume of space, which gives

$$\int_{(a)} \rho \frac{\partial u_a}{\partial x_i} (dx)^3 = \int_{(\infty)} \rho_a \frac{\partial u_a}{\partial x_i} (dx)^3 = \frac{1}{4\pi\gamma} \int_{(\infty)} \frac{\partial q_{ik}^{(a)}}{\partial x_k} (dx)^3 = 0 \tag{71.19}$$

since at infinity the $q_{ik}^{(a)}$ become zero.

We now turn to the evaluation of the second integral in (71.11). Expanding the potential $U^{(a)}$ of the external masses in a Taylor series we get

$$\frac{\partial U^{(a)}}{\partial x_i} = \left(\frac{\partial U^{(a)}}{\partial x_i}\right)_a + \left(\frac{\partial^2 U^{(a)}}{\partial x_i \, \partial x_k}\right)_a (x_k - a_k)$$
$$+ \frac{1}{2}\left(\frac{\partial^3 U^{(a)}}{\partial x_i \, \partial x_k \, \partial x_l}\right)_a (x_k - a_k)(x_l - a_l) + \dots \tag{71.20}$$

Multiplying this expression by ρ, integrating over the volume of the mass (a) and using (71.06), we obtain

$$\int_{(a)} \rho \frac{\partial U^{(a)}}{\partial x_i} (dx)^3 = M_a\left(\frac{\partial U^{(a)}}{\partial x_i}\right)_a + \frac{1}{2} I_{kl}^{(a)}\left(\frac{\partial^3 U^{(a)}}{\partial x_i \, \partial x_k \, \partial x_l}\right)_a + \dots \tag{71.21}$$

where $I_{kl}^{(a)}$ denotes the quantities

$$I_{kl}^{(a)} = \int (a)\rho\, (x_k - a_k)(x_l - a_l)(dx)^3 \tag{71.22}$$

which we shall call the moments of inertia of the mass (a). (In mechanics this name is applied to somewhat different quantities.) We now have to find the value of the potential $U^{(a)}$. We have

$$U^{(a)}(\mathbf{r}) = \sum_b{}' \gamma \int_{(b)} \frac{\rho'}{|\mathbf{r} - \mathbf{r}'|} (dx')^3 \tag{71.23}$$

where the prime attached to the summation sign signifies that the mass (a) is excluded from the summation. Each term in the sum represents the potential due to the corresponding mass. We consider a single term such as

$$u_b(\mathbf{r}) = \gamma \int_{(b)} \frac{\rho'(dx')^3}{|\mathbf{r} - \mathbf{r}'|} \tag{71.24}$$

We insert the expansion

$$\frac{1}{|\mathbf{r} - \mathbf{r}'|} = \frac{1}{|\mathbf{r} - \mathbf{b}|} - (x_k' - b_k)\frac{\partial}{\partial x_k}\frac{1}{|\mathbf{r} - \mathbf{b}|}$$
$$+ \frac{1}{2}(x_k' - b_k)(x_l' - b_l)\frac{\partial^2}{\partial x_k \, \partial x_l}\frac{1}{|\mathbf{r} - \mathbf{b}|} + \dots \tag{71.25}$$

integrate term by term and use (71.06) and the definition (71.22). This gives

$$u_b(\mathbf{r}) = \frac{\gamma M_b}{|\mathbf{r} - \mathbf{b}|} + \frac{1}{2}\gamma I^{(b)}_{kl}\frac{\partial^2}{\partial x_k\,\partial x_l}\frac{1}{|\mathbf{r} - \mathbf{b}|} + \cdots \qquad (71.26)$$

Therefore we have

$$U^{(a)}(\mathbf{r}) = {\sum_b}'\frac{\gamma M_b}{|\mathbf{r} - \mathbf{b}|} + \frac{1}{2}{\sum_b}'\gamma I^{(b)}_{kl}\frac{\partial^2}{\partial x_k\,\partial x_l}\frac{1}{|\mathbf{r} - \mathbf{b}|} + \cdots \qquad (71.27)$$

Let us estimate the order of the terms in the two sums occurring here. Let L be a length that characterizes the linear dimensions of the bodies and R a length of the order of magnitude of the distances between them. (See Section 64.) Let q characterize the order of magnitude of the velocities of the bodies. We shall take it that in orders of magnitude

$$q^2 \sim \frac{\gamma M}{R} \qquad (71.28)$$

The order of magnitude of the moments of inertia will evidently be given by

$$I_{kl} \sim ML^2 \qquad (71.29)$$

therefore the first sum in (71.27) will be of order q^2 and the second of order $q^2 L^2/R^2$. The omitted terms indicated by the dots will be of yet higher order in the small quantity L/R and we neglect them. On the other hand it is readily seen that in (71.21) the second term will be of order L^2/R^2 relative to the first. Therefore when calculating the second term we can discard terms in $U^{(a)}$ that are of order $q^2 L^2/R^2$ whereas they must be retained in the first term. With a little manipulation we get

$$\int\limits_{(a)}\rho\,\frac{\partial U^{(a)}}{\partial x_i}\,(dx)^3 = \frac{\partial}{\partial a_i}{\sum_b}'\left\{\frac{\gamma M_a M_b}{|\mathbf{a} - \mathbf{b}|} + \frac{\gamma}{2}(M_a I^{(b)}_{kl} + M_b I^{(a)}_{kl})\frac{\partial^2}{\partial a_k\,\partial a_l}\frac{1}{|\mathbf{a} - \mathbf{b}|}\right\} \qquad (71.30)$$

Since the quantity

$$\frac{\partial^2}{\partial a_k\,\partial a_l}\frac{1}{|\mathbf{a} - \mathbf{b}|} = -\frac{\delta_{kl}}{|\mathbf{a} - \mathbf{b}|^3} + \frac{3(a_k - b_k)(a_l - b_l)}{|\mathbf{a} - \mathbf{b}|^5} \qquad (71.31)$$

is symmetric in $\mathbf{a}$ and $\mathbf{b}$ the expression in curly brackets in (71.30) will also be symmetric. Introducing the double sum

$$\Phi = -\frac{1}{2}\sum_{\substack{a,\,b\\(a\neq b)}}\left\{\frac{\gamma M_a M_b}{|\mathbf{a} - \mathbf{b}|} + \frac{\gamma}{2}(M_a I^{(b)}_{kl} + M_b I^{(a)}_{kl})\frac{\partial^2}{\partial a_k\,\partial a_l}\frac{1}{|\mathbf{a} - \mathbf{b}|}\right\} \qquad (71.32)$$

we can therefore write

$$\int\limits_{(a)}\rho\,\frac{\partial U}{\partial x_i}\,(dx)^3 = \int\limits_{(a)}\rho\,\frac{\partial U^{(a)}}{\partial x_i}\,(dx)^3 = -\frac{\partial\Phi}{\partial a_i} \qquad (71.33)$$

Equation (70.27), which we restate,

$$\frac{d}{dt}\int\limits_{(a)}\rho v_i(dx)^3 = \int\limits_{(a)}\rho\,\frac{\partial U}{\partial x_i}\,(dx)^3 \qquad (71.34)$$

then assumes the form

$$M_a\ddot{a}_i = -\frac{\partial\Phi}{\partial a_i} \qquad (71.35)$$

The quantity Φ is evidently the Newtonian potential energy of our mechanical system expressed in terms of the coordinates and the moments of inertia. We note that our derivation has as yet not required any assumptions concerning the distribution of velocity within the body, apart from what is implied by (71.01).

If all bodies under discussion possess spherical symmetry the inertia tensor I_{kl} of each body will be proportional to the unit tensor

$$I_{kl} = I\delta_{kl} \tag{71.36}$$

In that case the potential energy will not contain the moments of inertia at all, but will depend only on the coordinates a_i (and, of course, on the constant masses M_a). Then the system of equations (71.35) is fully determinate: it contains as many equations as unknown mass centre coordinates. It is just the usual system of equations for the motion of a set of mass points subject to an attraction given by Newton's Law.

In the general case, on the other hand, when the bodies are not spherically symmetric the equations of motion involve not only the mass centre coordinates of the masses but also their moments of inertia, and the system of equations (71.35) is then not fully determinate. In that case a determinate system of equations may be obtained if it is assumed that the bodies rotate about their mass centres in the manner of rigid bodies. This means that the distribution of velocities within each body has the form

$$v_i = \dot{a}_i + \omega_{ji}^{(a)}(x_j - a_j) \tag{71.37}$$

where $\omega_{ji}^{(a)}$ is the three-dimensional antisymmetric tensor of angular velocity of the body (a). Omitting the label (a) we can alternatively write its components as

$$\omega_{23} = \omega_1 ; \qquad \omega_{31} = \omega_2 ; \qquad \omega_{12} = \omega_3 \tag{71.38}$$

Under such an assumption the complete system of equations is obtained by adjoining to (71.35) some equations which prescribe the rates of change of the angular momentum of each body. The derivation of these equations will be given in the following section.

72. Newton's Equations for Rotational Motion

We put

$$M_{ik}^{(a)} = \int_{(a)} \rho[(x_i - a_i)v_k - (x_k - a_k)v_i](dx)^3 \tag{72.01}$$

Evidently, this is the angular momentum of body (a) referred to its own mass centre. The law governing the change of this quantity can be obtained from (70.29) after separating terms referring to the orbital angular momentum. This is effected by use of the relation

$$\frac{d}{dt}\left\{ a_i \int_{(a)} \rho v_k (dx)^3 - a_k \int_{(a)} \rho v_i (dx)^3 \right\} = a_i \int_{(a)} \rho \frac{\partial U}{\partial x_k}(dx)^3 - a_k \int_{(a)} \rho \frac{\partial U}{\partial x_i}(dx)^3 \tag{72.02}$$

which follows from the equations of motion (71.34) and from equation (71.08), by virtue of which

$$\dot{a}_i \int_{(a)} \rho v_k (dx)^3 - \dot{a}_k \int_{(a)} \rho v_i (dx)^3 = 0 \tag{72.03}$$

We restate equations (70.29)

$$\frac{d}{dt} \int_{(a)} \rho(x_i v_k - x_k v_i)(dx)^3 = \int_{(a)} \rho\left(x_i \frac{\partial U}{\partial x_k} - x_k \frac{\partial U}{\partial x_i}\right)(dx)^3 \qquad (72.04)$$

Subtracting from them the relations (72.02) we get

$$\frac{d}{dt} \int_{(a)} \rho[(x_i - a_i)v_k - (x_k - a_k)v_i](dx)^3$$

$$= \int_{(a)} \rho\left[(x_i - a_i) \frac{\partial U}{\partial x_k} - (x_k - a_k) \frac{\partial U}{\partial x_i}\right](dx)^3 \qquad (72.05)$$

or, using the definition (72.01) :

$$\frac{d}{dt} M_{ik}^{(a)} = \int_{(a)} \rho\left[(x_i - a_i) \frac{\partial U}{\partial x_k} - (x_k - a_k) \frac{\partial U}{\partial x_i}\right](dx)^3 \qquad (72.06)$$

We now calculate the quantity $M_{ik}^{(a)}$. Inserting the expression (71.37) for the velocity into (72.01) and using the definition (71.22) for the three-dimensional inertia tensor we get

$$M_{ik}^{(a)} = \omega_{jk}^{(a)} I_{ji}^{(a)} - \omega_{ji}^{(a)} I_{jk}^{(a)} \qquad (72.07)$$

In more detailed notation these relations appear as

$$M_{23} = (I_{22} + I_{33})\omega_{23} - I_{12}\omega_{31} - I_{13}\omega_{12}$$
$$M_{31} = -I_{12}\omega_{23} + (I_{33} + I_{11})\omega_{31} - I_{23}\omega_{12} \qquad (72.08)$$
$$M_{12} = -I_{13}\omega_{23} - I_{23}\omega_{31} + (I_{11} + I_{22})\omega_{12}$$

For brevity the label (a) has been omitted. These are the well known equations in the mechanics of a rigid body, which relate angular momentum to angular velocity.

We now evaluate the right-hand side of equation (72.06) ; it evidently represents the moment of the forces acting on the body. In the sense of the separation into external and internal forces that was given in (71.10) let us first consider the moment of the internal forces. With the aid of (71.18) it is easy to verify that it vanishes. For by the same argument as was used to derive (71.19) we obtain the equation

$$\int_{(a)} \rho\left\{(x_i - a_i) \frac{\partial u_a}{\partial x_k} - (x_k - a_k) \frac{\partial u_a}{\partial x_i}\right\}(dx)^3$$

$$= \frac{1}{4\pi\gamma} \int_{(\infty)} \frac{\partial}{\partial x_j} \{(x_i - a_i)q_{kj}^{(a)} - (x_k - a_k)q_{ij}^{(a)}\}(dx)^3 = 0 \qquad (72.09)$$

The moment of the external forces remains to be calculated. Using the expansion (71.20) of which only the constant and the linear terms need be retained, we get

$$\int_{(a)} \rho\left[(x_i - a_i) \frac{\partial U^{(a)}}{\partial x_k} - (x_k - a_k) \frac{\partial U^{(a)}}{\partial x_i}\right](dx)^3$$

$$= I_{ij}^{(a)}\left(\frac{\partial^2 U^{(a)}}{\partial x_k \partial x_j}\right)_a - I_{kj}^{(a)}\left(\frac{\partial^2 U^{(a)}}{\partial x_i \partial x_j}\right)_a \qquad (72.10)$$

We insert into this the expression (71.27) for $U^{(a)}$, of which only the first sum need be retained. This gives

$$\int\limits_{(a)} \rho \left[(x_i - a_i) \frac{\partial U^{(a)}}{\partial x_k} - (x_k - a_k) \frac{\partial U^{(a)}}{\partial x_i} \right] (dx)^3$$

$$= \sum_b{}' \cdot \gamma M_b \left\{ I_{ij}^{(a)} \frac{\partial^2}{\partial a_k \, \partial a_j} \frac{1}{|\mathbf{a} - \mathbf{b}|} - I_{kj}^{(a)} \frac{\partial^2}{\partial a_i \, \partial a_j} \frac{1}{|\mathbf{a} - \mathbf{b}|} \right\} \qquad (72.11)$$

Since by (72.09) the moment of the external forces is equal to the total moment, we may replace $U^{(a)}$ by U; then (72.11) gives the right-hand side of (72.06), so that we may write the law for the rate of change of the angular momentum of body (a) as[†]

$$\frac{d}{dt} M_{ik}^{(a)} = \sum_b{}' \gamma M_b \left\{ I_{ij}^{(a)} \frac{\partial^2}{\partial a_k \, \partial a_j} \frac{1}{|\mathbf{a} - \mathbf{b}|} - I_{kj}^{(a)} \frac{\partial^2}{\partial a_i \, \partial a_j} \frac{1}{|\mathbf{a} - \mathbf{b}|} \right\} \qquad (72.12)$$

Introducing the explicit expression (71.31) for the second derivatives we can also write

$$\frac{d}{dt} M_{ik}^{(a)} = \sum_b{}' \frac{3\gamma M_b(a_j - b_j)}{|\mathbf{a} - \mathbf{b}|^5} [(a_k - b_k)I_{ij}^{(a)} - (a_i - b_i)I_{kj}^{(a)}] \qquad (72.13)$$

These equations supplement the previously derived equations of motion of the mass centres

$$M_a \ddot{a}_i = - \frac{\partial \Phi}{\partial a_i} \qquad (72.14)$$

and render the system of equations determinate. That this is so may be seen in various ways. We can consider as our unknowns characterizing the motion of each mass the quantities

$$a_i, \qquad I_{ij}^{(a)}, \qquad \omega_{ij}^{(a)} \qquad (72.15)$$

twelve quantities in all. (The components of angular momentum can be expressed in terms of these by equation (72.07)). For these quantities we have: the three equations (72.14) (the mass centre motion), the three equations (72.13) (the law describing the change of angular momentum) and, in addition, the six equations

$$\frac{dI_{ik}^{(a)}}{dt} = \omega_{ji}^{(a)} I_{jk}^{(a)} + \omega_{jk}^{(a)} I_{ij}^{(a)} \qquad (72.16)$$

which hold for any tensor whose components are constant in a coordinate system fixed to the body. (These equations will be derived below.) Thus we have twelve equations for the twelve unknowns, so that the system of equations is fully determinate.

We could also have argued differently by considering for each body a co-ordinate system (x_1^*, x_2^*, x_3^*) rotating with the body (we again omit the label (a) for brevity). Denoting by α_{ri} the direction cosines which satisfy the relations

$$\alpha_{ri}\alpha_{rj} = \delta_{ij}; \qquad \alpha_{ri}\alpha_{si} = \delta_{rs} \qquad (72.17)$$

[†] This equation was first derived from Einstein's equations (by another method) by V. P. Kashkarov [39].

we may put

$$x_r^* = \alpha_{ri}(x_i - a_i); \qquad x_i - a_i = \alpha_{ri}x_r^* \tag{72.18}$$

The derivatives of the direction cosines are related to the components of the angular velocity by the relations

$$\dot{\alpha}_{ri} = \alpha_{rj}\omega_{ji}; \qquad \omega_{ji} = \alpha_{rj}\dot{\alpha}_{ri} \tag{72.19}$$

By well-known relations in the kinematics of a rigid body the nine direction cosines may be expressed in terms of the three Eulerian angles ϑ, φ and ψ. For each of the masses we could have replaced the unknown functions (72.15) by the six quantities

$$a_1, a_2, a_3, \vartheta^{(a)}, \varphi^{(a)}, \psi^{(a)} \tag{72.20}$$

and could have expressed all other quantities in terms of these, in particular those given in (72.15). For instance, (72.19) already expresses the angular velocity in terms of the direction cosines and their derivatives. As for the moments of inertia, they may be expressed as

$$I_{ij} = \alpha_{ri}\alpha_{sj}I_{zs}^* \tag{72.21}$$

where the I_{zs}^* are the constant values of the components of this tensor in a coordinate system fixed in the body. For the six quantities (72.20) related to each mass we would then have six equations (72.13) and (72.14), i.e. the required number of equations to make the scheme determinate.

The calculations just described of the equations of motion in Newtonian approximation presuppose the possibility of discarding (in addition to relativistic corrections) all terms of higher order in the small quantity L/R. If we wished to retain these terms we would have to discuss third and higher moments such as

$$I_{ikl}^{(a)} = \int\limits_{(a)} \rho(x_i - a_i)(x_k - a_k)(x_l - a_l)(dx)^3 \tag{72.22}$$

However this would not destroy the determinateness of the system of equations, for we could regard the additional quantities introduced as functions of the Eulerian angles, e.g.

$$I_{ikl} = \alpha_{ri}\alpha_{sk}\alpha_{ul}I_{rsu}^* \tag{72.23}$$

where the I_{rsu}^* are constants. Then the quantities (72.20) would remain the only unknown functions, so that the number of these would not increase. Using the other procedure we would include the newly introduced quantities among the unknowns and correspondingly we would augment the system of equations by writing down, e.g. for the quantities (72.22) the equations

$$\frac{d}{dt}I_{ikl}^{(a)} = \omega_{ji}^{(a)}I_{jkl}^{(a)} + \omega_{jk}^{(a)}I_{ijl}^{(a)} + \omega_{jl}^{(a)}I_{ikj}^{(a)} \tag{72.24}$$

In the general case of an arbitrary three-dimensional tensor $A_{i_1 i_2 \ldots i_n}$ having the constant components $A_{r_1 r_2 \ldots r_n}^*$ in the system fixed to the body we would have

$$\frac{d}{dt}A_{i_1 i_2 \ldots i_n} = \omega_{ji_1}A_{j, i_2 \ldots i_n} + \omega_{ji_k}A_{i_1, \ldots i_{k-1}, j, i_k, \ldots i_n}$$
$$+ \omega_{ji_n}A_{i_1, i_2, \ldots i_{n-1}, j} \tag{72.25}$$

These equations follow directly from the transformation equation

$$A_{t_1, t_2 \cdots t_n} = \alpha_{r_1 t_1} \alpha_{r_2 t_2} \cdots, \qquad \alpha_{r_n t_n} A^*_{r_1 r_2} \cdots r_n \qquad (72.26)$$

in conjunction with (72.19).

In conclusion, we verify that the law of conservation of energy is satisfied for the system of equations (72.13) and (72.14). We introduce the rotational kinetic energy of a body about its mass centre

$$T_a = \tfrac{1}{2} \omega^{(a)}_{kj} \omega^{(a)}_{lj} I^{(a)}_{kl} = \tfrac{1}{4} M^{(a)}_{ik} \omega^{(a)}_{ik} \qquad (72.27)$$

When forming the time-derivative of T_a one must bear in mind that by (72.16)

$$\omega^{(a)}_{kj} \omega^{(a)}_{lj} \frac{dI^{(a)}_{kl}}{dt} = 0 \qquad (72.28)$$

so that in the differentiation of T_a the $I^{(a)}_{kl}$ may be treated as constants. Remembering this, it is easy to obtain the relation

$$\frac{dT_a}{dt} = \tfrac{1}{2} \omega^{(a)}_{ik} \frac{dM^{(a)}_{ik}}{dt} \qquad (72.29)$$

If we introduce the expression (72.12) for the derivative of $M^{(a)}_{ik}$ into this equation and if we use the antisymmetry of the $\omega^{(a)}_{ik}$ we get

$$\frac{dT_a}{dt} = \omega^{(a)}_{ik} \sum_b{}' \gamma M_b I^{(a)}_{ij} \frac{\partial^2}{\partial a_j \, \partial a_k} \frac{1}{|\mathbf{a} - \mathbf{b}|} \qquad (72.30)$$

or, after symmetrization with respect to j and k and subsequent relabelling

$$\frac{dT_a}{dt} = \frac{1}{2} \sum_b{}' \gamma M_b (\omega^{(a)}_{ji} I^{(a)}_{jk} + \omega^{(a)}_{jk} I^{(a)}_{ij}) \frac{\partial^2}{\partial a_i \, \partial a_k} \frac{1}{|\mathbf{a} - \mathbf{b}|} \qquad (72.31)$$

or, finally, by (72.16)

$$\frac{dT_a}{dt} = \frac{1}{2} \sum_b{}' \gamma M_b \frac{dI^{(a)}_{ik}}{dt} \frac{\partial^2}{\partial a_i \, \partial a_k} \frac{1}{|\mathbf{a} - \mathbf{b}|} \qquad (72.32)$$

We recall that the expression (71.32) for the potential energy was

$$\Phi = -\frac{1}{2} \sum_{\substack{a, b \\ (a \neq b)}} \left\{ \frac{\gamma M_a M_b}{|\mathbf{a} - \mathbf{b}|} + \frac{\gamma}{2} (M_a I^{(b)}_{ik} + M_b I^{(a)}_{ik}) \frac{\partial^2}{\partial a_i \, \partial a_k} \frac{1}{|\mathbf{a} - \mathbf{b}|} \right\} \qquad (72.33)$$

The quantity Φ depends on time through the coordinates a_i and through the moments of inertia $I^{(a)}_{ik}$. This latter dependence leads to the following terms in the total derivative of Φ with respect to time:

$$\frac{d\Phi}{dt} - \sum_a \frac{\partial \Phi}{\partial a_i} \dot{a}_i = - \sum_a \frac{dT_a}{dt} \qquad (72.34)$$

this may be seen by comparing (72.33) and (72.32). Hence using the equations of motion for the mass centres we get

$$\frac{d}{dt} \left\{ \sum_a (\tfrac{1}{2} M_a \dot{a}^2_i + T_a) + \Phi \right\} = 0 \qquad (72.35)$$

and, therefore, we have the law of conservation of energy in the form

$$\sum_a (\tfrac{1}{2} M_a \dot{a}^2_i + T_a) + \Phi = E \qquad (72.36)$$

where E is the energy constant. One should note that even for a very fast rotation of the bodies, when the linear velocities of the translational and the rotational motions are of the same order, the rotational terms in the equation of energy balance (72.34) still remain smaller by a factor L/R than the main terms, while in the integrated equation (72.36) they are of the same order as the main term.

73. The Internal Structure of a Body. Liapunov's Equation

At the end of Section 70 we found the second approximation to the equations for translational motion in integral form. We now write them down in more detail. By inserting the components of the mass tensor of an elastic body (70.26) into the equations of motion (70.23) we obtain

$$\frac{d}{dt} \int\limits_{(a)} \left\{ \rho v_i \left[1 + \frac{1}{c^2} \left(\tfrac{1}{2} v^2 + \Pi + 3U \right) \right] - \frac{1}{c^2} p_{ik} v_k \right\} (dx)^3$$

$$= \int\limits_{(a)} \left(\frac{\partial U^*}{\partial x_i} + \frac{4}{c^2} \frac{\partial U_i}{\partial t} \right) \left\{ \rho + \frac{\rho}{c^2} \left(\tfrac{3}{2} v^2 + \Pi - U \right) - \frac{p_{kk}}{c^2} \right\} (dx)^3$$

$$+ \frac{4}{c^2} \int\limits_{(a)} \left(\frac{\partial U_i}{\partial x_k} - \frac{\partial U_k}{\partial x_i} \right) \rho v_k (dx)_3 \qquad (73.01)$$

According to (68.30) the quantity U^* appearing here satisfies the equation

$$\Delta U^* - \frac{1}{c^2} \frac{\partial^2 U^*}{\partial t^2} = -4\pi\gamma \left\{ \rho + \frac{\rho}{c^2} \left(\tfrac{3}{2} v^2 + \Pi - U \right) - \frac{p_{kk}}{c^2} \right\} \qquad (73.02)$$

In first approximation U^* is equal to the Newtonian potential U, but we require U^* in second approximation, including retardation corrections and including terms arising from the additional terms on the right of (73.02). On the other hand it is sufficient to know the first approximation to the quantities U_i which satisfy the equations

$$\Delta U_i = -4\pi\gamma \rho v_i \qquad (73.03)$$

We have pointed out in Section 71 that in order to obtain from (73.01) the explicit form of the relativistic equations of motion it is necessary to consider the internal structure of the body in the Newtonian approximation described by the equations (71.03)

$$\rho \left(\frac{\partial v_i}{\partial t} + v_k \frac{\partial v_i}{\partial x_k} \right) - \rho \frac{\partial U}{\partial x_i} = \frac{\partial p_{ik}}{\partial x_k} \qquad (73.04)$$

We confine ourselves to the study of those cases in which the body rotates as a whole, in the manner of a rigid body. Then (see (71.37)) the distribution of velocities within the body has the form

$$v_i = \dot{a}_i + \omega_{ji}(x_j - a_j) \qquad (73.05)$$

(We again take the label (a) on ω_{ji} for granted.) Hence the acceleration of a particle in the body

$$w_i = \frac{\partial v_i}{\partial t} + v_k \frac{\partial v_i}{\partial x_k} \qquad (73.06)$$

is given by

$$w_i = \ddot{a}_i + (\dot{\omega}_{ji} - \omega_{ik}\omega_{jk})(x_j - a_j) \qquad (73.07)$$

We again split the Newtonian potential U appearing in (73.04) into an internal and an external potential, u_a and $U^{(a)}$ respectively and replace the latter by the first term in its Taylor expansion about the point $x_j = a_j$. We also insert the expression (73.07) for the acceleration w_i. Then we get

$$\rho \ddot{a}_i - \rho \left(\frac{\partial U^{(a)}}{\partial x_i} \right)_a - \rho \, \frac{\partial u_a}{\partial x_i}$$

$$+ \rho \left[\dot{\omega}_{ji} - \omega_{ik}\omega_{jk} - \left(\frac{\partial^2 U^{(a)}}{\partial x_i \, \partial x_j} \right)_a \right] (x_j - a_j) = \frac{\partial p_{ik}}{\partial x_k} \qquad (73.08)$$

We now estimate the order of magnitude of the various terms, retaining only the leading ones. A simple consequence of the Newtonian equations of motion (71.35) is that

$$\ddot{a}_i \sim \frac{q^2}{R} \qquad (73.09)$$

The quantity $(\partial U^{(a)} / \partial x_i)_a$ in the second term of (73.08) will be of the same order as $\ddot{a}_i$, but the difference of the two quantities will be small. A comparison of (71.21) and (72.33) shows that

$$\ddot{a}_i - \left(\frac{\partial U^{(a)}}{\partial x_i} \right)_a \sim \frac{q^2}{R} \cdot \frac{L^2}{R^2} \qquad (73.10)$$

(For almost spherical bodies this difference will be even smaller because its value is determined by differences of moments of inertia and not by the moments themselves.) We can therefore take the first two terms of (73.08) to cancel. We now proceed to estimate the terms in the square brackets. Here the main term is $\omega_{ik}\,\omega_{jk}$; it has the order of magnitude of the angular velocity squared. We assume that the order of the angular velocity is given by

$$\omega \sim \frac{q}{L} \qquad (73.11)$$

The order of magnitude of the time derivative of the angular velocity is determined by the rate of change of the angular momentum. It is easy to obtain the estimate

$$\dot{\omega} \sim \frac{q^2}{R^2} \qquad (73.12)$$

Comparing this with the estimate for ω we get

$$\dot{\omega} \sim \omega^2 \, \frac{L^2}{R^2} \qquad (73.13)$$

Further, the second derivatives of the external potential with respect to the coordinates will be of the following order :

$$\left(\frac{\partial^2 U^{(a)}}{\partial x_i \, \partial x_j} \right)_a \sim \frac{q^2}{R^2} \qquad (73.14)$$

i.e. of the same order as $\dot{\omega}$. Neglecting terms of this order[†] we retain in the square brackets only the term $\omega_{ik}\omega_{jk}$. With these simplifications we can write

---

[†] This approximation is made only in the equations of the internal problem (see (80.13)).

the internal equations of motion (73.08) in the form

$$\rho\left\{\frac{\partial u_a}{\partial x_i} + \omega_{ik}\omega_{jk}(x_j - a_j)\right\} + \frac{\partial p_{ik}}{\partial x_k} = 0 \tag{73.15}$$

Let us put

$$u_a + \tfrac{1}{2}\omega_{ik}\omega_{jk}(x_i - a_i)(x_j - a_j) = V_a \tag{73.16}$$

This is the sum of the gravitational potential and the potential of the centrifugal force. Equation (73.15) may be written as

$$\rho\frac{\partial V_a}{\partial x_i} + \frac{\partial p_{ik}}{\partial x_k} = 0 \tag{73.17}$$

This equation can be satisfied on the assumption that the stress tensor within the body reduces to an isotropic pressure p:

$$p_{ik} = -p\delta_{ik} \tag{73.18}$$

(a liquid always satisfies this condition). If we had not neglected the quantities $\dot{\omega}_{ji}$ in (73.08) we would have been obliged to consider non-diagonal elements in the stress tensor p_{ik}. Indeed it is evident that a change of the angular velocity of an elastic body must give rise to stresses that do not reduce to an isotropic pressure.

Under the condition (73.18) equation (73.17) reduces to the following

$$\rho\frac{\partial V_a}{\partial x_i} = \frac{\partial p}{\partial x_i} \tag{73.19}$$

The equation

$$\frac{\partial\rho}{\partial x_k}\frac{\partial V_a}{\partial x_i} - \frac{\partial\rho}{\partial x_i}\frac{\partial V_a}{\partial x_k} = 0 \tag{73.20}$$

follows from it and shows that V_a and ρ must be connected by a relation not involving the coordinates, so that if ρ is a function of one parameter α, the potential V_a must be a function of the same quantity

$$\rho = \rho(\alpha); \qquad V_a = V_a(\alpha) \tag{73.21}$$

The internal potential u_a is a functional of ρ; inserting its explicit expression into (73.16) we obtain

$$\gamma\int_{(a)}\frac{\rho'(dx')^3}{|\mathbf{r} - \mathbf{r}'|} + \tfrac{1}{2}\omega_{ik}\omega_{jk}(x_i - a_i)(x_j - a_j) = V_a \tag{73.22}$$

Our problem consists in finding the shape of the body, i.e. the shape of the region of integration (a), for a given density ρ. This shape must be such that condition (73.21) is satisfied at all points within the body, i.e. such that the value of the left-hand side of (73.22) depends only on the density, or on the parameter on which the density also depends. In particular, the conditions $\alpha = $ const. and $V_a = $ const. must hold on the surface of the body.

If the body does not rotate, so that $\omega_{ik} = 0$, all conditions are evidently satisfied by a spherically symmetric distribution of density over a spherical body. In the case of rotation ($\omega_{ik} \neq 0$) the problem of finding the shape of the body is a very difficult mathematical problem which has been studied by many mathematicians. The most complete results were obtained by A. I. Liapunov who studied the near-ellipsoidal equilibrium shapes of a rotating liquid, and also the question of their stability [21, 22]. We shall therefore call equation (73.22) Liapunov's equation.

If condition (73.20) or (73.21) is satisfied the pressure p can be found from the equation

$$dp = \rho dV_a \tag{73.23}$$

or

$$p = \int^{\alpha} \rho \cdot (\alpha) \frac{dV_a}{d\alpha} \, d\alpha \tag{73.24}$$

We determine the additive constant from the condition that the pressure shall vanish on the surface of the body.

The expression for the mass tensor and also the equations (73.01) and (73.02) involve the elastic energy per unit mass Π which, according to (30.11), is determined by the equation

$$\Pi = \int^{p} \frac{dp}{\rho} - \frac{p}{\rho} \tag{73.25}$$

As a result of (73.23) the integral appearing here is just V_a or a quantity differing from V_a by a constant. This constant can be so determined that one has

$$p = \rho(V_a - \Pi) \tag{73.26}$$

This expression will be of use in deriving the equations of motion from the integral relations (73.01).

74. Evaluation of Some Integrals that Characterize the Internal Structure of a Body

In order to derive equations of motion from the integral relations (73.01) it is necessary to evaluate a series of integrals whose values depend on the density distribution inside a body and on its internal structure in general. To avoid interrupting our subsequent discussion we shall collect all such calculations of integrals in the present section.

We begin with integrals that depend on the moments of inertia of the body and on its angular velocity. We denote by Ω_a the potential of the centrifugal forces

$$\Omega_a = \tfrac{1}{2}\omega_{ik}^{(a)}\omega_{jk}^{(a)} (x_i - a_i)(x_j - a_j) \tag{74.01}$$

Liapunov's equation (73.16) then assumes the form

$$u_a + \Omega_a = V_a \tag{74.02}$$

We consider the integral

$$T_a = \int_{(a)} \rho\Omega_a(dx)^3 \tag{74.03}$$

We have, evidently,

$$T_a = \tfrac{1}{2}\omega_{ik}^{(a)}\omega_{jk}^{(a)} I_{ij}^{(a)} \tag{74.04}$$

so that T_a is the rotational kinetic energy of body (a). We consider also the first moments weighted by the function $\rho\Omega_a$, i.e. the quantities

$$T_{ai} = \int_{(a)} \rho\Omega_a(x_i - a_i)(dx)^3 \tag{74.05}$$

Using the definition (72.22) we can write

$$T_{at} = \tfrac{1}{2}\omega_{kj}^{(a)}\omega_{lj}^{(a)}I_{ikl}^{(a)} \tag{74.06}$$

These quantities vanish if the body has three planes of symmetry.

We now consider the integral

$$\varepsilon_a = \tfrac{1}{2}\int\limits_{(a)} \rho u_a (dx)^3 \tag{74.07}$$

which represents the negative of the energy of mutual attraction of the constituent particles of the body and we consider also the first moments

$$\varepsilon_{at} = \tfrac{1}{2}\int\limits_{(a)} \rho u_a (x_i - a_i)(dx)^3 \tag{74.08}$$

With the use of Poisson's equation (71.12) the quantity ε_a may be represented in the form

$$\varepsilon_a = \frac{1}{8\pi\gamma}\int\limits_{(\infty)} (\mathrm{grad}\, u_a)^2 (dx)^3 \tag{74.09}$$

The moments ε_{at} may be similarly transformed as follows :

$$\varepsilon_{at} = \frac{1}{8\pi\gamma}\int\limits_{(\infty)} (\mathrm{grad}\, u_a)^2 (x_i - a_i)(dx)^3 \tag{74.10}$$

Remembering the definition (71.16) of the quantities $q_{ik}^{(a)}$

$$q_{ik}^{(a)} = \tfrac{1}{2}\delta_{ik}(\mathrm{grad}\, u_a)^2 - \frac{\partial u_a}{\partial x_i}\frac{\partial u_a}{\partial x_k} \tag{74.11}$$

with

$$q_{kk}^{(a)} = \tfrac{1}{2}(\mathrm{grad}\, u_a)^2 \tag{74.12}$$

we can replace (74.09) and (74.10) by

$$\varepsilon_a = \frac{1}{4\pi\gamma}\int\limits_{(\infty)} q_{kk}^{(a)}(dx)^3 \tag{74.13}$$

and

$$\varepsilon_{at} = \frac{1}{4\pi\gamma}\int\limits_{(\infty)} q_{kk}^{(a)}(x_i - a_i)(dx)^3 \tag{74.14}$$

These integrals are special cases of the more general integrals

$$B_{kl}^{(a)} = \frac{1}{4\pi\gamma}\int\limits_{(\infty)} q_{kl}^{(a)}(dx)^3 \tag{74.15}$$

and

$$B_{i,kl}^{(a)} = \frac{1}{4\pi\gamma}\int\limits_{(\infty)} q_{kl}^{(a)}(x_i - a_i)(dx)^3 \tag{74.16}$$

In addition to the integrals discussed above,

$$\varepsilon_a = B_{kk}^{(a)}; \qquad \varepsilon_{at} = B_{i,kk}^{(a)} \tag{74.17}$$

other useful integrals may be expressed in terms of the quantities (74.15) and (74.16).

We consider the volume integral of the pressure p

$$I = \int_{(a)} p(dx)^3 \qquad (74.18)$$

Since the pressure vanishes outside the mass we obtain by partial integration

$$3I = - \int_{(a)} (x_i - a_i) \frac{\partial p}{\partial x_i} (dx)^3 \qquad (74.19)$$

Using the relations (73.19) we can also write

$$3I = - \int_{(a)} (x_i - a_i)\rho \frac{\partial V_a}{\partial x_i} (dx)^3 \qquad (74.20)$$

However, in view of the fact that Ω_a is a homogeneous quadratic function of the differences $x_i - a_i$, it follows from Liapunov's equation that

$$(x_i - a_i) \frac{\partial V_a}{\partial x_i} = (x_i - a_i) \frac{\partial u_a}{\partial x_i} + 2\Omega_a \qquad (74.21)$$

On the other hand we have by (71.18)

$$\rho \frac{\partial u_a}{\partial x_i} = \frac{1}{4\pi\gamma} \frac{\partial q_{ik}^{(a)}}{\partial x_k} \qquad (74.22)$$

Inserting (74.21) into (74.20) and using (74.22) we get

$$3I = - \frac{1}{4\pi\gamma} \int (x_i - a_i) \frac{\partial q_{ik}^{(a)}}{\partial x_k} (dx)^3 - 2 \int \rho \Omega_a (dx)^3 \qquad (74.23)$$

Integrating by parts and using the expressions (74.03) and (74.13) for T_a and ε_a we finally get

$$3 \int_{(a)} p(dx)^3 = \varepsilon_a - 2T_a \qquad (74.24)$$

This relation shows that when the body rotates the mean pressure within it is less than in the absence of rotation, as is to be expected.

Similarly we get the relation

$$2 \int_{(a)} p \cdot (x_i - a_i)(dx)^3 = \eta_{ai} - T_{ai} \qquad (74.25)$$

where

$$\eta_{ai} = \frac{1}{8\pi\gamma} \int_{(\infty)} \{(x_k - a_k)q_{ik}^{(a)} + (x_i - a_i)q_{kk}^{(a)}\}(dx)^3 \qquad (74.26)$$

or, in the notation of (74.16),

$$\eta_{ai} = \tfrac{1}{2}(B_{k,ik}^{(a)} + B_{i,kk}^{(a)}) \qquad (74.27)$$

Equations (74.15) and (74.16) give a representation of $B_{kl}^{(a)}$ and $B_{i,kl}^{(a)}$ as integrals over all space, but they may also be represented as integrals extended only over the volume occupied by the mass (a). To make the transformation to this form we introduce a function w_a which is defined by the equation

$$w_a = \frac{\gamma}{2} \int_{(a)} \rho' |\mathbf{r} - \mathbf{r}'| (dx')^3 \qquad (74.28)$$

by virtue of which we have

$$\Delta w_a = u_a \tag{74.29}$$

It is then not difficult to prove the equation

$$\frac{1}{4\pi\gamma} \int\limits_{(\infty)} \frac{\partial u_a}{\partial x_i} \frac{\partial u_a}{\partial x_k} (dx)^3 = \int\limits_{(a)} \rho \frac{\partial^2 w_a}{\partial x_i \partial x_k} (dx)^3 \tag{74.30}$$

whence, by the use of (74.11), we get

$$B_{ik}^{(a)} = \int\limits_{(a)} \rho \left(\tfrac{1}{2}\delta_{ik}\Delta w_a - \frac{\partial^2 w_a}{\partial x_i \partial x_k} \right)(dx)^3 \tag{74.31}$$

Here the integral extends only over the volume of the mass (a).

Inserting the integral representation (74.28) for w_a into (74.31) and performing the differentiations we are able to write

$$B_{ik}^{(a)} = \frac{\gamma}{2} \int\limits_{(a)}\int \rho\rho' \frac{(x_i - x_i')(x_k - x_k')}{|\mathbf{r} - \mathbf{r}'|^3} (dx)^3(dx')^3 \tag{74.32}$$

In analogy with equation (74.31), which may be written as

$$\int\limits_{(a)} \rho \frac{\partial^2 w_a}{\partial x_i \partial x_k} (dx)^3 = \varepsilon_a\delta_{ik} - B_{ik}^{(a)} \tag{74.33}$$

one can also prove the relation

$$\int\limits_{(a)} \rho \frac{\partial^2 w_a}{\partial x_i \partial x_k}(x_j - a_j)(dx)^3 = \varepsilon_{aj}\delta_{ik} - B_{j,ik}^{(a)} \tag{74.34}$$

These relations will also be needed in the following.

In conclusion we note that as a result of (74.22) and of the equations of motion (73.04) the quantity $q_{ik}^{(a)}$ divided by $4\pi\gamma$ may be interpreted, within the framework of Newtonian theory, as the stress tensor of the gravitational field of the mass (a).

75. Transformation of the Integral Form of the Equations of Motion

We take as our starting point the integral form of the equations of motion that was given at the beginning of Section 73. We restate these equations taking into account that by (73.18) the stresses reduce to an isotropic pressure p. We have

$$\frac{d}{dt} \int\limits_{(a)} \left\{ \rho v_i \left[1 + \frac{1}{c^2} (\tfrac{1}{2}v^2 + \Pi + 3U) \right] + \frac{1}{c^2} p v_i \right\}(dx)^3$$

$$= \int\limits_{(a)} \left(\frac{\partial U^*}{\partial x_i} + \frac{4}{c^2} \frac{\partial U_i}{\partial t} \right) \left[\rho + \frac{\rho}{c^2} (\tfrac{3}{2}v^2 + \Pi - U) + \frac{3p}{c^2} \right](dx)^3$$

$$+ \frac{4}{c^2} \int\limits_{(a)} \left(\frac{\partial U_i}{\partial x_k} - \frac{\partial U_k}{\partial x_i} \right) \rho v_k (dx)^3 \tag{75.01}$$

with $\quad \Delta U^* - \dfrac{1}{c^2} \dfrac{\partial^2 U^*}{\partial t^2} = -4\pi\gamma \left[\rho + \dfrac{\rho}{c^2} (\tfrac{3}{2}v^2 + \Pi - U) + \dfrac{3p}{c^2} \right] \tag{75.02}$

and
$$\Delta U_i = - 4\pi\gamma\rho v_i \tag{75.03}$$

Putting for brevity

$$\sigma = \rho + \frac{\rho}{c^2}(\tfrac{3}{2}v^2 + \Pi - U) + \frac{3p}{c^2} \tag{75.04}$$

we can write (75.02) as

$$\Delta U^* - \frac{1}{c^2}\frac{\partial^2 U^*}{\partial t^2} = - 4\pi\gamma\sigma \tag{75.05}$$

Neglecting small quantities we get from (75.01)

$$\frac{d}{dt}\int\limits_{(a)}\left\{\rho v_i\left[1 + \frac{1}{c^2}(\tfrac{1}{2}v^2 + \Pi + 3U)\right] + \frac{1}{c^2}pv_i\right\}(dx)^3$$
$$= \int\limits_{(a)}\frac{\partial U^*}{\partial x_i}\sigma\,(dx)^3 + \frac{4}{c^2}\int\limits_{(a)}\rho\left(\frac{\partial U_i}{\partial t} + v_k\frac{\partial U_i}{\partial x_k}\right)(dx)^3 - \frac{4}{c^2}\int\limits_{(a)}\rho v_k\frac{\partial U_k}{\partial x_i}\,(dx)^3 \tag{75.06}$$

We note first that

$$\frac{4}{c^2}\int\limits_{(a)}\rho\left(\frac{\partial U_i}{\partial t} + v_k\frac{\partial U_i}{\partial x_k}\right)(dx)^3 = \frac{4}{c^2}\frac{d}{dt}\int\limits_{(a)}\rho U_i(dx)^3 \tag{75.07}$$

so that this term may be taken over on to the left-hand side and combined with the other terms that are differentiated with respect to time.

We then consider the first term on the right of (75.06). It is a generalization of the expression (71.11) evaluated in Section 71 which referred to the Newtonian approximation. As in (71.10) we split the potential U^* into an internal and an external part

$$U^* = u_a^* + U^{*(a)} \tag{75.08}$$

and then have

$$\int\limits_{(a)}\frac{\partial U^*}{\partial x_i}\sigma\,(dx)^3 = \int\limits_{(a)}\frac{\partial u_a^*}{\partial x_i}\sigma\,(dx)^3 + \int\limits_{(a)}\frac{\partial U^{*(a)}}{\partial x_i}\sigma\,(dx)^3 \tag{75.09}$$

In Newtonian approximation the first term on the right would vanish by (71.19), being the resultant of the internal gravitational forces. But in relativistic approximation, when Poisson's equation has to be replaced by (75.05), this is no longer so owing to the retardation. We insert into our integral the value for σ given by the relation

$$\Delta u_a^* - \frac{1}{c^2}\frac{\partial^2 u_a^*}{\partial t^2} = - 4\pi\gamma\sigma \tag{75.10}$$

which holds within the mass (a) and we use the fact that the integral of the term involving the Laplace operator vanishes. This gives

$$\int\limits_{(a)}\frac{\partial u_a^*}{\partial x_i}\sigma\,(dx)^3 = \frac{1}{4\pi\gamma c^2}\int\limits_{(\infty)}\frac{\partial u_a^*}{\partial x_i}\frac{\partial^2 u_a^*}{\partial t^2}\,(dx)^3 \tag{75.11}$$

or
$$\int_{(a)} \frac{\partial u_a^*}{\partial x_i} \sigma \, (dx)^3 = \frac{1}{4\pi\gamma c^2} \frac{d}{dt} \int_{(\infty)} \frac{\partial u_a^*}{\partial x_i} \frac{\partial u_a^*}{\partial t} (dx)^3 \tag{75.12}$$

because
$$\int_{(\infty)} \frac{\partial^2 u_a^*}{\partial x_i \partial t} \frac{\partial u_a^*}{\partial t} (dx)^3 = 0 \tag{75.13}$$

Owing to the smallness of the factor outside the integral we can replace the quantity u_a^* on the right-hand side by the Newtonian potential u_a; equation (75.12) then becomes

$$\int_{(a)} \frac{\partial u_a^*}{\partial x_i} \sigma \, (dx)^3 = \frac{1}{4\pi\gamma c^2} \frac{d}{dt} \int_{(\infty)} \frac{\partial u_a}{\partial x_i} \frac{\partial u_a}{\partial t} (dx)^3 \tag{75.14}$$

Following (74.28) we introduce the quantity w_a related to u_a by

$$\Delta w_a = u_a \tag{75.15}$$

This allows us to transform the integral on the right-hand side of (75.14) and to write that equation as

$$\int_{(a)} \frac{\partial u_a^*}{\partial x_i} \sigma \, (dx)^3 = \frac{1}{c^2} \frac{d}{dt} \int_{(a)} \rho \frac{\partial^2 w_a}{\partial x_i \partial t} (dx)^3 \tag{75.16}$$

The last relation could have been derived more directly by inserting the approximate solution of (75.10) into the integral on the left-hand side.

Thus the first term on the right-hand side of (75.06) may be written as

$$\int_{(a)} \frac{\partial U^*}{\partial x_i} \sigma \, (dx)^3 = \int_{(a)} \frac{\partial U^{*(a)}}{\partial x_i} \sigma \, (dx)^3 + \frac{1}{c^2} \frac{d}{dt} \int_{(a)} \rho \frac{\partial^2 w_a}{\partial x_i \partial t} (dx)^3 \tag{75.17}$$

We make yet another transformation. We introduce the function

$$W = \tfrac{1}{2}\gamma \int_{(\infty)} \rho' |\mathbf{r} - \mathbf{r}'| (dx')^3 \tag{75.18}$$

which is a solution of the equation

$$\Delta W = U \tag{75.19}$$

U being the Newtonian potential. It is evident from a comparison of (74.25) and (75.18) that

$$W = \sum_a w_a \tag{75.20}$$

just as the Newtonian potential U is the sum of the potentials of the separate masses

$$U = \sum_a u_a \tag{75.21}$$

The analogue of the splitting (71.10) of the Newtonian potential into an internal and an external part is

$$W = w_a + W^{(a)} \tag{75.22}$$

Using this, we can replace (75.17) by

$$\int_{a)} \frac{\partial U^*}{\partial x_i} \sigma \, (dx)^3 = \int_{(a)} \frac{\partial U^{*(a)}}{\partial x_i} \sigma \, (dx)^3 - \frac{1}{c^2} \frac{d}{dt} \int_{(a)} \rho \frac{\partial^2 W^{(a)}}{\partial x_i \partial t} (dx)^3 + \frac{1}{c^2} \frac{d}{dt} \int_{(a)} \rho \frac{\partial^2 W}{\partial x_i \partial t} (dx)^3 \tag{75.23}$$

Repeating the arguments that led us to equation (75.16), now applied to the total mass, we obtain the relation

$$\int\limits_{(\infty)} \frac{\partial U^*}{\partial x_i} \, \sigma \, (dx)^3 = \frac{1}{c^2} \frac{d}{dt} \int\limits_{(\infty)} \rho \, \frac{\partial^2 W}{\partial x_i \, \partial t}(dx)^3 \tag{75.24}$$

whence it follows that

$$\sum_a \left\{ \int\limits_{(a)} \frac{\partial U^{*(a)}}{\partial x_i} \, \sigma \, (dx)^3 - \frac{1}{c^2} \frac{d}{dt} \int\limits_{(a)} \rho \, \frac{\partial^2 W^{(a)}}{\partial x_i \, \partial t} \, (dx)^3 \right\} = 0 \tag{75.25}$$

We now consider the last term in (75.06). We divide the " vector potential " U_k into an internal and an external part

$$U_k = u_{ak} + U_k^{(a)} \tag{75.26}$$

and conclude as before (see Section 71) that by virtue of Poisson's equation (75.03) we have

$$\int\limits_{(a)} \rho v_k \frac{\partial u_{ak}}{\partial x_i} \, (dx)^3 = 0 \tag{75.27}$$

and that therefore the last term in (75.06) will be equal to

$$-\frac{4}{c^2} \int\limits_{(a)} \rho v_k \frac{\partial U_k}{\partial x_i}(dx)^3 = -\frac{4}{c^2} \int\limits_{(a)} \rho v_k \frac{\partial U_k^{(a)}}{\partial x_i}(dx)^3 \tag{75.28}$$

We also have

$$\int\limits_{\infty)} \rho v_k \frac{\partial U_k}{\partial x_i} \, (dx)^3 = 0 \tag{75.29}$$

We have discussed all the terms on the right-hand side of (75.06). Of these terms we transfer (75.07) and the last term on the right of (75.23), both of the form of time derivatives, to the left-hand side ; then the equations of motion (75.06) assume the form

$$\frac{dP_{ai}}{dt} = F_{ai} \tag{75.30}$$

where

$$P_{ai} = \int\limits_{(a)} \left\{ \rho v_i \left[1 + \frac{1}{c^2} \left(\tfrac{1}{2} v^2 + \Pi + 3U \right) \right] + \frac{1}{c^2} \, p v_i - \frac{4}{c^2} \rho U_i - \frac{1}{c^2} \rho \frac{\partial^2 W}{\partial x_i \, \partial t} \right\} (dx)^3 \tag{75.31}$$

and

$$F_{ai} = \int\limits_{(a)} \frac{\partial U^{*(a)}}{\partial x_i} \, \sigma \, (dx)^3 - \frac{1}{c^2} \frac{d}{dt} \int\limits_{(a)} \rho \, \frac{\partial^2 W^{(a)}}{\partial x_i \, \partial t}(dx)^3 - \frac{4}{c^2} \int\limits_{(a)} \rho v_k \frac{\partial U_k^{(a)}}{\partial x_i}(dx)^3 \tag{75.32}$$

As a consequence of equations (75.25) to (75.29) we have

$$\sum_a F_{ai} = 0 \tag{75.33}$$

and therefore

$$\sum_a P_{ai} \equiv P_i = \text{const.} \tag{75.34}$$

By analogy with Newtonian mechanics the quantity P_{ai} may be interpreted as a component of the momentum of the mass (a). Then the quantity F_{ai} will be the component of the force acting on that mass. Such an interpretation is very natural in Newtonian approximation, but here it is somewhat artificial because according to (75.31) the momentum P_{ai} then depends not only on the internal structure of the body and its velocity, but also on the potentials U, U_i and W.

We shall now separate off those terms of P_{ai} in (75.31) which depend only on the internal structure.

Within the mass (a) the quantities u_a and u_{ai} satisfy the equations

$$\Delta u_a = -\,4\pi\gamma\rho\;;\qquad \Delta u_{ai} = -\,4\pi\gamma\rho v_i \tag{75.35}$$

Hence it follows that

$$\int\limits_{(a)} \rho v_i u_a (dx)^3 = \int\limits_{(a)} \rho u_{ai}(dx)^3 \tag{75.36}$$

Using this relation we can express P_{ai} as

$$P_{ai} = \int\limits_{(a)} \left\{ \rho v_i + \frac{1}{c^2}\,\rho v_i \left(\tfrac{1}{2}v^2 + \Pi - u_a\right) + \frac{1}{c^2}\,\rho v_i - \frac{\rho}{c^2}\,\frac{\partial^2 w_a}{\partial x_i\,\partial t} \right\} (dx)^3$$

$$+ \frac{3}{c^2}\int\limits_{(a)} \rho v_i U^{(a)}(dx)^3 - \frac{4}{c^2}\int\limits_{(a)} \rho U_i^{(a)}(dx)^3 - \frac{1}{c^2}\int\limits_{(a)} \rho \frac{\partial^2 W^{(a)}}{\partial x_i\,\partial t}(dx)^3 \tag{75.37}$$

Here the first integral depends only on the motion and the internal structure of body (a) whereas the remaining three terms depend also on the potentials of the external field, i.e. on the interaction of (a) with the other bodies. We shall deal with the evaluation of these integrals in the following section.

76. Evaluation of the Momentum in Second Approximation

In the preceding section we reduced the equations of motion to the form

$$\frac{dP_{ai}}{dt} = F_{ai} \tag{76.01}$$

where the momentum P_{ai} and the force F_{ai} were expressed as the integrals (75.31) and (75.32). We must now evaluate these integrals and express them in terms of the parameters that characterize the motion of the bodies as a whole.

In order to evaluate P_{ai} we use its representation in the form (75.37). We split the momentum into the part intrinsic or " proper " to the body and the part arising from the interaction, writing

$$P_{ai} = (P_{ai})_{\text{prop}} + (P_{ai})_{\text{inter}} \tag{76.02}$$

with

$$(P_{ai})_{\text{prop}} = \int\limits_{(a)} \rho v_i (dx)^3 + \frac{1}{c^2}\int\limits_{(a)} v_i (\tfrac{1}{2}\rho v^2 + \rho\Pi - \rho u_a + p)(dx)^3$$

$$- \frac{1}{c^2}\int\limits_{(a)} \rho \frac{\partial^2 w_a}{\partial x_i\,\partial t}(dx)^3 \tag{76.03}$$

and

$$(P_{ai})_{\text{inter}} = \frac{3}{c^2}\int\limits_{(a)} \rho v_i U^{(a)}(dx)^3 - \frac{4}{c^2}\int\limits_{(a)} \rho U_i^{(a)}(dx)^3 - \frac{1}{c^2}\int\limits_{(a)} \rho \frac{\partial^2 W^{(a)}}{\partial x_i\,\partial t}(dx)^3 \tag{76.04}$$

We first calculate the integrals appearing in (76.03). The first gives the momentum in Newtonian approximation—it is

$$\int_{(a)} \rho v_i (dx)^3 = M_a \dot{a}_i \tag{76.05}$$

in agreement with (71.08). In the evaluation of the second integral we utilize the relation

$$\rho \Pi - \rho u_a + p = \rho \Omega_a \tag{76.06}$$

which follows from (73.26) and (74.02) and also the relation

$$\tfrac{1}{2} v^2 = \tfrac{1}{2} \dot{a}_k^2 + \dot{a}_k \omega_{jk}^{(a)} (x_j - a_j) + \Omega_a \tag{76.07}$$

which is a consequence of the equation

$$v_i = \dot{a}_i + \omega_{ji}^{(a)} (x_j - a_j) \tag{76.08}$$

for the velocity within the body (a). The second integral may be seen to be equal to

$$\int_{(a)} \rho v_i (\tfrac{1}{2} v^2 + \Omega_a)(dx)^3 = (\tfrac{1}{2} M_a \dot{a}_k^2) \, \dot{a}_i + 2 T_a \dot{a}_i + \omega_{ri}^{(a)} \omega_{sk}^{(a)} I_{rs}^{(a)} \dot{a}_k + 2 \omega_{ji}^{(a)} T_{aj} \tag{76.09}$$

with the notation of (74.03) and (74.05). The last integral in (76.03) may be transformed as follows :

$$-\int_{(a)} \rho \, \frac{\partial^2 w_a}{\partial x_i \, \partial t}(dx)^3 = \int_{(a)} \rho v_k \, \frac{\partial^2 w_a}{\partial x_i \, \partial x_k}(dx)^3 \tag{76.10}$$

With the use of (74.33) and (74.34) we then get

$$-\int_{(a)} \rho \, \frac{\partial^2 w_a}{\partial x_i \, \partial t}(dx)^3 = \varepsilon_a \dot{a}_i - B_{ik}^{(a)} \dot{a}_k + \omega_{ji}^{(a)} \varepsilon_{aj} - \omega_{jk}^{(a)} B_{j,ik}^{(a)} \tag{76.11}$$

We collect all three terms and introduce the notation

$$Z_{ik}^{(a)} = (2 T_a + \varepsilon_a) \, \delta_{ik} + \omega_{ri}^{(a)} \omega_{sk}^{(a)} I_{rs}^{(a)} - B_{ik}^{(a)} \tag{76.12}$$

and

$$Z_i^{(a)} = 2 \omega_{ji}^{(a)} T_{aj} + \omega_{ji}^{(a)} \varepsilon_{aj} - \omega_{jk}^{(a)} B_{j,ik}^{(a)} \tag{76.13}$$

This gives for the intrinsic part of the momentum

$$(P_{ai})_{\text{prop}} = M_a \dot{a}_i + \frac{1}{c^2} (\tfrac{1}{2} M_a \dot{a}_k^2) \, \dot{a}_i + \frac{1}{c^2} (Z_{ik}^{(a)} \dot{a}_k + Z_i^{(a)}) \tag{76.14}$$

Here the first term represents the Newtonian expression for the momentum, as we have already noted. The second term gives a correction well-known from point mechanics. The last term may be interpreted in terms of the notion of a tensor of effective mass, which is the matrix occurring when the components of momentum are expressed as linear functions of the components of velocity. If we put

$$K = \sum_a (\tfrac{1}{2} M_a \dot{a}_i^2 + T_a) + \frac{1}{c^2} \sum_a [\tfrac{1}{8} M_a (\dot{a}_k^2)^2 + \tfrac{1}{2} Z_{ik}^{(a)} \dot{a}_i \dot{a}_k + Z_i^{(a)} \dot{a}_i] \tag{76.15}$$

we evidently have

$$(P_{ai})_{\text{prop}} = \frac{\partial K}{\partial \ddot{a}_i} \tag{76.16}$$

This equation determines the quantity K apart from a function independent of the a_i. In (76.15) we have included a term $\sum T_a$ in order to ensure that in non-relativistic approximation K should go over into the usual expression for the kinetic energy of the system of bodies.

We note that for non-rotating bodies with spherical symmetry we have

$$B_{ik}^{(a)} = \tfrac{1}{3}\varepsilon_a \delta_{ik}; \qquad Z_{ik}^{(a)} = \tfrac{2}{3}\varepsilon_a \delta_{ik}; \qquad Z_i^{(a)} = 0 \tag{76.17}$$

Therefore, if we introduce the effective mass

$$m_a = M_a + \frac{2}{3c^2}\varepsilon_a \tag{76.18}$$

we shall have, apart from small corrections,

$$K = \sum_a \tfrac{1}{2} m_a \dot{a}_i^2 + \frac{1}{c^2} \sum_a \tfrac{1}{8} m_a (\dot{a}_k^2)^2 \tag{76.19}$$

just as for a set of mass points. Equation (76.18) shows that in this case the effective mass tensor reduces to a scalar.

We now go on to the evaluation of that part of the momentum which depends on the interaction. We begin by estimating the order of magnitude of this part. It is readily seen that all three terms in (76.04) will be of the same order of magnitude, namely

$$(P_{ai})_{\text{inter}} = O\left(M\frac{q^3}{c^2}\right) \tag{76.20}$$

where q is the quantity already used on several occasions which is of the order of the velocities in question. When calculating the integrals in (76.04) we retain not only the leading terms, which are of the order of magnitude just mentioned, but also terms of order L/R in relation to the main terms; terms of higher order in L/R will be discarded.

To calculate the integrals to the required accuracy it is sufficient to retain only the first term in the expression (71.27) for the Newtonian potential, so that we take

$$U^{(a)}(\mathbf{r}) = \sum_b{}' \frac{\gamma M_b}{|\mathbf{r} - \mathbf{b}|} \tag{76.21}$$

In the expression

$$U_i^{(a)}(\mathbf{r}) = \sum_b{}' \gamma \int\limits_{(b)} \rho' v_i' \frac{(dx')^3}{|\mathbf{r} - \mathbf{r}'|} \tag{76.22}$$

for the vector potential, on the other hand, we must retain not only the main term but one more. Using (71.25) we get

$$U_i^{(a)}(\mathbf{r}) = \sum_b{}' \frac{\gamma M_b \dot{b}_i}{|\mathbf{r} - \mathbf{b}|} - \sum_b{}' \gamma \omega_{ri}^{(b)} I_{rk}^{(b)} \frac{\partial}{\partial x_k} \frac{1}{|\mathbf{r} - \mathbf{b}|} \tag{76.23}$$

Finally the function

$$W^{(a)}(\mathbf{r}) = \sum_b{}' \frac{1}{2}\gamma \int\limits_{(b)} \rho' |\mathbf{r} - \mathbf{r}'| (dx')^3 \tag{76.24}$$

will be equal to

$$W^{(a)}(\mathbf{r}) = \frac{1}{2}\sum_b{}' \gamma M_b|\mathbf{r} - \mathbf{b}| + \frac{1}{4}\sum_b{}' \gamma I_{jk}^{(b)} \frac{\partial^2 |\mathbf{r} - \mathbf{b}|}{\partial x_j \, \partial x_k} \qquad (76.25)$$

to the accuracy required.

Here we have retained one term beyond the first in order to ensure that the derivative of $W^{(a)}$ with respect to time may be obtained to the required accuracy.

Inserting into the first integral of (76.04) the expansion of $U^{(a)}(\mathbf{r})$ into a Taylor series about the point $x_k = a_k$, i.e.

$$U^{(a)}(\mathbf{r}) = U^{(a)}(\mathbf{a}) + (x_k - a_k)\left(\frac{\partial U^{(a)}}{\partial x_k}\right)_a + \dots \qquad (76.26)$$

we get

$$3 \int\limits_{(a)} \rho v_i U^{(a)}(\mathbf{r})(dx)^3 = 3M_a \dot{a}_i U^{(a)}(\mathbf{a}) + 3\omega_{ji}^{(a)} I_{ji}^{(a)}\left(\frac{\partial U^{(a)}}{\partial x_k}\right)_a \qquad (76.27)$$

Here the expression (76.21) for the Newtonian potential due to the external masses must be inserted. We then get

$$3 \int \rho v_i U^{(a)}(\mathbf{r})(dx)^3 = \sum_b{}' \frac{3\gamma M_a M_b \dot{a}_i}{|\mathbf{a} - \mathbf{b}|} + \sum_b{}' 3\gamma M_b \omega_{ji}^{(a)} I_{jk}^{(a)} \frac{\partial}{\partial a_k} \frac{1}{|\mathbf{a} - \mathbf{b}|} \qquad (76.28)$$

The second integral in (76.04) may be evaluated similarly. We have

$$-4 \int\limits_{(a)} \rho U_i^{(a)}(\mathbf{r})(dx)^3 = -4M_a U_i^{(a)}(\mathbf{a}) \qquad (76.29)$$

and if the expression (76.23) for $U_i^{(a)}$ is inserted :

$$-4 \int\limits_{(a)} \rho U_i^{(a)}(\mathbf{r})(dx)^3 = -\sum_b{}' \frac{4\gamma M_a M_b \dot{b}_i}{|\mathbf{a} - \mathbf{b}|} + \sum_b{}' 4\gamma M_a \omega_{si}^{(b)} I_{sk}^{(b)} \frac{\partial}{\partial a_k} \frac{1}{|\mathbf{a} - \mathbf{b}|} \qquad (76.30)$$

Finally, the last integral in (76.04) is

$$-\int\limits_{(a)} \rho \frac{\partial^2 W^{(a)}}{\partial x_i \, \partial t}(dx)^3 = -M_a\left(\frac{\partial^2 W^{(a)}}{\partial x_i \, \partial t}\right)_a \qquad (76.31)$$

Differentiating (76.25) with respect to time we get

$$\frac{\partial W^{(a)}}{\partial t} = -\frac{1}{2}\sum_b{}' \gamma M_b \dot{b}_k \frac{\partial |\mathbf{r} - \mathbf{b}|}{\partial x_k} + \frac{1}{4}\sum_b{}' \gamma \dot{I}_{jk}^{(b)} \frac{\partial^2 |\mathbf{r} - \mathbf{b}|}{\partial x_j \, \partial x_k} \qquad (76.32)$$

To the accuracy here considered we must neglect terms containing third derivatives of $|\mathbf{r} - \mathbf{b}|$. According to (72.16) the quantity $\dot{I}_{jk}^{(b)}$ has the value

$$\dot{I}_{jk}^{(b)} = \omega_{sj}^{(b)} I_{sk}^{(b)} + \omega_{sk}^{(b)} I_{sj}^{(b)} \qquad (76.33)$$

By differentiating (76.32) we obtain

$$\frac{\partial^2 W^{(a)}}{\partial x_i \, \partial t} = -\frac{1}{2}\sum_b{}' \gamma M_b \dot{b}_k \frac{\partial^2 |\mathbf{r} - \mathbf{b}|}{\partial x_i \, \partial x_k} + \frac{1}{4}\sum_b{}' \gamma \dot{I}_{jk}^{(b)} \frac{\partial^3 |\mathbf{r} - \mathbf{b}|}{\partial x_i \, \partial x_j \, \partial x_k} \qquad (76.34)$$

and therefore

$$-\int \rho \frac{\partial^2 W^{(a)}}{\partial x_i \, \partial t}(dx)^3 = \frac{1}{2}\sum_b{}' \gamma M_a M_b \dot{b}_k \frac{\partial^2 |\mathbf{a} - \mathbf{b}|}{\partial a_i \, \partial a_k} - \frac{1}{4}\sum_b{}' \gamma M_a \dot{I}_{jk}^{(b)} \frac{\partial^3 |\mathbf{a} - \mathbf{b}|}{\partial a_i \, \partial a_j \, \partial a_k} \qquad (76.35)$$

According to (76.04) the sum of the expressions (76.28), (76.30) and (76.35), divided by c^2, gives the quantity $(P_{ai})_{\text{inter}}$.

We now introduce two functions K_1 and K_2 such that the first is homogeneous quadratic in the velocities and homogeneous of degree -1 in the coordinates, while the second is homogeneous and linear in the velocities and homogeneous of degree (-2) in the coordinates.

We do this by putting

$$K_1 = \frac{1}{4c^2} \sum_{\substack{a,b \\ (a \neq b)}} \frac{\gamma M_a M_b}{|a-b|} (3\dot{a}_i^2 + 3\dot{b}_i^2 - 8\dot{a}_i\dot{b}_i) + \frac{1}{4c^2} \sum_{\substack{a,b \\ (a \neq b)}} \gamma M_a M_b \dot{a}_i \dot{b}_k \frac{\partial^2 |a-b|}{\partial a_i \, \partial a_k}$$

$$(76.36)$$

and

$$K_2 = \frac{1}{2c^2} \sum_{\substack{a,b \\ (a \neq b)}} \gamma [M_b \omega_{ji}^{(a)} I_{jk}^{(a)} (3\dot{a}_i - 4\dot{b}_i) - M_a \omega_{ji}^{(b)} I_{jk}^{(b)} (3\dot{b}_i - 4\dot{a}_i)] \frac{\partial}{\partial a_k} \frac{1}{|a-b|}$$

$$+ \frac{1}{8c^2} \sum_{\substack{a,b \\ (a \neq b)}} \gamma (M_b \dot{b}_j I_{kl}^{(a)} - M_a \dot{a}_j I_{kl}^{(b)}) \frac{\partial^3 |a-b|}{\partial a_j \, \partial a_k \, \partial a_l}$$

$$(76.37)$$

It is then easy to verify that

$$(P_{ai})_{\text{inter}} = \frac{\partial K_1}{\partial \dot{a}_i} + \frac{\partial K_2}{\partial \dot{a}_i} \tag{76.38}$$

Remembering the estimates

$$\omega \sim \frac{q}{L}; \qquad I \sim ML^2; \qquad \dot{I} \sim MqL \tag{76.39}$$

it is readily seen that the order of the functions K_1 and K_2 is given by

$$K_1 \sim M \frac{q^4}{c^2}; \qquad K_2 \sim M \frac{q^4}{c^2} \cdot \frac{L}{R} \tag{76.40}$$

Thus K_2 will be small in comparison with K_1.

Using (76.16) and (76.38) we can write the total momentum in the form

$$P_{ai} = \frac{\partial}{\partial \dot{a}_i} (K + K_1 + K_2) \tag{76.41}$$

where K, K_1 and K_2 have the values (76.15), (76.36) and (76.37) respectively.

77. Evaluation of the Force

In order to evaluate the integrals which according to (75.32) are involved in the expression for the force

$$F_{ai} = \int_{(a)} \frac{\partial U^{*(a)}}{\partial x_i} \sigma \, (dx)^3 - \frac{1}{c^2} \frac{d}{dt} \int_{(a)} \rho \frac{\partial^2 W^{(a)}}{\partial x_i \, \partial t} (dx)^3 - \frac{4}{c^2} \int_{(a)} \rho v_k \frac{\partial U_k^{(a)}}{\partial x_i} (dx)^3$$

$$(77.01)$$

we must first of all find the potential U^* to sufficient approximation. As regards the potentials W and U_k the first order expressions already derived for them, (76.32) and (76.25), will be sufficient.

According to (75.05) the potential U^* satisfies the equation

$$\Delta U^* - \frac{1}{c^2} \frac{\partial^2 U^*}{\partial t^2} = -4\pi\gamma\sigma \tag{77.02}$$

where σ is given by

$$\sigma = \rho + \frac{1}{c^2}(\tfrac{3}{2}\rho v^2 + \rho\Pi - \rho U + 3p) \tag{77.03}$$

and differs little from ρ. If we know the Newtonian potential U that satisfies the equation

$$\Delta U = -4\pi\gamma\rho \tag{77.04}$$

the generalized Newtonian potential U^* may be obtained from U by introducing two corrections. The first is for retardation, the second arises from the replacement of ρ by σ. The latter can be written as

$$U_{\text{add}} = \gamma \int\limits_{(\infty)} \frac{(\sigma' - \rho')}{|\mathbf{r} - \mathbf{r}'|}\,(dx')^3 \tag{77.05}$$

As regards the retardation correction, it can be expressed in terms of the function W already introduced by (75.18)

$$W = \frac{1}{2}\gamma \int\limits_{(\infty)} \rho'\,|\mathbf{r} - \mathbf{r}'|(dx')^3 \tag{77.06}$$

We then have

$$U^* = U + \frac{1}{c^2}\frac{\partial^2 W}{\partial t^2} + U_{\text{add}} \tag{77.07}$$

We now deal with the evaluation of U_{add}. We write the difference of σ and ρ as

$$\sigma - \rho = \frac{1}{c^2}(\tfrac{3}{2}\rho v^2 + \rho\Pi - \rho u_a + 3p) - \frac{1}{c^2}\rho U^{(a)} \tag{77.08}$$

Here the first term depends only on the internal structure of the body and on its velocity while the second depends also on the external potential. Using the equations (76.06) and (76.07) we get

$$\int\limits_{(a)} (\tfrac{3}{2}\rho v^2 + \rho\Pi - \rho u_a + 3p)(dx)^3 = \tfrac{3}{2}M_a \dot{a}_k^2 + \xi_a \tag{77.09}$$

where

$$\xi_a = \int\limits_{(a)} (4\rho\Omega_a + 2p)(dx)^3 \tag{77.10}$$

Also, the first moment becomes

$$\int\limits_{(a)} (\tfrac{3}{2}\rho v^2 + \rho\Pi - \rho u_a + 3p)(x_i - a_i)(dx)^3 = 3\dot{a}_k\omega_{jk}^{(a)}I_{ji}^{(a)} + \xi_{ai} \tag{77.11}$$

where

$$\xi_{ai} = \int\limits_{(a)} (4\rho\Omega_a + 2p)(x_i - a_i)(dx)^3 \tag{77.12}$$

The integrals appearing here were evaluated in Section 74 :

$$\xi_a = \tfrac{2}{3}\epsilon_a + \tfrac{8}{3}T_a \tag{77.13}$$

and

$$\xi_{ai} = \eta_{ai} + 3T_{ai} \tag{77.14}$$

Hence we get, approximately

$$\int_{(a)} (\tfrac{3}{2}\rho v^2 - \rho\Pi - \rho\mu_a + 3p)' \frac{(dx')^3}{|\mathbf{r} - \mathbf{r}'|}$$

$$= (\tfrac{3}{2}M_a \dot{a}_k^2 + \xi_a)\frac{1}{|\mathbf{r} - \mathbf{a}|} + (3\dot{a}_k \omega_{jk}^{(a)} I_{ji}^{(a)} + \xi_{ai})\frac{x_i - a_i}{|\mathbf{r} - \mathbf{a}|^3} \qquad (77.15)$$

Further we have, to the accuracy required,

$$\int_{(a)} \frac{\rho' U^{(a)}(\mathbf{r}')}{|\mathbf{r} - \mathbf{r}'|}(dx')^3 = \frac{M_a U^{(a)}(\mathbf{a})}{|\mathbf{r} - \mathbf{a}|} \qquad (77.16)$$

Combining these results we can express the quantity (77.07) as

$$U_{\mathrm{add}} = \frac{\gamma}{c^2} \sum_a (\tfrac{3}{2}M_a \dot{a}_k^2 - M_a U^{(a)}(\mathbf{a}) + \xi_a)\frac{1}{|\mathbf{r} - \mathbf{a}|}$$

$$+ \frac{\gamma}{c^2} \sum_a (3\dot{a}_k \omega_{jk}^{(a)} I_{ji}^{(a)} + \xi_{ai})\frac{x_i - a_i}{|\mathbf{r} - \mathbf{a}|^3} \qquad (77.17)$$

The equation (77.01) for the force acting on mass (a) involves not the whole of $U*$ but only that part which is due to the external masses.

This part is

$$U*^{(a)} = U^{(a)} + \frac{1}{c^2}\frac{\partial^2 W^{(a)}}{\partial t^2} + U_{\mathrm{add}}^{(a)} \qquad (77.18)$$

where $U^{(a)}(\mathbf{r})$ and $W^{(a)}(\mathbf{r})$ are the quantities already determined in Section 76, and the additional term $U_{\mathrm{add}}^{(a)}$ is given by

$$U_{\mathrm{add}}^{(a)} = \frac{\gamma}{c^2} \sum_b (\tfrac{3}{2}M_b b_k^2 - M_b U^{(b)}(\mathbf{b}) + \xi_b)\frac{1}{|\mathbf{r} - \mathbf{b}|}$$

$$+ \frac{\gamma}{c^2} {\sum_b}' (3b_k \omega_{jk}^{(b)} I_{ji}^{(b)} + \xi_{bi})\frac{x_i - b_i}{|\mathbf{r} - \mathbf{b}|^3} \qquad (77.19)$$

The values of potential obtained must now be inserted into the expression (77.01) for the force. We get

$$F_{ai} = \int_{(a)} \frac{\partial U^{(a)}}{\partial x_i}\rho\,(dx)^3 + \int_{(a)} \frac{\partial U_{\mathrm{add}}^{(a)}}{\partial x_i}\rho\,(dx)^3 + \int_{(a)} \frac{\partial U^{(a)}}{\partial x_i}(\sigma - \rho)(dx)^3$$

$$+ \frac{1}{c^2}\int_{(a)} \rho\frac{\partial^3 W^{(a)}}{\partial x_i\,\partial t^2}(dx)^3 - \frac{1}{c^2}\frac{d}{dt}\int_{(a)} \rho\frac{\partial^2 W^{(a)}}{\partial x_i\,\partial t}(dx)^3$$

$$- \frac{4}{c^2}\int_{(a)} \rho v_k\frac{\partial U_k^{(a)}}{\partial x_i}(dx)^3 \qquad (77.20)$$

Here the first integral is the Newtonian expression for the force ; it has already been evaluated in Section 71. We have, by (71.33)

$$\int\limits_{(a)} \rho \frac{\partial U^{(a)}}{\partial x_i}(dx)^3 = -\frac{\partial \Phi}{\partial a_i} \tag{77.21}$$

where Φ is the Newtonian potential energy of a system of bodies, as in (71.32). To the accuracy required the second integral may be written as

$$\int\limits_{(a)} \frac{\partial U_{\mathrm{add}}^{(a)}}{\partial x_i} \rho \,(dx)^3 = M_a \left(\frac{\partial U_{\mathrm{add}}^{(a)}}{\partial x_i}\right)_a \tag{77.22}$$

Here the expression (77.19) can be taken for $U_{\mathrm{add}}^{(a)}$. The third integral can be evaluated by use of the relations (77.08) to (77.14). We obtain

$$\int\limits_{(a)} \frac{\partial U^{(a)}}{\partial x_i}(\sigma - \rho)(dx)^3 = \frac{1}{c^2}\left(\frac{\partial U^{(a)}}{\partial x_i}\right)_a(\tfrac{3}{2}M_a \dot{a}_k^2 + \xi_a)$$

$$+ \frac{1}{c^2}\left(\frac{\partial^2 U^{(a)}}{\partial x_i \partial x_j}\right)_a(3\dot{a}_k \omega_{sk}^{(a)} I_{sj}^{(a)} + \xi_{aj}) - \frac{1}{c^2}M_a\left(U^{(a)}\frac{\partial U^{(a)}}{\partial x_i}\right)_a \tag{77.23}$$

where the expression (76.21) may be used for $U^{(a)}$.

We add the expressions (77.22) and (77.23) and represent the sum as a derivative with respect to a_i. In (77.23) we may put $x_i = a_i$ before differentiating, but in (77.22) we must take into account that one of the terms in $U^{(b)}(\mathbf{b})$ itself depends on a_i, namely

$$U^{(b)}(\mathbf{b}) = \frac{\gamma M_a}{|\mathbf{a} - \mathbf{b}|} + \cdots \tag{77.24}$$

where the dots denote terms not containing a_i. As a consequence of (77.24) we have

$$U^{(b)}(\mathbf{b})\frac{\partial}{\partial a_i}\frac{1}{|\mathbf{a} - \mathbf{b}|} = \frac{\partial}{\partial a_i}\left\{U^{(b)}(\mathbf{b})\frac{1}{|\mathbf{a} - \mathbf{b}|} - \frac{1}{2}\frac{\gamma M_a}{|\mathbf{a} - \mathbf{b}|^2}\right\} \tag{77.25}$$

Using this relation we get

$$\int\limits_{(a)} \frac{\partial U_{\mathrm{add}}^{(a)}}{\partial x_i}\rho\,(dx)^3 + \int\limits_{(a)} \frac{\partial U^{(a)}}{\partial x_i}(\sigma - \rho)(dx)^3 = \frac{\partial}{\partial a_i}(L_1 + L_2) - \frac{\partial \Psi}{\partial a_i} \tag{77.26}$$

where we have put

$$L_1 = \frac{1}{4c^2}\sum_{\substack{a,\,b \\ (a \neq b)}}[3\gamma M_a M_b(\dot{a}_k^2 + b_k^2) + 2\gamma(\xi_b M_a + \xi_a M_b)]\frac{1}{|\mathbf{a} - \mathbf{b}|} \tag{77.27}$$

and

$$L_2 = \frac{1}{2c^2}\sum_{\substack{a,\,b \\ (a \neq b)}}[3\gamma M_a \omega_{sk}^{(b)} I_{sj}^{(b)} b_k - 3\gamma M_b \omega_{sk}^{(a)} I_{sj}^{(a)} \dot{a}_k + \gamma(M_a \xi_{bj} - M_b \xi_{aj})]\frac{a_j - b_j}{|\mathbf{a} - \mathbf{b}|^3} \tag{77.28}$$

and where the function Ψ is equal to

$$\Psi = \frac{1}{c^2} \sum_b' \left(\gamma M_a M_b U^{(b)}(b) \frac{1}{|a-b|} - \frac{1}{2} \gamma^2 \frac{M_a^2 M_b}{|a-b|^2} \right) + \frac{1}{2c^2} M_a U^{(a)}(a)^2 + \dots$$

$$(77.29)$$

with dots again denoting terms independent of a_t. We arrange these terms in such a way as to make Ψ symmetric in all masses and the corresponding position vectors. We put

$$\Psi(a, b) = \frac{\gamma^2}{2c_0^2} \cdot \frac{M_a M_b (M_a + M_b)}{|a-b|^2} \tag{77.30}$$

and

$$\Psi(a, b, c) = \frac{\gamma^2}{c_0^2} M_a M_b M_c$$
$$\times \left(\frac{1}{|a-b||a-c|} + \frac{1}{|b-c||b-a|} + \frac{1}{|c-a||c-b|} \right)$$

$$(77.31)$$

where, temporarily, we have denoted the speed of light by c_0, to avoid confusion with the suffix in M_c. Thus it is readily seen that in the function

$$\Psi = \frac{1}{2} \sum_{\substack{a, b \\ (a \neq b)}} \Psi(a, b) + \frac{1}{6} \sum_{\substack{a, b, c \\ (a \neq b,\, b \neq c,\, c \neq a)}} \Psi(a, b, c) \tag{77.32}$$

the terms depending on a_t are the same as in (77.29). Thus in the equation (77.26) for the sum of the two integrals Ψ may be understood to stand for (77.32). The terms $\Psi(a, b, c)$ give peculiar "triple interactions" of the masses.

We now consider those integrals in (77.20) which involve the function $W^{(a)}$. We have, evidently

$$\frac{1}{c^2} \int_{(a)} \rho \frac{\partial^3 W^{(a)}}{\partial x_i \partial t^2} (dx)^3 - \frac{1}{c^2} \frac{d}{dt} \int_{(a)} \rho \frac{\partial^2 W^{(a)}}{\partial x_i \partial t} (dx)^3$$

$$= -\frac{1}{c^2} \int_{(a)} \frac{\partial \rho}{\partial t} \frac{\partial^2 W^{(a)}}{\partial x_i \partial t} (dx)^3 = -\frac{1}{c^2} \int_{(a)} \rho v_j \frac{\partial^3 W^{(a)}}{\partial x_i \partial x_j \partial t} (dx)^3 \tag{77.33}$$

This expression can be evaluated by use of the relation (76.34) for the derivative of $W^{(a)}$. We get

$$-\frac{1}{c^2} \int_{(a)} \rho v_j \frac{\partial^3 W^{(a)}}{\partial x_i \partial x_j \partial t} (dx)^3 = \frac{\partial L_3}{\partial a_i} + \frac{\partial L_4}{\partial a_i} \tag{77.34}$$

where

$$L_3 = \frac{1}{4c^2} \sum_{\substack{a, b \\ a \neq b}} \gamma M_a M_b \dot{a}_j b_k \frac{\partial^2 |a-b|}{\partial a_j \partial a_k} \tag{77.35}$$

and

$$L_4 = \frac{1}{8c^2} \sum_{\substack{a, b \\ (a \neq b)}} \gamma (M_b \dot{b}_j I_{kl}^{(a)} - M_a \dot{a}_j I_{kl}^{(b)}) \frac{\partial^3 |a-b|}{\partial a_j \partial a_k \partial a_l} \tag{77.36}$$

It remains to examine the last integral in (77.20). Its evaluation presents no difficulties and we get

$$-\frac{4}{c^2}\int_{(a)} \rho v_k \frac{\partial U_k^{(a)}}{\partial x_i}(dx)^3 = \frac{\partial L_5}{\partial a_i} + \frac{\partial L_6}{\partial a_i} \tag{77.37}$$

where

$$L_5 = -\frac{2}{c^2}\sum_{\substack{a,\,b\\(a\neq b)}}\frac{\gamma M_a M_b(\dot{a}_k \dot{b}_k)}{|\mathbf{a}-\mathbf{b}|} \tag{77.38}$$

and

$$L_6 = \frac{2}{c^2}\sum_{\substack{a,\,b\\(a\neq b)}}\gamma(M_b \dot{b}_k \omega_{sk}^{(a)}I_{sj}^{(a)} - M_a \dot{a}_k \omega_{sk}^{(b)}I_{sj}^{(b)})\frac{a_j - b_j}{|\mathbf{a}-\mathbf{b}|^3} \tag{77.39}$$

We collect all integrals and so get the following expression for the force

$$F_{ai} = -\frac{\partial \Phi}{\partial a_i} - \frac{\partial \Psi}{\partial a_i} + \frac{\partial}{\partial a_i}(L_1 + L_3 + L_5) + \frac{\partial}{\partial a_i}(L_2 + L_4 + L_6) \tag{77.40}$$

Let us compare this expression for the force with the previously derived expression (76.41) for the momentum. We put

$$\Phi_1 = -\frac{1}{2c^2}\sum_{\substack{a,\,b\\(a\neq b)}}\gamma(\xi_b M_a + \xi_a M_b)\frac{1}{|\mathbf{a}-\mathbf{b}|} \tag{77.41}$$

and

$$\Phi_2 = -\frac{1}{2c^2}\sum_{\substack{a,\,b\\(a\neq b)}}\gamma(\xi_{bj} M_a - \xi_{aj} M_b)\frac{a_j - b_j}{|\mathbf{a}-\mathbf{b}|^3} \tag{77.42}$$

The negative of these quantities also enters the expressions (77.27) and (77.28) for L_1 and L_2.

It is simple to check that we have

$$L_1 + L_3 + L_5 = K_1 - \Phi_1 \tag{77.43}$$

and similarly

$$L_2 + L_4 + L_6 = K_2 - \Phi_2 \tag{77.44}$$

where K_1 and K_2 have the values (76.36) and (76.37). Therefore

$$F_{ai} = \frac{\partial}{\partial a_i}(K_1 + K_2 - \Phi - \Phi_1 - \Phi_2 - \Psi) \tag{77.45}$$

On the other hand, by (76.41)

$$P_{ai} = \frac{\partial}{\partial \dot{a}_i}(K + K_1 + K_2) \tag{77.46}$$

where K is given by (76.15).

Here K is independent of the coordinates a_i while the quantities Φ, Φ_1, Φ_2 and Ψ are independent of the velocities $\dot{a}_i$. Putting

$$L = K + K_1 + K_2 - \Phi - \Phi_1 - \Phi_2 - \Psi \tag{77.47}$$

we can therefore write

$$P_{at} = \frac{\partial L}{\partial \dot{a}_i} \; ; \quad F_{ai} = \frac{\partial L}{\partial a_i} \qquad (77.48)$$

The equations of motion

$$\frac{dP_{at}}{dt} = F_{at} \qquad (77.49)$$

then appear in the Lagrangian form

$$\frac{d}{dt}\frac{\partial L}{\partial \dot{a}_i} - \frac{\partial L}{\partial a_i} = 0 \qquad (77.50)$$

78. The Equations of Translational Motion in Lagrangian Form

In the preceding sections we have derived the equations of motion for the mass centres of a set of masses, by use of the condition

$$\int_{(a)} g \nabla_\alpha T^{\alpha i}(dx)^3 = 0 \qquad (78.01)$$

which in turn was derived from the harmonic condition (see Section 70). It was assumed in the derivation that each mass rotates about its own mass centre in the manner of a rigid body.

As we saw, the equations of motion are expressible in the Lagrangian form

$$\frac{d}{dt}\frac{\partial L}{\partial \dot{a}_i} - \frac{\partial L}{\partial a_i} = 0 \qquad (78.02)$$

where the Lagrangian is obtained by inserting into (77.47) the expressions previously found for K, K_1, K_2, Φ, Φ_1, Φ_2 and Ψ. (See equations (76.15), (76.36), (76.37), (71.32), (77.41), (77.42) and (77.32).)† We restate these equations. We have

$$L = K + K_1 + K_2 - \Phi - \Phi_1 - \Phi_2 - \Psi \qquad (78.03)$$

where the various terms have the values set out in the following :

$$K = \sum_a (\tfrac{1}{2}M_a \dot{a}_i^2 + T_a) + \frac{1}{c^2}\sum_a (\tfrac{1}{8}M_a(\dot{a}_k^2)^2 + \tfrac{1}{2}Z_{ik}^{(a)}\dot{a}_i\dot{a}_k + Z_i^{(a)}\dot{a}_i) \qquad (78.04)$$

Here the first sum represents the usual Newtonian kinetic energy of the translational and rotational motion of a system of bodies. (In forming the left-hand side of Lagrange's equations it is inessential to include the term T_a.) The second sum gives a correction to the " kinetic " part of the Lagrangian, i.e. to that part which depends on the velocities. In the absence of rotation this correction reduces, according to (76.19), to the usual correction term well-known from the mechanics of mass points ; when rotation is present this cor-

† For non-rotating masses the reduction to Lagrangian form was first performed by I. Fichtenholz [40].

rection also involves "mixed" terms which depend both on the velocities of translational motion and on the angular velocities of rotation of the body. The quantity K does not depend on the position of the mass centre of the body.

We now state the values of K_1 and K_2. According to (76.36) and (76.37) we have :

$$K_1 = \frac{1}{4c^2} \sum_{a,b} \frac{\gamma M_a M_b}{|\mathbf{a}-\mathbf{b}|}(3\dot{a}_i^2 + 3\dot{b}_i^2 - 8\dot{a}_i\dot{b}_i) + \frac{1}{4c^2} \sum_{a,b} \gamma M_a M_b \dot{a}_i\dot{b}_k \frac{\partial^2 |\mathbf{a}-\mathbf{b}|}{\partial a_i\,\partial a_k}$$

$$(78.05)$$

and

$$K_2 = \frac{1}{2c^2} \sum_{a,b} [\gamma M_a \omega_{si}^{(b)} I_{sj}^{(b)}(3\dot{b}_i - 4\dot{a}_i) - \gamma M_b \omega_{si}^{(a)} I_{sj}^{(a)}(3\dot{a}_i - 4\dot{b}_i)] \frac{a_j - b_j}{|\mathbf{a}-\mathbf{b}|^2}$$

$$+ \frac{1}{8c^2} \sum_{a,b} (\gamma M_b \dot{b}_i I_{kl}^{(a)} - \gamma M_a \dot{a}_i I_{kl}^{(b)}) \cdot \frac{\partial^3 |\mathbf{a}-\mathbf{b}|}{\partial a_i\,\partial a_k\,\partial a_l} \qquad (78.06)$$

These terms depend both on the coordinates and on the velocities and represent, so to speak, the result of an interaction of kinetic and potential energies. As we already noted in Section 76 the quantity K_1 is homogeneous and quadratic in the velocities of translational motion $\dot{a}_i$ whereas K_2 is bilinear in the velocities of translation and the angular velocities.

The next term in the Lagrangian is :

$$-\Phi = \frac{1}{2} \sum_{a,b} \frac{\gamma M_a M_b}{|\mathbf{a}-\mathbf{b}|} + \frac{1}{4} \sum_{a,b} \gamma(M_a I_{ik}^{(b)} + M_b I_{ik}^{(a)}) \frac{\partial^2}{\partial a_i\,\partial a_k} \frac{1}{|\mathbf{a}-\mathbf{b}|}$$

$$(78.07)$$

It represents the Newtonian potential energy of the system of bodies. It is augmented by the corrections Φ_1 and Φ_2 which, by (77.41) and (77.42) are

$$-\Phi_1 = \frac{1}{2c^2} \sum_{a,b} \gamma(\xi_b M_a + \xi_a M_b) \frac{1}{|\mathbf{a}-\mathbf{b}|} \qquad (78.08)$$

and

$$-\Phi_2 = \frac{1}{2c^2} \sum_{a,b} \gamma(\xi_{bj} M_a - \xi_{aj} M_b) \frac{a_j - b_j}{|\mathbf{a}-\mathbf{b}|^3} \qquad (78.09)$$

The quantity Φ_1 may be interpreted as the result of replacing the mass M_a in the Newtonian potential energy, or more precisely in its leading term[†]

$$\Phi_0 = -\tfrac{1}{2} \sum_{a,b} \frac{\gamma M_a M_b}{|\mathbf{a}-\mathbf{b}|} \qquad (78.10)$$

by the effective mass $M_a + \delta M_a$, where

$$\delta M_a = \frac{1}{c^2} \xi_a \qquad (78.11)$$

On the other hand, the quantity Φ_2 may be interpreted as the result of dis-

---

† In the equation (78.07) for Φ the correction term is of order L^2/R^2 relative to the main term. Consequently relativistic corrections to the correction term will be of the same order as terms already neglected. Therefore it is immaterial whether such corrections are introduced into the complete expression for Φ or only into the main term Φ_0.

placing the mass centre of body (a), so that a_i goes over into $a_i + \delta a_i$, where

$$\delta a_i = \frac{1}{c^2 M_a} \xi_{ai} \tag{78.12}$$

Indeed we have, apart from small quantities,

$$-\tfrac{1}{2} \sum_{a, b} \frac{\gamma(M_a + \delta M_a)(M_b + \delta M_b)}{|\mathbf{a} + \delta\mathbf{a} - \mathbf{b} - \delta\mathbf{b}|} = \Phi_0 + \Phi_1 + \Phi_2 \tag{78.13}$$

We note that the quantity ξ_a involved in the equation for the effective mass is equal to the intrinsic energy of body (a), which is composed of the kinetic energy of its rotation around its mass centre, of its elastic energy and of the gravitational energy of its component particles. Indeed it can be shown that the expression

$$\xi_a = T_a + \int\limits_{(a)} \rho\Pi \, (dx)^3 - \tfrac{1}{2} \int\limits_{(a)} \rho u_a (dx)^3 \tag{78.14}$$

for the intrinsic energy goes over into the form (77.10) for ξ_a if Liapunov's equation and (73.26) are used.

It might be expected that the presence of the mass related to the intrinsic energy of a body would give rise not only to a change of the effective mass but also to a displacement of its mass centre. However, in view of the fact that the kinetic energy of rotation about its mass centre refers to the body as a whole and is not related to the individual constituent particles, it would be difficult to predict the correct expression for the displacement of the mass centre. Actually the calculation has proved it to be given by (78.12) with ξ_{ai} given by (77.12).

It remains for us to write down the last term in the Lagrangian. It is convenient to denote the three position vectors occurring in it by $\mathbf{a}$, $\mathbf{b}$ and $\mathbf{c}$ and we therefore adopt the notation c_0 for the speed of light, as was done in Section 77. According to (77.30), (77.31) and (77.32) we have

$$-\Psi = -\frac{\gamma^2}{4c_0^2} \sum_{a, b} \frac{M_a M_b (M_a + M_b)}{|\mathbf{a} - \mathbf{b}|^2} - \frac{\gamma^2}{6c_0^2} \sum_{a, b, c} M_a M_b M_c$$

$$\times \left(\frac{1}{|\mathbf{a} - \mathbf{b}| \, |\mathbf{a} - \mathbf{c}|} + \frac{1}{|\mathbf{b} - \mathbf{c}| \, |\mathbf{b} - \mathbf{a}|} + \frac{1}{|\mathbf{c} - \mathbf{a}| \, |\mathbf{c} - \mathbf{b}|} \right) \tag{78.15}$$

Here the last sum gives the triple interaction of the masses.† If in the sense of a remark made above we call the terms K_1 and K_2 the " kinetic-potential " part of the Lagrangian the quantity Ψ may be called its " potential-potential " part. These names stress the fact that in the second approximation of Einstein's theory the additivity of kinetic and potential parts of the Lagrangian, characteristic of Newtonian theory, no longer prevails.

According to (78.03) the total Lagrangian is the sum of the expression (78.04)

---

† In the triple sum the labels satisfy the relations $a \neq b$, $b \neq c$, $c \neq a$, and in all double sums we must take $a \neq b$

to (78.09) and (78.15). To the present degree of approximation it leads to the equations of translational motion with relativistic corrections.

As for the equations of rotational motion, they may be obtained from the relations (70.28) which have the form

$$- \int_{(a)} g(x_i \nabla_\alpha T^{\alpha k} - x_k \nabla_\alpha T^{\alpha i})(dx)^3 = 0 \tag{78.16}$$

In Section 72 it was shown that in Newtonian approximation these equations determine the rate of change of the angular momentum

$$M_{ik}^{(a)} = \omega_{jk}^{(a)} I_{ji}^{(a)} - \omega_{ji}^{(a)} I_{jk}^{(a)} \tag{78.17}$$

of each body, giving

$$\frac{d}{dt} M_{ik}^{(a)} = \sum_b{}' \frac{3\gamma M_b(a_j - b_j)}{|\mathbf{a} - \mathbf{b}|^5} [(a_k - b_k)I_{ij}^{(a)} - (a_i - b_i)I_{kj}^{(a)}] \tag{78.18}$$

(see equations (72.07) and (72.13)).

The relativistic corrections to the Newtonian equations of rotational motion may be obtained by a more exact evaluation of the left-hand side of (78.16). These calculations can be performed on the pattern of those performed for translational motion in the preceding sections. They do not present any difficulties apart from the complexity of the manipulations involved. However, since relativistic corrections to the rotational motion of celestial bodies are quite insignificant and are even harder to observe than the corrections to their translational motion, we shall not evaluate them here.

79. The Integrals of the Equations of Motion for Systems of Bodies

Just as was the case in Sections 26 to 28 for a system of particles interacting by means of the electromagnetic field, a system of gravitating bodies has the property that its equations of motion possess the ten classical integrals, or constants of the motion, namely the integrals of momentum and energy and those of angular momentum and of mass centre motion.

We shall now derive general expressions for these constants of motion in the form of definite integrals. In doing this we shall proceed as in Section 71 and make use, for the internal motion, of the general equations of motion of an elastic body in non-relativistic approximation. We restate these equations. We have the equation of continuity

$$\frac{\partial \rho}{\partial t} + \frac{\partial(\rho v_i)}{\partial x_i} = 0 \tag{79.01}$$

the equations of motion proper

$$\rho w_i - \rho \frac{\partial U}{\partial x_i} = \frac{\partial p_{ik}}{\partial x_k} \tag{79.02}$$

in which the acceleration w_i is given by

$$w_i = \frac{\partial v_i}{\partial t} + v_k \frac{\partial v_i}{\partial x_k} \tag{79.03}$$

and finally the relation giving the elastic potential energy :

$$\rho \frac{d\Pi}{dt} = \tfrac{1}{2} p_{ik} \left(\frac{\partial v_i}{\partial x_k} + \frac{\partial v_k}{\partial x_i} \right) \tag{79.04}$$

We shall not at present introduce the assumption that each body rotates in a rigid manner.

To obtain the constants of motion we may start from the relations which, according to Section 70, result from the harmonic conditions. The relations

$$- \int_{(\infty)} g \nabla_\alpha T^{\alpha i} (dx)^3 = 0 \tag{79.05}$$

integrated with respect to time give us the three momentum integrals, and the relation

$$- \int_{(\infty)} g \nabla_\alpha T^{\alpha 0} (dx)^3 = 0 \tag{79.06}$$

integrated with respect to time gives the energy integral. Similarly the relations

$$- \int_{(\infty)} g(x_i \nabla_\alpha T^{\alpha k} - x_k \nabla_\alpha T^{\alpha i})(dx)^3 = 0 \tag{79.07}$$

will give us the three integrals of angular momentum and finally the relation

$$- \int_{(\infty)} g x_i \nabla_\alpha T^{\alpha 0}(dx)^3 + x_0 \int_{(\infty)} g \nabla_\alpha T^{\alpha i}(dx)^3 = 0 \tag{79.08}$$

(in which, incidentally, the second term vanishes by virtue of (79.05)) leads to the three integrals for the motion of the mass centre.

We begin with the evaluation of the momentum. In deriving the conservation law from (79.05) we can use the results of Section 75. Generalizing equation (75.31) a little we put

$$P_i = \int_{(\infty)} \left\{ \rho v_i \left[1 + \frac{1}{c^2}(\tfrac{1}{2}v^2 + \Pi + 3U) \right] - \frac{1}{c^2} p_{ik} v_k - \frac{4}{c^2} \rho U_i - \frac{1}{c^2} \rho \frac{\partial^2 W}{\partial x_i \, \partial t} \right\} (dx)^3 \tag{79.09}$$

and then form the derivative of this quantity with respect to time. Using (73.01) we first find

$$\frac{dP_i}{dt} = \int \frac{\partial U^*}{\partial x_i} \sigma \, (dx)^3 - \frac{1}{c^2} \frac{d}{dt} \int \rho \frac{\partial^2 W}{\partial x_i \, \partial t}(dx)^3 - \frac{4}{c^2} \int \rho v_k \frac{\partial U_k}{\partial x_i}(dx)^3 \tag{79.10}$$

where

$$\sigma = \rho + \frac{\rho}{c^2}(\tfrac{3}{2}v^2 + \Pi - U) - \frac{p_{kk}}{c^2} \tag{79.11}$$

and the function U^* satisfies the equation

$$\Delta U^* - \frac{1}{c^2} \frac{\partial^2 U^*}{\partial t^2} = - 4\pi\gamma\sigma \tag{79.12}$$

But since all integrals in (79.10) are to be taken over the whole of space, relations (75.24) and (75.29) may be applied to them, according to which

$$\int \frac{\partial U^*}{\partial x_i} \sigma \, (dx)^3 = \frac{1}{c^2} \frac{d}{dt} \int \rho \, \frac{\partial^2 W}{\partial x_i \, \partial t} (dx)^3 \tag{79.13}$$

and

$$\int \rho v_k \frac{\partial U_k}{\partial x_i} (dx)^3 = 0 \tag{79.14}$$

Hence it follows that

$$\frac{dP_i}{dt} = 0 \; ; \quad P_i = \text{const.} \tag{79.15}$$

so that P_i is a constant of the motion. This result represents a generalization of the relation (75.34) for the general case of a system of elastic bodies interacting by means of the gravitational field.

We now go on to the formulation of the conservation law for the angular momentum of such a system. Introducing the expression (70.22) for $g\nabla_\alpha T^{\alpha i}$ into (79.07) and using the relation (70.26) for the components of the mass tensor we get

$$\frac{d}{dt} \int \left\{ \left[\rho + \frac{\rho}{c^2} (\tfrac{1}{2} v^2 + \Pi + 3U) \right] (x_i v_k - x_k v_i) - \frac{1}{c^2} (p_{jk} v_j x_i - p_{ji} v_j x_k) \right\} (dx)^3$$

$$= \int \left(x_i \frac{\partial U^*}{\partial x_k} - x_k \frac{\partial U^*}{\partial x_i} \right) \sigma \, (dx)^3 + \frac{4}{c^2} \int \rho \left(x_i \frac{dU_k}{dt} - x_k \frac{dU_i}{dt} \right) (dx)^3$$

$$- \frac{4}{c^2} \int \rho v_j \left(x_i \frac{\partial U_j}{\partial x_k} - x_k \frac{\partial U_j}{\partial x_i} \right) (dx)^3 \tag{79.16}$$

where for brevity we have put

$$\frac{dU_i}{dt} = \frac{\partial U_i}{\partial t} + v_j \frac{\partial U_i}{\partial x_j} \tag{79.17}$$

If in (79.16) we extend all integrals over the region occupied by one of the masses we obtain a generalization of the relation (72.04) that gives the law of the change of angular momentum in Newtonian approximation. We are here interested in the total angular momentum so that the integrals must be extended over the whole of space.

We introduce the notation

$$G_i = \left[\rho + \frac{\rho}{c^2} (\tfrac{1}{2} v^2 + \Pi + 3U) \right] v_i - \frac{1}{c^2} p_{ij} v_j - \frac{4}{c^2} \rho U_i - \frac{1}{c^2} \rho \frac{\partial^2 W}{\partial x_i \partial t} \tag{79.18}$$

using which, we can write equation (79.09) for the total momentum as

$$P_i = \int G_i (dx)^3 \tag{79.19}$$

We can then represent (79.16) in the form

$$\frac{d}{dt} \int (x_i G_k - x_k G_i)(dx)^3$$

$$= \int \left(x_i \frac{\partial U^*}{\partial x_k} - x_k \frac{\partial U^*}{\partial x_i} \right) \sigma \, (dx)^3 - \frac{1}{c^2} \frac{d}{dt} \int \rho \left(x_i \frac{\partial^2 W}{\partial x_k \, \partial t} - x_k \frac{\partial^2 W}{\partial x_i \, \partial t} \right) (dx)^3$$

$$- \frac{4}{c^2} \int \rho v_j \left(x_i \frac{\partial U_j}{\partial x_k} - x_k \frac{\partial U_j}{\partial x_i} \right) (dx)^3 - \frac{4}{c^2} \int \rho (v_i U_k - v_k U_i)(dx)^3 \tag{79.20}$$

We prove that the first two integrals on the right cancel and the remaining two are separately zero, so that the entire right-hand side vanishes.

In evaluating these integrals we shall use the following lemma :

If the function ψ may be expressed in terms of the density μ as

$$\psi = \int f(|\mathbf{r} - \mathbf{r}'|)\mu(\mathbf{r}')(dx')^3 \tag{79.21}$$

where f is some function of the distance $|\mathbf{r} - \mathbf{r}'|$, then the relation

$$\int \left(x_i \frac{\partial \psi}{\partial x_k} - x_k \frac{\partial \psi}{\partial x_i} \right)\mu \, (dx)^3 = 0 \tag{79.22}$$

is true. It is assumed here that in equation (79.21) one may differentiate under the integral sign. To prove this it is sufficient to insert the values of the derivatives of ψ, as calculated from (79.21), into (79.22) and to note that in the resulting double integral the integrand is antisymmetric in the coordinates of the two points $\mathbf{r}$ and $\mathbf{r}'$.

We have already encountered a similar relation when deriving (71.14).

Remembering equation (77.07) we may write

$$U^* = U_\sigma + \frac{1}{c^2} \frac{\partial^2 W}{\partial t^2} \tag{79.23}$$

where $U_\sigma = U + U_{\text{add}}$ is a solution of the equation

$$\Delta U_\sigma = -4\pi\gamma\sigma \tag{79.24}$$

The second term in (79.23), in which W denotes the quantity

$$W = \tfrac{1}{2}\gamma \int_{(\infty)} \rho' |\mathbf{r} - \mathbf{r}'| (dx')^3 \tag{79.25}$$

is a retardation correction.

We consider the first integral on the right-hand side of (79.20). By the lemma just proved

$$\int \left(x_i \frac{\partial U_\sigma}{\partial x_k} - x_k \frac{\partial U_\sigma}{\partial x_i} \right)\sigma \, (dx)^3 = 0 \tag{79.26}$$

Therefore we have

$$\int \left(x_i \frac{\partial U^*}{\partial x_k} - x_k \frac{\partial U^*}{\partial x_i} \right)\sigma \, (dx)^3 = \frac{1}{c^2} \int \left(x_i \frac{\partial^3 W}{\partial t^2 \, \partial x_k} - x_k \frac{\partial^3 W}{\partial t^2 \, \partial x_i} \right)\rho \, (dx)^3 \tag{79.27}$$

On the other hand, for

$$f = \tfrac{1}{2}\gamma |\mathbf{r} - \mathbf{r}'| \; ; \qquad \mu = \frac{\partial \rho}{\partial t} ; \qquad \psi = \frac{\partial W}{\partial t} \tag{79.28}$$

the lemma gives the relation

$$\int \left(x_i \frac{\partial^2 W}{\partial t \, \partial x_k} - x_k \frac{\partial^2 W}{\partial t \, \partial x_i} \right)\frac{\partial \rho}{\partial t} \, (dx)^3 = 0 \tag{79.29}$$

Using this we get

$$\frac{d}{dt} \int \rho \left(x_i \frac{\partial^2 W}{\partial t \, \partial x_k} - x_k \frac{\partial^2 W}{\partial t \, \partial x_i} \right)(dx)^3 = \int \rho \left(x_i \frac{\partial^3 W}{\partial t^2 \, \partial x_k} - x_k \frac{\partial^3 W}{\partial t^2 \, \partial x_i} \right)(dx)^3 \tag{79.30}$$

and therefore

$$\int \left(x_i \frac{\partial U^*}{\partial x_k} - x_k \frac{\partial U^*}{\partial x_i} \right) \sigma \, (dx)^3 = \frac{1}{c^2} \frac{d}{dt} \int \rho \left(x_i \frac{\partial^2 W}{\partial t \, \partial x_k} - x_k \frac{\partial^2 W}{\partial t \, \partial x_i} \right) (dx)^3 \tag{79.31}$$

so that the first two integrals on the right of (79.20) do indeed cancel.

The third integral on the right of (79.20) vanishes as a result of the same lemma; one has simply to apply it to

$$f = \frac{\gamma}{|\mathbf{r} - \mathbf{r}'|}; \qquad \mu = \rho v_j; \qquad \psi = U_j \tag{79.32}$$

Finally, the last integral vanishes because Poisson's equation holds for U_i. Thus the entire right-hand side of (79.20) is zero and we have

$$\frac{d}{dt} \int_{(\infty)} (x_i G_k - x_k G_i)(dx)^3 = 0 \tag{79.33}$$

If we introduce the total angular momentum of the system,

$$M_{ik} = \int_{(\infty)} (x_i G_k - x_k G_i)(dx)^3 \tag{79.34}$$

we have

$$M_{ik} = \text{const.} \tag{79.35}$$

We recall that in these equations the quantity G_i has the value (79.18) and differs little from the momentum density ρv_i.

We now go on to the formulation of the law of energy conservation for a system of bodies. In contrast to the other conservation laws, the law of energy conservation can be derived from (79.06) only in Newtonian approximation, the accuracy of calculations being the same as for other laws. A more exact form of the energy conservation law can be obtained by discussing the Lagrangian form of the equations for the system of bodies. For non-rotating masses this will be done in the next section.

Since the main terms ρ and ρv_i in the components $c^2 T^{00}$ and $c^2 T^{0i}$ satisfy the equation of continuity (79.01) the relation (79.06) amounts to the same as

$$c^2 \int \nabla_\alpha T^{\alpha 0}(dx)^3 = 0 \tag{79.36}$$

to the order of approximation considered. Introducing the expression (65.23) for the divergence into the last equation we find

$$\frac{d}{dt} \int c^2 T^{00}(dx)^3 + \int \frac{\partial U}{\partial t} T^{00}(dx)^3 = 0 \tag{79.37}$$

and, using the value (70.26) for T^{00} we get

$$\frac{d}{dt} \int \rho \left\{ 1 + \frac{1}{c^2} (\tfrac{1}{2} v^2 + \Pi - U) \right\} (dx)^3 + \frac{1}{c^2} \int \rho \frac{\partial U}{\partial t} \, (dx)^3 = 0 \tag{79.38}$$

Since separately

$$M^0 = \int \rho (dx)^3 = \text{const.} \tag{79.39}$$

we must have

$$\frac{d}{dt} \int \rho(\tfrac{1}{2}v^2 + \Pi - U)(dx)^3 + \int \rho \frac{\partial U}{\partial t} (dx)^3 = 0 \qquad (79.40)$$

To obtain from this a conservation law in the narrower sense we must transform the second integral in (79.40) into the form of a time derivative. This is easily done with the aid of the relation

$$\int \left(\rho \frac{\partial U}{\partial t} - U \frac{\partial \rho}{\partial t} \right)(dx)^3 = 0 \qquad (79.41)$$

which follows from Poisson's equation for U. Subtracting half of (79.41) from (79.40) and putting

$$E = \int \rho(\tfrac{1}{2}v^2 + \Pi - \tfrac{1}{2}U)(dx)^3 \qquad (79.42)$$

we get

$$\frac{dE}{dt} = 0 ; \qquad E = \text{const.} \qquad (79.43)$$

The integrals of the separate terms in (79.42) represent the kinetic, elastic and gravitational energies of the system of bodies in Newtonian approximation. If we do not separate off the terms (79.39) from (79.38) and put

$$M = \int \rho \left\{ 1 + \frac{1}{c^2}(\tfrac{1}{2}v^2 + \Pi - \tfrac{1}{2}U) \right\}(dx)^3 \qquad (79.44)$$

we also get

$$M = \text{const.} \qquad (79.45)$$

The quantity M is the total mass of the system of bodies. It is equal to

$$M = M^0 + \frac{E}{c^2} \qquad (79.46)$$

where M^0 and E are defined by (79.39) and (79.42).

It remains for us to examine the integrals of the mass centre motion of the system of bodies. They may be obtained starting from the relation (79.08). This amounts to transforming the expression

$$\frac{d}{dt} \int x_i \rho \left\{ 1 + \frac{1}{c^2}(\tfrac{1}{2}v^2 + \Pi - U) \right\}(dx)^3$$

$$= \int \rho v_i \left\{ 1 + \frac{1}{c^2}(\tfrac{1}{2}v^2 + \Pi - U) \right\}(dx)^3$$

$$+ \frac{1}{c^2} \int x_i \rho v_j w_j (dx)^3 + \frac{1}{c^2} \int x_i \rho \frac{d(\Pi - U)}{dt}(dx)^3 \qquad (79.47)$$

with the aid of the equations (79.01) to (79.04). Inserting the value for ρw_j

given by (79.02) into (79.47) we get as the sum of the last two integrals

$$\frac{1}{c^2}\int x_i\rho\left\{v_jw_j + \frac{d\Pi}{dt} - \frac{dU}{dt}\right\}(dx)^3 = -\frac{1}{c^2}\int p_{ji}v_j(dx)^3 - \frac{1}{c^2}\int x_i\rho\frac{\partial U}{\partial t}(dx)^3 \tag{79.48}$$

Using the notation (79.18) we can write the result of inserting (79.48) into (79.47) as

$$\frac{d}{dt}\int x_i\rho\left\{1 + \frac{1}{c^2}(\tfrac{1}{2}v^2 + \Pi - U)\right\}(dx)^3$$

$$= \int G_i\,(dx)^3 - \frac{4}{c^2}\int \rho v_i U\,(dx)^3 + \frac{4}{c^2}\int \rho U_i\,(dx)^3$$

$$+ \frac{1}{c^2}\int \rho\frac{\partial^2 W}{\partial x_i\,\partial t}(dx)^3 - \frac{1}{c^2}\int x_i\rho\frac{\partial U}{\partial t}(dx)^3 \tag{79.49}$$

Adding to this the obvious equation

$$\frac{1}{2c^2}\frac{d}{dt}\int x_i\rho U\,(dx)^3 = \frac{1}{2c^2}\int x_i\left(\rho\frac{\partial U}{\partial t} + U\frac{\partial\rho}{\partial t}\right)(dx)^3 \tag{79.50}$$

we can replace (79.49) by

$$\frac{d}{dt}\int x_i\rho\left\{1 + \frac{1}{c^2}(\tfrac{1}{2}v^2 + \Pi - \tfrac{1}{2}U)\right\}(dx)^3$$

$$= \int G_i\,(dx)^3 - \frac{4}{c^2}\int \rho v_i U\,(dx)^3 + \frac{4}{c^2}\int \rho U_i\,(dx)^3$$

$$+ \frac{1}{c^2}\int \rho\frac{\partial^2 W}{\partial x_i\,\partial t}(dx)^3 - \frac{1}{2c^2}\int x_i\left(\rho\frac{\partial U}{\partial t} - U\frac{\partial\rho}{\partial t}\right)(dx)^3 \tag{79.51}$$

This equation is valid if the region of integration includes one or some of the masses, but if the integration is extended over all space it can be simplified. By using the Poisson equations satisfied by U and U_i we get

$$\int \rho v_i U\,(dx)^3 = \int \rho U_i\,(dx)^3 \tag{79.52}$$

We also have

$$\int \rho\frac{\partial^2 W}{\partial x_i\,\partial t}(dx)^3 = \tfrac{1}{2}\int x_i\left(\rho\frac{\partial U}{\partial t} - U\frac{\partial\rho}{\partial t}\right)(dx)^3 \tag{79.53}$$

The latter relation can be most simply verified by noting that the function

$$Q_i = x_i U - 2\frac{\partial W}{\partial x_i} \tag{79.54}$$

satisfies a Poisson equation of the form

$$\Delta Q_i = -4\pi\gamma\rho x_i \tag{79.55}$$

As a result of (79.52) and (79.53) all integrals on the right-hand side of the equation, except the first, cancel and we get

$$\frac{d}{dt} \int x_i \rho \left\{ 1 + \frac{1}{c^2}(\tfrac{1}{2}v^2 + \Pi - \tfrac{1}{2}U) \right\}(dx)^3 = \int G_i(dx)^3 = P_i \qquad (79.56)$$

where, by (79.15), P_i is constant. Therefore equation (79.56) may be written in an integrated form, namely as

$$\int x_i \rho \left\{ 1 + \frac{1}{c^2}(\tfrac{1}{2}v^2 + \Pi - \tfrac{1}{2}U) \right\}(dx)^3 - tP_i = K_i \qquad (79.57)$$

where K_i is a new constant. Remembering that the total mass M as defined by (79.44) is constant we can introduce three quantities X_i by means of the relations

$$MX_i = \int x_i \rho \left\{ 1 + \frac{1}{c^2}(\tfrac{1}{2}v^2 + \Pi - \tfrac{1}{2}U) \right\}(dx)^3 \qquad (79.58)$$

These quantities can be interpreted as the coordinates of the mass centre of the system of masses, and equation (79.57), written as

$$MX_i - tP_i = K_i \qquad (79.59)$$

can be interpreted as the law of motion for the mass centre. Equation (79.08), which was our starting point, may be considered to be the result of differentiating (79.59) with respect to time.

80. Additional Remarks on the Problem of the Motion of a System of Bodies. The Explicit Form of the Integrals of Motion for the Case of Non-Rotating Masses

In the preceding section we introduced the integrals of motion for a system of bodies,. assuming the validity within each body of the non-relativistic equations of a motion for a continuous medium (79.01) to (79.04). The question arises whether the integrals of motion so found are still constant if the equations of motion of a continuous medium are taken to be only approximately valid within the bodies, as was assumed in Section 73, and if instead it is only postulated that the equations of motion of the bodies as a whole are satisfied. In this case one has, of course, to reintroduce the assumption that the bodies rotate as if rigid.

As regards the momentum, the question just posed is very simply answered. The equations of motion obtained in Sections 75 and 77 amounted precisely to the statement that the quantities

$$P_{ai} = \int\limits_{(a)} G_i(dx)^3 \qquad (80.01)$$

satisfy the relation

where, by (75.33)

$$\frac{dP_{ai}}{dt} = F_{ai} \qquad (80.02)$$

$$\sum_a F_{ai} = 0 \qquad (80.03)$$

Therefore the fact that the quantities

$$P_i = \int G_i(dx)^3 \qquad (80.04)$$

are constant, is a consequence of the equations of motion of the bodies as a whole.

The same applies to the quantities

$$M_{ik} = \int (x_i G_k - x_k G_i)(dx)^3 \qquad (80.05)$$

which represent the angular momentum of the system. In Section 72 we wrote down the equations of rotational motion only in Newtonian approximation. But the more precise equations for the sum of orbital and intrinsic angular momentum are precisely of the form

$$\frac{d}{dt} \int_{(a)} (x_i G_k - x_k G_i)(dx)^3 = L_{ik}^{(a)} \qquad (80.06)$$

where $L_{ik}^{(a)}$ is the sum of the same integrals that appear on the right-hand side of (79.20), except that here the integrals are extended over the region of mass (a) and not over the whole of space. Now, as was proved in Section 79, the relation

$$\sum_a L_{ik}^{(a)} = 0 \qquad (80.07)$$

is valid and hence the constancy of the M_{ik} is a consequence of the rotational equations (80.06).

We now verify that the relation

$$\int_{(a)} g \nabla_\alpha T^{\alpha 0}(dx)^3 = 0 \qquad (80.08)$$

is satisfied. It must hold in order that the corresponding harmonic condition be satisfied. On the other hand, if it does hold, so will the relation (79.06) which is connected with the energy integral.

The transformations that took us from (79.06) to (79.38) are also applicable in the case when all integrals are extended over the volume of a single mass. Therefore we may write immediately

$$\frac{d}{dt} \int_{(a)} \rho \Big\{ 1 + \frac{1}{c^2}(\tfrac{1}{2}v^2 + \Pi - U) \Big\}(dx)^3 + \frac{1}{c^2} \int_{(a)} \rho \frac{\partial U}{\partial t}(dx)^3 = 0 \qquad (80.09)$$

and since, separately

$$\int_{(a)} \rho (dx)^3 = M_a = \text{const.} \qquad (80.10)$$

we must have

$$\frac{d}{dt} \int_{(a)} \rho(\tfrac{1}{2}v^2 + \Pi - U)(dx)^3 + \int_{(a)} \rho \frac{\partial U}{\partial t}(dx)^3 = 0 \qquad (80.11)$$

This relation is fulfilled as a result of the equations of motion of a continuous medium (79.01) to (79.04). We must show that they will also be approximately satisfied if the equations of motion of a continuous medium are satisfied only in the mean and the body is taken to be rotating as if rigid, but not necessarily with constant angular velocity (see section 73). In this case our problem reduces to verifying the relation

$$\int\limits_{(a)} \rho v_i \left(w_i - \frac{\partial U}{\partial x_i} \right)(dx)^3 = 0 \tag{80.12}$$

which follows from (80.11) by differentiation when account is taken of the fact that the elastic energy remains constant. Here w_i is the acceleration for which the expression (73.07) was deduced in Section 73; the integrand in (80.12) is v_i times the left-hand side of (73.08). The equation (80.12) is readily verifiable with the use of the relation

$$\int\limits_{(a)} \rho v_i \left[\dot{\omega}_{ji}^{(a)} - \left(\frac{\partial^2 U^{(a)}}{\partial x_i \, \partial x_j} \right)_a \right](x_j - a_j)(dx)^3 = 0 \tag{80.13}$$

which may be written as

$$\frac{dT_a}{dt} = \frac{1}{2} I_{ij}^{(a)} \left(\frac{\partial^2 U^{(a)}}{\partial x_i \, \partial x_j} \right)_a \tag{80.14}$$

This relation coincides with (72.32) and is satisfied by virtue of the equation of the rotational motion of the body. The verification of (80.11) may also be performed as follows. Dividing the potential U into an internal and an external part and using equations (71.19) and (72.09) which express the fact that the resultant of the internal forces and of their moments is zero, we may write

$$\int \rho \frac{\partial u_a}{\partial t}(dx)^3 = -\int \rho v_i \frac{\partial u_a}{\partial x_i}(dx)^3 = 0 \tag{80.15}$$

Further it is evident that

$$\frac{d}{dt}\int\limits_{(a)} \rho(\Pi - u_a)(dx)^3 = 0 \tag{80.16}$$

Therefore (80.11) reduces to an equation involving only the external potential $U^{(a)}$, namely

$$\frac{d}{dt}\int\limits_{(a)} \rho(\tfrac{1}{2}v^2 - U^{(a)})(dx)^3 + \int\limits_{(a)} \rho \frac{\partial U^{(a)}}{\partial t}(dx)^3 = 0 \tag{80.17}$$

Inserting the value (71.27) for $U^{(a)}(\mathbf{r})$ into this equation and using the equations (71.35) and (72.32) for the translational and rotational motions we see that (80.17) is satisfied.

Thus the validity of the relation (80.08) which must be required to ensure that the harmonic condition is satisfied is, in fact, a consequence of the remaining relations of the form (70.21), just as in point mechanics the equation expressing the conservation of energy is a consequence of the equations of motion.

Similarly it can be verified that the equations of translational and of rotational motion ensure the validity of the relation (79.51) and hence of the law of motion of the mass centre.

As we have already noted in Section 79 the accuracy of our approximation permits a derivation of the law of conservation of energy from (79.06) only in Newtonian approximation. However, for non-rotating bodies with spherical symmetry it is not difficult to write down the energy integral in the next approximation also. In this case the motion will be purely translational, and for such motion we have derived the Lagrangian form of its equations. Therefore we can base the derivation of the energy integral on the Lagrangian examined in Section 78. We introduce the effective mass

$$m_a = M_a + \frac{2}{3}\frac{\varepsilon_a}{c^2} \tag{80.18}$$

and then have, by (78.03)

$$L = K + K_1 - \Phi - \Psi \tag{80.19}$$

where by (76.19)

$$K = \sum_a \tfrac{1}{2} m_a \dot{a}_i^2 + \frac{1}{c^2} \sum_a \tfrac{1}{8} m_a (\dot{a}_i^2)^2 \tag{80.20}$$

As before, the quantity K_1 is given by the equation (78.05) in which we can replace M_a and M_b by the effective masses m_a and m_b:

$$K_1 = \frac{1}{4c^2} \sum_{a,b} \frac{\gamma m_a m_b}{|\mathbf{a}-\mathbf{b}|}(3\dot{a}_i^2 + 3\dot{b}_i^2 - 8\dot{a}_i\dot{b}_i) + \frac{1}{4c^2}\sum_{a,b}\gamma m_a m_b \dot{a}_i \dot{b}_k \frac{\partial^2}{\partial a_i\,\partial a_k}|\mathbf{a}-\mathbf{b}| \tag{80.21}$$

Φ is the Newtonian potential energy for the effective masses.

$$\Phi = -\frac{1}{2}\sum_{a,b}\frac{\gamma m_a m_b}{|\mathbf{a}-\mathbf{b}|} \tag{80.22}$$

In view of (78.13) this expression includes the terms Φ_1, and Φ_2 (incidentally $\Phi_2 = 0$ because of the spherical symmetry). Finally, Ψ has its previous value (78.15), but in the approximation considered the masses involved may also be replaced by effective masses:

$$\Psi = \frac{\gamma^2}{4c_0^2}\sum_{a,b}\frac{m_a m_b(m_a + m_b)}{|\mathbf{a}-\mathbf{b}|^2} + \frac{\gamma^2}{6c_0^2}\sum_{a,b,c}m_a m_b m_c$$
$$\times\left(\frac{1}{|\mathbf{a}-\mathbf{b}|\,|\mathbf{a}-\mathbf{c}|} + \frac{1}{|\mathbf{b}-\mathbf{c}|\,|\mathbf{b}-\mathbf{a}|} + \frac{1}{|\mathbf{c}-\mathbf{a}|\,|\mathbf{c}-\mathbf{b}|}\right) \tag{80.23}$$

Using the relation

$$\sum_a \dot{a}_i \frac{\partial L}{\partial \dot{a}_i} - L = E \tag{80.24}$$

we obtain the energy integral (with the non-relativistic choice of the zero of energy) in the form

$$E = \sum_a \tfrac{1}{2} m_a \dot{a}_i^2 + \frac{1}{c^2}\sum_a \tfrac{3}{8} m_a (\dot{a}_i^2)^2 + K_1 + \Phi + \Psi \tag{80.25}$$

The remaining integrals of the motion can also be readily derived from the Lagrangian. We obtain the momentum integrals

$$\sum_a P_{ai} = P_i \tag{80.26}$$

where

$$P_{ai} = \frac{\partial L}{\partial \dot{a}_i} = \dot{a}_i \left(m_a + \frac{1}{2c^2} m_a \dot{a}_k^2 - \frac{1}{2c^2} \sideset{}{'}\sum_b \frac{\gamma m_a m_b}{|a-b|} \right)$$
$$+ \frac{7}{2c^2} \sideset{}{'}\sum_b \frac{\gamma m_a m_b (\dot{a}_i - \dot{b}_i)}{|a-b|} - \frac{1}{2c^2} \sideset{}{'}\sum_b \gamma m_a m_b \dot{b}_k \frac{(a_i - b_i)(a_k - b_k)}{|a-b|^3} \tag{80.27}$$

the angular momentum integrals

$$\sum_a (a_i P_{ak} - a_k P_{ai}) = M_{ik} \tag{80.28}$$

and the integrals of the mass centre motion†

$$M X_i - P_i t = K_i = \text{const.} \tag{80.29}$$

where

$$M X_i = \sum_a a_i \left(m_a + \frac{1}{2c^2} m_a \dot{a}_k^2 - \frac{1}{2c^2} \sideset{}{'}\sum_b \frac{\gamma m_a m_b}{|a-b|} \right) \tag{80.30}$$

and where

$$M = \sum_a \left(m_a + \frac{1}{2c^2} m_a \dot{a}_k^2 \right) - \frac{1}{2c^2} \sum_{a,b} \frac{\gamma m_a m_b}{|a-b|} \tag{80.31}$$

is the total mass of the system.

A more exact value of the total mass is

$$M = \sum_a m_a + \frac{E}{c^2} \tag{80.32}$$

where E has the value (80.25).

81. The Problem of Two Bodies of Finite Mass

In the case of two bodies the equations of motion obtainable from the Lagrangian (80.19) can be integrated. In this connection it is convenient to change to a notation which is more usual in mechanics. To label the two masses we shall now use the numbers 1 and 2 instead of the letters a and b, and we shall denote the coordinates of the two particles by x_1, y_1, z_1, and x_2, y_2, z_2 respectively instead of using a and b here also.

We shall also use the three-dimensional vector symbols $\mathbf{r}_1$ and $\mathbf{r}_2$ to describe the positions of the two masses. In the new notation the Lagrangian becomes

$$L = \frac{1}{2} m_1 \dot{\mathbf{r}}_1^2 + \frac{1}{2} m_2 \dot{\mathbf{r}}_2^2 + \frac{m_1}{8c^2} (\dot{\mathbf{r}}_1^2)^2 + \frac{m_2}{8c^2} (\dot{\mathbf{r}}_2^2)^2$$
$$+ \frac{1}{2c^2} \frac{\gamma m_1 m_2}{|\mathbf{r}_1 - \mathbf{r}_2|} (3\dot{\mathbf{r}}_1^2 + 3\dot{\mathbf{r}}_2^2 - 7\dot{\mathbf{r}}_1 \cdot \dot{\mathbf{r}}_2)$$
$$- \frac{1}{2c^2} \frac{\gamma m_1 m_2}{|\mathbf{r}_1 - \mathbf{r}_2|^3} \{\dot{\mathbf{r}}_1 \cdot (\mathbf{r}_1 - \mathbf{r}_2)\}\{(\dot{\mathbf{r}}_2 \cdot (\mathbf{r}_1 - \mathbf{r}_2)\}$$
$$+ \frac{\gamma m_1 m_2}{|\mathbf{r}_1 - \mathbf{r}_2|} - \frac{\gamma^2}{2c^2} \frac{m_1 m_2 (m_1 + m_2)}{|\mathbf{r}_1 - \mathbf{r}_2|^2} \tag{81.01}$$

† The constants K_i should not be confused with the quantities K_1 and K_2 appearing in the Lagrangian.

and the energy integral appears as

$$E = \frac{1}{2} m_1 \dot{\mathbf{r}}_1^2 + \frac{1}{2} m_2 \dot{\mathbf{r}}_2^2 + \frac{3m_1}{8c^2} (\dot{\mathbf{r}}_1^2)^2 + \frac{3m_2}{8c_2} (\dot{\mathbf{r}}_2^2)^2$$

$$+ \frac{1}{2c^2} \frac{\gamma m_1 m_2}{|\mathbf{r}_1 - \mathbf{r}_2|} (3\dot{\mathbf{r}}_1^2 + 3\dot{\mathbf{r}}_2^2 - 7\dot{\mathbf{r}}_1 \cdot \dot{\mathbf{r}}_2)$$

$$- \frac{1}{2c^2} \frac{\gamma m_1 m_2}{|\mathbf{r}_1 - \mathbf{r}_2|^3} \{\dot{\mathbf{r}}_1 \cdot (\mathbf{r}_1 - \mathbf{r}_2)\}\{\dot{\mathbf{r}}_2 \cdot (\mathbf{r}_1 - \mathbf{r}_2)\}$$

$$- \frac{\gamma m_1 m_2}{|\mathbf{r}_1 - \mathbf{r}_2|} + \frac{\gamma^2}{2c^2} \frac{m_1 m_2 (m_1 + m_2)}{|\mathbf{r}_1 - \mathbf{r}_2|^2} \tag{81.02}$$

The equation (80.27) for the momentum of one of the masses should also be restated in the new notation. The component $P_x^{(1)}$, for instance, is given by

$$P_x^{(1)} = \dot{x}_1 \left(m_1 + \frac{1}{2c^2} m_1 \dot{\mathbf{r}}_1^2 - \frac{1}{2c^2} \frac{\gamma m_1 m_2}{|\mathbf{r}_1 - \mathbf{r}_2|} \right)$$

$$+ \frac{7}{2c^2} \frac{\gamma m_1 m_2 (\dot{x}_1 - \dot{x}_2)}{|\mathbf{r}_1 - \mathbf{r}_2|} - \frac{\gamma m_1 m_2 (x_1 - x_2)}{2c^2 |\mathbf{r}_1 - \mathbf{r}_2|^3} \{\dot{\mathbf{r}}_2 \cdot (\mathbf{r}_1 - \mathbf{r}_2)\} \tag{81.03}$$

The momentum of the other mass can be obtained from the last expression by interchanging the suffixes 1 and 2, and the total momentum will be given by

$$P_x = P_x^{(1)} + P_x^{(2)}, \text{ etc.} \tag{81.04}$$

Further, we state the equation for one of the components of angular momentum, for instance

$$M_{xy} = x_1 P_y^{(1)} - y_1 P_x^{(1)} + x_2 P_y^{(2)} - y_2 P_x^{(2)} \tag{81.05}$$

We have

$$M_{xy} = (x_1 \dot{y}_1 - y_1 \dot{x}_1) \left(m_1 + \frac{1}{2c^2} m_1 \dot{\mathbf{r}}_1^2 + \frac{3}{c^2} \frac{\gamma m_1 m_2}{|\mathbf{r}_1 - \mathbf{r}_2|} \right)$$

$$+ (x_2 \dot{y}_2 - y_2 \dot{x}_2) \left(m_2 + \frac{1}{2c^2} m_2 \dot{\mathbf{r}}_2^2 + \frac{3}{c^2} \frac{\gamma m_1 m_2}{|\mathbf{r}_1 - \mathbf{r}_2|} \right)$$

$$- \frac{7\gamma m_1 m_2}{2c^2 |\mathbf{r}_1 - \mathbf{r}_2|} (x_1 \dot{y}_2 - y_1 \dot{x}_2 + x_2 \dot{y}_1 - y_2 \dot{x}_1)$$

$$+ \frac{\gamma m_1 m_2}{2c^2 |\mathbf{r}_1 - \mathbf{r}_2|} \{(\dot{\mathbf{r}}_1 + \dot{\mathbf{r}}_2) \cdot (\mathbf{r}_1 - \mathbf{r}_2)\}(x_1 y_2 - x_2 y_1) \tag{81.06}$$

If we introduce a system of coordinates fixed to the mass centre we can write the mass centre integral as

$$m_1 \mathbf{r}_1 \left(1 + \frac{\dot{\mathbf{r}}_1^2}{2c^2} - \frac{1}{2c^2} \frac{\gamma m_2}{|\mathbf{r}_1 - \mathbf{r}_2|} \right) + m_2 \mathbf{r}_2 \left(1 + \frac{\dot{\mathbf{r}}_2^2}{2c^2} - \frac{1}{2c^2} \frac{\gamma m_1}{|\mathbf{r}_1 - \mathbf{r}_2|} \right) = 0$$

$$\tag{81.07}$$

We now introduce the coordinates of the mass centre in the Newtonian sense

$$\mathbf{r}_0 = \frac{m_1\mathbf{r}_1 + m_2\mathbf{r}_2}{m_1 + m_2} \qquad (81.08)$$

and also the relative coordinates

$$\mathbf{r} = \mathbf{r}_1 - \mathbf{r}_2 \qquad (81.09)$$

Then we have

$$\mathbf{r}_1 = \mathbf{r}_0 + \frac{m_2}{m_0}\mathbf{r}$$

$$\mathbf{r}_2 = \mathbf{r}_0 - \frac{m_1}{m_0}\mathbf{r} \qquad (81.10)$$

where

$$m_0 = m_1 + m_2 \qquad (81.11)$$

is the total mass. Further, we introduce the notation

$$m^* = \frac{m_1 m_2}{m_1 + m_2} \qquad (81.12)$$

for the reduced mass and note that

$$m_0 m^* = m_1 m_2 \qquad (81.13)$$

We also have

$$m_1\dot{\mathbf{r}}_1^2 + m_2\dot{\mathbf{r}}_2^2 = m_0\dot{\mathbf{r}}_0^2 + m^*\dot{\mathbf{r}}^2 \qquad (81.14)$$

$$m_1(x_1\dot{y}_1 - y_1\dot{x}_1) + m_2(x_2\dot{y}_2 - y_2\dot{x}_2) = m_0(x_0\dot{y}_0 - y_0\dot{x}_0) + m^*(x\dot{y} - y\dot{x}) \qquad (81.15)$$

and

$$x_2 y_1 - x_1 y_2 = x_0 y - x y_0 \qquad (81.16)$$

Equation (81.07) shows directly that the radius vector of the Newtonian mass centre will always remain small and its rate of change will also be small. If we take the orders of $\mathbf{r}$ and $\dot{\mathbf{r}}$ to be R and q respectively, we have

$$\mathbf{r}_0 \sim R\frac{q^2}{c^2}; \qquad \dot{\mathbf{r}}_0 \sim \frac{q^3}{c^2} \qquad (81.17)$$

Therefore in all correction terms that contain the factor $1/c^2$ we may replace (81.10) by

$$\mathbf{r}_1 = \frac{m_2}{m_0}\mathbf{r}; \qquad \mathbf{r}_2 = -\frac{m_1}{m_0}\mathbf{r} \qquad (81.18)$$

and

$$\dot{\mathbf{r}}_1 = \frac{m_2}{m_0}\dot{\mathbf{r}}; \qquad \dot{\mathbf{r}}_2 = -\frac{m_1}{m_0}\dot{\mathbf{r}} \qquad (81.19)$$

Making these approximations in equation (81.07) itself we can write it in the form†

$$m_0\mathbf{r}_0 = \frac{(m_1 - m_2)}{2c^2 m_0}\mathbf{r}\left(m^*\dot{\mathbf{r}}^2 - \frac{\gamma m^* m}{r}\right) \qquad (81.20)$$

Hence it can be concluded that in the case of a bounded motion the Newtonian

---

† This form was first derived in the author's paper of 1941 [38].

mass centre $\mathbf{r}_0$ will oscillate about its mean position.

We rewrite the integrals of energy and angular momentum using the assumption that $\mathbf{r}_0$ is small. We can neglect the quantities $\mathbf{r}_0$ and $\dot{\mathbf{r}}_0$ even in the main (Newtonian) terms of (81.02) and (81.06) since according to (81.14) and (81.15) they appear quadratically in these; this means that the values (81.18) and (81.19) may be used everywhere. Introducing these values into the energy integral (81.02) and dividing the result by the reduced mass m^* we find for the quantity

$$E_0 = \frac{E}{m^*} \qquad (81.21)$$

the expression

$$E_0 = \frac{1}{2}\dot{\mathbf{r}}^2 - \frac{\gamma m_0}{r}$$
$$+ \frac{1}{c^2}\left\{\frac{3}{8}\left(1 - \frac{3m^*}{m_0}\right)(\dot{\mathbf{r}}^2)^2 + \frac{\gamma}{2r}(3m_0 + m^*)\dot{\mathbf{r}}^2 + \frac{\gamma}{2r^3}m^*(\mathbf{r}\cdot\dot{\mathbf{r}})^2 + \frac{\gamma^2 m_0^2}{2r^2}\right\}$$

$$(81.22)$$

We now introduce the values of $\mathbf{r}_1$ and $\mathbf{r}_2$ into the angular momentum integral. By (81.16) and (81.20) the last term of (81.06) is equal to zero in high approximation and the remaining terms give

$$\frac{1}{m^*}M_{xy} = \left\{1 + \frac{1}{2c^2}\left(1 - \frac{3m^*}{m_0}\right)\dot{\mathbf{r}}^2 + \frac{\gamma}{c^2 r}(3m_0 + m^*)\right\}(x\dot{y} - y\dot{x}) \quad (81.23)$$

Similar expressions result for the other components of angular momentum. It is evident from these expressions that in the space of the relative coordinates x, y, z the orbit will be plane. Taking the plane of the orbit to be the xy plane we can put in the usual way

$$z = 0; \qquad \dot{z} = 0 \qquad (81.24)$$

and we can introduce the polar coordinates r and φ by the equations

$$x = r\cos\varphi; \qquad y = r\sin\varphi \qquad (81.25)$$

Denoting the constant on the left-hand side of (81.23) by μ we get

$$\mu = \left\{1 + \frac{1}{2c^2}\left(1 - \frac{3m^*}{m_0}\right)\dot{\mathbf{r}}^2 + \frac{\gamma}{c^2 r}(3m_0 + m^*)\right\}r^2\dot{\varphi} \qquad (81.26)$$

Before continuing we compare the integrals of energy and angular momentum just derived with those obtained in Section 58 in our investigation of the motion of an infinitesimal mass in the field of a large or finite mass. We must expect that for $m^* = 0$ the equations of the two-body problem go over into the equations of the one-body problem. Let us verify this. As the equations (58.26) to (58.31) show, the following relations held in Section 58:

$$\frac{r-\alpha}{r+\alpha}\frac{dt}{d\tau} = \varepsilon = 1 + \frac{E_0}{c^2} \qquad (81.27)$$

and

$$(r+\alpha)^2\frac{d\varphi}{d\tau} = \mu \qquad (81.28)$$

where

$$\left(\frac{d\tau}{dt}\right)^2 = \frac{r-\alpha}{r+\alpha} - \frac{1}{c^2}\left[\left(\frac{r+\alpha}{r-\alpha}\right)\left(\frac{dr}{dt}\right)^2 + (r+\alpha)^2\left(\frac{d\varphi}{dt}\right)^2\right] \qquad (81.29)$$

and where α is the gravitational radius of the large mass ; it may be taken to be

$$\alpha = \frac{\gamma m_0}{c^2} \tag{81.30}$$

Putting

$$v^2 = \dot{\mathbf{r}}^2 = \left(\frac{dr}{dt}\right)^2 + r^2\left(\frac{d\varphi}{dt}\right)^2 . \tag{81.31}$$

we may replace (81.29) approximately by

$$\left(\frac{d\tau}{dt}\right)^2 = \frac{r - \alpha}{r + \alpha} \cdot \left[1 - \frac{1}{c^2}\left(1 + \frac{4\alpha}{r}\right)v^2\right] \tag{81.32}$$

whence

$$\frac{dt}{d\tau} = \sqrt{\left(\frac{r + \alpha}{r - \alpha}\right) \cdot \left[1 + \frac{1}{2c^2}\left(1 + \frac{4\alpha}{r}\right)v^2 + \frac{3}{8}\frac{v^4}{c^4}\right]} \tag{81.33}$$

and then

$$\frac{r - \alpha}{r + \alpha}\frac{dt}{d\tau} = 1 - \frac{\alpha}{r} + \frac{v^2}{2c^2} + \frac{3\alpha}{2c^2 r}v^2 + \frac{3}{8}\frac{v^4}{c^4} + \frac{\alpha^2}{2r^2} \tag{81.34}$$

Introducing this expression into (81.27) and replacing α by its value (81.30) we obtain for E_0 the value

$$E_0 = \frac{1}{2}v^2 - \frac{\gamma m_0}{r} + \frac{1}{c^2}\left(\frac{3}{8}v^4 + \frac{3}{2}\frac{\gamma m_0}{r}v^2 + \frac{\gamma^2 m_0^2}{2r^2}\right) \tag{81.35}$$

which agrees with that given in (81.22) if in the latter m^* is equated to zero.

In order to compare the equations (81.26) and (81.28) we separate off the factor $r^2\dot{\varphi}$ in the latter and write

$$\left(1 + \frac{\alpha}{r}\right)^2\frac{dt}{d\tau}r^2\frac{d\varphi}{dt} = \mu \tag{81.36}$$

The value of $dt/d\tau$ may be taken from equation (81.33) in which terms of order v^4/c^4 may be neglected. Then we get

$$\left(1 + \frac{\alpha}{r}\right)^2\frac{dt}{d\tau} = 1 + \frac{3\alpha}{r} + \frac{v^2}{2c^2} \tag{81.37}$$

Here we replace the gravitational radius α by its value (81.30) and insert (81.37) into (81.36), so getting

$$\left(1 + \frac{v^2}{2c^2} + \frac{3\gamma m_0}{c^2 r}\right)r^2\frac{d\varphi}{dt} = \mu \tag{81.38}$$

If m^* is equated to zero in (81.26) that equation agrees with (81.38).

Thus in the limit the integrals of motion in the two-body problem do indeed go over into the corresponding integrals of the equations of the geodesic which determine the motion of an infinitesimal mass in the field of a finite mass. We note that this comparison has been possible only because we have treated both problems in terms of the same, namely harmonic, coordinates.

We now continue the discussion of the equations for two finite masses and derive the equations of the trajectory of their relative motion. We shall retain the symbol v^2 in place of $\dot{r}^2$ to denote the square of the velocity. If we put also

$$u = \frac{1}{r} \tag{81.39}$$

we have the identity

$$v^2 = \left(r^2 \frac{d\varphi}{dt}\right)^2 \left\{\left(\frac{du}{d\varphi}\right)^2 + u^2\right\} \tag{81.40}$$

whence, after multiplying by the square of the quantity that appears multiplied by $r^2\dot{\varphi}$ in (81.26) we find

$$v^2 + \frac{1}{c^2}\left(1 - \frac{3m^*}{m_0}\right)v^4 + \frac{2\gamma}{c^2 r}(3m_0 + m^*)v^2 = \mu^2\left\{\left(\frac{du}{d\varphi}\right)^2 + u^2\right\} \tag{81.41}$$

We can now insert on the left the value of v^2 given by the energy integral (81.22) with $(\mathbf{r} \cdot \dot{\mathbf{r}})^2$ expressed as

$$(\mathbf{r} \cdot \dot{\mathbf{r}})^2 = r^2 \cdot v^2 - \mu^2 \tag{81.42}$$

This insertion reduces (81.22) for E_0 to

$$E_0 = \frac{1}{2}v^2 - \frac{\gamma m_0}{r} + \frac{3}{8c^2}\left(1 - \frac{3m^*}{m_0}\right)v^4 + \frac{\gamma}{2c^2 r}(3m_0 + 2m^*)v^2 + \frac{\gamma^2 m_0^2}{2c^2 r^2} - \frac{\gamma m^* \mu^2}{2c^2 r^3} \tag{81.43}$$

We solve this equation approximately for v^2 and insert the solution into (81.41). Replacing $1/r$ by u we then get

$$\mu^2\left\{\left(\frac{du}{d\varphi}\right)^2 + u^2\right\} = 2E_0 + \frac{1}{c^2}\left(1 - \frac{3m^*}{m_0}\right)E_0^2$$

$$+ 2\gamma m_0\left\{1 + \frac{1}{c^2}\left(4 - \frac{3m^*}{m_0}\right)E_0\right\}u$$

$$+ \frac{3\gamma^2 m_0^2}{c^2}\left(2 - \frac{m^*}{m_0}\right)u^2 + \frac{\gamma m^*}{c^2}\mu^2 u^3 \tag{81.44}$$

For $m^* = 0$ this equation goes over into (58.36) in the approximation considered. To make the discussion of this equation more convenient we replace the integration constants E_0 and μ by two new constants a and p, where

$$E_0 = -\frac{\gamma m_0}{2a}; \qquad \mu^2 = \gamma m_0 p \tag{81.45}$$

Further we put, as in (81.30) :

$$\frac{\gamma m_0}{c^2} = \alpha; \qquad \frac{\gamma m^*}{c^2} = \alpha^* \tag{81.46}$$

In Newtonian approximation the quantities a and p represent the major semi-axis and the parameter of an ellipse (we confine ourselves to the case of a bounded motion). With the new notation (81.44) appears as

$$\left(\frac{du}{d\varphi}\right)^2 = -\frac{1}{ap} + \frac{\alpha - 3\alpha^*}{4a^2 p} + \left(\frac{2}{p} - \frac{4\alpha}{ap} + \frac{3\alpha^*}{ap}\right)u$$

$$- \left(1 - \frac{6\alpha}{p} + \frac{3\alpha^*}{p}\right)u^2 + \alpha^* u^3 \tag{81.47}$$

For $a > p$ the polynomial on the right-hand side of this equation has two positive roots u_1 and u_2 that are close to the roots of the equation

$$-\frac{1}{ap} + \frac{2}{p}u - u^2 = 0 \tag{81.48}$$

which are

$$u_1^0 = \frac{1+e}{p}; \qquad u_2^0 = \frac{1-e}{p} \tag{81.49}$$

with

$$1 - e^2 = \frac{p}{a} \tag{81.50}$$

In addition there is a large root u_3 for which one easily finds the relation

$$\alpha^* u_3 = 1 - \frac{6\alpha - \alpha^*}{p} \tag{81.51}$$

The differential equation (81.47) can therefore be written as

$$\left(\frac{du}{d\varphi}\right)^2 = (u_1 - u)(u - u_2)\left(1 - \frac{6\alpha - \alpha^*}{p} - \alpha^* u\right) \tag{81.52}$$

We make the substitution

$$u = \frac{u_1 + u_2}{2} + \frac{u_1 - u_2}{2}\cos\psi \tag{81.53}$$

Then the equation for ψ is

$$\left(\frac{d\psi}{d\varphi}\right)^2 = 1 - \frac{6\alpha}{p} - \frac{\alpha^* e}{p}\cos\psi \tag{81.54}$$

Here we have introduced the approximate values for the roots given by (81.49) into the correction term. Hence

$$\frac{d\varphi}{d\psi} = 1 + \frac{3\alpha}{p} + \frac{\alpha^* e}{2p}\cos\psi \tag{81.55}$$

If r varies from its greatest to its least value and back, ψ changes by 2π. In that time the angle φ increases by somewhat more than 2π, say by $2\pi + \Delta\varphi$ where

$$\Delta\varphi = \frac{6\pi\alpha}{p} \tag{81.56}$$

This equation has the same form as the equation (58.43) which gives the displacement of the perihelion in one period of revolution, but the constants involved have a somewhat different meaning. For a given parameter p the displacement depends only on the sum of the masses of the two components of the system (e.g. a double star). Of the constants of integration only the angular momentum is involved in this expression for the displacement.

The presence of the cubic term in the differential equations (81.47) has the effect that the orbit of relative motion is not a precessing ellipse, but a precessing curve of a more complicated form which, however, does not differ greatly from an ellipse [19].

CHAPTER VII

APPROXIMATE SOLUTIONS, CONSERVATION LAWS AND SOME QUESTIONS OF PRINCIPLE

82. The Gravitational Potentials for Non-Rotating Bodies (Spatial Components)

In the preceding chapter we determined the gravitational potentials only with the accuracy required to derive the equations of motion of a system of bodies. We shall now concern ourselves with a more precise evaluation of the gravitational potentials, but in view of the complexity of the problem we shall only deal with the case of non-rotating spherically symmetric masses.

In Section 67 we stated the equations

$$\mathfrak{g}^{00} = \frac{1}{c} + \frac{4U}{c^3} + \frac{4S}{c^5} \tag{82.01}$$

$$\mathfrak{g}^{0i} = \frac{4U_i}{c^3} + \frac{4S_i}{c^5} \tag{82.02}$$

and

$$\mathfrak{g}^{ik} = -c\delta_{ik} + \frac{4S_{ik}}{c^3} \tag{82.03}$$

in which U is the Newtonian potential and U_i the gravitational vector potential. The terms involving S, S_i and S_{ik} are corrections. We did not evaluate these in detail because it was sufficient for the derivation of the equations of motion to know, in addition to the vector potential U_i, the single quantity

$$U^* = U + \frac{1}{c^2}(S + S_{kk} - 2U^2) \tag{82.04}$$

(see equation (67.11)) which, by (68.30), satisfies the equation

$$\Delta U^* - \frac{1}{c^2}\frac{\partial^2 U^*}{\partial t^2} = -4\pi\gamma(c^2 T^{00} + T^{kk}) \tag{82.05}$$

Now we shall also evaluate the correction terms, taking as our starting point the approximate form of Einstein's equations obtained in Section 68.

$$\frac{1}{2c}\Delta\mathfrak{g}^{\mu\nu} - \frac{1}{2c^3}\frac{\partial^2\mathfrak{g}^{\mu\nu}}{\partial t^2} + N^{\mu\nu} = \frac{8\pi\gamma g}{c^4}T^{\mu\nu} \tag{82.06}$$

We consider first the equation for the $\mathfrak{g}^{ik}$. In it we retain terms of fourth order in $1/c$, but discard all terms of higher orders.

According to (66.07) we can then put

$$-gT^{ik} = \rho v_i v_k - p_{ik} \tag{82.07}$$

318

and in the expression (68.16) for N^{ik} we can take the main terms

$$N^{ik} = -\frac{2}{c^4}\, Q_{ik} \tag{82.08}$$

Here we have put

$$Q_{ik} = \tfrac{1}{2}\, \delta_{ik}(\operatorname{grad} U)^2 - \frac{\partial U}{\partial x_i}\frac{\partial U}{\partial x_k} \tag{82.09}$$

as in (71.16). We can neglect the second derivative with respect to time in the equation for $\mathfrak{g}^{ik}$. Introducing the value (82.03) for $\mathfrak{g}^{ik}$, multiplying by $\tfrac{1}{2}c^4$ and transferring the term Q_{ik} to the right-hand side we obtain the following equation for S_{ik}:

$$\Delta S_{ik} = Q_{ik} - 4\pi\gamma(\rho v_i v_k - p_{ik}) \tag{82.10}$$

We note that the gravitational vector potential U_i satisfies the equation

$$\Delta U_i = -4\pi\gamma\rho v_i \tag{82.11}$$

and that, since the Newtonian potential U satisfies Poisson's equation we have

$$\frac{\partial Q_{ik}}{\partial x_k} = 4\pi\gamma\rho\,\frac{\partial U}{\partial x_i} \tag{82.12}$$

Therefore equations (82.10) and (82.11) lead to

$$\Delta\!\left(\frac{\partial U_i}{\partial t} + \frac{\partial S_{ik}}{\partial x_k}\right) = -4\pi\gamma\left\{\frac{\partial(\rho v_i)}{\partial t} + \frac{\partial(\rho v_i v_k)}{\partial x_k} - \rho\frac{\partial U}{\partial x_i} - \frac{\partial p_{ik}}{\partial x_k}\right\} \tag{82.13}$$

and by virtue of the equations of motion for a continuous medium written in the form (66.13) we get

$$\Delta\!\left(\frac{\partial U_i}{\partial t} + \frac{\partial S_{ik}}{\partial x_k}\right) = 0 \tag{82.14}$$

Since this last relation holds throughout space we must have

$$\frac{\partial U_i}{\partial t} + \frac{\partial S_{ik}}{\partial x_k} = 0 \tag{82.15}$$

i.e. the harmonic conditions are satisfied. When we obtain the explicit expressions for the S_{ik} we shall be able to verify by direct substitution that (82.15) is valid.

We shall seek to find the functions S_{ik} in the form

$$S_{ik} = U_{ik} + V_{ik} \tag{82.16}$$

where U_{ik} and V_{ik} satisfy the equations

$$\Delta U_{ik} = -4\pi\gamma(\rho v_i v_k - p_{ik}) \tag{82.17}$$

and

$$\Delta V_{ik} = Q_{ik} \tag{82.18}$$

Inserting the expression

$$U = \sum_a u_a \tag{82.19}$$

for the Newtonian potential into the equation (82.09) for Q_{ik} we can write

$$Q_{ik} = \sum_a Q_{ik}^{(aa)} + \sum_{a \neq b} Q_{ik}^{(ab)} \tag{82.20}$$

where†

$$Q_{ik}^{(aa)} = \tfrac{1}{2}\delta_{ik}(\operatorname{grad} u_a)^2 - \frac{\partial u_a}{\partial x_i}\frac{\partial u_a}{\partial x_k} \tag{82.21}$$

and

$$Q_{ik}^{(ab)} = \tfrac{1}{2}\delta_{ik}(\operatorname{grad} u_a \cdot \operatorname{grad} u_b) - \tfrac{1}{2}\left(\frac{\partial u_a}{\partial x_i}\frac{\partial u_b}{\partial x_k} + \frac{\partial u_a}{\partial x_k}\frac{\partial u_b}{\partial x_i}\right) \tag{82.22}$$

In accordance with (82.20) we assume that the solution V_{ik} of (82.18) is of the form

$$V_{ik} = \sum_a V_{ik}^{(aa)} + \sum_{a \neq b} V_{ik}^{(ab)} \tag{82.23}$$

with the separate terms satisfying the equations

$$\Delta V_{ik}^{(aa)} = Q_{ik}^{(aa)} \tag{82.24}$$

and

$$\Delta V_{ik}^{(ab)} = Q_{ik}^{(ab)} \tag{82.25}$$

We shall find explicit solutions of these last equations for the case of non-rotating, spherically symmetric masses. In this case the Newtonian potential of mass (a) in the space outside that mass is

$$u_a = \frac{\gamma M_a}{|\mathbf{r} - \mathbf{a}|} \tag{82.26}$$

and the expressions (82.21) and (82.22) for the $Q_{ik}^{(aa)}$ and the $Q_{ik}^{(ab)}$ take on the form

$$Q_{ik}^{(aa)} = \gamma^2 M_a^2\left\{\tfrac{1}{2}\frac{\delta_{ik}}{|\mathbf{r} - \mathbf{a}|^4} - \frac{(x_i - a_i)(x_k - a_k)}{|\mathbf{r} - \mathbf{a}|^6}\right\} \tag{82.27}$$

$$Q_{ik}^{(ab)} = \gamma^2 M_a M_b \tfrac{1}{2}\left\{\frac{(x_j - a_j)(x_j - b_j)}{|\mathbf{r} - \mathbf{a}|^3|\mathbf{r} - \mathbf{b}|^3}\delta_{ik}\right.$$
$$\left. - \frac{(x_i - a_i)(x_k - b_k) + (x_i - b_i)(x_k - a_k)}{|\mathbf{r} - \mathbf{a}|^3|\mathbf{r} - \mathbf{b}|^3}\right\} \tag{82.28}$$

These expressions are valid outside the masses. Within the masses one must, strictly speaking, use the more accurate expressions (82.21) and (82.22).

However, the difference between the exact and the approximate values of the $Q_{ik}^{(ab)}$ will not appreciably influence the values of the V_{ik}, at least in the case that the linear dimensions of the masses are small in comparison with their mutual distances. Therefore we shall take the quantity $Q_{ik}^{(ab)}$ appearing on the right-hand side of (82.25) to be given by the expression (82.28) throughout space. At the points $\mathbf{r} = \mathbf{a}$ and $\mathbf{r} = \mathbf{b}$ this expression has singularities that are

---

† In Section 71 the quantity now called $Q_{ik}^{(aa)}$ was denoted by $q_{ik}^{(a)}$.

no higher than of dipole character. Consequently, the equation (82.25) for $V_{ik}^{(ab)}$ will have a solution which remains finite throughout space, including the points $\mathbf{r} = \mathbf{a}$ and $\mathbf{r} = \mathbf{b}$ and which tends to zero at infinity.

This solution can be given in closed form. To do this we express the quantity (82.28) in terms of derivatives of the function $1/|\mathbf{r} - \mathbf{a}| \, |\mathbf{r} - \mathbf{b}|$ with respect to the parameters a_i and b_j. We have

$$Q_{ik}^{(ab)} = \gamma^2 \frac{M_a M_b}{2} \left(\delta_{ik} \frac{\partial^2}{\partial a_j \, \partial b_j} - \frac{\partial^2}{\partial a_i \, \partial b_k} - \frac{\partial^2}{\partial a_k \, \partial b_i} \right) \frac{1}{|\mathbf{r} - \mathbf{a}| \, |\mathbf{r} - \mathbf{b}|} \tag{82.29}$$

Therefore (82.25) may be reduced to the simpler equation

$$\Delta \varphi = \frac{1}{|\mathbf{r} - \mathbf{a}| \, |\mathbf{r} - \mathbf{b}|} \tag{82.30}$$

Indeed, if φ is a solution of (82.30) then the quantity

$$V_{ik}^{(ab)} = \frac{\gamma^2 M_a M_b}{2} \left(\delta_{ik} \frac{\partial^2 \varphi}{\partial a_j \, \partial b_j} - \frac{\partial^2 \varphi}{\partial a_i \, \partial b_k} - \frac{\partial^2 \varphi}{\partial a_k \, \partial b_i} \right) \tag{82.31}$$

is a solution of (82.25).

Now, it is simple to write down the required solution of (82.30). We denote by s the perimeter of the triangle whose vertices are at the points $\mathbf{a}$, $\mathbf{b}$ and $\mathbf{r}$:

$$s = |\mathbf{r} - \mathbf{a}| + |\mathbf{r} - \mathbf{b}| + |\mathbf{a} - \mathbf{b}| \tag{82.32}$$

Then the function

$$\varphi = \log s = \log \left(|\mathbf{r} - \mathbf{a}| + |\mathbf{r} - \mathbf{b}| + |\mathbf{a} - \mathbf{b}| \right) \tag{82.33}$$

satisfies (82.30), for we have

$$\Delta \log s = \frac{1}{|\mathbf{r} - \mathbf{a}| \, |\mathbf{r} - \mathbf{b}|} \tag{82.34}$$

Therefore the required solution of (82.25) has the form

$$V_{ik}^{(ab)} = \frac{\gamma^2 M_a M_b}{2} \left(\delta_{ik} \frac{\partial^2 \log s}{\partial a_j \, \partial b_j} - \frac{\partial^2 \log s}{\partial a_i \, \partial b_k} - \frac{\partial^2 \log s}{\partial a_k \, \partial b_i} \right) \tag{82.35}$$

It is easy to verify that this expression remains finite everywhere and tends to zero at infinity.

We now turn to the equation (82.24) for $V_{ik}^{(aa)}$. Shifting the origin of coordinates to the point $\mathbf{a}$ and using the spherical symmetry of our problem we can write the equation as

$$\Delta V_{ik}^{(aa)} = \left(\tfrac{1}{2} \delta_{ik} - \frac{x_i x_k}{r^2} \right) u'(r)^2 \tag{82.36}$$

For brevity we have put

$$u_a = u(r) \tag{82.37}$$

We try to find a solution of (82.36) of the form

$$V_{ik}^{(aa)} = - \delta_{ik} q_0(r) + \left(x_i x_k - \tfrac{1}{3} \delta_{ik} r^2 \right) q_2(r) \tag{82.38}$$

Then q_0 and q_2 must satisfy the equations

$$\frac{d^2 q_0}{dr^2} + \frac{2}{r}\frac{dq_0}{dr} = -\frac{1}{6}u'(r)^2 \tag{82.39}$$

and

$$\frac{d^2 q_2}{dr^2} + \frac{6}{r}\frac{dq_2}{dr} = -\frac{1}{r^2}u'(r)^2 \tag{82.40}$$

Hence, using the boundary conditions, we obtain

$$q_0(r) = \frac{1}{6}\int_r^\infty ru'(r)^2\,dr + \frac{1}{6r}\int_0^r r^2 u'(r)^2\,dr \tag{82.41}$$

and

$$q_2(r) = \frac{1}{5}\int_r^\infty \frac{1}{r}u'(r)^2\,dr + \frac{1}{5r^5}\int_0^r r^4 u'(r)^2\,dr \tag{82.42}$$

If the radius of the body is L we have for $r > L$:

$$u(r) = \frac{\gamma M_a}{r} \tag{82.43}$$

and the expressions for $q_0(r)$ and $q_2(r)$ reduce to the following:

$$q_0(r) = -\frac{\gamma^2 M_a^2}{12r^2} + \frac{\gamma \varepsilon_a}{3r} \tag{82.44}$$

and

$$q_2(r) = \frac{\gamma^2 M_a^2}{4r^4} - \frac{\gamma^2 M_a^2}{5r^5}\lambda_a \tag{82.45}$$

Here

$$\lambda_a = L - \frac{1}{\gamma^2 M_a^2}\int_0^L r^4 u'(r)^2\,dr \tag{82.46}$$

is a length of the order of L and the quantity

$$\varepsilon_a = \frac{1}{8\pi\gamma}\int (\text{grad } u_a)^2(dx)^3 = \frac{1}{2\gamma}\int_0^\infty r^2 u'(r)^2\,dr \tag{82.47}$$

is the negative of the gravitational energy of the body. If we insert the expressions obtained for $q_0(r)$ and $q_2(r)$ into (82.38) we get

$$V_{ik}^{(aa)} = \frac{\gamma^2 M_a^2 x_i x_k}{4r^4} - \frac{1}{3}\delta_{ik}\frac{\gamma \varepsilon_a}{r} - \frac{\gamma^2 M_a^2 \lambda_a}{5r^5}\left(x_i x_k - \frac{1}{3}\delta_{ik}r^2\right) \tag{82.48}$$

or if we return to our original variables by replacing x_i by $x_i - a_i$:

$$V_{ik}^{(aa)} = \frac{\gamma^2 M_a^2(x_i - a_i)(x_k - a_k)}{4|\mathbf{r} - \mathbf{a}|^4} - \frac{1}{3}\delta_{ik}\frac{\gamma \varepsilon_a}{|\mathbf{r} - \mathbf{a}|}$$

$$- \frac{\gamma^2 M_a^2 \lambda_a}{5|\mathbf{r} - \mathbf{a}|^5}\left[(x_i - a_i)(x_k - a_k) - \frac{1}{3}\delta_{ik}(\mathbf{r} - \mathbf{a})^2\right] \tag{82.49}$$

Here the last term is small compared to the first as long as the distance from body (a) is great compared to its radius. Strictly speaking that term should be discarded because the same approximation has already been used in calculating $V_{ik}^{(ab)}$.

It remains to write down the solution of (82.17). For non-rotating masses we can put

$$v_i = \dot{a}_i; \qquad p_{ik} = -p\delta_{ik} \tag{82.50}$$

with p determined from the equations

$$dp = \rho \, du_a \tag{82.51}$$

whereby, according to (74.24)

$$\int_{(a)} p(dx)^3 = \tfrac{1}{3} \varepsilon_a \tag{82.52}$$

We then have

$$U_{ik} = \sum_a \frac{\gamma M_a \dot{a}_i \dot{a}_k}{|\mathbf{r} - \mathbf{a}|} + \sum_a \tfrac{1}{3} \delta_{ik} \frac{\gamma \varepsilon_a}{|\mathbf{r} - \mathbf{a}|} \tag{82.53}$$

Here the dipole terms are zero because of the spherical symmetry of the bodies and terms of higher order in L/R (i.e. of the same order as the last term in (82.49)) will be discarded.

We now put

$$S_{ik}^{(aa)} = \frac{\gamma M_a \dot{a}_i \dot{a}_k}{|\mathbf{r} - \mathbf{a}|} + \frac{\gamma^2 M_a^2 (x_i - a_i)(x_k - a_k)}{4 |\mathbf{r} - \mathbf{a}|^4} \tag{82.54}$$

and

$$S_{ik}^{(ab)} = V_{ik}^{(ab)} = \frac{\gamma^2 M_a M_b}{2} \left(\delta_{ik} \frac{\partial^2 \log s}{\partial a_j \, \partial b_j} - \frac{\partial^2 \log s}{\partial a_i \, \partial b_k} - \frac{\partial^2 \log s}{\partial a_k \, \partial b_i} \right) \tag{82.55}$$

Denoting by S_{ik} the sum

$$S_{ik} = \sum S_{ik}^{(aa)} + \sum_{a \neq b} S_{ik}^{(ab)} \tag{82.56}$$

and inserting this expression into the equation

$$\mathfrak{g}^{ik} = -c\delta_{ik} + \frac{4}{c^3} S_{ik} \tag{82.03}$$

we obtain explicit expressions for the spatial components of the metric tensor. These expressions are also valid in the region of the system itself, outside the actual masses.

For the mixed components of the metric tensor we had the approximate expression

$$\mathfrak{g}^{0i} = \frac{4}{c^3} U_i \tag{82.57}$$

where U_i is a solution of (82.11) which, in the approximation considered, is equal to

$$U_i = \sum_a \frac{\gamma M_a \dot{a}_i}{|\mathbf{r} - \mathbf{a}|} \tag{82.58}$$

(see equation (76.23)).

We can now verify that the explicit expressions found for S_{ik} and for U_i satisfy the harmonic condition (82.15). We have

$$\frac{\partial U_i}{\partial t} + \sum_a \frac{\partial S_{ik}^{(aa)}}{\partial x_k} = \sum_a \frac{\gamma M_a \ddot{a}_i}{|\mathbf{r} - \mathbf{a}|} \tag{82.59}$$

Also, using the relation

$$\frac{\partial^2 \log s}{\partial a_j \, \partial b_j} = - \frac{(|\mathbf{r} - \mathbf{a}| + |\mathbf{r} - \mathbf{b}| - |\mathbf{a} - \mathbf{b}|)}{2|\mathbf{r} - \mathbf{a}| \, |\mathbf{r} - \mathbf{b}| \, |\mathbf{a} - \mathbf{b}|} \tag{82.60}$$

and the two further relations that may be obtained from (82.60) by permutation of the letters $\mathbf{a}$, $\mathbf{b}$ and $\mathbf{r}$, we can verify that

$$\frac{\partial S_{ik}^{(ab)}}{\partial x_k} = \tfrac{1}{2}\gamma^2 M_a M_b \frac{a_i - b_i}{|\mathbf{a} - \mathbf{b}|^3} \left(\frac{1}{|\mathbf{r} - \mathbf{a}|} - \frac{1}{|\mathbf{r} - \mathbf{b}|} \right) \tag{82.61}$$

Summing this expression over a and b we get

$$\sum_{a \neq b} \frac{\partial S_{ik}^{(ab)}}{\partial x_k} = \sum_{a \neq b} \gamma^2 M_a M_b \frac{(a_i - b_i)}{|\mathbf{a} - \mathbf{b}|^3} \frac{1}{|\mathbf{r} - \mathbf{a}|} \tag{82.62}$$

Hence, putting

$$\Phi = -\tfrac{1}{2} \sum_{a \neq b} \frac{\gamma M_a M_b}{|\mathbf{a} - \mathbf{b}|} \tag{82.63}$$

we have

$$\sum_{a \neq b} \frac{\partial S_{ik}^{(ab)}}{\partial x_k} = \sum_a \frac{\gamma}{|\mathbf{r} - \mathbf{a}|} \frac{\partial \Phi}{\partial a_i} \tag{82.64}$$

Combination of (82.59) and (82.64) finally gives

$$\frac{\partial U_i}{\partial t} + \frac{\partial S_{ik}}{\partial x_k} = \sum_a \frac{\gamma}{|\mathbf{r} - \mathbf{a}|} \left(M_a \ddot{a}_i + \frac{\partial \Phi}{\partial a_i} \right) \tag{82.65}$$

Now, Φ is the Newtonian potential energy of the bodies. Therefore

$$M_a \ddot{a}_i + \frac{\partial \Phi}{\partial a_i} = 0 \tag{82.66}$$

by virtue of Newton's equations of motion. Hence the entire expression (82.65) will vanish, in agreement with (82.15). By reversing the argument (as was done in our paper of 1939[34]) we could have derived Newton's equations of motion (82.66) from (82.15) and (82.65).

83. The Gravitational Potentials for Non-Rotating Bodies (Mixed and Temporal Components)

We now derive expressions for the mixed components $\mathfrak{g}^{0i}$ of the gravitational potential to the next approximation beyond that represented by equations (82.57) and (82.58). We must put $\mu = 0$ and $\nu = i$ in (82.06) and insert into that equation the value of N^{0i} given by (68.15) and the value of T^{0i} given by

(66.07), but with the simplification that the stress p_{ik} reduces to an isotropic pressure p and that the velocities $v_i = \dot{a}_i$ within each body are constant. We write equation (68.15) for N^{oi} in the form

$$N^{oi} = -\frac{2}{c^6} Q_i \tag{83.01}$$

where $$Q_i = -3 \frac{\partial U}{\partial t} \frac{\partial U}{\partial x_i} + 4\left(\frac{\partial U_i}{\partial x_j} - \frac{\partial U_j}{\partial x_i}\right)\frac{\partial U}{\partial x_j} \tag{83.02}$$

Equation (82.06) then appears as

$$\frac{1}{2c}\Delta g^{oi} - \frac{1}{2c^3}\frac{\partial^2 g^{oi}}{\partial t^2} = \frac{2}{c^6}Q_i - \frac{8\pi\gamma}{c^4}(c^2 + 4U)T^{oi} \tag{83.03}$$

where, according to (66.07), we have for isotropic pressure :

$$(c^2 + 4U)T^{oi} = v_i\left(\rho + \frac{\rho}{c^2}(\tfrac{1}{2}v^2 + \Pi + 3U) + \frac{p}{c^2}\right) \tag{83.04}$$

If we insert into (83.03) the expression

$$g^{oi} = \frac{4U_i}{c^3} + \frac{4S_i}{c^5} \tag{83.05}$$

for g^{oi} we can satisfy that equation if we demand that

$$\Delta U_i - \frac{1}{c^2}\frac{\partial^2 U_i}{\partial t^2} = -4\pi\gamma(c^2 + 4U)T^{oi} \tag{83.06}$$

and $$\Delta S_i - \frac{1}{c^2}\frac{\partial^2 S_i}{\partial t^2} = Q_i \tag{83.07}$$

Since these expressions involve the speed of light as a parameter the quantities U_i and S_i will no longer be coefficients in the expansion of g^{oi} in inverse powers of c. However, this inconsistency in their definition is unimportant because equation (83.06) for U_i coincides to first approximation with (82.11).

To write down the solution of (83.06) for the region outside the masses we must know the value of the volume integral of the right-hand side of that equation taken over the volume of each mass. To evaluate this integral we recall the relation

$$\rho\Pi - \rho u_a + p = 0 \tag{83.08}$$

to which equation (73.26) reduces in the absence of rotation. According to (74.07) and (74.24) we have

$$\int_{(a)} \rho u_a (dx)^3 = 2\varepsilon_a ; \qquad \int_{(a)} p(dx)^3 = \tfrac{1}{3}\varepsilon_a \tag{83.09}$$

Hence (83.08) gives the relation

$$\int_{(a)} \rho\Pi(dx)^3 = \tfrac{5}{3}\varepsilon_a \tag{83.10}$$

Using these results we obtain

$$\int_{(a)} (c^2 + 4U)T^{oi}(dx)^3 = M_a\dot{a}_i\left\{1 + \frac{1}{c^2}[\tfrac{1}{2}v_a^2 + 3U^{(a)}(a)]\right\} + \frac{8}{c^2}\varepsilon_a\dot{a}_i \tag{83.11}$$

where $U^{(a)}$ is the external potential introduced in Section 71. Here the evaluation is much simpler than in Section 76 because we do not consider rotations.

We note that the quantity (83.10) is the internal (elastic) energy of the body. Since its gravitational energy is the negative of ε_a the sum of the two quantities, $(2/3)\varepsilon_a$, is the energy that must be taken in calculating the effective mass. The latter will be†

$$m_a = M_a + \frac{2}{3}\frac{\varepsilon_a}{c^2} \tag{83.12}$$

in agreement with (76.18) and (80.18).

Using (83.11) we can write the approximate solution of (83.06) in the form

$$U_i = \sum_a \frac{\gamma \dot{a}_i}{|\mathbf{r}-\mathbf{a}|}\left\{M_a + \frac{M_a}{c^2}[\tfrac{1}{2}v_a^2 + 3U^{(a)}(\mathbf{a})] + \frac{8\varepsilon_a}{c^2}\right\}$$
$$+ \frac{1}{2c^2}\frac{\partial^2}{\partial t^2}\sum_a \gamma M_a \dot{a}_i|\mathbf{r}-\mathbf{a}| \tag{83.13}$$

Here the last term represents a retardation correction.

We now pass to the equation (83.07) for S_i. Here the second derivative with respect to time may be neglected so that the equation takes on the form

$$\Delta S_i = Q_i \tag{83.14}$$

As in (82.20) the quantity Q_i can be decomposed in the form

$$Q_i = \sum_a Q_i^{(aa)} + \sum_{a \neq b} Q_i^{(ab)} \tag{83.15}$$

where $Q_i^{(aa)}$ is a quadratic function of the first derivatives of the potential of mass (a) and $Q_i^{(ab)}$ is a bilinear function of first derivatives of the potentials of two masses (a) and (b). Corresponding to this decomposition the solution of (83.14) can be written in the form

$$S_i = \sum_a S_i^{(aa)} + \sum_{a \neq b} S_i^{(ab)} \tag{83.16}$$

with the separate terms satisfying

$$\Delta S_i^{(aa)} = Q_i^{(aa)} \tag{83.17}$$

and

$$\Delta S_i^{(ab)} = Q_i^{(ab)} \tag{83.18}$$

For $Q_i^{(aa)}$ we take an expression analogous to (82.21) which is valid even within the mass in question :

$$Q_i^{(aa)} = \dot{a}_j\left\{-\frac{\partial u_a}{\partial x_i}\frac{\partial u_a}{\partial x_j} + 4\delta_{ij}(\operatorname{grad} u_a)^2\right\} \tag{83.19}$$

For $Q_i^{(ab)}$ we confine ourselves to an expression that is correct outside the masses and is analogous to (82.28), namely

$$Q_i^{(ab)} = \tfrac{1}{2}\gamma^2 M_a M_b\left\{(3\dot{a}_j - 4\dot{b}_j)\frac{(x_j - a_j)(x_i - b_i)}{|\mathbf{r}-\mathbf{a}|^3\,|\mathbf{r}-\mathbf{b}|^3}\right.$$
$$\left. + (3\dot{b}_j - 4\dot{a}_j)\frac{(x_i - a_i)(x_j - b_j)}{|\mathbf{r}-\mathbf{a}|^3|\mathbf{r}-\mathbf{b}|^3} + 4(\dot{a}_i + \dot{b}_i)\frac{(x_j - a_j)(x_j - b_j)}{|\mathbf{r}-\mathbf{a}|^3|\mathbf{r}-\mathbf{b}|^3}\right\} \tag{83.20}$$

† It is important to bear in mind the relation (83.12) when comparing the present equations with those of our 1939 paper [34].

To solve (83.17) we express its right-hand side in the form

$$Q_i^{(aa)} = \dot{a}_j Q_{ij}^{(aa)} + 7\dot{a}_i Q_{jj}^{(aa)} \tag{83.21}$$

where the $Q_{ij}^{(aa)}$ are the same as in Section 82. It evidently has the solution

$$S_i^{(aa)} = \dot{a}_j V_{ij}^{(aa)} + 7\dot{a}_i V_{jj}^{(aa)} \tag{83.22}$$

where $V_{ij}^{(aa)}$ is the previously determined solution (82.38) or (82.49) of equation (82.24).

Passing on to equation (83.18) we represent its right-hand side, i.e. the expression (83.20), in the form

$$Q_i^{(ab)} = \frac{1}{2}\gamma^2 M_a M_b \left\{ (3\dot{a}_j - 4b_j)\frac{\partial^2}{\partial a_j\,\partial b_i} + (3b_j - 4\dot{a}_j)\frac{\partial^2}{\partial a_i\,\partial b_j} + 4(\dot{a}_i + b_i)\frac{\partial^2}{\partial a_j\,\partial b_j} \right\}$$

$$\times \frac{1}{|\mathbf{r}-\mathbf{a}|\,|\mathbf{r}-\mathbf{b}|} \tag{83.23}$$

It follows from (82.34) that (83.18) is solved by

$$S_i^{(ab)} = \frac{1}{2}\gamma^2 M_a M_b \left\{ (3\dot{a}_j - 4b_j)\frac{\partial^2 \log s}{\partial a_j\,\partial b_i} \right.$$

$$\left. + (3b_j - 4\dot{a}_j)\frac{\partial^2 \log s}{\partial a_i\,\partial b_j} + 4(\dot{a}_i + b_i)\frac{\partial^2 \log s}{\partial a_j\,\partial b_j} \right\} \tag{83.24}$$

We shall also write down the value of $S_i^{(aa)}$ outside the masses. To do this we must insert the value (82.49) of $V_{ij}^{(aa)}$ into (83.22). The terms containing λ_a rapidly tend to zero at large distances and can be omitted. In the expression so obtained for $S_i^{(aa)}$ it is convenient to separate off a harmonic term, writing

$$S_i^{(aa)} = -\frac{22}{3}\dot{a}_i \frac{\gamma\varepsilon_a}{|\mathbf{r}-\mathbf{a}|} + \bar{S}_i^{(aa)} \tag{83.25}$$

where

$$\bar{S}_i^{(aa)} = \gamma^2 M_a^2 \left\{ \dot{a}_j \frac{(x_i - a_i)(x_j - a_j)}{4|\mathbf{r}-\mathbf{a}|^4} + \frac{7}{4}\frac{\dot{a}_i}{|\mathbf{r}-\mathbf{a}|^2} \right\} \tag{83.26}$$

Insertion of these expressions into (83.16) gives the value of S_i which can be combined with the value (83.13) of U_i to determine $\mathfrak{g}^{0i}$ from (83.05). The equation for $\mathfrak{g}^{0i}$ may be written in the form

$$\mathfrak{g}^{0i} = \frac{4\bar{U}_i}{c^3} + \frac{4\bar{S}_i}{c^5} \tag{83.27}$$

where $\bar{U}_i = \sum_a \frac{\gamma\dot{a}_i}{|\mathbf{r}-\mathbf{a}|}\left\{ M_a + \frac{2\varepsilon_a}{3c^2} + \frac{M_a}{c^2}[\frac{1}{2}v_a^2 + 3U^{(a)}(\mathbf{a})] \right\}$

$$+ \frac{1}{2c^2}\frac{\partial^2}{\partial t^2}\sum_a \gamma M_a \dot{a}_i |\mathbf{r}-\mathbf{a}| \tag{83.28}$$

and

$$\bar{S}_i = \sum_a \bar{S}_i^{(aa)} + \sum_{a\neq b} S_i^{(ab)} \tag{83.29}$$

Here the quantities $\bar{U}_i$ and $\bar{S}_i$ differ respectively from U_i and S_i by harmonic terms containing ε_a. We note that ε_a enters $\bar{U}_i$ only through the effective mass (83.12). The sum $\bar{S}_i$ is a homogeneous quadratic function of the masses, whereas $\bar{U}_i$ depends on them linearly (apart from terms containing $U^{(a)}(\mathbf{a})$).

It remains for us to find an explicit expression for the temporal component of the gravitational potential, i.e. for the quantity $\mathfrak{g}^{00}$. In Section 68 we have already written down the equations determining $\mathfrak{g}^{00}$. By (68.43) and (68.41) we have

$$\mathfrak{g}^{00} = \frac{1}{c} + \frac{4}{c^3}\,\bar{U} + \frac{7}{c^5}\,\bar{U}^2 \tag{83.30}$$

where $\bar{U}$ is a generalized Newtonian potential satisfying the equation

$$\Delta\bar{U} - \frac{1}{c^2}\frac{\partial^2\bar{U}}{\partial t^2} = -4\pi\gamma\,(c^2 + \tfrac{1}{2}U)\,T^{00} \tag{83.31}$$

This equation has on its right-hand side the expression

$$(c^2 + \tfrac{1}{2}U)T^{00} = \rho + \frac{\rho}{c^2}\,(\tfrac{1}{2}v^2 + \Pi - \tfrac{1}{2}U) \tag{83.32}$$

which follows from (66.07) and was used in Section 79. The potential $\bar{U}$ can be evaluated in a manner similar to the procedure followed for U in Section 77, with the simplification that now the masses are taken to be spherically symmetric and non-rotating. Using (83.09) and (83.10) we get

$$\int_{(a)} (c^2 + \tfrac{1}{2}U)T^{00}(dx)^3 = M_a + \frac{2}{3c^2}\,\varepsilon_a + \frac{M_a}{2c^2}\,\{v_a^2 - U^{(a)}\,(\mathbf{a})\} \tag{83.33}$$

and therefore

$$\bar{U} = \sum_a \frac{\gamma}{|\mathbf{r} - \mathbf{a}|}\left(M_a + \frac{2}{3c^2}\,\varepsilon_a + \frac{M_a}{2c^2}\,\{v_a^2 - U^{(a)}\,(\mathbf{a})\}\right)$$
$$+ \frac{1}{2c^2}\frac{\partial^2}{\partial t^2}\sum_a \gamma M_a|\mathbf{r} - \mathbf{a}| \tag{83.34}$$

Insertion of this expression into (83.30) gives $\mathfrak{g}^{00}$. This concludes the determination of the gravitational potentials in second approximation.

We must still verify that the expressions obtained for $\mathfrak{g}^{00}$ and $\mathfrak{g}^{0i}$ satisfy the harmonic condition

$$\frac{\partial\mathfrak{g}^{00}}{\partial t} + \frac{\partial\mathfrak{g}^{0i}}{\partial x_i} = 0 \tag{83.35}$$

Differentiation of the expressions (83.34) and (83.28) for $\bar{U}$ and $\bar{U}_i$ gives directly

$$\frac{\partial\bar{U}}{\partial t} + \frac{\partial\bar{U}_i}{\partial x_i} = \frac{7}{2c^2}\frac{\partial}{\partial x_i}\sum_a \frac{\gamma M_a \dot{a}_i U^{(a)}\,(\mathbf{a})}{|\mathbf{r} - \mathbf{a}|} + \frac{1}{c^2}\sum_a \frac{\gamma M_a}{|\mathbf{r} - \mathbf{a}|}\left(\dot{a}_i\ddot{a}_i - \frac{1}{2}\frac{dU^{(a)}\,(\mathbf{a})}{dt}\right) \tag{83.36}$$

Further we have by (83.26)

$$\frac{\partial\bar{S}_i^{(aa)}}{\partial x_i} = -\frac{7}{4}\frac{\partial}{\partial t}\frac{\gamma^2 M_a^2}{|\mathbf{r} - \mathbf{a}|^2} \tag{83.37}$$

In calculating the expression

$$\frac{\partial S_i^{(ab)}}{\partial x_i} = \frac{1}{2}\,\gamma^2 M_a M_b$$
$$\times\left\{(3\dot{a}_j - 4\dot{b}_j)\frac{\partial}{\partial a_j}\frac{\partial^2\log s}{\partial b_i\,\partial x_i} + (3\dot{b}_j - 4\dot{a}_j)\frac{\partial}{\partial b_j}\frac{\partial^2\log s}{\partial a_i\,\partial x_i} + 4(\dot{a}_j + \dot{b}_j)\frac{\partial}{\partial x_j}\frac{\partial^2\log s}{\partial a_i\,\partial b_i}\right\} \tag{83.38}$$

we must use equation (82.60) and two further equations obtained from it by permutation of a, b and x; in addition we must bear in mind when transforming (83.38) that log s and its derivatives depend only on coordinate differences, so that, for instance

$$\left(\frac{\partial}{\partial a_j} + \frac{\partial}{\partial b_j} + \frac{\partial}{\partial x_j}\right)\log s = 0 \tag{83.39}$$

We can combine all terms in (83.38) which contain $|\mathbf{r} - \mathbf{a}|\,|\mathbf{r} - \mathbf{b}|$, then terms containing $|\mathbf{r} - \mathbf{a}|\,|\mathbf{a} - \mathbf{b}|$ and finally terms containing $|\mathbf{r} - \mathbf{b}|\,|\mathbf{a} - \mathbf{b}|$, getting

$$\frac{\partial S_i^{(ab)}}{\partial x_i} = \frac{1}{4}\,\gamma^2 M_a M_b\left\{-7\dot{a}_j\frac{\partial}{\partial a_j} - 7b_j\frac{\partial}{\partial b_j}\right\}\frac{1}{|\mathbf{r} - \mathbf{a}|\,|\mathbf{r} - \mathbf{b}|}$$

$$+ \frac{1}{4}\,\gamma^2 M_a M_b\left\{-7\dot{a}_j\frac{\partial}{\partial x_j} + (\dot{a}_j + b_j)\frac{\partial}{\partial b_j}\right\}\frac{1}{|\mathbf{r} - \mathbf{a}|\,|\mathbf{a} - \mathbf{b}|}$$

$$+ \frac{1}{4}\,\gamma^2 M_a M_b\left\{-7b_j\frac{\partial}{\partial x_j} + (\dot{a}_j + b_j)\frac{\partial}{\partial a_j}\right\}\frac{1}{|\mathbf{r} - \mathbf{b}|\,|\mathbf{a} - \mathbf{b}|} \tag{83.40}$$

Summing this expression over a and b (omitting the term $a = b$) and adding to (83.37) summed over a, we get

$$\frac{\partial \bar{S}_i}{\partial x_i} = -\frac{7}{2}\,U\frac{\partial U}{\partial t} - \frac{7}{2}\frac{\partial}{\partial x_i}\sum_a\frac{\gamma M_a \dot{a}_i U^{(a)}(\mathbf{a})}{|\mathbf{r} - \mathbf{a}|}$$

$$+ \sum_a\frac{\gamma M_a}{|\mathbf{r} - \mathbf{a}|}\left\{\frac{1}{2}\frac{dU^{(a)}(\mathbf{a})}{dt} - \dot{a}_i\left(\frac{\partial U^{(a)}(\mathbf{r})}{\partial x_i}\right)_a\right\} \tag{83.41}$$

Now if in equation (83.30) $\bar{U}$ is replaced by U in the correction term the left-hand side of the harmonic condition (83.35) differs only by the factor $4/c^3$ from the expression

$$\frac{\partial \bar{U}}{\partial t} + \frac{\partial \bar{U}_i}{\partial x_i} + \frac{1}{c^2}\left(\frac{7}{2}\,U\frac{\partial U}{\partial t} + \frac{\partial \bar{S}_i}{\partial x_i}\right) = \frac{1}{c^2}\sum_a\frac{\gamma M_a}{|\mathbf{r} - \mathbf{a}|}\,\dot{a}_i\left\{\ddot{a}_i - \left(\frac{\partial U^{(a)}(\mathbf{r})}{\partial x_i}\right)_a\right\} \tag{83.42}$$

which is obtained by adding to (83.36) the expression (83.41) divided by c^2 and transferring one term to the left-hand side.

But we have

$$M_a\left(\frac{\partial U^{(a)}(\mathbf{r})}{\partial x_i}\right)_a = -\frac{\partial \Phi}{\partial a_i} \tag{83.43}$$

where Φ is the Newtonian potential energy

$$\Phi = -\frac{1}{2}\sum_{a \neq b}\gamma\,\frac{M_a M_b}{|\mathbf{a} - \mathbf{b}|} \tag{83.44}$$

Therefore, by virtue of Newton's equations of motion, we have

$$\ddot{a}_i = \left(\frac{\partial U^{(a)}(\mathbf{r})}{\partial x_i}\right)_a \tag{83.45}$$

and the right-hand side of (83.42) vanishes. Thus the harmonic condition (83.35) is satisfied.

In order to obtain for the gravitational potentials not too complicated explicit expressions which remain valid in the region of the masses (though outside the actual masses) we were obliged to limit the discussion of this and the preceding section rather drastically. We had to assume that the masses were spherically symmetric and that they did not rotate. In the following sections, in a discussion of the gravitational potentials at large distances from a system of bodies, we shall free ourselves from these limitations.

84. Gravitational Potentials at Large Distances from a System of Bodies (Spatial Components)

In this section and the next we shall derive explicit expressions for the gravitational potentials which are valid at moderately large distances from a system of bodies. We call distances " moderately large " if they are large compared to the dimensions of the system yet small in comparison with the lengths of the waves radiated by the system (see Section 64). Our assumptions concerning the internal structure of the system will be as general as those used in Section 79 in deriving the integrals of the motion for a system of bodies.

We begin with the determination of the spatial components $\mathfrak{g}^{ik}$. As in Section 82 we have

$$\mathfrak{g}^{ik} = -c\delta_{ik} + \frac{4}{c^3}S_{ik} \tag{84.01}$$

where, as in (82.16) to (82.18),

$$S_{ik} = U_{ik} + V_{ik} \tag{84.02}$$

and the functions U_{ik} and V_{ik} satisfy the equations

$$\Delta U_{ik} = -4\pi\gamma(\rho v_i v_k - p_{ik}) \tag{84.03}$$

and

$$\Delta V_{ik} = \tfrac{1}{2}\delta_{ik}\,(\operatorname{grad} U)^2 - \frac{\partial U}{\partial x_i}\frac{\partial U}{\partial x_k} \tag{84.04}$$

The right-hand side of (84.03) differs from zero only within the masses and, using mathematical terminology, it has moments of all orders (see Section 70). This means that if it is multiplied by a product of coordinates of any order and then integrated over all space, the integral is convergent. It is, therefore, possible to write a solution of (84.03) valid outside the system of masses as a series of spherical harmonics, i.e. as a multipole expansion. We shall take as the origin of coordinates some point within the system of masses, not necessarily their mass centre. We obtain

$$U_{ik} = U_{ik}^0 + U_{ik}^{(1)} + \dots \tag{84.05}$$

where the first two terms are

$$U_{ik}^0 = \frac{\gamma}{r}\int (\rho v_i v_k - p_{ik})(dx)^3 \tag{84.06}$$

and

$$U_{ik}^{(1)} = \frac{\gamma x_j}{r^3}\int (\rho v_i v_k - p_{ik})x_j(dx)^3 \tag{84.07}$$

On the other hand the right-hand side of (84.04) is different from zero throughout space and only decreases as the inverse fourth power of distance. Therefore only a zero order moment exists and the solution of the equation cannot be represented as a series similar to (84.05).

To find a solution of (84.04) we introduce into its right-hand side the integral representation of the Newtonian potential

$$U = \gamma \int \frac{\rho' \, (dx')^3}{|\mathbf{r} - \mathbf{r}'|} \tag{84.08}$$

We then obtain a relation which may be written as

$$\Delta V_{ik} = \frac{1}{2} \gamma^2 \int \int \rho' \, (dx')^3 \rho'' \, (dx'')^3$$

$$\left\{ \delta_{ik} \frac{\partial^2}{\partial x'_l \, \partial x''_l} - \frac{\partial^2}{\partial x'_i \, \partial x''_k} - \frac{\partial^2}{\partial x'_k \, \partial x''_i} \right\} \frac{1}{|\mathbf{r} - \mathbf{r}'| \, |\mathbf{r} - \mathbf{r}''|} \tag{84.09}$$

We know from Section 82 (equations (82.33) and (82.34)) that the function

$$\log s = \log(|\mathbf{r} - \mathbf{r}'| + |\mathbf{r} - \mathbf{r}''| + |\mathbf{r}' - \mathbf{r}''|) \tag{84.10}$$

satisfies the equation

$$\Delta \log s = \frac{1}{|\mathbf{r} - \mathbf{r}'| \, |\mathbf{r} - \mathbf{r}''|} \tag{84.11}$$

Hence it is simple to deduce that the solution of (84.09) that is everywhere finite and that tends to zero at infinity, may be represented in the form

$$V_{ik} = \frac{1}{2} \gamma^2 \int \int \rho' \, (dx')^3 \rho'' \, (dx'')^3 \left\{ \delta_{ik} \frac{\partial^2 \log s}{\partial x'_l \, \partial x''_l} - \frac{\partial^2 \log s}{\partial x'_i \, \partial x''_k} - \frac{\partial^2 \log s}{\partial x'_k \, \partial x''_i} \right\} \tag{84.12}$$

We are interested in the value of this expression at large distances. To evaluate it we must find an expansion of s and of $\log s$ in inverse powers of r which is valid for large r and finite r' and r''. We have

$$s = 2r + \left(|\mathbf{r}' - \mathbf{r}''| - \frac{x_i x'_i}{r} - \frac{x_i x''_i}{r} \right) + \frac{1}{2} \left(x'_i x'_k + x''_i x''_k \right) \left(\frac{\delta_{ik}}{r} - \frac{x_i x_k}{r^3} \right) + \dots \tag{84.13}$$

whence

$$\log s = \log 2r + \frac{1}{2r} \left(|\mathbf{r}' - \mathbf{r}''| - \frac{x_i (x'_i + x''_i)}{r} \right)$$

$$+ \frac{x_j}{4r^3} (x'_j + x''_j) |\mathbf{r}' - \mathbf{r}''| + \frac{1}{8r^2} (r'^2 + r''^2 + 2x'_j x''_j)$$

$$- \frac{x_i x_k}{8r^4} (3x'_i x'_k + 3x''_i x''_k + x''_i x'_k + x'_i x''_k) + \dots \tag{84.14}$$

By differentiation we obtain the symmetrized and antisymmetrized second derivatives with respect to x'_i and x''_k.

$$\frac{1}{2}\left(\frac{\partial^2 \log s}{\partial x'_i \, \partial x''_k} + \frac{\partial^2 \log s}{\partial x''_i \, \partial x'_k}\right) = \frac{1}{4r^2}\left(\delta_{ik} - \frac{x_i x_k}{r^2}\right)$$
$$- \left(\frac{1}{2r} + \frac{x_j(x'_j + x''_j)}{4r^3}\right)\left(\frac{\delta_{ik}}{|\mathbf{r}' - \mathbf{r}''|} - \frac{(x'_i - x''_i)(x'_k - x''_k)}{|\mathbf{r}' - \mathbf{r}''|^3}\right) \qquad (84.15)$$

and

$$\frac{1}{2}\left(\frac{\partial^2 \log s}{\partial x'_i \, \partial x''_k} - \frac{\partial^2 \log s}{\partial x''_i \, \partial x'_k}\right) = \frac{x_k}{4r^3}\frac{x'_i - x''_i}{|\mathbf{r}' - \mathbf{r}''|} - \frac{x_i}{4r^3}\frac{x'_k - x''_k}{|\mathbf{r}' - \mathbf{r}''|} \qquad (84.16)$$

Here we have discarded terms that decrease more rapidly than $1/r^2$. We put $i = l$ and $k = l$ in (84.15) and sum over l. This gives

$$\frac{\partial^2 \log s}{\partial x'_l \, \partial x''_l} = \frac{1}{2r^2} - \left(\frac{1}{r} + \frac{x_j(x'_j + x''_j)}{2r^3}\right)\frac{1}{|\mathbf{r}' - \mathbf{r}''|} \qquad (84.17)$$

in agreement with the exact relation

$$\frac{\partial^2 \log s}{\partial x'_l \, \partial x''_l} = \frac{1}{2|\mathbf{r} - \mathbf{r}'| \, |\mathbf{r} - \mathbf{r}''|} - \frac{1}{2}\left(\frac{1}{|\mathbf{r} - \mathbf{r}'|} + \frac{1}{|\mathbf{r} - \mathbf{r}''|}\right)\frac{1}{|\mathbf{r}' - \mathbf{r}''|} \qquad (84.18)$$

We insert (84.15) and (84.17) into (84.12) and consider first the terms that decrease as $1/r$. Denoting the corresponding terms in V_{ik} by V^0_{ik} we obtain

$$V^0_{ik} = -\frac{\gamma^2}{2r}\int\int \rho' \, (dx')^3 \rho'' \, (dx'')^3 \frac{(x'_i - x''_i)(x'_k - x''_k)}{|\mathbf{r}' - \mathbf{r}''|^3} \qquad (84.19)$$

Only the part of the integrand symmetric in x' and x'' is important. We therefore replace the factor $x'_i - x''_i$ by $2x'_i$ and perform the integration over x''. This gives

$$V^0_{ik} = \frac{\gamma}{r}\int x_i \frac{\partial U}{\partial x_k}\rho \, (dx)^3 \qquad (84.20)$$

or, since this expression is known to be symmetric in i and k

$$V^0_{ik} = \frac{\gamma}{2r}\int\left(x_i \frac{\partial U}{\partial x_k} + x_k \frac{\partial U}{\partial x_i}\right)\rho \, (dx)^3 \qquad (84.21)$$

(see also the lemma in Section 79). We note that this expression is also equal to

$$V^0_{ik} = -\frac{1}{4\pi r}\int\left(\frac{1}{2}\delta_{ik}(\mathrm{grad}\ U)^2 - \frac{\partial U}{\partial x_i}\frac{\partial U}{\partial x_k}\right)(dx)^3 \qquad (84.22)$$

as was to be expected because V_{ik} satisfies (84.04) and the volume integral of the right-hand side of that equation is finite.

We now examine the terms in (84.15) and (84.17) which decrease as $1/r^2$. Among them are some that are independent of x' and x''. These contribute to V_{ik} the quantity

$$V'_{ik} = \frac{\gamma^2 M^2 x_i x_k}{4r^4} \qquad (84.23)$$

where M is the total mass of the system.

The remaining terms of order $1/r^2$ are of dipole character. They are

$$V_{ik}^{(1)} = -\frac{\gamma^2 x_j}{2r^3} \int \rho' \,(dx')^3 \rho'' \,(dx'')^3 \frac{x_j' + x_j''}{2} \frac{(x_i' - x_i'')(x_k' - x_k'')}{|\mathbf{r}' - \mathbf{r}''|^3} \qquad (84.24)$$

But we have the identity

$$[x_i' x_j'(x_k' - x_k'') + x_k' x_j'(x_i' - x_i'') - x_i' x_k'(x_j' - x_j'')]$$
$$+ [x_i'' x_j''(x_k'' - x_k') + x_k'' x_j''(x_i'' - x_i') - x_i'' x_k''(x_j'' - x_j')]$$
$$= (x_j' + x_j'')(x_i' - x_i'')(x_k' - x_k'') \qquad (84.25)$$

in which the two expressions in square brackets on the left are related by the interchange of x' and x''. When performing the integration in (84.24) we can therefore replace the factor (84.25) by twice one of the square brackets. We then perform the integration over the variable that enters the square bracket linearly, so obtaining

$$V_{ik}^{(1)} = \frac{\gamma x_j}{2r^3} \int \left(x_j x_i \frac{\partial U}{\partial x_k} + x_j x_k \frac{\partial U}{\partial x_i} - x_i x_k \frac{\partial U}{\partial x_j} \right) \rho \,(dx)^3 \qquad (84.26)$$

We now combine those terms in U_{ik} and V_{ik} that have the same multipole character. Putting

$$S_{ik}^0 = U_{ik}^0 + V_{ik}^0 \qquad (84.27)$$

and adding (84.06) and (84.21) we get

$$S_{ik}^0 = \frac{\gamma}{2r} \int \left\{ 2\rho v_i v_k \quad 2p_{ik} + \rho \left(x_i \frac{\partial U}{\partial x_k} + x_k \frac{\partial U}{\partial x_i} \right) \right\} (dx)^3 \qquad (84.28)$$

Writing the term involving p_{ik} in the form

$$-2 \int p_{ik}(dx)^3 = \int \left(x_i \frac{\partial p_{jk}}{\partial x_j} + x_k \frac{\partial p_{ji}}{\partial x_j} \right) (dx)^3 \qquad (84.29)$$

and using the equations of motion for the internal problem

$$\rho w_i = \rho \frac{\partial U}{\partial x_i} + \frac{\partial p_{ji}}{\partial x_j} \qquad (84.30)$$

we obtain from (84.28)

$$S_{ik}^0 = \frac{\gamma}{2r} \int \rho(x_i w_k + x_k w_i + 2v_i v_k)(dx)^3 \qquad (84.31)$$

or

$$S_{ik}^0 = \frac{\gamma}{2r} \frac{d^2}{dt^2} \int \rho x_i x_k (dx)^3 \qquad (84.32)$$

Thus, the quantity S_{ik}^0 has been finally transformed to a form involving the second time derivative of the corresponding moment of inertia.

We now transform the quantity

$$S_{ik}^{(t)} = U_{ik}^{(1)} + V_{ik}^{(1)} \qquad (84.33)$$

From (84.07) and (84.26) we get

$$S_{ik}^{(1)} = \frac{\gamma x_j}{2r^3} \int \left\{ 2\rho v_i v_k x_j - 2p_{ik}x_j + \rho\left(x_j x_i \frac{\partial U}{\partial x_k} + x_j x_k \frac{\partial U}{\partial x_i} - x_i x_k \frac{\partial U}{\partial x_j} \right) \right\}(dx)^3 \tag{84.34}$$

Using the identity

$$\frac{\partial}{\partial x_s}(x_j x_i p_{ks} + x_j x_k p_{is} - x_i x_k p_{js}) = 2x_j p_{ik} + x_j x_i \frac{\partial p_{ks}}{\partial x_s} + x_j x_k \frac{\partial p_{is}}{\partial x_s} - x_i x_k \frac{\partial p_{js}}{\partial x_s} \tag{84.35}$$

we represent the integral involving p_{ik} as

$$-2\int p_{ik}x_j(dx)^3 = \int \left(x_j x_i \frac{\partial p_{ks}}{\partial x_s} + x_j x_k \frac{\partial p_{is}}{\partial x_s} - x_i x_k \frac{\partial p_{js}}{\partial x_s} \right)(dx)^3 \tag{84.36}$$

With the aid of the equations of motion (84.30) we can then write

$$S_{ik}^{(1)} = \frac{\gamma x_j}{2r^3} \int \rho(2x_j v_i v_k + x_j x_i w_k + x_j x_k w_i - x_i x_k w_j)(dx)^3 \tag{84.37}$$

or

$$S_{ik}^{(1)} = \frac{\gamma x_j}{2r^3} \frac{d}{dt} \int \rho(x_j x_i v_k + x_j x_k v_i - x_i x_k v_j)(dx)^3 \tag{84.38}$$

Hence, the equation

$$S_{ik} = S_{ik}^{(0)} + S_{ik}^{(1)} + V_{ik}' \tag{84.39}$$

gives us S_{ik} and if we insert this value of S_{ik} into (84.01) we obtain the following final expression for $\mathfrak{g}^{ik}$:

$$\mathfrak{g}^{ik} = -c\delta_{ik} + \frac{2\gamma}{c^3 r} \frac{d^2}{dt^2} \int \rho x_i x_k (dx)^3$$

$$+ \frac{2\gamma x_j}{c^3 r^3} \frac{d}{dt} \int \rho(x_j x_i v_k + x_j x_k v_i - x_i x_k v_j)(dx)^3 + \frac{\gamma^2 M^2 x_i x_k}{c^3 r^4} \tag{84.40}$$

We have obtained explicit expressions for the spatial components of the gravitational potential which are valid at large distances (in the sense defined above), from the system of bodies. Among the terms containing c^3 in the denominator those have been omitted which decrease more rapidly than $1/r^2$.

We note that for a single concentrated mass the expression (84.40) reduces to that obtained by rigorous solution of the gravitational equations (equation (58.12)).

85. Gravitational Potentials at Large Distances from a System of Bodies (Mixed and Temporal Components)

To determine the mixed components at large distances we return to the equations given at the beginning of Section 83. We have

$$\frac{1}{2c}\Delta\mathfrak{g}^{0i} - \frac{1}{2c^3}\frac{\partial^2 \mathfrak{g}^{0i}}{\partial t^2} = \frac{2}{c^6}Q_i - \frac{8\pi\gamma}{c^4}(c^2 + 4U)T^{0i} \tag{85.01}$$

where

$$Q_i = -3\frac{\partial U}{\partial t}\frac{\partial U}{\partial x_i} + 4\left(\frac{\partial U_i}{\partial x_j} - \frac{\partial U_j}{\partial x_i} \right)\frac{\partial U}{\partial x_j} \tag{85.02}$$

and, according to (66.07)

$$(c^2 + 4U)T^{oi} = \rho v_i \left(1 + \frac{1}{c^2}(\tfrac{1}{2}v^2 + \Pi + 3U)\right) - \frac{1}{c^2}\, p_{ik}v_k \qquad (85.03)$$

As before, we put

$$\mathfrak{g}^{oi} = \frac{4U_i}{c^3} + \frac{4S_i}{c^5} \qquad (85.04)$$

and subject U_i and S_i to the equations

$$\Delta U_i - \frac{1}{c^2}\frac{\partial^2 U_i}{\partial t^2} = -4\pi\gamma(c^2 + 4U)T^{oi} \qquad (85.05)$$

and

$$\Delta S_i - \frac{1}{c^2}\frac{\partial^2 S_i}{\partial t^2} = Q_i \qquad (85.06)$$

As in (75.18) we introduce the quantity

$$W = \frac{1}{2}\gamma \int \rho'|\mathbf{r} - \mathbf{r}'|(dx')^3 \qquad (85.07)$$

and also

$$W_i = \frac{1}{2}\gamma \int (\rho v_i)'|\mathbf{r} - \mathbf{r}'|(dx')^3 \qquad (85.08)$$

We can then write

$$U_i = \gamma \int \frac{\{(c^2 + 4U)T^{oi}\}'}{|\mathbf{r} - \mathbf{r}'|}(dx')^3 + \frac{1}{c^2}\frac{\partial^2 W_i}{\partial t^2} \qquad (85.09)$$

Here the last term is a correction for retardation. We now perform the expansion of the integral into multipoles and confine ourselves to the first two terms and an approximate value of the third term. This gives

$$U_i = \frac{\gamma}{r}\int (c^2 + 4U)T^{oi}(dx)^3 + \frac{\gamma x_j}{r^3}\int (c^2 + 4U)T^{oi}x_j(dx)^3$$

$$+ \frac{\partial^2}{\partial x_j\,\partial x_k}\frac{\gamma}{2r}\int \rho v_i x_j x_k(dx)^3 + \frac{1}{c^2}\frac{\partial^2 W_i}{\partial t^2} \qquad (85.10)$$

In this expression terms containing the momentum and the angular momentum of the system can be separated off. According to (79.19) and (79.34) those constants of the motion can be expressed in terms of the function G_i which, according to (79.18), is related to the quantity in (85.03) by

$$(c^2 + 4U)T^{oi} = G_i + \frac{\rho}{c^2}\left(4U_i + \frac{\partial^2 W_i}{\partial x_i\,\partial t}\right) \qquad (85.11)$$

We then have

$$P_i = \int G_i(dx)^3 \qquad (85.12)$$

and

$$M_{ik} = \int (x_i G_k - x_k G_i)(dx)^3 \qquad (85.13)$$

We shall perform the transformation indicated after we have evaluated S_i because a number of terms in this quantity can be combined with terms of U_i.

In the equation (85.06) for S_i we again neglect the second time derivative and write

$$\Delta S_i = Q_i \qquad (85.14)$$

Just as was done in (84.09), Q_i can be written as a twofold volume integral

$$Q_i = \gamma^2 \int \int (dx')^3 (dx'')^3 (\rho v_k)' \rho'' \left\{ -\frac{1}{2} \left(\frac{\partial^2}{\partial x'_i \, \partial x''_k} + \frac{\partial^2}{\partial x'_k \, \partial x''_i} \right) \right.$$
$$\left. + 4\delta_{ik} \frac{\partial^2}{\partial x'_s \, \partial x''_s} - \frac{7}{2} \left(\frac{\partial^2}{\partial x'_i \, \partial x''_k} - \frac{\partial^2}{\partial x'_k \, \partial x''_i} \right) \right\} \frac{1}{|\mathbf{r} - \mathbf{r}'| \, |\mathbf{r} - \mathbf{r}''|} \quad (85.15)$$

whence we immediately obtain the solution of (85.14) as

$$S_i = \gamma^2 \int \int (dx')^3 (dx'')^3 (\rho v_k)' \rho'' \left\{ -\frac{1}{2} \left(\frac{\partial^2 \log s}{\partial x'_i \, \partial x''_k} + \frac{\partial^2 \log s}{\partial x'_k \, \partial x''_i} \right) \right.$$
$$\left. + 4\delta_{ik} \frac{\partial^2 \log s}{\partial x'_i \, \partial x''_i} - \frac{7}{2} \left(\frac{\partial^2 \log s}{\partial x'_i \, \partial x''_k} - \frac{\partial^2 \log s}{\partial x'_k \, \partial x''_i} \right) \right\} \quad (85.16)$$

Here we must insert the expressions (84.15) and (84.16) and integrate over x' and x''.

We first split off the term that decreases as $1/r$. It can be written as

$$S_i^0 = \frac{\gamma}{r} \left\{ -4 \int \rho U_i (dx)^3 + \int \rho v_k \frac{\partial^2 W}{\partial x_i \, \partial x_k} (dx)^3 \right\} \quad (85.17)$$

On the other hand, if the obvious relation

$$\int \rho \frac{\partial W}{\partial x_i} (dx)^3 = 0 \quad (85.18)$$

is differentiated with respect to time, it gives

$$\int \rho \left(\frac{\partial^2 W}{\partial x_i \, \partial t} + v_k \frac{\partial^2 W}{\partial x_i \, \partial x_k} \right) (dx)^3 = 0 \quad (85.19)$$

and this enables us to write

$$S_i^0 = \frac{\gamma}{r} \left\{ -4 \int \rho U_i (dx)^3 - \int \rho \frac{\partial^2 W}{\partial x_i \, \partial t} (dx)^3 \right\} \quad (85.20)$$

We now consider the terms in (85.16) which decrease as $1/r^2$. Among these there are some in which the integrand does not depend on x' or x''. These give

$$S'_i = \frac{7\gamma^2 M P_i}{4r^2} + \frac{\gamma^2 M P_k x_i x_k}{4r^4} \quad (85.21)$$

The remaining terms of order $1/r^2$ are of dipole character. Denoting them by $S_i^{(1)}$, we have

$$S_i^{(1)} = -\frac{7}{4} \gamma^2 \frac{x_j}{r^3} \int \int (\rho v_i)' \, \rho'' \frac{(x'_j + x''_j)}{|\mathbf{r}' - \mathbf{r}''|} (dx')^3 (dx'')^3$$
$$- \frac{1}{4} \gamma^2 \frac{x_j}{r^3} \int \int (\rho v_k)' \rho'' \frac{(x'_j + x''_j)(x'_i - x''_i)(x'_k - x''_k)}{|\mathbf{r}' - \mathbf{r}''|^3} (dx')^3 (dx'')^3$$
$$- \frac{7}{4} \gamma^2 \frac{x_j}{r^3} \int \int (\rho v_j)' \rho'' \frac{(x'_i - x''_i)}{|\mathbf{r}' - \mathbf{r}''|} (dx')^3 (dx'')^3$$
$$+ \frac{7}{4} \gamma^2 \frac{x_j}{r^3} \delta_{ij} \int \int (\rho v_k)' \rho'' \frac{(x'_k - x''_k)}{|\mathbf{r}' - \mathbf{r}''|} (dx')^3 (dx'')^3 \quad (85.22)$$

We write this expression in the form

$$S_i^{(1)} = \frac{\gamma x_j}{r^3} (A_{ji} + B_{ji}) \quad (85.23)$$

where A_{ji} and B_{ji} are, respectively, the antisymmetric and the symmetric parts of the coefficient.

$$A_{ij} = -A_{ji} ; \qquad B_{ij} = B_{ji} \tag{85.24}$$

We then have

$$\begin{aligned}
A_{ji} = &-\frac{7}{4}\gamma \iint (\rho v_i)'\rho'' \frac{x_j''}{|\mathbf{r}' - \mathbf{r}''|} (dx')^3(dx'')^3 \\
&+\frac{7}{4}\gamma \iint (\rho v_j)'\rho'' \frac{x_i''}{|\mathbf{r}' - \mathbf{r}''|} (dx')^3(dx'')^3 \\
&-\frac{1}{4}\gamma \iint (\rho v_k)'\rho'' \frac{(x_j'' x_i' - x_i'' x_j')(x_k' - x_k'')}{|\mathbf{r}' - \mathbf{r}''|^3} (dx')^3(dx'')^3
\end{aligned} \tag{85.25}$$

and

$$\begin{aligned}
B_{ji} = &-\frac{7}{4}\gamma \iint (\rho v_i)'\rho'' \frac{x_j'}{|\mathbf{r}' - \mathbf{r}''|} (dx')^3(dx'')^3 \\
&-\frac{7}{4}\gamma \iint (\rho v_j)'\rho'' \frac{x_i'}{|\mathbf{r}' - \mathbf{r}''|} (dx')^3(dx'')^3 \\
&-\frac{1}{4} \iint (\rho v_k)'\rho'' \frac{(x_i' x_j' - x_i'' x_j'')(x_k' - x_k'')}{|\mathbf{r}' - \mathbf{r}''|^3} (dx')^3(dx'')^3 \\
&+\frac{7}{4}\gamma \delta_{ij} \iint (\rho v_k)'\rho'' \frac{x_k' - x_k''}{|\mathbf{r}' - \mathbf{r}''|} (dx')^3(dx'')^3
\end{aligned} \tag{85.26}$$

After some manipulation we can express A_{ji} as

$$A_{ji} = -2\int \rho(x_j U_i - x_i U_j)(dx)^3 - \frac{1}{2}\int \rho\left(x_j \frac{\partial^2 W}{\partial x_i\, \partial t} - x_i \frac{\partial^2 W}{\partial x_j\, \partial t}\right)(dx)^3 \tag{85.27}$$

Here we have used the relation

$$\frac{\partial W}{\partial t} + \frac{\partial W_k}{\partial x_k} = 0 \tag{85.28}$$

which follows from the definitions of W and W_i in (85.07) and (85.08) together with the equation of continuity.

For the symmetric part B_{ji} of the dipole coefficient we get

$$\begin{aligned}
B_{ji} = &-\frac{7}{4}\int \rho(x_j v_i + x_i v_j)U\, (dx)^3 + \frac{1}{4}\int \rho x_i x_j\left(v_k \frac{\partial U}{\partial x_k} - \frac{\partial U}{\partial t}\right)(dx)^3 \\
&+\frac{7}{2}\delta_{ij}\int \rho \frac{\partial W}{\partial t}(dx)^3
\end{aligned} \tag{85.29}$$

Here we have used the relation (85.28) and the analogous relation for the potentials U and U_k. It remains to form the sum $U_i + (1/c^2)S_i$ and to combine similar terms. Denoting by U_i^0 the first term in (85.10) and using (85.20) we obtain

$$U_i^0 + \frac{1}{c^2}S_i^0 = \frac{\gamma}{r}\int\left\{(c^2 + 4U)T^{0i} - \frac{\rho}{c^2}\left(4U_i + \frac{\partial^2 W}{\partial x_i\, \partial t}\right)\right\}(dx)^3 \tag{85.30}$$

But, by virtue of (85.11) and (85.12), this can be expressed as

$$U_i^0 + \frac{1}{c^2}S_i^0 = \frac{\gamma P_i}{r} \tag{85.31}$$

where P_t is the total momentum of the system, including corrections of the order $1/c^2$. We now consider those parts of the dipole terms which have anti-symmetric coefficients. It follows from (85.27), (85.11) and (85.13) that they are equal to

$$\frac{\gamma x_j}{r^3}\left\{\frac{1}{2}\int (c^2 + 4U)(x_j T^{0i} - x_i T^{0j})(dx)^3 + \frac{1}{c^2} A_{ji}\right\} = \frac{\gamma x_j}{2r^3} M_{ji} \quad (85.32)$$

where M_{ji} is the total angular momentum of the system, including relativistic corrections.

The complete set of dipole terms can be written in the form

$$U_i^{(1)} + \frac{1}{c^2} S_i^{(1)} = \frac{\gamma x_j}{2r^3}(M_{ji} + \dot{D}_{ji}) \quad (85.33)$$

where $\dot{D}_{ji}$ is the symmetric part of the coefficient. The use of a dotted symbol for it anticipates the result that this quantity can be represented as a time derivative of a certain quantity D_{ji} which has a simple physical meaning. Comparing the last equation with (85.10) and (85.23) we can express $\dot{D}_{ji}$ as

$$\dot{D}_{ji} = \int (c^2 + 4U)(T^{0i}x_j + T^{0j}x_i)(dx)^3 + \frac{2}{c^2} B_{ji} \quad (85.34)$$

If we insert the value of T^{0i} given by (85.03) and the value of B_{ji} given by (85.29) we get

$$\dot{D}_{ji} = \int \rho(v_i x_j + v_j x_i)(dx)^3 + \frac{1}{c^2}\int \rho\left(\frac{1}{2}v^2 + \Pi - \frac{1}{2}U\right)(v_i x_j + v_j x_i)(dx)^3$$

$$- \frac{1}{c^2}\int (p_{ik}v_k x_j + p_{jk}v_k x_i)(dx)^3 + \frac{1}{2c^2}\int \rho x_i x_j\left(v_k \frac{\partial U}{\partial x_k} - \frac{\partial U}{\partial t}\right)(dx)^3$$

$$+ \frac{7}{c^2}\delta_{ij}\int \rho\,\frac{\partial W}{\partial t}\,(dx)^3 \quad (85.35)$$

Adding to this the expression

$$\frac{1}{c^2}\int x_i x_j v_k\left(\rho w_k - \rho\frac{\partial U}{\partial x_k} - \frac{\partial p_{sk}}{\partial x_s}\right)(dx)^3 = 0 \quad (85.36)$$

which vanishes by virtue of the internal equations of motion, and using the relation

$$\int \rho\frac{\partial W}{\partial t}\,(dx)^3 = \frac{d}{dt}\frac{1}{2}\int \rho W\,(dx)^3 \quad (85.37)$$

as well as equation (79.04) for the total time derivative of the elastic energy Π we can write $\dot{D}_{ji}$ in the form

$$\dot{D}_{ji} = \frac{dD_{ji}}{dt} \quad (85.38)$$

where

$$D_{ji} = \int \rho x_i x_j\left\{1 + \frac{1}{c^2}\left(\frac{1}{2}v^2 + \Pi - \frac{1}{2}U\right)\right\}(dx)^3 + \frac{7}{2c^2}\delta_{ij}\int \rho W(dx)^3 \quad (85.39)$$

The first term in this expression is the moment of inertia of the system of bodies, calculated with inclusion of the masses of the kinetic and potential energies.

Now we can write down the complete expression for $U_i + (1/c^2)S_i$. According to (85.10), (85.21), (85.31) and (85.33) we have

$$U_i + \frac{1}{c^2} S_i = \frac{\gamma}{r} P_i + \frac{\gamma x_j}{2r^3} M_{ji} + \frac{\gamma x_j}{2r^3} \frac{dD_{ji}}{dt}$$

$$+ \frac{\partial^2}{\partial x_j \, \partial x_k} \frac{\gamma}{2r} \int \rho v_i x_j x_k (dx)^3 + \frac{7\gamma^2 M P_i}{4c^2 r^2} + \frac{\gamma^2 M P_k x_i x_k}{4c^2 r^4} + \frac{1}{c^2} \frac{\partial^2 W_i}{\partial t^2}$$

$$(85.40)$$

and therefore

$$\mathfrak{g}^{0i} = \frac{4\gamma}{c^3 r} P_i + \frac{2\gamma x_j}{c^3 r^3} M_{ji} - \frac{\partial^2}{\partial x_j \, \partial t} \frac{2\gamma}{c^3 r} D_{ji}$$

$$+ \frac{\partial^2}{\partial x_j \, \partial x_k} \frac{2\gamma}{c^3 r} \int \rho v_i x_j x_k (dx)^3 + \frac{7\gamma^2 M P_i}{c^5 r^2} + \frac{\gamma^2 M P_k x_i x_k}{c^5 r^4} + \frac{4}{c^5} \frac{\partial^2 W_i}{\partial t^2}$$

$$(85.41)$$

It remains to find the temporal component $\mathfrak{g}^{00}$, which by equation (83.30) is expressible in terms of the generalized Newtonian potential $\bar{U}$. By (83.31) and (83.32)

$$\bar{U} = \frac{\gamma M}{r} + \frac{\gamma x_j}{r^3} M X_j + \frac{1}{2} \frac{\partial^2}{\partial x_j \, \partial x_k} \frac{\gamma}{r} D_{jk}$$

$$- \frac{1}{6} \frac{\partial^3}{\partial x_j \, \partial x_k \, \partial x_i} \frac{\gamma}{r} \int \rho x_j x_k x_i (dx)^3 + \frac{1}{c^2} \frac{\partial^2 W}{\partial t^2} \qquad (85.42)$$

Here M is the total mass

$$M = \int \rho \left[1 + \frac{1}{c^2} \left(\tfrac{1}{2} v^2 + \Pi - \tfrac{1}{2} U \right) \right] (dx)^3 \qquad (85.43)$$

which is constant by virtue of (79.45) and the X_j are the mass centre coordinates

$$M X_j = \int x_j \rho \left[1 + \frac{1}{c^2} \left(\tfrac{1}{2} v^2 + \Pi - \tfrac{1}{2} U \right) \right] (dx)^3 \qquad (85.44)$$

which, by (79.59), are linear functions of the time. The quantities D_{ij} are defined by (85.39). The last term in that equation, which is proportional to δ_{ij} drops out of the expression (85.42). In the octopole moments we have discarded relativistic corrections. The last term in (85.42) is a retardation correction.

Inserting the expression obtained for $\bar{U}$ into the equation

$$\mathfrak{g}^{00} = \frac{1}{c} + \frac{4\bar{U}}{c^3} + \frac{7\bar{U}^2}{c^5} \qquad (85.45)$$

we obtain $\mathfrak{g}^{00}$ as

$$\mathfrak{g}^{00} = \frac{1}{c} + \frac{4\gamma M}{c^3 r} + \frac{4\gamma x_j}{c^3 r^3} M X_j + \frac{\partial^2}{\partial x_j \, \partial x_k} \frac{2\gamma}{c^3 r} D_{jk} - \frac{\partial^3}{\partial x_i \, \partial x_j \, \partial x_k} \frac{2\gamma}{3c^3 r} \int \rho x_i x_j x_k (d\bar{x})^3$$

$$+ \frac{7\gamma^2 M^2}{c^5 r^2} + \frac{14\gamma^2 M^2 X_j x_j}{c^5 r^4} + \frac{4}{c^5} \frac{\partial^2 W}{\partial t^2} \qquad (85.46)$$

It is easy to verify by direct insertion that this expression, together with the expression (85.41) for $\mathfrak{g}^{0i}$ satisfies the relation

$$\frac{\partial \mathfrak{g}^{00}}{\partial t} + \frac{\partial \mathfrak{g}^{0i}}{\partial x_i} = 0 \qquad (85.47)$$

exactly. In the equation (84.40) for the spatial components, which may be written as

$$g^{ik} = -c\delta_{ik} + \frac{\partial^2}{\partial t^2} \frac{2\gamma}{c^3 r} \int \rho x_i x_k (dx)^3$$
$$- \frac{\partial^2}{\partial x_j \partial t} \frac{2\gamma}{c^3 r} \int \rho(x_j x_i v_k + x_j x_k v_i - x_i x_k v_j)(dx)^3 + \frac{\gamma^2 M^2 x_i x_k}{c^3 r^4} \qquad (85.48)$$

terms of order $1/c^3$ (more precisely q^4/c^3) have been retained, but higher terms have been dropped. If the quantity g^{0i} is taken to the same accuracy it is easy to verify that the relation

$$\frac{\partial g^{0i}}{\partial t} + \frac{\partial g^{ik}}{\partial x_k} = 0 \qquad (85.49)$$

is also satisfied.

86. Solution of the Wave Equation in the Wave Zone

The expressions derived above for the gravitational potentials are valid at " moderately large " distances from a system of bodies. As was explained at the beginning of Section 84, this term is understood to mean distances that are large compared to the dimensions of the system, but small compared to the length of the waves radiated by the system. If, on the other hand, the distances are large compared to these wave lengths one is concerned with the so-called " wave-zone ". In the wave-zone the term in the wave equation involving the second time derivative may no longer be treated as a correction and the method of solving the equation must be different.

In the case of the Solar System " moderately large " distances extend as as far as the nearest stars, i.e. into such a region of space in which the system may no longer be treated as isolated. In practice, therefore, the study of the Solar System does not take one beyond moderately large distances. However, in some theoretical questions, such as that of the emission of gravitational waves, or that of the uniqueness of the solution of the gravitational equations one must consider distances which belong to the wave-zone, and are arbitrarily great in a mathematical sense.

Before going on to the solution of Einstein's equations for arbitrarily large distances we shall clarify the notions of " moderately large distances " and of the " wave-zone " with the aid of the example of a simple wave equation with an inhomogeneous term

$$\Delta\psi - \frac{1}{c^2} \frac{\partial^2 \psi}{\partial t^2} = -4\pi\sigma \qquad (86.01)$$

The quantity corresponding to ψ in gravitational theory will be the difference between $g^{\mu\nu}$ and its limiting value at infinity.

If the " density " σ is taken to be known the solution of the wave equation which is of interest to us may be stated as the retarded potential

$$\psi = \int \frac{[\sigma]}{|\mathbf{r} - \mathbf{r}'|} (dx')^3 \qquad (86.02)$$

where
$$[\sigma] = \sigma(t', \mathbf{r}') \qquad (86.03)$$

with
$$t' = t - \frac{1}{c} |\mathbf{r} - \mathbf{r}'| \qquad (86.04)$$

The fact that we choose this solution and not any other corresponds to our conception that the system is isolated and that the only sources of waves shall be the bodies that make up the system. The exact form of initial conditions is of no importance ; it is sufficient to assume that the initial disturbance was concentrated in a finite region around the system and that we are dealing with such times and distances at which the initial disturbance has dispersed.

We assume that the density σ possesses both time derivatives of various orders and " moments " of various orders, for which we introduce the notation

$$\mu_0(\tau) = \int \sigma(\tau, \mathbf{r}')(dx')^3$$
$$\mu_i(\tau) = \int x_i'\sigma(\tau, \mathbf{r}')(dx')^3 \qquad (86.05)$$
$$\mu_{ik}(\tau) = \int x_i'x_k'\sigma(\tau, \mathbf{r}')(dx')^3$$

where τ is a quantity independent of $\mathbf{r}'$.

The technique of solving the wave equation used in the preceding sections amounted to an expansion of the argument t' of σ and of σ itself in inverse powers of c. Since such an expansion leads to the appearance of increasing positive powers of $|\mathbf{r} - \mathbf{r}'|$ in the integrands this method clearly gives a well converging series only for " moderately large " distances r. (The region of " moderately large " distances can, in fact, be more precisely defined as the region in which the series converges rapidly.) Each term of the series can in turn be expanded in inverse powers of r, and then the coefficients of the expansion will involve the " moments " (86.05) taken at $\tau = t$.

But we can instead split off the quantity

$$\tau = t - \frac{r}{c} \qquad (86.06)$$

in the expression (86.04) for t' which then appears in the form

$$t' = \tau + \frac{1}{c}(r - |\mathbf{r} - \mathbf{r}'|) \qquad (86.07)$$

If then t' and σ are expanded in powers of $1/c$, *only in so far as this quantity is not involved in* τ, we obtain a series of a different form, and one that converges for arbitrarily large values of r.

If in this series we take all terms which have the slowest decrease with increasing r, we obtain an expression for ψ which is valid in the wave-zone, i.e. for very large values of r. The retention of none but the most slowly decreasing terms corresponds to the replacement of the quantity (86.07) by

$$t' = \tau + \frac{\mathbf{n} \cdot \mathbf{r}'}{c} \qquad (86.08)$$

where

$$\mathbf{n} = \frac{\mathbf{r}}{r}; \qquad n_i = \frac{x_i}{r} \qquad (86.09)$$

is a unit vector in the direction of $\mathbf{r}$. In this way we obtain for ψ an expression of the form

$$\psi = \frac{1}{r}\mu(\tau, \mathbf{n}) \qquad (86.10)$$

where the function

$$\mu(\tau, \mathbf{n}) = \int \sigma\left(\tau + \frac{\mathbf{n} \cdot \mathbf{r}'}{c}, \mathbf{r}'\right)(dx')^3 \qquad (86.11)$$

depends on *three* arguments, namely the quantity τ and the two angles that determine **n**. We note that if μ is an arbitrary function of these three arguments, ψ is an approximate solution of the homogeneous wave equation.

If the moments (86.05) exist we can expand μ as follows :

$$\mu(\tau, \mathbf{n}) = \mu_0 + \frac{n_i}{c}\,\dot\mu_i + \frac{1}{2}\frac{n_i n_k}{c^2}\,\ddot\mu_{ik} + \dots \tag{86.12}$$

or

$$\mu(\tau, \mathbf{n}) = \mu_0 + \frac{x_i}{cr}\,\dot\mu_i + \frac{1}{2}\frac{x_i x_k}{c^2 r^2}\,\ddot\mu_{ik} + \dots \tag{86.13}$$

where the dots denote differentiation of the quantities (86.05) with respect to their argument τ, or, equivalently, with respect to time.

The region in which the solution of the wave equation for ψ can accurately be given in the form (86.10) is known as the wave-zone.

When the dimensions of the system are small compared to the length of the waves emitted by it, the expansion (86.12) converges rapidly, and its first non-vanishing term will be the main one. If this term is μ_0 the function ψ will be spherically symmetric.

87. The Gravitational Potentials in the Wave Zone

We now turn to Einstein's equations as stated in Section 68. As in (68.13) we introduce the quantities

$$N^{\mu\nu} = \left(\frac{-g}{c^2}\right)\{\Pi^{\mu,\,\alpha\beta}\,\Pi^\nu_{\alpha\beta} - \tfrac{1}{2}y^\mu y^\nu + \tfrac{1}{2}g^{\mu\nu}L\} \tag{87.01}$$

where L is the Lagrangian

$$L = -\frac{1}{2\sqrt{(-g)}}\,\Pi^\nu_{\alpha\beta}\frac{\partial g^{\alpha\beta}}{\partial x_\nu} + \tfrac{1}{2}y_\nu y^\nu \tag{87.02}$$

and the other quantities involved are defined as follows :

$$\Pi^{\mu,\,\alpha\beta} = \frac{1}{2g}\left(g^{\alpha\rho}\frac{\partial g^{\mu\beta}}{\partial x_\rho} + g^{\beta\rho}\frac{\partial g^{\mu\alpha}}{\partial x_\rho} - g^{\mu\rho}\frac{\partial g^{\alpha\beta}}{\partial x_\rho}\right) \tag{87.03}$$

$$\Pi^\nu_{\alpha\beta} = g_{\alpha\mu}g_{\beta\lambda}\Pi^{\nu,\,\mu\lambda} \tag{87.04}$$

$$y_\nu = \frac{\partial \log \sqrt{(-g)}}{\partial x_\nu}; \qquad y^\nu = g^{\mu\nu}y_\mu \tag{87.05}$$

Then Einstein's equations in harmonic coordinates appear as

$$\left(\frac{-g}{c^2}\right)(R^{\mu\nu} - \tfrac{1}{2}g^{\mu\nu}R) = -\frac{1}{2c^2}\,g^{\alpha\beta}\frac{\partial^2 g^{\mu\nu}}{\partial x_\alpha\,\partial x_\beta} + N^{\mu\nu} = \frac{8\pi\gamma g}{c^4}\,T^{\mu\nu} \tag{87.06}$$

We must investigate the asymptotic form assumed at large distances by the solutions of these equations. To do this we consider first the wave equation

$$\sqrt{(-g)}\cdot\Box\,\psi \equiv g^{\alpha\beta}\frac{\partial^2\psi}{\partial x_\alpha\,\partial x_\beta} = 0 \tag{87.07}$$

and replace in it the coefficients $g^{\alpha\beta}$ by their " static " values; for simplicity we shall assume that the origin of coordinates is at the mass centre of the system.

We can here use the expressions (85.41), (85.46) and (85.48) in which, how-ever, we discard all terms that decrease more rapidly than $1/r$ and of the static terms we retain (for the time being) only those of order $1/r$. We introduce the gravitational radius of a mass by the relation

$$\alpha = \frac{\gamma M}{c^2} \tag{87.08}$$

and go over to the spherical polar coordinates which are connected with the harmonic coordinates by the usual relations (57.03). Then we can write the wave equation (87.07) in the form

$$\Box^0\psi = \frac{1}{c^2}\left(1 + \frac{4\alpha}{r}\right)\frac{\partial^2\psi}{\partial t^2} - \left(\frac{\partial^2\psi}{\partial r^2} + \frac{2}{r}\frac{\partial\psi}{\partial r} + \frac{1}{r^2}\Delta^*\psi\right) = 0 \tag{87.09}$$

Here $\Delta^*\psi$ is the ordinary Laplacian on a sphere (see equation (57.06)). We are interested in solutions of the nature of an outgoing wave. For such solutions the term $\Delta^*\psi/r^2$ will decrease at infinity more rapidly than the remaining terms in the equation and we can discard it. Then equation (87.09) becomes

$$\frac{1}{c^2}\left(1 + \frac{4\alpha}{r}\right)\frac{\partial^2\psi}{\partial t^2} - \left(\frac{\partial^2\psi}{\partial r^2} + \frac{2}{r}\frac{\partial\psi}{\partial r}\right) = 0 \tag{87.10}$$

Here only r and t are independent variables, the angles ϑ and φ enter merely as parameters.

We make the substitution

$$r\psi = f \tag{87.11}$$

and we introduce in place of r the variable

$$r^* = r + 2\alpha(\log r - \log r_0) \tag{87.12}$$

where r_0 is some constant. Then, apart from small quantities, we get

$$\frac{1}{c^2}\frac{\partial^2 f}{\partial t^2} - \frac{\partial^2 f}{\partial r^{*2}} = 0 \tag{87.13}$$

A solution of the nature of an outgoing wave will be

$$f = f(\tau, \mathbf{n}) \tag{87.14}$$

where, as before, $\mathbf{n}$ is the unit vector (86.09) and τ now has the value

$$\tau = t - \frac{1}{c}r^* \tag{87.15}$$

or

$$\tau = t - \frac{1}{c}\left\{r + 2\alpha\log\left(\frac{r}{r_0}\right)\right\}. \tag{87.16}$$

Thus the solution of (87.09) which is of the form of an outgoing wave, has the asymptotic form

$$\psi = \frac{1}{r}f(\tau, \mathbf{n}) \tag{87.17}$$

Here τ is assumed to be finite while r may be arbitrarily great.

Under these conditions the asymptotic values of the derivatives of ψ with respect to the space and time coordinates can be evaluated as if ψ depended on them only through the quantity τ. Putting

$$k_\alpha = \frac{\partial \tau}{\partial x_\alpha} \tag{87.18}$$

we have in the approximation in question

$$\frac{\partial \psi}{\partial x_\alpha} = k_\alpha \dot{\psi} \tag{87.19}$$

Neglecting terms of order α/r in comparison with unity we can take the k_α to be given by

$$k_0 = 1; \qquad k_i = -\frac{n_i}{c} \tag{87.20}$$

In agreement with this we may put

$$k^0 = \frac{1}{c^2}; \qquad k^i = +\frac{n_i}{c} \tag{87.21}$$

whence

$$k_\alpha k^\alpha = 0 \tag{87.22}$$

The quantities k_α are proportional to the components of a four-dimensional null vector (in the Galilean space corresponding to the limiting values of the $\mathfrak{g}^{\mu\nu}$).

We now add to the static values of the $\mathfrak{g}^{\mu\nu}$ in the coefficients of the wave equation (87.07) their wave part $b^{\mu\nu}$, putting

$$\begin{aligned}
\mathfrak{g}^{00} &= \frac{1}{c} + \frac{4\alpha}{cr} + b^{00} \\
\mathfrak{g}^{0i} &= b^{0i} \\
\mathfrak{g}^{ik} &= -c\delta_{ik} + b^{ik}
\end{aligned} \tag{87.23}$$

We shall assume of the $b^{\mu\nu}$ that in the wave zone they either have the form (87.17) or, at any rate, that they satisfy the condition (87.19). Therefore we can calculate the derivatives of the $b^{\mu\nu}$ according to the rule

$$\frac{\partial b^{\mu\nu}}{\partial x_\alpha} = k_\alpha b^{\mu\nu} \tag{87.24}$$

Since the derivatives of the static terms in $\mathfrak{g}^{\mu\nu}$ will decrease as $1/r^2$ and may be discarded, we also have

$$\frac{\partial \mathfrak{g}^{\mu\nu}}{\partial x_\alpha} = k_\alpha b^{\mu\nu} \tag{87.25}$$

The harmonic conditions for the $\mathfrak{g}^{\mu\nu}$ appear as

$$k_\mu b^{\mu\nu} = 0 \tag{87.26}$$

and they may be integrated with respect to τ. Since we have already split off the static part of the $\mathfrak{g}^{\mu\nu}$ the constants of integration may be set equal to zero and we get

$$k_\mu b^{\mu\nu} = 0 \tag{87.27}$$

Hence the mixed and temporal components among the $b^{\mu\nu}$ can be expressed in terms of the spatial components as follows :

$$b^{0i} = \frac{n_k}{c} b^{ik}; \qquad b^{00} = \frac{n_i n_k}{c^2} b^{ik} \tag{87.28}$$

The more precise form of $\sqrt{(-g)}/c$ times the d'Alembertian which may be obtained by inserting the values (87.23) for the $g^{\mu\nu}$ into (87.07) now appears as

$$\frac{1}{c} \sqrt{(-g)} \cdot \Box\psi = \Box^{\circ}\psi + \frac{1}{c} b^{\alpha\beta} \frac{\partial^2\psi}{\partial x_\alpha \, \partial x_\beta} \tag{87.29}$$

But if ψ is of the nature of a diverging wave which depends on the space and time coordinates mainly through τ and which satisfies (87.19), we have

$$b^{\alpha\beta} \frac{\partial^2\psi}{\partial x_\alpha \, \partial x_\beta} = k_\alpha k_\beta b^{\alpha\beta} \ddot{\psi} = 0 \tag{87.30}$$

as a result of (87.27). Therefore the additional term in the d'Alembertian will vanish separately and we can discuss the outgoing wave solution as if the coefficients of the d'Alembertian in the wave equation (87.07) and in Einstein's equations (87.06) involved only their static parts. By this we have, so to speak, freed ourselves from the non-linear parts of those terms in Einstein's equations which contain second derivatives.

We now pass on to examine the non-linear terms containing first derivatives. We cannot discard them straightaway because in the wave zone they decrease no more rapidly than $1/r^2$ so that they may strongly influence the asymptotic form of the solution. But when evaluating them we can introduce the simplifications that follow from equation (87.25) and from the fact that outside the differentiation signs the components of the metric tensor may be replaced by their limiting values. Raising and lowering indices by means of these limiting values we can write for instance

$$k^\alpha = g^{\alpha\beta} k_\beta; \qquad b^\mu_\nu = g_{\nu\alpha} b^{\mu\alpha} \qquad \text{etc.} \tag{87.31}$$

just as if we were dealing with tensors. Using the rigorous relation

$$y_\alpha = \frac{1}{2\sqrt{(-g)}} g_{\mu\nu} \frac{\partial g^{\mu\nu}}{\partial x_\alpha} \tag{87.32}$$

we can then write

$$y_\alpha = \frac{k_\alpha}{2c} b^\nu_\nu; \qquad y^\alpha = \frac{k^\alpha}{2c} b^\nu_\nu \tag{87.33}$$

The quantities (87.03) and (87.04) will then be given by

$$\Pi^{\mu,\,\alpha\beta} = -\frac{1}{2c} (k^\alpha b^{\mu\beta} + k^\beta b^{\mu\alpha} - k^\mu b^{\alpha\beta}) \tag{87.34}$$

and

$$\Pi^\nu_{\alpha\beta} = -\frac{1}{2c} (k_\alpha b^\nu_\beta + k_\beta b^\nu_\alpha - k^\nu b_{\alpha\beta}) \tag{87.35}$$

It follows from (87.22) and (87.26) that

$$k_\nu \Pi^\nu_{\alpha\beta} = 0; \qquad y_\nu y^\nu = 0 \tag{87.36}$$

Therefore, in the wave zone the Lagrangian has the value zero

$$L = 0 \tag{87.37}$$

just as for electromagnetic waves.

If we form products of the three terms in (87.34) with the three terms of (87.35) we get nine sums, of which, however, only one differs from zero, namely

$$\Pi^{\mu,\,\alpha\beta}\Pi^{\nu}_{\alpha\beta} = \frac{1}{4c^2}\,k^\mu k^\nu b^{\alpha\beta}b_{\alpha\beta} \tag{87.38}$$

Inserting the expressions obtained into (87.01) and replacing the factor $(-g/c^2)$ by unity, we get

$$N^{\mu\nu} = \frac{1}{4c^2}\,k^\mu k^\nu\left(b^{\alpha\beta}b_{\alpha\beta} - \tfrac{1}{2}b^\alpha_\alpha b^\beta_\beta\right) \tag{87.39}$$

Here the following properties of $N^{\mu\nu}$ are important. In the first place it is proportional to the product $k^\mu k^\nu$ and when it is inserted into Einstein's equation (87.06) it can give rise only to such terms in $\mathfrak{g}^{\mu\nu}$ and $\dot{\mathfrak{g}}^{\mu\nu}$, and also in $b^{\mu\nu}$ and $\dot{b}^{\mu\nu}$, which are also proportional to this product. But if one augments $\dot{b}^{\mu\nu}$ by terms proportional to $k^\mu k^\nu$, i.e. if one makes the substitution

$$b^{\alpha\beta} \to b^{\alpha\beta} + \lambda k^\alpha k^\beta \tag{87.40}$$

then, by virtue of the harmonic conditions (87.26) and of (87.22), there is no change in $N^{\mu\nu}$. As a consequence the problem of determining the $\mathfrak{g}^{\mu\nu}$, including the effects of non-linear terms, reduces to the solution of linear equations.

We put

$$\sigma_g = \frac{1}{32\pi\gamma}\left(b_{\alpha\beta}b^{\alpha\beta} - \tfrac{1}{2}b^\alpha_\alpha b^\beta_\beta\right) \tag{87.41}$$

As will be seen below, this quantity plays the role of the energy density of gravitational waves. Equation (87.39) then appears as

$$N^{\mu\nu} = \frac{8\pi\gamma}{c^2}\sigma_g k^\mu k^\nu \tag{87.42}$$

Inserting this equation into Einstein's equations (87.06) we obtain

$$\frac{1}{2c}\square\mathfrak{g}^{\mu\nu} = \frac{8\pi\gamma}{c^2}(T^{\mu\nu} + \sigma_g k^\mu k^\nu) \tag{89.43}$$

In forming the mass tensor in earlier sections we entirely neglected electromagnetic energy. But we may now take into account the energy of the electromagnetic radiation of a system of bodies. Denoting its density by σ_{em}, so that

$$\sigma_{em} = \frac{1}{8\pi}(\mathbf{E}^2 + \mathbf{H}^2) \tag{87.44}$$

we get for the electromagnetic energy tensor in the wave zone the expression

$$T^{\mu\nu} = \sigma_{em}k^\mu k^\nu \tag{87.45}$$

(We are retaining the symbol $T^{\mu\nu}$ for this tensor because in the wave zone the entire mass tensor reduces to (87.45), the part corresponding to the material medium being zero.)

Thus we can write Einstein's equations for the wave zone in the form

$$\frac{1}{2c}\square\mathfrak{g}^{\mu\nu} = \frac{8\pi\gamma}{c^2}\sigma k^\mu k^\nu \tag{87.46}$$

where σ can be taken as the sum of σ_{em} and σ_g if we include electromagnetic radiation, and simply as σ_g if we deal with the purely gravitational problem.

To solve (87.46) we split off the term in $b^{\mu\nu}$ which is proportional to $k^\mu k^\nu$, writing $b^{\mu\nu}$ as

$$b^{\mu\nu} = h^{\mu\nu} + hk^\mu k^\nu \qquad (87.47)$$

As has already been noted, the expression (87.41) for σ_g does not change if $b^{\mu\nu}$ is replaced by $h^{\mu\nu}$, so that we have

$$\sigma_g = \frac{1}{32\pi\gamma}(h^{\alpha\beta}h_{\alpha\beta} - \tfrac{1}{2}h_\alpha^\alpha h_\beta^\beta) \qquad (87.48)$$

The relations (87.27) and (87.28) also remain valid; we may write

$$k_\mu h^{\mu\nu} = 0 \qquad (87.49)$$

The quantities $h^{\mu\nu}$ and h appearing in (87.47) can be subjected to the conditions

$$\Box h^{\mu\nu} = 0 \qquad (87.50)$$

and

$$\Box h = \frac{16\pi\gamma}{c}\sigma \qquad (87.51)$$

in which, according to the remark made above, we may replace the complete wave operator $\Box$ by the " static " wave operator $\Box^0$ (equation (87.09)).

Then the $h^{\mu\nu}$ satisfy a *linear* wave equation and by (87.17) we can require that they have the asymptotic form

$$h^{\mu\nu} = \frac{2\gamma}{c^3 r}f^{\mu\nu}(\tau, \mathbf{n}) \qquad (87.52)$$

The coefficient $2\gamma/c^3$ has been introduced for convenience in estimating the order of magnitude of the $h^{\mu\nu}$; the spatial components f^{ik} will be of the order of the kinetic energy of the system.

Inserting these values for $h^{\mu\nu}$ into (87.48) we obtain an expression for σ_g that is inversely proportional to r^2. The r-dependence of the electromagnetic part of the energy density will be of the same form. Therefore the total energy density σ in (87.51) will also be of the form

$$\sigma = \frac{\sigma_0(\tau, \mathbf{n})}{r^2} \qquad (87.53)$$

The gravitational part σ_{0g} of the function σ_0 can be expressed in terms of the quantities $f^{\mu\nu}$ by a relation analogous to (87.48) namely

$$\sigma_{0g} = \frac{\gamma}{8\pi c^6}(\dot{f}^{\alpha\beta}\dot{f}_{\alpha\beta} - \tfrac{1}{2}\dot{f}_\alpha^\alpha \dot{f}_\beta^\beta) \qquad (87.54)$$

Inserting the expression (87.53) for σ into (87.51) we get for h the equation

$$\Box h = \frac{16\pi\gamma}{cr^2}\sigma_0(\tau, \mathbf{n}) \qquad (87.55)$$

The right-hand side of this equation can be considered to be known. Thus not only the $h^{\mu\nu}$ but also h satisfies a *linear* equation. The asymptotic form of the solution of this equation will be

$$h = \frac{8\pi\gamma \log r}{r} \int^\tau \sigma_0(\tau, \mathbf{n}) \, d\tau + \frac{h_0(\tau, \mathbf{n})}{r} \tag{87.56}$$

Let us put

$$4\pi c \int_{\tau_0}^\tau \sigma_0(\tau, \mathbf{n}) d\tau = \Delta\mathscr{E}(\tau, \mathbf{n}) \tag{87.57}$$

If this expression is multiplied by $d\Omega/4\pi$, where $d\Omega$ is an element of solid angle it gives the flow of energy in the time $\tau - \tau_0$ into such a solid angle situated in the direction $\mathbf{n}$. The result of inserting (87.57) into the previous equation may be stated in the form

$$h = \frac{2\gamma}{cr}[\log r \, \Delta\mathscr{E}(\tau, \mathbf{n}) + \varepsilon(\tau, \mathbf{n})] \tag{87.58}$$

where the quantity $\varepsilon(\tau, \mathbf{n})$ may be taken as of the same order as $\Delta\mathscr{E}(\tau, \mathbf{n})$ or alternatively it may be omitted, the corresponding terms in the equations for $\mathfrak{g}^{\mu\nu}$ being included in $f^{\mu\nu}$.

Inserting the values (87.52) and (87.58) for $h^{\mu\nu}$ and h first into equation (87.47) for $b^{\mu\nu}$ and then into equation (87.23) for $\mathfrak{g}^{\mu\nu}$, we obtain the following symptotic expressions for the $\mathfrak{g}^{\mu\nu}$ in the wave zone.

$$\mathfrak{g}^{00} = \frac{1}{c} + \frac{4\gamma M}{c^3 r} + \frac{2\gamma}{c^3 r} f^{00} + \frac{2\gamma}{c^5 r} (\log r \, \Delta\mathscr{E} + \varepsilon)$$

$$\mathfrak{g}^{0i} = \frac{2\gamma}{c^3 r} f^{0i} + \frac{2\gamma}{c^4 r} n_i (\log r \, \Delta\mathscr{E} + \varepsilon) \tag{87.59}$$

$$\mathfrak{g}^{ik} = -c\delta_{ik} + \frac{2\gamma}{c^3 r} f^{ik} + \frac{2\gamma}{c^3 r} n_i n_k (\log r \, \Delta\mathscr{E} + \varepsilon)$$

Here the quantities f^{0i} and f^{00} are expressible in terms of the f^{ik} by equations analogous to (87.28) namely

$$f^{0i} = \frac{n_k}{c} f^{ik} \; ; \quad f^{00} = \frac{n_i n_k}{c^2} f^{ik} \tag{87.60}$$

Let us compare the expression for the $\mathfrak{g}^{\mu\nu}$ in the wave zone with the corresponding expressions for moderately large distances as obtained in Section 85. In doing this we can first of all neglect terms involving $\log r$ and arising from the outflow of energy. As for the remaining terms, we can write them in such a form that they go over into corresponding terms in equations (85.41), (85.46) and (85.48). To do this we put

$$D_{ik}(t) = \int \rho x_i x_k (dx)^3 \tag{87.61}$$

and then replace t by τ and relate f^{ik} to $D_{ik}(\tau)$ by

$$f^{ik} = \frac{d^2}{d\tau^2} D_{ik}(\tau) \tag{87.62}$$

Then the equations

$$g^{00} = \frac{1}{c} + \frac{4\gamma M}{c^3 r} + \frac{2\gamma}{c^3} \frac{\partial^2}{\partial x_i\, \partial x_k} \frac{D_{ik}(\tau)}{r}$$

$$g^{0i} = -\frac{2\gamma}{c^3} \frac{\partial^2}{\partial x_k\, \partial t} \frac{D_{ik}(\tau)}{r} \tag{87.63}$$

$$g^{ik} = -c\delta_{ik} + \frac{2\gamma}{c^3} \frac{\partial^2}{\partial t^2} \frac{D_{ik}(\tau)}{r}$$

go over in the wave zone into (87.59), apart from terms arising from the out-flow of energy, while for moderately large distances they give the main terms of equations (85.41), (85.46) and (85.48). At moderately large distances the logarithmic term in the expression (87.15) for τ may be omitted, i.e. r^* may be replaced by r.

88. Some General Remarks on the Conservation Laws

Gravitational energy plays a very special role in the theory of gravitation, which is quite different from the role of all other forms of energy. It does not enter explicitly into the energy tensor but is accounted for indirectly through the gravitational potentials. The presence of a gravitational field and of the energy related to it reveals itself, as we know, in a change of the properties of space and time. Gravitational energy can be separated out in the form of additional terms in the energy tensor only in an artificial manner by fixing the coordinate system and reformulating the problem in such a way that the gravitational field is taken to be superimposed on a space-time of fixed properties, just as is done in Newtonian theory. The additional terms in the energy tensor that correspond to gravitational energy do not possess the property of covariance (i.e. they do not form a tensor). This is quite understandable because of the lack of uniqueness in the choice of the space of fixed properties into which the gravitational field is embedded. On the other hand, the difficulties that arise in the question of determining gravitational energy uniquely can be related to the fact that it cannot be localized. This property of gravitational energy shows itself physically in the fact that *a gravitational field cannot be screened*. The only way to avoid the action of a gravitational field is to remove oneself further from the masses producing it. This can be done with an isolated system of masses. The gravitational field produced by such a system can be regarded as a local non-uniformity in infinite Euclidean space (or in Galilean space-time). With this form of description it is possible (neglecting radiation, of which more will be said below) to form the ten integrals of Einstein's equations which correspond to the ten classical integrals of the equations of mechanics. Four of these—the integrals of energy and momentum—form a four-dimensional vector in the Galilean space-time in which the system of masses with its gravitational field is embedded. The remaining six integrals form an anti-symmetric tensor in the same space-time; they are the integrals of angular momentum and of the motion of the mass centre of the system.

It is important to note that the existence of the ten integrals of motion is related to the uniformity and isotropy of the Galilean space-time in which the system is embedded. If one gives up the requirement of uniformity and of Euclidean character at infinity this brings about a violation of all or some of the conservation laws of which the ten integrals of motion are the expression. From a physical point of view this is perfectly natural, for the isotropy and the Euclidean character at infinity express the fact that the system is isolated, and one can expect the conservation laws to hold only if the system is isolated.

One should note another reason why a system of moving masses can never be completely isolated in an active sense (i.e. in the sense of giving out energy rather than receiving it). This reason is provided by the radiation of electromagnetic and of gravitational waves by the system and, possibly, also of other kinds of waves. However, for a system like the Solar system the loss of energy by radiation, even over geological periods, is very small in comparison with the available store of energy. This is so in spite of the fact that in absolute measure the loss appears an impressive one (for the Sun the radiative power corresponds to a transmutation of four million tons of matter into radiation per second). As for the radiation of gravitational waves, it is completely negligible : a rough estimate using equations based on the results of the preceding section shows that the power radiated by the Solar system in the form of gravitational waves is 10^{23} or 10^{24} times less than that radiated electromagnetically and is, all in all, about a single kilowatt. (Such an estimate will be made in Section 90.) Therefore it is permissible to neglect the action of gravitational waves in all but, possibly, purely theoretical considerations. This result shows in particular that the problem studied in Chapter VI of the motion of systems of gravitating masses may be considered as a problem in mechanics, disregarding radiation, not only in the approximation in which it was solved there but also in further approximations, which otherwise present no practical interest.

89. Formulation of the Conservation Laws

In a theory working with Galilean space-time the classical conservation laws can be stated in differential form, namely in the form of relations (31.10). The generalization of these relations is

$$\nabla_{\mu} T^{\mu\nu} = 0 \tag{89.01}$$

and, according to (41.25), this can also be written as

$$\frac{1}{\sqrt{(-g)}} \frac{\partial}{\partial x_{\mu}} [\sqrt{(-g)} \cdot T^{\mu\nu}] + \Gamma^{\nu}_{\alpha\beta} T^{\alpha\beta} = 0 \tag{89.02}$$

However the relations (89.01) do not by themselves lead to conservation laws. The mathematical reason for this is the presence of the second term, standing outside the sign of differentiation, owing to which, one cannot, in general, conclude that any quantities of the form of volume integrals are constant. (See Section 49.) The physical reason is the fact that the gravitational field itself possesses energy which does not enter $T^{\mu\nu}$ explicitly, but which must, nevertheless, be included in the general balance.

To obtain a relation in which gravitational energy is explicitly included we consider Einstein's gravitational equations as stated at the beginning of Section 87.

We have

$$\left(\frac{-g}{c^2}\right)(R^{\mu\nu} - \tfrac{1}{2}g^{\mu\nu}R) = -\frac{1}{2c^2}\, g^{\alpha\beta}\, \frac{\partial^2 g^{\mu\nu}}{\partial x_\alpha\, \partial x_\beta} + N^{\mu\nu} \tag{89.03}$$

where $N^{\mu\nu}$ is determined by equations (87.01) to (87.05). On the other hand we have, in a harmonic coordinate system,

$$\frac{\partial^2}{\partial x_\alpha\, \partial x_\beta}(g^{\alpha\beta}g^{\mu\nu} - g^{\alpha\mu}g^{\beta\nu}) = g^{\alpha\beta}\, \frac{\partial^2 g^{\mu\nu}}{\partial x_\alpha\, \partial x_\beta} - \frac{\partial g^{\alpha\mu}}{\partial x_\beta}\, \frac{\partial g^{\beta\nu}}{\partial x_\alpha} \tag{89.04}$$

Multiplying this equation by $1/2c^2$ and adding it to the previous one we get

$$\left(-\frac{g}{c^2}\right)(R^{\mu\nu} - \tfrac{1}{2}g^{\mu\nu}R) + \frac{1}{2c^2}\, \frac{\partial^2}{\partial x_\alpha\, \partial x_\beta}(g^{\alpha\beta}g^{\mu\nu} - g^{\alpha\mu}g^{\beta\nu}) = L^{\mu\nu} \tag{89.05}$$

where

$$L^{\mu\nu} = N^{\mu\nu} - \frac{1}{2c^2}\, \frac{\partial g^{\alpha\mu}}{\partial x_\beta}\, \frac{\partial g^{\beta\nu}}{\partial x_\alpha} \tag{89.06}$$

Equation (89.05) would be an identity in an arbitrary coordinate system if $L^{\mu\nu}$ was understood to mean

$$L^{\mu\nu} = N^{\mu\nu} + \frac{1}{2c^2}\left(-\frac{\partial g^{\alpha\mu}}{\partial x_\beta}\, \frac{\partial g^{\beta\nu}}{\partial x_\alpha} + \frac{\partial g^{\alpha\beta}}{\partial x_\beta}\, \frac{\partial g^{\mu\nu}}{\partial x_\alpha} - \frac{\partial g^{\alpha\mu}}{\partial x_\alpha}\, \frac{\partial g^{\beta\nu}}{\partial x_\beta}\right) \tag{89.07}$$

This relation goes over into the preceding one if the coordinate system is harmonic. To prove equation (89.05) one has to use the complete expression (D.87) for the Einstein tensor which is derived in Appendix D.

Using Einstein's equations

$$R^{\mu\nu} - \tfrac{1}{2}g^{\mu\nu}R = -\frac{8\pi\gamma}{c^2}\, T^{\mu\nu} \tag{89.08}$$

and putting

$$U^{\mu\nu} = \left(-\frac{g}{c^2}\right)T^{\mu\nu} + \frac{c^2}{8\pi\gamma}\, L^{\mu\nu} \tag{89.09}$$

we can write equation (89.05) in the form

$$\frac{\partial^2}{\partial x_\alpha\, \partial x_\beta}(g^{\alpha\beta}g^{\mu\nu} - g^{\alpha\mu}g^{\beta\nu}) = 16\pi\gamma U^{\mu\nu} \tag{89.10}$$

Here we have on the left an expression of the form of the Krutkov tensor discussed in Section 31; the sum of the derivatives with respect to x_μ of the left-hand side of (89.10) is identically zero. We therefore have

$$\frac{\partial U^{\mu\nu}}{\partial x_\mu} = 0 \tag{89.11}$$

The set of quantities $U^{\mu\nu}$ is not a generally covariant tensor. It is a tensor only with respect to linear transformations ; in particular $U^{\mu\nu}$ is a tensor in a harmonic coordinate system. Adopting the somewhat artificial point of view that was described at the beginning of the preceding section the second term in (89.09) multiplied by c^2 can be interpreted as the energy tensor of the gravitational field and the first term multiplied by c^2 as the energy tensor of the material media and all fields other than gravitational. If other than harmonic systems of coordinates are also admitted such an interpretation will not be completely unique if the region of the mass system is considered. But at large distances from the masses, where space-time is nearly pseudo-Euclidean and the coordinates are, by choice, Galilean, the physical meaning of the $U^{\mu\nu}$ becomes unique in any case.

The conservation laws in integral form which follow from (89.11) are also obtained uniquely and do not depend on the arbitrariness connected with the deviation of the coordinate system from the harmonic within the region of masses. As we shall see, this is due to the fact that the volume integrals expressing the energy, the momentum and other quantities may be transformed into integrals over surfaces surrounding the masses.

We now go on to derive the integral form of the conservation laws. To do this we multiply the left-hand side of (89.11) by the Euclidean volume element

$$dx_1\, dx_2\, dx_3 = (dx)^3 \tag{89.12}$$

and integrate over some sufficiently large volume, including the system of masses. For the time being we leave the dimensions of the region of integration undetermined.

Using the Gauss-Ostrogradsky theorem we obtain equations of the form

$$\frac{d}{dt} \int U^{00}(dx)^3 = -\int n_i U^{0i}\, dS \tag{89.13}$$

and

$$\frac{d}{dt} \int U^{0i}(dx)^3 = -\int n_k U^{ik}\, dS \tag{89.14}$$

where n_i is the unit vector normal to the surface. If the boundary of the volume of integration is a sphere, we may put

$$n_i = \frac{x_i}{r}; \qquad dS = r^2 d\omega \tag{89.15}$$

where $d\omega$ is the element of solid angle.

As a consequence of the symmetry of the $U^{\mu\nu}$ in the indices μ and ν equations (89.11) also give rise to relations analogous to (31.06) and (31.07) which give, after integration

$$\frac{d}{dt} \int (x_i U^{0k} - x_k U^{0i})(dx)^3 = -\int n_j(x_i U^{jk} - x_k U^{ji})dS \tag{89.16}$$

and

$$\frac{d}{dt} \int (x_i U^{00} - t U^{0i})(dx)^3 = -\int n_j(x_i U^{j0} - t U^{ji})dS \tag{89.17}$$

We discuss the physical significance of the volume integrals on the left-hand sides of these equations. We put†

$$\overset{*}{M} = c^2 \int U^{00}(dx)^3 \tag{89.18}$$

$$\overset{*}{P^i} = c^2 \int U^{0i}(dx)^3 \tag{89.19}$$

$$\overset{*}{M^{ik}} = c^2 \int (x_i U^{0k} - x_k U^{0i})(dx)^3 \tag{89.20}$$

and

$$\overset{*}{M^{i0}} = c^2 \int (x_i U^{00} - t U^{0i})(dx)^3 \tag{89.21}$$

(We have written asterisks above the quantities (89.18) to (89.21) so that they should not be confused with the constants introduced when solving the equations of mechanics.) The quantity $\overset{*}{M}$ is the total mass of the system, including the mass pertaining to the field enclosed within the volume chosen. The $\overset{*}{P^i}$ represent the momentum and the $\overset{*}{M^{ik}}$ the angular momentum of the system. The $\overset{*}{M^{i0}}$ can be written in the form

$$\overset{*}{M^{i0}} = \overset{*}{M}\overset{*}{X^i} - \overset{*}{P^i}t \tag{89.22}$$

where the $\overset{*}{X^i}$ are the mass centre coordinates of the system. It is therefore clear that the $\overset{*}{M^{i0}}$ are the quantities involved in the law of mass centre motion.

The value of the volume integrals (89.18) to (89.21) may change somewhat with the size of the region of integration. This is so because the field also possesses energy, momentum, etc. However it will be made clear in Section 90 that with an appropriate choice of the region of integration the resulting indeterminateness in the value of the integrals is negligible in comparison with their total value.

We show now that not only the time derivatives of the quantities (89.18) to (89.21), but the quantities themselves may be represented as surface integrals. To demonstrate this we consider the structure of the expression (89.10) for $U^{\mu\nu}$. Putting $\mu = \nu = 0$ we get

$$16\pi\gamma U^{00} = \frac{\partial^2}{\partial x_\alpha \, \partial x_\beta} (\mathfrak{g}^{\alpha\beta}\mathfrak{g}^{00} - \mathfrak{g}^{\alpha 0}\mathfrak{g}^{\beta 0}) \tag{89.23}$$

For $\alpha = \beta = 0$ and also for $\alpha = 0$, $\beta = i$ (where $i = 1, 2, 3$) the expression on the right becomes zero. Therefore the indices α and β in (89.23) actually take on only spatial values and we can write

$$16\pi\gamma U^{00} = \frac{\partial^2}{\partial x_i \, \partial x_k} (\mathfrak{g}^{ik}\mathfrak{g}^{00} - \mathfrak{g}^{i0}\mathfrak{g}^{k0}) \tag{89.24}$$

whence

$$\overset{*}{M} = \frac{c^2}{16\pi\gamma} \int n_i \frac{\partial}{\partial x_k} (\mathfrak{g}^{ik}\mathfrak{g}^{00} - \mathfrak{g}^{i0}\mathfrak{g}^{k0}) dS \tag{89.25}$$

Similarly we have

$$16\pi\gamma U^{0i} = \frac{\partial^2}{\partial x_\alpha \, \partial x_j} (\mathfrak{g}^{\alpha j}\mathfrak{g}^{0i} - \mathfrak{g}^{\alpha 0}\mathfrak{g}^{ji}) \tag{89.26}$$

† We write M^{ik}, P^i and X^i with upper indices.

where j takes on only spatial values, but the values of α include zero. (We note that the value $\alpha = i$ actually drops out.) Insertion of (89.26) into the volume integral (89.19) gives

$$\overset{*}{P}{}^i = \frac{c^2}{16\pi\gamma} \int n_j \frac{\partial}{\partial x_\alpha} (\mathfrak{g}^{\alpha j} \mathfrak{g}^{0i} - \mathfrak{g}^{\alpha 0} \mathfrak{g}^{ji}) dS \qquad (89.27)$$

From (89.26) it is easy to derive the relation

$$16\pi\gamma(x_i U^{0k} - x_k U^{0i}) = \frac{\partial}{\partial x_j} \left\{ x_i \frac{\partial}{\partial x_\alpha} (\mathfrak{g}^{\alpha j} \mathfrak{g}^{0k} - \mathfrak{g}^{\alpha 0} \mathfrak{g}^{jk}) \right.$$
$$\left. - x_k \frac{\partial}{\partial x_\alpha} (\mathfrak{g}^{\alpha j} \mathfrak{g}^{0i} - \mathfrak{g}^{\alpha 0} \mathfrak{g}^{ji}) + \mathfrak{g}^{jk} \mathfrak{g}^{0i} - \mathfrak{g}^{ji} \mathfrak{g}^{0k} \right\} \qquad (89.28)$$

the right-hand side of which represents a sum of derivatives with respect to space coordinates. Inserting (89.28) into (89.20) and using the Gauss-Ostrogradsky theorem we obtain an expression for the angular momentum in the form of a surface integral :

$$\overset{*}{M}{}^{ik} = \frac{c^2}{16\pi\gamma} \int n_j \left\{ x_i \frac{\partial}{\partial x_\alpha} (\mathfrak{g}^{\alpha j} \mathfrak{g}^{0k} - \mathfrak{g}^{\alpha 0} \mathfrak{g}^{jk}) \right.$$
$$\left. - x_k \frac{\partial}{\partial x_\alpha} (\mathfrak{g}^{\alpha j} \mathfrak{g}^{0i} - \mathfrak{g}^{\alpha 0} \mathfrak{g}^{ji}) + \mathfrak{g}^{jk} \mathfrak{g}^{0i} - \mathfrak{g}^{ji} \mathfrak{g}^{0k} \right\} dS \qquad (89.29)$$

Finally, the first term in the expression (89.22) for $\overset{*}{M}{}^{i0}$ may be written as

$$\overset{**}{M}X^i = \frac{c^2}{16\pi\gamma} \int n_j \left\{ x_i \frac{\partial}{\partial x_k} (\mathfrak{g}^{jk} \mathfrak{g}^{00} - \mathfrak{g}^{j0} \mathfrak{g}^{k0}) + \mathfrak{g}^{j0} \mathfrak{g}^{i0} - \mathfrak{g}^{ji} \mathfrak{g}^{00} \right\} dS \qquad (89.30)$$

Thus all the quantities (89.18) to (89.21) have been represented as surface integrals. The value of these integrals depends only on the behaviour of the gravitational potentials at large distances.

When writing down the conservation laws in differential form we have used the symmetry of the set† of quantities $U^{\mu\nu}$ defined by (89.09) ; as we have indicated these quantities represent an analogue of a contravariant symmetric tensor. In the literature it is, however, more usual, since the earliest papers of Einstein, to employ a different set of quantities which are the analogue of a mixed (non-symmetrical) tensor and which are defined as follows.‡

At the end of Section 60 we derived an equation for the variation of the action integral, according to which

$$\delta \int L\sqrt{(-g)} \cdot (dx) = \int (R^{\alpha\beta} - \tfrac{1}{2} g^{\alpha\beta} R) \, \delta g_{\alpha\beta} \sqrt{(-g)} \cdot (dx) \qquad (89.31)$$

---

† A different, but also symmetric set of quantities is used in the book by Landau and Lifshitz, *The Classical Theory of Fields* [23].

‡ The reader not specially interested in comparing our form of the conservation laws with Einstein's may skip the rather tedious calculations from here to the end of Section 89.

Here L is the Lagrangian (60.23) and (dx) stands for the product of four differentials

$$(dx) = dx_0 \, dx_1 \, dx_2 \, dx_3 \tag{89.32}$$

Since

$$\delta g_{\alpha\beta} = -g_{\alpha\mu}g_{\beta\nu}\delta g^{\mu\nu} \tag{89.33}$$

equation (89.31) may also be written as

$$\delta \int L\sqrt{(-g)}\cdot(dx) = -\int (R_{\mu\nu} - \tfrac{1}{2}g_{\mu\nu}R)\, \delta g^{\mu\nu}\sqrt{(-g)}\cdot(dx) \tag{89.34}$$

Putting

$$g_\sigma^{\mu\nu} = \frac{\partial g^{\mu\nu}}{\partial x_\sigma} \tag{89.35}$$

we can define the " partial derivative " with respect to $g_\sigma^{\mu\nu}$ and to $g^{\mu\nu}$ by the equation

$$\delta[L\sqrt{(-g)}] = \frac{\partial[L\sqrt{(-g)}]}{\partial g_\sigma^{\mu\nu}} \delta g_\sigma^{\mu\nu} + \frac{\partial[L\sqrt{(-g)}]}{\partial g^{\mu\nu}} \delta g^{\mu\nu} \tag{89.36}$$

Insertion of (89.36) into (89.34) and integration by parts shows that the conservative tensor

$$G_{\mu\nu} = R_{\mu\nu} - \tfrac{1}{2}g_{\mu\nu}R \tag{89.37}$$

multiplied by $\sqrt{(-g)}$ may be written as

$$\sqrt{(-g)}\cdot G_{\mu\nu} = \frac{\partial}{\partial x_\sigma} \frac{\partial[L\sqrt{(-g)}]}{\partial g_\sigma^{\mu\nu}} - \frac{\partial[L\sqrt{(-g)}]}{\partial g^{\mu\nu}} \tag{89.38}$$

We now introduce a set of quantities w_ρ^σ defined by the equation

$$2\sqrt{(-g)}\cdot w_\rho^\sigma = g_\rho^{\mu\nu}\frac{\partial[L\sqrt{(-g)}]}{\partial g_\sigma^{\mu\nu}} - \delta_\rho^\sigma[L\sqrt{(-g)}] \tag{89.39}$$

Forming the sum of derivatives of (89.39) with respect to the x_σ and using (89.38) we get

$$\frac{1}{\sqrt{(-g)}} \frac{\partial[\sqrt{(-g)}\cdot w_\rho^\sigma]}{\partial x_\sigma} = \frac{1}{2}\frac{\partial g^{\mu\nu}}{\partial x_\rho} G_{\mu\nu} \tag{89.40}$$

But for any symmetric tensor we have

$$\frac{1}{2}\frac{\partial g^{\mu\nu}}{\partial x_\rho} G_{\mu\nu} = -\frac{1}{2}\frac{\partial g_{\mu\nu}}{\partial x_\rho} G^{\mu\nu} = -\Gamma_{\nu\rho}^\mu G_\mu^\nu \tag{89.41}$$

Therefore the preceding equation may be written as

$$\frac{1}{\sqrt{(-g)}} \frac{\partial[\sqrt{(-g)}\cdot w_\rho^\sigma]}{\partial x_\sigma} = -\Gamma_{\nu\rho}^\mu G_\mu^\nu \tag{89.42}$$

On the other hand, the divergence of the conservative tensor (which vanishes identically) has the form

$$\nabla_\sigma G_\rho^\sigma = \frac{1}{\sqrt{(-g)}} \frac{\partial[\sqrt{(-g)}\cdot G_\rho^\sigma]}{\partial x_\sigma} - \Gamma_{\nu\rho}^\mu G_\mu^\nu = 0 \tag{89.43}$$

Here the second term coincides with the right-hand side of (89.42). Eliminating it from (89.42) and (89.43) we get

$$\frac{\partial}{\partial x_\sigma}[\sqrt{(-g)}\cdot G_\rho^\sigma + \sqrt{(-g)}\cdot w_\rho^\sigma] = 0 \tag{89.44}$$

We now express G_ρ^σ in terms of T_ρ^σ by the gravitational equations and put

$$-\frac{c^2}{8\pi\gamma}\, w_\rho^\sigma = t_\rho^\sigma \qquad (89.45)$$

Then we can write the preceding equation as

$$\frac{\partial}{\partial x_\sigma}\,[\sqrt{(-g)}\cdot T_\rho^\sigma + \sqrt{(-g)}\cdot t_\rho^\sigma] = 0 \qquad (89.46)$$

This equation represents the differential form of the conservation law as it is most frequently stated in the literature. The quantity

$$\overset{*}{U}{}_\rho^\sigma = \frac{\sqrt{(-g)}}{c}\,(T_\rho^\sigma + t_\rho^\sigma) \qquad (89.47)$$

corresponds to our $U^{\mu\nu}$, but it is not symmetric in its indices. Therefore it is not possible to derive from the relation

$$\frac{\partial \overset{*}{U}{}_\rho^\sigma}{\partial x_\sigma} = 0 \qquad (89.48)$$

equations corresponding to the conservation laws for angular momentum and for mass centre motion. As for the conservation laws for energy and momentum, both formulations, based on (89.11) and on (89.48) respectively, give equivalent results. We shall demonstrate this, with the omission of some fairly complicated manipulation

It follows from the definition (89.39) of the w_ρ^σ that

$$2w_\rho^\sigma = -\Gamma_{\alpha\beta}^\sigma \frac{\partial g^{\alpha\beta}}{\partial x_\rho} - \delta_\rho^\sigma L + y_\alpha \frac{\partial g^{\sigma\alpha}}{\partial x_\rho} + (y^\sigma - \Gamma^\sigma)y_\rho \qquad (89.49)$$

Hence, using the equations of Appendix D, we obtain

$$2\sqrt{(-g)}\cdot(G_\rho^\sigma + w_\rho^\sigma) = \frac{\partial}{\partial x_\beta}\left[\frac{g_{\rho\tau}}{\sqrt{(-g)}}\frac{\partial}{\partial x_\alpha}(g^{\sigma\alpha}g^{\tau\beta} - g^{\sigma\tau}g^{\alpha\beta})\right] \qquad (89.50)$$

and after multiplication by $-c$:

$$16\pi\gamma\overset{*}{U}{}_\rho^\sigma = \frac{\partial}{\partial x_\beta}\left[\frac{cg_{\rho\tau}}{\sqrt{(-g)}}\frac{\partial}{\partial x_\alpha}(g^{\sigma\tau}g^{\alpha\beta} - g^{\sigma\alpha}g^{\tau\beta})\right] \qquad (89.51)$$

This equation is analogous to (89.10). We obtain from it

$$\int \overset{*}{U}{}_\rho^0(dx)^3 = \frac{c}{16\pi\gamma}\int \frac{g_{\rho\tau}}{\sqrt{(-g)}}\,n_j\,\frac{\partial}{\partial x_\alpha}(g^{\alpha j}g^{0\tau} - g^{\alpha 0}g^{j\tau})dS \qquad (89.52)$$

Since the integration is over a distant surface we can take the limiting value of $g_{\rho\tau}/\sqrt{(-g)}$ outside the integral. Comparing the expression so obtained with (89.52) and (89.27) we may write

$$c\int \overset{*}{U}{}_\rho^0(dx)^3 = \left(\frac{g_{\rho\tau}}{\sqrt{(-g)}}\right)_\infty \overset{*}{P}{}^\tau \qquad (89.53)$$

where $\overset{*}{P}{}^0 = \overset{*}{M}$ and $\overset{*}{P}{}^i$ has the value (89.27). The last equation can also be written in the form

$$\int \overset{*}{U}{}_\rho^0(dx)^3 = \left(\frac{cg_{\rho\tau}}{\sqrt{(-g)}}\right)_\infty \cdot \int U^{0\tau}(dx)^3 \qquad (89.54)$$

These relations confirm the fact that in spite of the difference in the differential forms of the conservation laws, the corresponding integral laws are equivalent. In addition, the presence of the quantities $(g_{\rho\tau})_\infty$ in the relations (89.54) shows clearly that the total energy and total momentum of the system form a four-dimensional vector in the *Galilean* space-time in which the system is embedded.

90. The Emission of Gravitational Waves and its Role in the Energy Balance

In Section 89 we stated the conservation laws for energy and other quantities as equations expressing the balance of the quantity in question, i.e. expressing the fact that a change in the total amount of the quantity enclosed in some volume occurs only on account of the flux of the quantity across the surface bounding the volume.

We now examine the question to what extent the flux through the surface may be neglected and the quantity in question may be considered constant. In other words, we enquire to what extent one can speak of conservation laws in the narrower sense. We shall confine these considerations to the conservation laws for energy and momentum.

We use the definitions (89.18) and (89.19) for mass and momentum and take the surface of integration to be spherical. Then, according to (89.13) to (89.15), we can write:

$$\frac{d\overset{*}{M}}{dt} = -c^2 \int n_k U^{0k} r^2 \, d\omega \tag{90.01}$$

and

$$\frac{d\overset{*}{P^i}}{dt} = -c^2 \int n_k U^{ik} r^2 \, d\omega \tag{90.02}$$

the integration being over solid angle. We can take the surface of integration to be so distant that it lies entirely in the wave zone. Using the results of Section 87 it is simple to see that there the quantities $L^{\mu\nu}$ defined by (89.06) or (89.07) reduce to the $N^{\mu\nu}$. Taking for the $N^{\mu\nu}$ the values (87.42) and for the $T^{\mu\nu}$ the values (87.45) corresponding to electromagnetic radiation, we may put

$$U^{\mu\nu} = \sigma k^\mu k^\nu \tag{90.03}$$

where σ is the (electromagnetic and gravitational) energy density introduced in Section 87. Using equation (87.53) which gives the dependence of the energy density σ on the distance r, we can also write

$$U^{\mu\nu} = \frac{\sigma_0(\tau, \mathbf{n})}{r^2} k^\mu k^\nu \tag{90.04}$$

Taking the value of k^ν from (87.21) we have

$$U^{0k} = \frac{\sigma_0(\tau, \mathbf{n})}{c^3 r^2} n_k; \qquad U^{ik} = \frac{\sigma_0(\tau, \mathbf{n})}{c^2 r^2} n_i n_k \tag{90.05}$$

and therefore

$$n_k U^{0k} = \frac{\sigma_0(\tau, \mathbf{n})}{c^3 r^2}; \qquad n_k U^{ik} = \frac{\sigma_0(\tau, \mathbf{n})}{c^2 r^2} n_i \tag{90.06}$$

Inserting these values into (90.01) and (90.02) we get

$$\frac{d\overset{*}{M}}{dt} = -\frac{1}{c}\int \sigma_0(\tau, \mathbf{n})d\omega \tag{90.07}$$

and

$$\frac{d\overset{*}{P^i}}{dt} = -\int n_i\sigma_0(\tau, \mathbf{n})d\omega \tag{90.08}$$

But the density σ_0 is an even function of the n_i, both for the electromagnetic and the gravitational field. Therefore equation (90.08) gives

$$\frac{d\overset{*}{P^i}}{dt} = 0 \tag{90.09}$$

As for equation (90.07), the integral in it will not be zero because σ_0 is a positive quantity and it does not tend to zero for increasing r. Therefore an outward flux of mass will always take place.

We consider first that part of this flow of mass which arises from the emission of gravitational waves. To do this we must replace σ_0 by the expression σ_{0g} given in (87.54), into which we must insert the values of $f^{\alpha\beta}$ from (87.60) and (87.62). For brevity we put

$$A_{ik} = \frac{d^3}{d\tau^3} D_{ik}(\tau) \tag{90.10}$$

Equation (87.54) then gives

$$\sigma_{0g} = \frac{\gamma}{8\pi c^6}\{A^2 - 2A_iA_i + A_{ik}A_{ik} - \tfrac{1}{2}(A - A_{jj})^2\} \tag{90.11}$$

where we have introduced the short notation

$$A_i = A_{ik}n_k; \qquad A = A_in_i = A_{ik}n_in_k \tag{90.12}$$

It may be shown that σ_{0g} depends not on all six A_{ik} but only on five combinations of them, namely on the quantities

$$B_{ik} = A_{ik} - a\delta_{ik}; \qquad a = \tfrac{1}{3}A_{jj} \tag{90.13}$$

which are subject to the relation

$$B_{11} + B_{22} + B_{33} = 0 \tag{90.14}$$

The B_{ik} are the third derivatives of the quadrupole moments

$$\overset{*}{D}_{ik}(t) = \int \rho\,(x_ix_k - \tfrac{1}{3}\delta_{ik}r^2)(dx)^3 \tag{90.15}$$

for $t = \tau$. Expressing the A_{ik} in terms of the B_{ik} and inserting first into (90.12) and then into (90.11) we can verify that the quantity a drops out of these equations and that,

$$\sigma_{0g} = \frac{\gamma}{8\pi c^6}\{B_{ik}B_{ik} - 2B_iB_i + \tfrac{1}{2}B^2\} \tag{90.16}$$

where the quantities B_i and B should be expressed in terms of the B_{ik} by means of formulae similar to (90.12). We check that the quantity σ_{0g} is always positive. Since it is invariant under three-dimensional rotations, it is sufficient to make the check for any fixed direction of the vector $\mathbf{n}$ that enters the expressions for B_i and B. Putting •

$$n_1 = 1; \qquad n_2 = 0; \qquad n_3 = 0 \tag{90.17}$$

and using (90.14) we get from (90.16)

$$\sigma_{0g} = \frac{\gamma}{8\pi c^6}\{\tfrac{1}{2}(B_{22} - B_{33})^2 + 2B_{23}^2\} \tag{90.18}$$

which is indeed positive.

Equation (90.07) involves the integral of the expression (90.16) taken over all solid angles. To evaluate it we can use the relations

$$\frac{1}{4\pi}\int n_i n_k d\omega = \tfrac{1}{3}\delta_{ik} \tag{90.19}$$

and

$$\frac{1}{4\pi}\int n_i n_k n_l n_m \, d\omega = \tfrac{1}{15}(\delta_{ik}\delta_{lm} + \delta_{il}\delta_{km} + \delta_{im}\delta_{kl}) \tag{90.20}$$

which are most simply obtained by use of the identity

$$\frac{1}{4\pi}\int (a_i n_i)^{2p} \, d\omega = \frac{1}{2p+1}\,(a_1^2 + a_2^2 + a_3^2)^p \tag{90.21}$$

Taking first $p = 1$ and then $p = 2$ and examining the coefficients of the powers and products of the a_i we immediately get the required results. The integration in (90.21) is readily performed using a polar coordinate system with its axis in the direction of the vector **a**.

Using the relations (90.19) and (90.20) we get

$$\frac{1}{4\pi}\int (B_{ik}B_{ik} - 2B_iB_i + \tfrac{1}{2}B^2) \, d\omega = \tfrac{2}{5}B_{ik}B_{ik} \tag{90.22}$$

Inserting (90.16) into (90.07) and using (90.22) we get

$$\frac{d\overset{*}{M}}{dt} = -\frac{\gamma}{5c^7}\,B_{ik}B_{ik} \tag{90.23}$$

This expression gives us the rate at which mass flows out of the system as a result of gravitational radiation. The corresponding equation for the rate of energy loss is obtained by multiplying (90.23) by c^2 and has the form

$$\frac{d\overset{*}{W}}{dt} = -\frac{\gamma}{5c^5}\,B_{ik}B_{ik} \tag{90.24}$$

This loss of mass and of energy is completely negligible owing to the enormous value of the constant

$$\frac{5c^3}{\gamma} = 2 \times 10^{39} \text{ g/sec} \tag{90.25}$$

If B characterizes the order of magnitude of the B_{ik}, then taking the system formed by the Sun and Jupiter we can put, in round figures

$$\frac{B}{c^2} = 10^{14} \text{ g/sec} \tag{90.26}$$

since the mass of Jupiter, its angular velocity of revolution around the Sun and the ratio of the square of its orbital speed to c^2 have the values

$$m_J = 2 \cdot 10^{33} g; \qquad \omega_J = 2 \cdot 10^{-8} \text{ sec}; \qquad \frac{v_J^2}{c^2} = 2 \cdot 10^{-9} \qquad (90.27)$$

Dividing the square of the number (90.26) by the value of the constant (90.25) we get a loss of mass of $5 \cdot 10^{-12}$ g/sec. Translated into energy units this corresponds to the ridiculously small power of 450 W. For comparison we mention that the power of Solar electromagnetic radiation is about $4 \cdot 10^{12}$ g/sec., which is about 10^{24} times greater.

This estimate completely confirms the conclusion stated at the end of Section 88 that in the problem of the gravitational interaction of heavy bodies gravitational waves play no part at all.

Let us further examine the question with what accuracy a system of gravitating masses may be considered conservative if electromagnetic radiation is neglected.

When we solved the problem of mechanics in Chapter VI we deduced the equations of motion to an accuracy that allowed us to find corrections to the energy of order Mq^4/c^2 where q was some characteristic speed. Equation (90.24) shows that apart from electromagnetic radiation we could have gone further, up to terms of order Mq^6/c^4. This is the accuracy to which the many body problem can be formulated as a problem of mechanics, with its ten classical integrals. We recall that in the problem of interacting charges (Sections 26 to 28) the greatest attainable accuracy corresponds to the order Mq^4/c^2, because there radiation plays a much more important part.

91. The Connection between the Conservation Laws for the Field and the Integrals of Mechanics

In Section 89 we derived equations for the time derivatives of the quantities $\overset{*}{M}$, $\overset{*}{P^i}$, $\overset{*}{M^{ik}}$, $\overset{*}{M^{i0}}$ and found a representation of the quantities in the form of surface integrals. The expressions found for the total mass and for the momentum have the form

$$\overset{*}{M} = \frac{c^2}{16\pi\gamma} \int n_i \frac{\partial}{\partial x_k} (\mathfrak{g}^{ik}\mathfrak{g}^{00} - \mathfrak{g}^{i0}\mathfrak{g}^{k0}) dS \qquad (91.01)$$

and

$$\overset{*}{P^i} = \frac{c^2}{16\pi\gamma} \int n_j \frac{\partial}{\partial x_\alpha} (\mathfrak{g}^{\alpha j}\mathfrak{g}^{0i} - \mathfrak{g}^{\alpha 0}\mathfrak{g}^{ji}) dS \qquad (91.02)$$

The angular momentum is given by

$$\overset{*}{M^{ik}} = \frac{c^2}{16\pi\gamma} \int n_j \Big\{ x_i \frac{\partial}{\partial x_\alpha} (\mathfrak{g}^{\alpha j}\mathfrak{g}^{0k} - \mathfrak{g}^{\alpha 0}\mathfrak{g}^{jk})$$
$$- x_k \frac{\partial}{\partial x_\alpha} (\mathfrak{g}^{\alpha j}\mathfrak{g}^{0i} - \mathfrak{g}^{\alpha 0}\mathfrak{g}^{ji}) + \mathfrak{g}^{jk}\mathfrak{g}^{0i} - \mathfrak{g}^{ji}\mathfrak{g}^{0k} \Big\} dS \qquad (91.03)$$

The quantity $\overset{*}{M^{i0}}$ involved in the equation of mass centre motion is given by

$$\overset{*}{M^{i0}} = \overset{*}{M}X^i - \overset{*}{P^i}t \qquad (91.04)$$

where $\overset{*}{P^i}$ has the value (91.02) and the first term is given by

$$\overset{*}{M}\overset{*}{X^i} = \frac{c^2}{16\pi\gamma} \int n_j \left\{ x_i \frac{\partial}{\partial x_k} (\mathfrak{g}^{jk}\mathfrak{g}^{00} - \mathfrak{g}^{i0}\mathfrak{g}^{k0}) + \mathfrak{g}^{j0}\mathfrak{g}^{i0} - \mathfrak{g}^{ji}\mathfrak{g}^{00} \right\} dS \quad (91.05)$$

According to how distant the surface of integration S is chosen to be, the values of these integrals for the total mass, and the other quantities will be somewhat different because they will include a greater or lesser fraction of the mass, etc., pertaining to the " pure " gravitational and electromagnetic radiation. As we have demonstrated in the preceding section, the energy of gravitational radiation is completely negligible. If we also neglect electromagnetic radiation we can place the surface of integration not in the wave zone, but instead at "moderately large" distances from the system of masses; by doing this we, so to speak, cut off the mass and energy of the material media and the static fields, from the mass and energy of pure radiation.

In Sections 84 and 85 we derived approximate expressions for the gravitational potentials at moderately large distances from the bodies; these we shall now use. According to (85.46) the expression for $\mathfrak{g}^{00}$ has the form

$$\mathfrak{g}^{00} = \frac{1}{c} + \frac{4\gamma M}{c^3 r} + \frac{4\gamma x_j}{c^3 r^3} MX^j + \frac{\partial^2}{\partial x_j \partial x_k} \frac{2\gamma}{c^3 r} D_{jk} - \frac{\partial^3}{\partial x_i \partial x_j \partial x_k} \frac{2\gamma}{3c^3 r} \int \rho x_i x_j x_k (dx)^3$$
$$+ \frac{7\gamma^2 M^2}{c^5 r^2} + \frac{14\gamma^2 M^2 X^j x_j}{c^5 r^4} + \frac{4}{c^5} \frac{\partial^2 W}{\partial t^2} \quad (91.06)$$

The mixed components are given by (85.41) as

$$\mathfrak{g}^{0i} = \frac{4\gamma}{c^3 r} P^i + \frac{2\gamma x_j M_{ji}}{c^3 r^3} - \frac{\partial^2}{\partial x_j \partial t} \frac{2\gamma}{c^3 r} D_{ji} + \frac{\partial^2}{\partial x_j \partial x_k} \frac{2\gamma}{c^3 r} \int \rho v_i x_j x_k (dx)^3$$
$$+ \frac{7\gamma^2 M P^i}{c^5 r^2} + \frac{\gamma^2 M P^k x_i x_k}{c^5 r^4} + \frac{4}{c^5} \frac{\partial^2 W_i}{\partial t^2} \quad (91.07)$$

Finally, (85.48) gives the spatial components as

$$\mathfrak{g}^{ik} = - c\delta_{ik} + \frac{\partial^2}{\partial t^2} \frac{2\gamma}{c^3 r} D_{ik}$$
$$- \frac{\partial^2}{\partial x_j \partial t} \frac{2\gamma}{c^3 r} \int \rho(x_j x_i v_k + x_j x_k v_i - x_i x_k v_j)(dx)^3 + \frac{\gamma^2 M^2 x_i x_k}{c^3 r^4} \quad (91.08)$$

In the equations (91.06) to (91.08) we have written X^i and P^i instead of X_i and P_i in order to stress the vector character of these quantities. The value of the quantity D_{ji} is given by (85.39); it is

$$D_{ji}(t) = \int \rho x_i x_j \left\{ 1 + \frac{1}{c^2}(\tfrac{1}{2}v^2 + \Pi - \tfrac{1}{2}U) \right\} (dx)^3 + \frac{7}{2c^2} \delta_{ij} \int \rho W (dx)^3 \quad (91.09)$$

When inserting D_{ji} into equation (91.08) for $\mathfrak{g}^{ik}$ it is sufficient to retain the main terms which are just the usual moments of inertia. The argument of D_{ji} is the time t, and not $t - r^*/c$ as in the wave zone.

The expressions for $\mathfrak{g}^{00}$ and $\mathfrak{g}^{0i}$ also contain terms involving W and W_i which represent retardation corrections. These terms are approximately given by

$$\frac{4}{c^2}\frac{\partial^2 W}{\partial t^2} = \frac{\gamma}{c^5}\left(\frac{\delta_{jk}}{r} - \frac{x_j x_k}{r^3}\right)\frac{d^2 D_{jk}}{dt^2} - \frac{\gamma}{3c^5}\frac{\partial^3 r}{\partial x_i\,\partial x_k\,\partial x_l}\frac{d^2}{dt^2}\int \rho x_i x_k x_l (dx)^3$$

$$(91.10)$$

and

$$\frac{4}{c^5}\frac{\partial^2 W_i}{\partial t^2} = -\frac{\gamma}{c^5}\frac{x_j}{r}\frac{d^3 D_{ji}}{dt^3} + \frac{\gamma}{c^5}\left(\frac{\delta_{jk}}{r} - \frac{x_j x_k}{r^3}\right)\frac{d^2}{dt^2}\int \rho v_i x_j x_k (dx)^3 \qquad (91.11)$$

The expressions for the $\mathfrak{g}^{\mu\nu}$ just stated contain the quantities M, P^i, M^{ik} and $MX^i - P^i t$ the constancy of which is the expression of the mechanical conservation laws. We may therefore expect these quantities to coincide with the values of the integrals $\overset{*}{M}$, $\overset{*}{P^i}$, $\overset{*}{M^{ik}}$ and $\overset{*}{M^{i0}}$ which represent the total mass, momentum, etc., of the whole system, including the field. We now verify this.

We have to insert the expressions (91.06) to (91.08) for the $\mathfrak{g}^{\mu\nu}$ into the surface integrals (91.01) to (91.05) and to evaluate them approximately. In this calculation we shall retain terms of order q^2/c^2 relative to the main terms when calculating $\overset{*}{M}$ and $\overset{*}{P^i}$, but for simplicity we shall deal only with the main terms in the evaluation of $\overset{*}{M^{ik}}$ and $\overset{*}{M^{i0}}$.

Leaving out the retardation term, we see that in all first derivatives of the $\mathfrak{g}^{\mu\nu}$ the terms that decrease most slowly with distance are those of order $1/r^2$ which are all odd in the coordinates x_1, x_2, x_3, except for the derivative $\partial \mathfrak{g}^{ik}/\partial t$ which decreases as $1/r$ and is even in the coordinates. In general the retardation corrections decrease more slowly but the correction in $\partial \mathfrak{g}^{00}/\partial x_k$ also decreases as $1/r^2$ and is also odd in x_1, x_2. x_3.

Bearing in mind these remarks we form the expression

$$\frac{\partial}{\partial x_k}(\mathfrak{g}^{ik}\mathfrak{g}^{00} - \mathfrak{g}^{i0}\mathfrak{g}^{k0}) = \mathfrak{g}^{i\alpha}\frac{\partial \mathfrak{g}^{00}}{\partial x_\alpha} - \mathfrak{g}^{0\alpha}\frac{\partial \mathfrak{g}^{i0}}{\partial x_\alpha} \qquad (91.12)$$

that enters equation (91.01) for $\overset{*}{M}$. The right-hand side is obtained from the left by replacing the summation over k by summation over α, including the value 0, and by using the harmonic conditions. Since it is sufficient for the evaluation to know the odd terms of order $1/r^2$ we may replace by their limiting values all the $\mathfrak{g}^{\mu\nu}$ in (91.12) that are not differentiated. Doing this we get

$$\mathfrak{g}^{i\alpha}\frac{\partial \mathfrak{g}^{00}}{\partial x_\alpha} - \mathfrak{g}^{0\alpha}\frac{\partial \mathfrak{g}^{i0}}{\partial x_\alpha} = -c\frac{\partial \mathfrak{g}^{00}}{\partial x_i} - \frac{1}{c}\frac{\partial \mathfrak{g}^{i0}}{\partial t} \qquad (91.13)$$

This approximation is still valid if the retardation corrections are included, bearing in mind their order of magnitude in terms of q/c.

Using equations (91.06) and (91.07) for $\mathfrak{g}^{00}$ and $\mathfrak{g}^{i0}$, multiplying (91.13) by $n_i = x_i/r$ and summing over i, we get the following expression for the integrand in (91.01)

$$-cn_i\frac{\partial \mathfrak{g}^{00}}{\partial x_i} - \frac{n_i}{c}\frac{\partial \mathfrak{g}^{i0}}{\partial t} = \frac{4\gamma M}{c^2 r^2} + \frac{\gamma}{c^4 r^2}(\delta_{ij} - 3n_i n_j)\ddot{D}_{ij} \qquad (91.14)$$

It is easy to see that the second term on the right is proportional to a second order spherical harmonic so that it gives zero on integration over the sphere. There remains only the first term, and the integral for $\overset{*}{M}$ becomes

$$\overset{*}{M} = M \tag{91.15}$$

Thus, in this approximation, the total mass $\overset{*}{M}$ of the system including the field, is equal to the mechanical mass M.

Similarly we can calculate the quantity $\overset{*}{P^i}$. We have approximately

$$g^{\alpha j} \frac{\partial g^{0i}}{\partial x_\alpha} - g^{\alpha 0} \frac{\partial g^{ji}}{\partial x_\alpha} = -c \frac{\partial g^{0i}}{\partial x_j} - \frac{1}{c} \frac{\partial g^{ji}}{\partial t} \tag{91.16}$$

and further

$$-cn_j \frac{\partial g^{0i}}{\partial x_j} - \frac{1}{c} n_j \frac{\partial g^{ji}}{\partial t}$$

$$= \frac{4\gamma}{c^2 r^2} P^i - \frac{2\gamma}{c^4 r} n_j \frac{d^2 D_{ij}}{dt^2} + \frac{\gamma}{c^4 r^2} (\delta_{kl} - 3n_k n_l) \frac{d^2}{dt^2} \int \rho v_i x_k x_l (dx)^3 \tag{91.17}$$

Here terms of the order q^2/c^2 as compared with the main terms have been retained and in them the expansion in inverse powers of r has been taken up to terms in $1/r^2$. In forming the expression (91.17) both terms of the retardation correction were included.

On the right of (91.17) the second and third terms are proportional to spherical harmonics and give zero on integration. The first term gives

$$\overset{*}{P^i} = P^i \tag{91.18}$$

Thus the total momentum also is equal to the mechanical momentum.

We now pass on to the evaluation of $\overset{*}{M^{ik}}$. In the approximation stated we have

$$n_j(g^{jk} g^{0i} - g^{ji} g^{0k}) = -c(n_k g^{0i} - n_i g^{0k}) \tag{91.19}$$

We use equation (91.16) and the obvious identity

$$n_i x_j = n_j x_i \tag{91.20}$$

and can then write the integral (91.03) for $\overset{*}{M^{ik}}$, as

$$\overset{*}{M^{ik}} = \frac{c^2}{16\pi\gamma} \int \left\{ cn_i \left(g^{0k} - x_j \frac{\partial g^{0k}}{\partial x_j} - \frac{1}{c^2} x_j \frac{\partial g^{jk}}{\partial t} \right) \right.$$

$$\left. - cn_k \left(g^{0i} - x_j \frac{\partial g^{0i}}{\partial x_j} - \frac{1}{c^2} x_j \frac{\partial g^{ji}}{\partial t} \right) \right\} dS \tag{91.21}$$

To evaluate the integrals containing $\partial g^{jk}/\partial t$ we would need to know g^{jk}, including terms decreasing as $1/r^3$ (we have in mind terms in g^{jk} containing c^3 in the denominator). But in Section 84 we have determined g^{jk} only up to terms decreasing as $1/r^2$. Although the evaluation of the missing terms does not present any difficulties in principle, we can avoid it, if in (91.21) we confine ourselves to the main terms and observe that the integrals containing $\partial \mathfrak{g}^{ik}/\partial t$ contribute only corrections of order q^2/c^2. The integrand in (91.21) then becomes

$$c n_i \left(\mathfrak{g}^{0k} - x_j \frac{\partial \mathfrak{g}^{0k}}{\partial x_j} \right) - c n_k \left(\mathfrak{g}^{0i} - x_j \frac{\partial \mathfrak{g}^{0i}}{\partial x_j} \right)$$

$$= \frac{4\gamma}{c^2 r^2} M_{ik} + \frac{8\gamma}{c^2 r} (n_i P_k - n_k P_i) + \frac{2\gamma}{c^2 r^2} (\delta_{kj} - 3 n_k n_j)(M_{ji} + \dot{D}_{ji})$$

$$- \frac{2\gamma}{c^2 r^2} (\delta_{ij} - 3 n_i n_j)(M_{jk} + \dot{D}_{jk}) \qquad (91.22)$$

Here the right-hand side is expressed in terms of spherical harmonics and involves harmonics of zero, first and second orders†. On integration only the first term remains and we get

$$\overset{*}{M}{}^{ik} = M_{ik} \qquad (91.23)$$

as was to be expected.

It remains to evaluate (91.05). Using (91.13), we can write this integral as

$$\overset{*}{M}\overset{*}{X}{}^{i} = \frac{c^2}{16\pi\gamma} \int \left\{ c n_i \left(\mathfrak{g}^{00} - x_j \frac{\partial \mathfrak{g}^{00}}{\partial x_j} - \frac{1}{c^2} x_j \frac{\partial \mathfrak{g}^{j0}}{\partial t} \right) - \frac{1}{c} n_j (\mathfrak{g}^{ij} + c \delta_{ij}) \right\} (dx)^3 \cdot$$

$$(91.24)$$

Since $\partial \mathfrak{g}^{j0}/\partial t$ can be expressed in terms of the $\partial \mathfrak{g}^{jk}/\partial x_k$ by use of the harmonic conditions and the latter quantities may be calculated from (91.08) up to terms decreasing as $1/r^3$ we could evaluate all terms in the integral. But to simplify calculations which are of no great interest we restrict ourselves again to the main terms. Then we can write

$$c n_i \left(\mathfrak{g}^{00} - x_j \frac{\partial \mathfrak{g}^{00}}{\partial x_j} \right) = \frac{4\gamma M X^i}{c^2 r^2} + n_i \left(1 + \frac{8\gamma M}{c^2 r} \right) - \frac{4\gamma}{c^2 r^2} (\delta_{ij} - 3 n_i n_j) M X^j$$

$$(91.25)$$

Hence, arguing as before, we obtain

$$\overset{*}{M}\overset{*}{X}{}^{i} = M X^i \qquad (91.26)$$

and since we have already verified that $\overset{*}{P}{}^{i} = P^i$, we have

$$\overset{*}{M}{}^{i0} = M X^i - P^i t \qquad (91.27)$$

as it should be.

The calculations just performed can be thought of as a verification of the correctness of the approximate solution of Einstein's equations given by the equations (91.06) to (91.08). At the same time the results of these calculations illustrate clearly the relation between the conservation laws stated in general form and the integrals of mechanics.

---

† If terms of relative order q^2/c^2 were taken into account the integrand in (91.21) would involve harmonics of up to fourth order.

92. The Uniqueness Theorem for the Wave Equation

In the next section we shall deal with the problem whether for an isolated system harmonic coordinates are uniquely determined. In that investigation we shall need a theorem which establishes the condition of uniqueness for the solution of the wave equation

$$\Box\psi = 0 \tag{92.01}$$

We shall now prove this theorem for the wave equation with constant coefficients for which

$$\Box\psi = \frac{1}{c^2}\frac{\partial^2\psi}{\partial t^2} - \left(\frac{\partial^2\psi}{\partial x^2} + \frac{\partial^2\psi}{\partial y^2} + \frac{\partial^2\psi}{\partial z^2}\right) \tag{92.02}$$

We subject the function

$$\psi = \psi(x, y, z, t) \tag{92.03}$$

to the following conditions :—

(a) *The condition of boundedness :* for all x, y, z and t the inequality

$$|\psi| < M_0 \tag{92.04}$$

shall hold so that the function is uniformly bounded ;

(b) *The condition of decrease at infinity :* if the distance from the origin, $r = \sqrt{(x^2 + y^2 + x^2)}$ increases without limit the solution shall satisfy the inequality

$$|\psi| < \frac{M}{r} \tag{92.05}$$

for all t and its first derivatives shall satisfy

$$|\operatorname{grad}\psi| < \frac{M_1}{r}; \qquad \left|\frac{1}{c}\frac{\partial\psi}{\partial t}\right| < \frac{M_1}{r} \tag{92.06}$$

Thus the function ψ and its first derivatives are to decrease at infinity in inverse proportion to r, or more rapidly. The quantities M_0, M and M_1 are positive constants.

(c) *The condition of outward radiation :* for $r \to \infty$ and all values of $t'_0 = t + r/c$ in an arbitrary fixed interval the limiting condition

$$\lim_{r\to\infty}\left\{\frac{\partial(r\psi)}{\partial r} + \frac{1}{c}\frac{\partial(r\psi)}{\partial t}\right\} = 0 \tag{92.07}$$

shall be satisfied. It expresses the fact that there are outgoing waves only, waves coming from outside being absent.

We can now formulate the following *uniqueness theorem.*

The solution of the homogeneous wave equation $\Box\psi = 0$ *which satisfies the conditions* (a), (b) *and* (c) *is identically zero.*

In the proof of this theorem we start by using Kirchhoff's formula for the solution of the wave equation.† Kirchhoff's formula expresses the values of

---

† For Kirchhoff's formula and its generalizations, S. L. Sobolev's formulæ, see V. I. Smirnov, *A Course of Higher Mathematics*, Vol. II, Sec. 202, 1957, and Vol. IV, Sec. 148, 1958.

the function ψ at a point in space $\mathbf{r}_0$ at time t_0 in terms of the values of ψ and its derivatives on a surface S surrounding this point, the value of ψ on each point $\mathbf{r}$ of the surface being taken not at time t_0 but at the earlier time

$$t = t_0 - \frac{1}{c} |\mathbf{r} - \mathbf{r}_0| \tag{92.08}$$

Kirchhoff's formula reads as follows :

$$\psi(\mathbf{r}_0, t_0) = \frac{1}{4\pi} \int\int_S \left\{ \frac{1}{R}\left[\frac{\partial\psi}{\partial\nu}\right] - [\psi]\frac{\partial(1/R)}{\partial\nu} + \frac{1}{R}\frac{\partial R}{\partial\nu}\left[\frac{1}{c}\frac{\partial\psi}{\partial t}\right] \right\}dS \tag{92.09}$$

Here R denotes the distance

$$R = |\mathbf{r} - \mathbf{r}_0| \tag{92.10}$$

and $\partial\psi/\partial\nu$ is the derivative in the direction of the outward normal to S :

$$\frac{\partial\psi}{\partial\nu} = \frac{\partial\psi}{\partial x}\cos(nx) + \frac{\partial\psi}{\partial y}\cos(ny) + \frac{\partial\psi}{\partial z}\cos(nz) \tag{92.11}$$

The bracketed expression $[\psi]$ signifies that the argument t must be replaced by its value (92.08), this replacement being made in the derivatives $\partial\psi/\partial\nu$ and $\partial\psi/\partial t$ *after* the differentiation.

We take for S the surface of a sphere of radius R centred at $\mathbf{r}_0$. Then we can put

$$dS = R^2\, d\omega \tag{92.12}$$

where $d\omega$ is the element of solid angle. Further

$$\cos(nx) = \frac{x - x_0}{R}; \qquad \cos(ny) = \frac{y - y_0}{R}; \qquad \cos(nz) = \frac{z - z_0}{R} \tag{92.13}$$

and since

$$\frac{\partial R}{\partial\nu} = 1 \tag{92.14}$$

we can also write

$$\frac{\partial\psi}{\partial\nu} = \frac{\partial\psi}{\partial R} \tag{92.15}$$

Then Kirchhoff's formula becomes

$$\psi(\mathbf{r}_0, t_0) = \frac{1}{4\pi} \int\int \left\{ \frac{\partial[R\psi]}{\partial R} + \frac{1}{c}\frac{\partial[R\psi]}{\partial t} \right\}d\omega \tag{92.16}$$

The expression in curly brackets under the integral sign is given by

$$\frac{\partial[R\psi]}{\partial R} + \frac{1}{c}\frac{\partial[R\psi]}{\partial t} = \psi(\mathbf{r}, t)$$
$$+ (x - x_0)\frac{\partial\psi}{\partial x} + (y - y_0)\frac{\partial\psi}{\partial y} + (z - z_0)\frac{\partial\psi}{\partial z} + \frac{R}{c}\frac{\partial\psi}{\partial t} \tag{92.17}$$

where t has the meaning (92.08).

According to (92.16) the value of the function ψ at $\mathbf{r}_0$, t_0 is the mean over solid angles of (92.17). In order that ψ should be zero at $\mathbf{r}_0$, t_0 it is evidently sufficient if for increasing R the expression (92.17) tends to zero:

$$\lim_{R \to \infty} \left\{ \frac{\partial[R\psi]}{\partial R} + \frac{1}{c} \frac{\partial[R\psi]}{\partial t} \right\}_{t=t_0-(R/c)} = 0 \qquad (92.18)$$

For any point $\mathbf{r}_0$ remaining at a finite distance from the origin this requirement will certainly be satisfied if conditions (a), (b) and (c) hold, for (92.17) can be written in the form

$$\frac{\partial[R\psi]}{\partial R} + \frac{1}{c} \frac{\partial[R\psi]}{\partial t} = \varphi + \varphi_1 + \varphi_2 \qquad (92.19)$$

where

$$\varphi = \psi(\mathbf{r}, t) + x \frac{\partial \psi}{\partial x} + y \frac{\partial \psi}{\partial y} + z \frac{\partial \psi}{\partial z} + \frac{r}{c} \frac{\partial \psi}{\partial t} \qquad (92.20)$$

$$\varphi_1 = - \left(x_0 \frac{\partial \psi}{\partial x} + y_0 \frac{\partial \psi}{\partial y} + z_0 \frac{\partial \psi}{\partial z} \right) \qquad (92.21)$$

and

$$\varphi_2 = \frac{R-r}{c} \frac{\partial \psi}{\partial t} \qquad (92.22)$$

Since

$$|R - r| \leqslant r_0 \qquad (92.23)$$

the equations (92.06) of condition (b) give

$$|\varphi_1| < \frac{r_0}{r} M_1 ; \qquad |\varphi_2| < \frac{r_0}{r} M_1 \qquad (92.24)$$

If r_0 is fixed and $r \to \infty$ these expressions tend to zero. Therefore we have separately

$$\varphi_1 \to 0 ; \qquad \varphi_2 \to 0 \qquad \text{(for } r \to \infty) \qquad (92.25)$$

and for (92.18) to hold it is sufficient that

$$\varphi \to 0 \qquad \text{(for } r \to \infty) \qquad (92.26)$$

or

$$\lim_{r \to \infty} \left\{ \frac{\partial(r\psi)}{\partial r} + \frac{1}{c} \frac{\partial(r\psi)}{\partial t} \right\} = 0 \qquad (92.27)$$

This condition, as well as (92.18), is to be satisfied for values of r and t such that when $r \to \infty$, the quantity $t_0 = t + R/c$ remains fixed. Now let us introduce the quantity $t_0' = t + r/c$ into the formulation of condition (c). We have $|t_0 - t_0'| \leqslant r_0/c$, and since r_0 is also fixed, the quantities t_0 and t_0' will both belong to some arbitrary fixed intervals if one of them belongs to such an interval. One can therefore replace t_0 by t_0' in condition (92.27) which then becomes the condition of outward radiation (92.07). This latter is a sufficient condition for the limiting equation (92.18) to hold, whence $\psi = 0$ follows directly (see [43]).

We have proved that the function ψ is zero at the point $\mathbf{r}_0$, but since this point may be chosen arbitrarily this proves that ψ vanishes everywhere. Therefore the uniqueness theorem formulated above is proved.

We now consider the solution of the inhomogeneous wave equation

$$\Delta\psi - \frac{1}{c^2}\frac{\partial^2\psi}{\partial t^2} = -4\pi\rho \tag{92.28}$$

expressed in the familiar form of a retarded potential

$$\psi(\mathbf{r}_0, t_0) = \int \frac{[\rho]dV}{|\mathbf{r}-\mathbf{r}_0|} \tag{92.29}$$

where
$$[\rho] = \rho(\mathbf{r}, t); \qquad t = t_0 - \frac{1}{c}|\mathbf{r}-\mathbf{r}_0| \tag{92.30}$$

The integration in (92.29) is over the coordinates (x, y, z) and extends over all that volume where the " density " is non-zero, i.e. over the region of the masses. If this region lies entirely within the sphere $r \leqslant a$ and if the time t_0 satisfies the inequality $ct_0 > r + a$ the calculation of the integral (92.29) requires the values of ρ only for positive values of the argument t.

At large distances from the masses the function ψ, which satisfies the homogeneous equation outside the masses, has the asymptotic form

$$\psi(\mathbf{r}, t) = \frac{1}{r}\mu\left(t - \frac{r}{c}, \mathbf{n}\right) \tag{92.31}$$

where $\mathbf{n}$ is the unit vector in the direction of the radius vector $\mathbf{r}$. The function μ is expressible in terms of ρ as follows :—

$$\mu\left(t - \frac{r}{c}, \mathbf{n}\right) = \int \rho\left(\mathbf{r}', t - \frac{r}{c} + \frac{(\mathbf{n} \cdot \mathbf{r}')}{c}\right)dV' \tag{92.32}$$

These equations show that the retarded potential satisfies the conditions (a), (b) and (c) formulated above. By virtue of the theorem just proved it is therefore the only solution of the inhomogeneous wave equation (92.28) that satisfies these conditions. Thus, the theorem gives a mathematical justification for the use of the retarded potential ; usually it is derived from physical considerations.

The uniqueness theorem we have formulated has only been proved for the wave equation with constant coefficients. One should expect it to remain true also for such equations with variable coefficients $g^{\mu\nu}$ which have the asymptotic behaviour defined in Section 87. The proof of the theorem for the general case presents considerable difficulties and is an unsolved mathematical problem. It is, however, much simpler to prove the theorem for the case that one can restrict oneself to the " stationary " approximation for the $g^{\mu\nu}$, and may write the wave equation in the form

$$\frac{n^2}{c^2}\frac{\partial^2\psi}{\partial t^2} - \Delta\psi = 0 \tag{92.33}$$

where Δ is the Euclidean Laplace operator and the " refractive index " n has the value

$$n = 1 + \frac{2U}{c^2} \tag{92.34}$$

Here U is the Newtonian potential, which for this problem may be considered to be independent of time. One could construct the proof either with the aid of

S. L. Sobolev's formula† which is a generalization of Kirchhoff's for equations of the form (92.33) or one could expand ψ, considered as a function of t, in a Fourier integral and use the well-known Sommerfeld radiation conditions, which in this case are consequences of our condition (92.27).

In conclusion we remark that the statement of the problem adopted in this section differs from the more usual statement in terms of Cauchy's problem in that we do not explicitly introduce initial conditions, but instead study such solutions of the wave equation which do not depend on the initial conditions within the region of space and the interval of time in question. This formulation is dictated by the physical nature of the problem. In it the solution is made unique and independent of the initial conditions by limiting the space-time region : any initial disturbance that may have occurred in this region is supposed to have dispersed long ago and further disturbances cannot enter the region because of the condition of outward radiation ; in the case of the inhomogeneous equation they may be generated within the region, but then they are determined not by initial conditions but by the " density " ρ.

93. On the Uniqueness of the Harmonic Coordinate System

When solving Einstein's equations for an isolated system of masses we used harmonic coordinates and in this way obtained a perfectly unambiguous solution. We found unique results not only for finite and " moderately large " distances from the masses, when the wave-like, i.e. hyperbolic, character of Einstein's equations was not essential and was accounted for by the introduction of retardation corrections, but also for the " wave zone ". This would lead us to expect that the harmonic conditions together with the requirement of Euclidean behaviour at infinity and with the condition ensuring uniqueness of a wave type solution should determine the coordinate system uniquely apart from a Lorentz transformation.

We now consider this question in detail. If $\Box \psi$ is the invariant d'Alembertian

$$\Box \psi = \frac{1}{\sqrt{(-g)}} \frac{\partial}{\partial x_\mu} \left(\mathfrak{g}^{\mu\nu} \frac{\partial \psi}{\partial x_\nu} \right) \tag{93.01}$$

the harmonic conditions

$$\frac{\partial \mathfrak{g}^{\mu\nu}}{\partial x_\mu} = 0 \tag{93.02}$$

may be written in the form

$$\frac{1}{\sqrt{(-g)}} \frac{\partial \mathfrak{g}^{\mu\nu}}{\partial x_\mu} \equiv \Box \, x_\nu = 0 \tag{93.03}$$

so that each of the functions

$$\psi = x_0 ; \qquad \psi = x_1 ; \qquad \psi = x_2 ; \qquad \psi = x_3 \tag{93.04}$$

is a solution of d'Alembert's equation

$$\Box \psi = 0 \tag{93.05}$$

† Sobolev's formula differs from Kirchhoff's formula (92.09) essentially in that it involves not only a surface integral but also a volume integral. Reasoning as described above, we can take the integral over the infinitely distant surface to vanish by virtue of the conditions on ψ. This then gives not directly $\psi = 0$, but instead a homogeneous integral equation which has zero as its only solution. The quantity $t_0' = t + r/c$ in the statement of condition (c) of the theorem is to be replaced by $t_0^* = t + r^*/c$ with r^* from (87.12).

Evidently this equation is also satisfied by any constant and any linear function of the harmonic coordinates.

We first consider the case that the metric of space-time is Galilean. In Galilean coordinates

$$x_0 = ct; \qquad x_1 = x; \qquad x_2 = y; \qquad x_3 = z \qquad (93.06)$$

the components of the metric tensor are†

$$g^{\mu\nu} = e_\mu \delta_{\mu\nu} \qquad (93.07)$$

and the d'Alembertian has the form

$$\Box\psi = e_\mu \frac{\partial^2\psi}{\partial x_\mu \, \partial x_\mu} \qquad (93.08)$$

Evidently each of the Galilean coordinates is harmonic.

We seek the most general form for harmonic coordinates. Let us assume transformation equations to new coordinates of the form

$$x'_\alpha = f^\alpha(x_0, x_1, x_2, x_3) \qquad (93.09)$$

The new coordinates, like the old, must satisfy d'Alembert's equation, they must be Galilean at large distances and must lead to values of the $g^{\mu\nu}$ with the correct asymptotic behaviour. Remembering these requirements we shall write the functions f^α in the form

$$f^\alpha = a_\alpha + e_\beta a_{\alpha\beta} x_\beta + \eta^\alpha(x_0, x_1, x_2, x_3) \qquad (93.10)$$

Here the a_α and the $a_{\alpha\beta}$ are the coefficients of a Lorentz transformation and so satisfy the relations

$$e_\alpha a_{\mu\alpha} a_{\nu\alpha} = e_\mu \delta_{\mu\nu}; \qquad e_\alpha a_{\alpha\mu} a_{\alpha\nu} = e_\mu \delta_{\mu\nu} \qquad (93.11)$$

Since the functions f^α must satisfy the equation

$$\Box f^\alpha = 0 \qquad (93.12)$$

and the linear terms satisfy this equation separately, we must have

$$\Box\eta^\alpha = 0 \qquad (93.13)$$

This equation must hold throughout space and at all t (i.e. all x_0). Since the equations (93.13) involve second derivatives it is natural to require that the functions η^α themselves and their first derivatives should be bounded throughout space and at all t. This requirement is all the more necessary because the first derivatives of the new coordinates with respect to the old enter the transformation equations for any tensor. As for the conditions at infinity, since there the new coordinates are to be Galilean, the functions η^α which represent additions to the Lorentz transformation, must tend to zero together with all their first derivatives. In addition, the requirements resulting from the asymptotic behaviour of the $g^{\mu\nu}$ must also be satisfied at infinity. We consider these requirements in more detail. Without restricting generality we can assume that the Lorentz transformation occurring in (93.10) is the identity, so that that equation can be written as

$$f^\alpha = x_\alpha + \eta^\alpha(x_0, x_1, x_2, x_3) \qquad (93.14)$$

† When using the summation convention for indices occurring twice the index of e_μ ($e_0 = 1$; $e_1 = e_2 = e_3 = -1$) is not to be counted.

Calculating the components of the metric tensor in the new coordinate system by the general rule

$$g'^{\alpha\beta} = g^{\mu\nu} \frac{\partial x'_\alpha}{\partial x_\mu} \frac{\partial x'_\beta}{\partial x_\nu} \qquad (93.15)$$

we get
$$g'^{\alpha\beta} = e_\alpha \delta_{\alpha\beta} + e_\alpha \frac{\partial \eta^\beta}{\partial x_\alpha} + e_\beta \frac{\partial \eta^\alpha}{\partial x_\beta} + e_\mu \frac{\partial \eta^\alpha}{\partial x_\mu} \frac{\partial \eta^\beta}{\partial x_\mu} \qquad (93.16)$$

By the condition at infinity the quantities $\partial \eta^\alpha / \partial x_\beta$ tend to zero. Therefore the asymptotic behaviour of the $g'^{\alpha\beta}$ is characterized by the terms linear in these quantities. But this asymptotic behaviour must be such that the difference between $g^{\alpha\beta}$ and its limiting value at infinity is an outgoing wave. (Corresponding relations for the $\mathfrak{g}^{\alpha\beta}$ were introduced in Section 87, and similar relations for the $g^{\alpha\beta}$ follow from them.) Thus we must have at infinity

$$g^{\alpha\beta} - (g^{\alpha\beta})_\infty = \text{outgoing wave} \qquad (93.17)$$

This requirement must be satisfied in any harmonic coordinate system, so that the $g'^{\alpha\beta}$ of equation (93.16) must also satisfy it. It follows therefore that

$$e_\alpha \frac{\partial \eta^\beta}{\partial x_\alpha} + e_\beta \frac{\partial \eta^\alpha}{\partial x_\beta} = \text{outgoing wave} \qquad (93.18)$$

If we put
$$\eta^\alpha = e_\alpha \eta_\alpha \qquad (93.19)$$

and divide through by $e_\alpha e_\beta$ we can write this condition in the form

$$\frac{\partial \eta_\beta}{\partial x_\alpha} + \frac{\partial \eta_\alpha}{\partial x_\beta} = \text{outgoing wave} \qquad (93.20)$$

Using the identity

$$\frac{\partial}{\partial x_\beta}\left(\frac{\partial \eta_\alpha}{\partial x_\nu} + \frac{\partial \eta_\nu}{\partial x_\alpha}\right) + \frac{\partial}{\partial x_\alpha}\left(\frac{\partial \eta_\nu}{\partial x_\beta} + \frac{\partial \eta_\beta}{\partial x_\nu}\right) - \frac{\partial}{\partial x_\nu}\left(\frac{\partial \eta_\beta}{\partial x_\alpha} + \frac{\partial \eta_\alpha}{\partial x_\beta}\right) = 2\frac{\partial^2 \eta_\nu}{\partial x_\alpha \, \partial x_\beta} \qquad (93.21)$$

and passing from the η_ν to the η^ν we conclude that

$$\frac{\partial^2 \eta^\nu}{\partial x_\alpha \, \partial x_\beta} = \text{outgoing wave} \qquad (93.22)$$

Hence one can deduce that η^ν is the sum of a linear function and of a function which at infinity represents an outgoing wave. The same conclusion evidently applies not only to the functions η^α entering (93.14) but also to the η^α entering (93.10). Since in (93.10) the linear function has already been split off and since we have the condition at infinity $\eta^\alpha \to 0$, we arrive at the conclusion that the function η^α itself represents an outgoing wave:

$$\eta^\alpha = \text{outgoing wave} \qquad (93.23)$$

The conditions satisfied by the additional function η^α in (93.10) can now be made more precise. This additional function satisfies the wave equation (93.13) and remains bounded everywhere together with its first derivatives. At infinity both η^α and its first derivatives decrease as $1/r$. Finally, from (93.23) we can infer that at infinity η^α satisfies a condition of outward radiation of the form (92.27). All these conditions must be satisfied for all values of t. By virtue of the uniqueness theorem proved in Section 92 a quantity η^α satisfying these conditions vanishes identically. Therefore the function f^α that enters (93.09) and (93.10) reduces to a linear function and the most general form of transformation from one system of harmonic coordinates to another is

$$x'_\alpha = a_\alpha + e_\beta a_{\alpha\beta} x_\beta \qquad (93.24)$$

i.e. it amounts to a Lorentz transformation.

We have proved this result for the case of Galilean space-time with the metric (93.07), because the uniqueness theorem formulated in Section 92 was proved for that case. However, it appears certain that this theorem can also be proved for the general case of an Einstein space-time whose metric tensor has the asymptotic behaviour established in Section 87. If we accept this we reach the conclusion that in the general case also the harmonic coordinate system is uniquely defined apart from a Lorentz transformation. Indeed, the reasoning of this section remains valid in the general case. In a harmonic coordinate system the d'Alembertian has the form

$$\Box \psi = g^{\mu\nu} \frac{\partial^2 \psi}{\partial x_\mu \, \partial x_\nu} \qquad (93.25)$$

and does not involve any first derivatives. Consequently any linear function of the coordinates satisfies the wave equation. Therefore, if we write down a transformation of the coordinates in the form (93.09), where f^α has the value (93.10) and if we require that the new coordinates should also be harmonic (equation (93.12)) we shall again obtain for the additional function the wave equation (93.13), but with $\Box$ now denoting the operator in (93.25). The additions η^α and their first derivatives must evidently be bounded throughout space. As for the remaining conditions imposed on the η^α, they all refer to the infinitely distant regions of space, where the metric differs little from the Euclidean. Therefore these conditions may be safely taken over from the previous case. In particular, the left-hand side of (93.18) will represent the difference between the asymptotic expressions for the $g^{\alpha\beta}$ in initial and transformed coordinates and must, therefore, correspond to an outgoing wave. Hence we conclude as before that the relations (93.22) and (92.23) are valid and then the uniqueness theorem leads to the conclusion that the additions η^α vanish.

Thus in the general case also, the harmonic coordinate system is uniquely determined apart from a Lorentz transformation.

We should note that we have not explicitly introduced any initial conditions for the functions f^α that define the coordinate transformation. This statement of the problem corresponds to the statement of the problem of determining the gravitational potentials $g^{\mu\nu}$. In that case there is sense in introducing initial conditions only for the distribution of the gravitating masses, but not for the gravitational waves and not for the gravitational potentials themselves. The problem of determining the gravitational potentials is not Cauchy's problem, i.e. not a problem with initial conditions, but rather the problem of finding a steady state which sets in when all gravitational waves have dispersed, other than those produced by the motion of the masses under consideration. (See above, end of Section 92.)

Our discussion shows that the conditions ensuring the uniqueness of the coordinate system arise directly from the formulation of the physical problem.

Since this is not Cauchy's problem as regards the determination of the gravitational potentials it will not be Cauchy's problem in relation to the determination of the coordinate system. The determinateness in the formulation of the problem of the gravitational potentials is achieved by excluding "transient" gravitational waves by the condition of outward radiation. But by the same means we exclude the corresponding wave terms in the equations for the coordinate transformations, and thus in turn we achieve the uniqueness of the coordinate system.

The question of the uniqueness of the harmonic coordinate system in the non-stationary case may also be approached from another direction, namely from the approximate method for solving the gravitational equations used in Chapter VI. If one follows the calculations performed there one finds that at all stages the solution, and therefore the coordinate system also, are obtained uniquely. Thus the uniqueness of the harmonic coordinate system can also be taken as proved in all cases in which the method of Chapter VI is applicable.

Let us formulate our conclusions once again. *In the case of an isolated system of masses there exists a coordinate system which is determined uniquely apart from a Lorentz transformation if suitable supplementary conditions are imposed. This is the harmonic coordinate system, characterized by a first order linear differential equation and by boundary conditions for the* $\mathfrak{g}^{\mu\nu}$.

The question may arise: can any coordinate systems other than the harmonic, exist, defined apart from a Lorentz transformation? This seems to us to be unlikely. The harmonic coordinates are characterized by the fact that each of them, and also any linear combination, satisfies a linear, generally covariant equation. One could hardly find other coordinates with this property; other coordinate conditions, even when very similar to the harmonic condition (93.02), for instance $\partial g^{\mu\nu}/\partial x_\mu = 0$ do not reduce to a linear equation.

The fact that for determinateness Einstein's ten gravitational equations must be supplemented by four additional equations is in itself evident. The difficulty consists in choosing these supplementary equations and in formulating boundary conditions.

In contrast with our statement of the problem, the formulation given to it by Einstein leaves it mathematically indeterminate and there can be no question of uniqueness of the solution. According to Einstein there are no privileged systems of coordinates and the system of coordinates remains indeterminate to the end. Einstein and those who support this point of view raise this indeterminacy to a virtue and see in it a deep meaning, namely the expression of some " general principle of relativity ", on the strength of which Einstein's theory is called by its author the " General Theory of Relativity ".

We cannot agree at all with such a point of view. The indeterminateness existing in Einstein's formulation is by no means a matter of principle and has no deep significance whatsoever. It arises in any physical theory that can be formulated in a generally covariant manner. The so-called " special " theory of relativity has actually been formulated in a generally covariant manner (Chapter IV of this book) and thus possesses, in this formulation, the property of indeterminateness to just the same degree as the so-called "general" theory of relativity (the theory of gravitation). What really matters is not the possibility of an indeterminate formulation (which is trivial) but just the opposite, namely, a formulation that is as determinate as is allowed by the nature of the problem. From this point of view, the existence of a preferred set of coordinates, determined apart from a Lorentz transformation, is by no means trivial, but reflects intrinsic properties of space-time. This is most clearly seen in the case of the "special" theory of relativity, where the existence of Galilean coordinates reflects the uniformity of space-time.

If this is made clear, the obvious necessity of introducing additional equations in order to define privileged coordinate systems (and thus to achieve a more determinate formulation of the problem) cannot give rise to any serious objections. This necessity exists in the theory of Einsteinian as well as in that of Galilean space-time. The fact that in the latter case no such equations are usually written down does not alter anything, because such equations *can* be written down or alternatively may be replaced by the verbal statement that Galilean coordinates should be used.

It is obvious that the additional equations mentioned are *not* generally covariant (otherwise they would not restrict the coordinate system.) Thus the objection may be raised that the additional equations destroy the beauty of the theory which according to the current opinion, lies in its general covariance. But this argument provides no real objection, in the first place because these equations *must be compatible* with the generally covariant Einsteinian equations, the simple form of which constitutes the real beauty of his theory. It should be added that the simplicity and beauty of the theory is due not so much to its covariant form as to its idea of unifying metric and gravitation.

The uniqueness of the solution achieved by the use of a well-defined privileged coordinate system seems to us an undoubted advantage rather than the contrary. This uniqueness shows the physical meaning of the privileged system, while the actual physical significance of any other coordinate system only becomes clear given the equations relating it to the privileged system.

As for the so-called " General Principle of Relativity " no such physical principle can exist, as was explained in detail in Section 49*. In contrast the Galilean relativity principle for uniform straight line motion, and its generalization expressed by the Lorentz transformations, are physical principles.

With the assumption of a rigid metric (i.e. one that does not depend on the physical processes occurring in space and time) the Galileo–Lorentz relativity principle leads to uniform space-time and, conversely, is an expression of this uniformity. In the case of non-uniform space-time one can consider the existence of harmonic coordinates to be a further generalization (or wider application) of the Galilean principle of relativity; this reasoning corresponds to the generalized definition of the principle of relativity put forward in Section 49*, as a statement about the equivalence of frames of reference within a certain class. As an illustration let us consider the expressions (91.06)–(91.08) for the $\mathfrak{g}^{\mu\nu}$. If we assume that the constants involved in these expressions are fixed and perform a Lorentz transformation we shall change the form of the expression for the $\mathfrak{g}^{\mu\nu}$, because the space-time is not uniform. But if we also transform the constants $(M,\ P^i)$ and $(M^{oi},\ M^{ji})$ by the same Lorentz transformation we restore the form of the $\mathfrak{g}^{\mu\nu}$. This just means that if a process (the motion of masses) is possible in which the constants of motion have some given values in one frame of reference, then a process is also possible in which these constants have those values in another frame of reference; in other words it means that the principle of relativity is satisfied in the form that was given to it in Section 49*.

Here we have considered the approximate expressions for the $g^{\mu\nu}$ and only the constants of motion, not any other quantities characterizing a system of bodies. But our conclusions also remain in force for the exact solutions, because the gravitational equations, the harmonic conditions and also the boundary conditions are strictly covariant with respect to Lorentz transformations. Thus *the principle of relativity expressed by the Lorentz transformations can hold in non-uniform space also, but a general principle of relativity cannot be valid.*

We have stressed repeatedly the fundamental significance of the existence of a preferred coordinate system, defined apart from a Lorentz transformation. It reveals itself, among other facts, in the following. Only if the existence of such a coordinate system is recognized can one speak of the correctness of the heliocentric Copernican system in the same sense as this is possible in Newtonian mechanics. If the existence of the preferred coordinates is denied, one is led to the inadmissible point of view that the heliocentric Copernican system and the geocentric Ptolemaic system are equivalent. Such a point of view is counter to the definition of physical equivalence of frames of reference given in Section 49* and is therefore inadmissible.

The above remarks concerning the privileged character of the harmonic system of coordinates should not be understood, in any case, as some kind of prohibition of the use of other coordinate systems. Nothing is more alien to our point of view than such an interpretation. Our aim was to clarify the question of coordinate systems in the restricted statement of the problem of the theory of gravitation discussed in the preceding chapters, where an "insular" distribution of matter is assumed. The intention was to show that this question has the same answer as in the case of the Galilean space-time of the "special" theory of relativity. Nobody would assert that in the latter case the existence of Galilean coordinates implies a prohibition of the use of other coordinates. Likewise, in the case of the Theory of Gravitation, the existence of harmonic coordinates though a fact of primary theoretical and practical importance, does not in any way preclude the use of other, non-harmonic, coordinate systems. The harmonic coordinates in Einstein space are no more (though no less) privileged than Galilean coordinates in uniform Galilean space.

94. Friedmann-Lobachevsky Space

When we stated the problem of solving the gravitational equations for a system of masses, we postulated that this system should be isolated and embedded in infinite Euclidean space or, more accurately, in Galilean space-time. Such a statement of the problem is undoubtedly admissible when considering objects of the dimensions of the Solar system. These dimensions may be characterized by the radii of the orbits of the heaviest planet, i.e. of Jupiter (778 million km) and of the most distant planet, i.e. Pluto (5900 million km). Light from the Sun reaches Pluto in about 5·5 hours. The nearest fixed star (α Centauri) is at a distance of 4·3 light years from the Sun, i.e. about 7,000 times more distant than Pluto.

It is possible that such a statement of the problem is still permissible when considering a single star cluster or even the whole Galaxy. The dimensions of the galaxies† are still some tens of times smaller than their mutual distances. But if one considers regions of space so great as to include many galaxies—and such regions of space are observable with large modern telescopes—the notion of an isolated system embedded in Euclidean space evidently becomes inapplicable.

The question arises with what to replace the Euclidean background which we have hitherto considered? What kind of space-time should one take to be the background from which the separate mass systems stand out?

Another reason for the need to replace the Euclidean background by some other is that if one considers masses distributed throughout Euclidean space with a uniform mean density the well-known paradox of Seeliger arises which amounts to the fact that the Newtonian potential of a uniform mass distribution does not exist. At the same time astronomical observation shows that throughout the region of space accessible to observation, up to distances of the order of 10^9 light years, the distribution of galaxies seems to be uniform on the average. On the other hand, if the Newtonian potential does not exist it is clear that the form of the solution of Einstein's equations must be essentially different from that which corresponds to an isolated system of masses and which allows the gravitational potentials $g^{\mu\nu}$ to be approximately expressed in terms of the Newtonian potential. Owing to the altered character of the problem the choice of coordinates must also be made anew.

The solution of Einstein's equations which corresponds to an isotropic space with a uniform mass density and which may be taken as the background in the study of enormous distances that include many galaxies was obtained in 1922 by the Russian scientist A. A. Friedmann [24]. As we shall see this solution permits the introduction of coordinates in which space possesses the properties of Lobachevsky's geometry. We shall therefore call the corresponding space-time manifold the *Friedmann-Lobachevsky* space.

The theory of Friedmann-Lobachevsky space may be derived starting from the assumption that the expression for ds^2 is invariant under the *homogeneous Lorentz group*. It may then always be reduced to the form

$$ds^2 = H^2(S)(dx_0^2 - dx_1^2 - dx_2^2 - dx_3^2) \qquad (94.01)$$

where

$$S = \sqrt{(x_0^2 - x_1^2 - x_2^2 - x_3^2)} \qquad (94.02)$$

Though this space-time is not itself Galilean, equation (94.01) shows that it may nevertheless be mapped conformally on a Galilean space-time. The group of homogeneous Lorentz transformations exists in this space and this ensures the *isotropy of the space*. In particular, the origin of the spatial coordinates is in no way singled out from any other point in the space ; any fixed point may be transformed so as to become the origin by means of a homogeneous Lorentz transformation. Thus the homogeneous Lorentz transformations play a twofold role : they effect both a transfer of the origin of coordinates and a passage to a moving reference frame.

† By the Galaxy (with a capital " g ") one means that stellar system to which the Sun belongs. Other similar stellar systems are termed galaxies (with a small " g ").

We write ds^2 in the form

$$ds^2 = H^2 \left(e_\mu \, dx_\mu^2\right) \tag{94.03}$$

We then see that

$$g_{\mu\nu} = H^2 e_\mu \, \delta_{\mu\nu} \, ; \qquad g^{\mu\nu} = \frac{1}{H^2} e_\mu \, \delta_{\mu\nu} \tag{94.04}$$

For the Christoffel symbols we get the expressions

$$\Gamma^\rho_{\alpha\beta} = \frac{H'(S)}{SH} \left(e_\alpha \, \delta_{\rho\beta} x_\alpha + e_\beta \, \delta_{\rho\alpha} x_\beta - e_\alpha \, \delta_{\alpha\beta} x_\rho\right) \tag{94.05}$$

We use the equation

$$R^\rho_{\mu,\,\alpha\beta} = \frac{\partial \Gamma^\rho_{\mu\alpha}}{\partial x_\beta} - \frac{\partial \Gamma^\rho_{\mu\beta}}{\partial x_\alpha} + \Gamma^\sigma_{\mu\alpha} \Gamma^\rho_{\sigma\beta} - \Gamma^\sigma_{\mu\beta} \Gamma^\rho_{\sigma\alpha} \tag{94.06}$$

to form the mixed fourth rank curvature tensor (see (44.01)) and obtain

$$R^\rho_{\mu,\,\alpha\beta} = \left[\frac{d^2 \log H}{dS^2} - \frac{1}{S} \frac{d \log H}{dS} - \left(\frac{d \log H}{dS}\right)^2\right]$$

$$\times \frac{e_\mu}{S^2} \left(e_\alpha \, \delta_{\mu\beta} x_\alpha x_\rho - e_\beta \, \delta_{\mu\alpha} x_\beta x_\rho + e_\beta \, \delta_{\rho\alpha} x_\beta x_\mu - e_\alpha \, \delta_{\rho\beta} x_\alpha x_\mu\right)$$

$$+ \left[\frac{2}{S} \frac{d \log H}{dS} + \left(\frac{d \log H}{dS}\right)^2\right] e_\mu (\delta_{\alpha\rho} \, \delta_{\beta\mu} - \delta_{\beta\rho} \, \delta_{\alpha\mu}) \tag{94.07}$$

Here we put $\alpha = \rho$, $\beta = \nu$ and sum over ρ, getting

$$R_{\mu\nu} = \left[\frac{d^2 \log H}{dS^2} + \frac{5}{S} \frac{d \log H}{dS} + 2\left(\frac{d \log H}{dS}\right)^2\right] e_\mu \, \delta_{\mu\nu}$$

$$+ 2 \left[\frac{d^2 \log H}{dS^2} - \frac{1}{S} \frac{d \log H}{dS} - \left(\frac{d \log H}{dS}\right)^2\right] e_\mu e_\nu \frac{x_\mu x_\nu}{S^2} \tag{94.08}$$

We calculate the invariant

$$R = \frac{6}{H^2} \left[\frac{d^2 \log H}{dS^2} + \frac{3}{S} \frac{d \log H}{dS} + \left(\frac{d \log H}{dS}\right)^2\right] \tag{94.09}$$

or

$$R = \frac{6}{H^3} \left(\frac{d^2 H}{dS^2} + \frac{3}{S} \frac{dH}{dS}\right) \tag{94.10}$$

Now we can form the conservative tensor

$$G_{\mu\nu} = R_{\mu\nu} - \tfrac{1}{2} g_{\mu\nu} R \tag{94.11}$$

From (94.08), (94.09) and (94.04) we obtain

$$G_{\mu\nu} = -\left[2 \frac{d^2 \log H}{dS^2} + \frac{4}{S} \frac{d \log H}{dS} + \left(\frac{d \log H}{dS}\right)^2\right] e_\mu \, \delta_{\mu\nu}$$

$$+ 2 \left[\frac{d^2 \log H}{dS^2} - \frac{1}{S} \frac{d \log H}{dS} - \left(\frac{d \log H}{dS}\right)^2\right] e_\mu e_\nu \frac{x_\mu x_\nu}{S^2} \tag{94.12}$$

By Einstein's equations we have

$$G_{\mu\nu} = -\frac{8\pi\gamma}{c^2} T_{\mu\nu} \tag{94.13}$$

As we have indicated in the derivation of these equations, the mass tensor $T_{\mu\nu}$ in the cosmological case, when conditions at infinity are absent, is determined only up to an additive term of the form $\lambda g_{\mu\nu}$; in this case the constant characterizes not only the mass tensor itself but also the properties of space as a whole, and choosing a value for it represents a special hypothesis.

Our basic aim is the examination of Friedmann-Lobachevsky space, but before we pass on to this task we shall touch briefly on the case of a maximally uniform space, to which we referred repeatedly in our previous discussions. In maximally uniform space the relations (49.12) must be satisfied. They may be written in the form

$$R^{\rho}_{\mu, \alpha\beta} \equiv K(\delta^{\rho}_{\alpha}g_{\mu\beta} - \delta^{\rho}_{\beta}g_{\mu\alpha}) \tag{94.14}$$

Comparing this expression with (94.07) we obtain agreement if we put

$$\frac{d^2 \log H}{dS^2} - \frac{1}{S}\frac{d \log H}{dS} - \left(\frac{d \log H}{dS}\right)^2 = 0 \tag{94.15}$$

$$\frac{2}{S}\frac{d \log H}{dS} + \left(\frac{d \log H}{dS}\right)^2 = KH^2 \tag{94.16}$$

Taking $1/H$ as our new unknown function we obtain from (94.15) a linear equation, the solution of which has the form

$$\frac{1}{H} = a - bS^2 \tag{94.17}$$

Insertion of this expression into (94.16) gives a relation between the constants

$$4ab = K \tag{94.18}$$

Putting $a = 1$ we get $b = \frac{1}{4}K$ so that

$$\frac{1}{H} = 1 - \frac{1}{4}KS^2 \tag{94.19}$$

and therefore

$$dS^2 = \frac{dx_0^2 - dx_1^2 - dx_2^2 - dx_3^2}{[1 - \frac{1}{4}K \cdot (x_0^2 - x_1^2 - x_2^2 - x_3^2)]^2} \tag{94.20}$$

In addition to the group of homogeneous Lorentz transformations, which contains 6 parameters, the expression (94.20) also allows a more general group of transformations with 10 parameters; we shall not state these here (see ref. [14]).

It follows from equation (94.14) that

$$R_{\mu\nu} = 3Kg_{\mu\nu}; \qquad R = 12K \tag{94.21}$$

whence

$$G_{\mu\nu} = -3Kg_{\mu\nu} \tag{94.22}$$

Thus a maximally uniform space corresponds formally to a mass tensor given by

$$T_{\mu\nu} = \frac{3K}{\varkappa}g_{\mu\nu} \tag{94.23}$$

Coming back now to the Friedmann-Lobachevsky space we assume that the mass tensor has the form

$$T_{\mu\nu} = \rho^* u_\mu u_\nu \tag{94.24}$$

where ρ^* is the invariant density and the u_ν are the covariant components of the four-dimensional velocity normalized by the relation

$$u_\nu u^\nu = 1 \tag{94.25}$$

In the usual (non-cosmological) statement of the problem the mass tensor (94.24) corresponds to "dust-like" matter at zero pressure (see equation (32.17)). In the cosmological statement the choice of the additive constant in the pressure (as of the constant K in equation (94.23)) represents a special hypothesis, as was mentioned, which characterizes the properties of the space as a whole. Our choice of mass tensor, though not the only one possible, allows us to construct a theory which reflects correctly some features of observed phenomena.

If the conservative tensor (94.12) and the mass tensor (94.24) are to be proportional, the first term in (94.12) must be zero. This gives

$$2 \frac{d^2 \log H}{dS^2} + \frac{4}{S} \frac{d \log H}{dS} + \left(\frac{d \log H}{dS}\right)^2 = 0 \tag{94.26}$$

If we put

$$H = H_1^2; \qquad \log H = 2 \log H_1 \tag{94.27}$$

equation (94.16) becomes linear

$$\frac{d^2 H_1}{dS^2} + \frac{4}{S} \frac{dH_1}{dS} = 0 \tag{94.28}$$

and may readily be integrated. If we assume that at $S = \infty$ we have $H_1 = 1$, which means that space-time is Galilean and the scale factor is the usual one, we get

$$H_1 = 1 - \frac{A}{S} \tag{94.29}$$

and therefore

$$H = 1 - \frac{2A}{S} + \frac{A^2}{S^2} \tag{94.30}$$

With this value of H we have

$$G_{\mu\nu} = -\frac{12A}{S^5(1 - A/S)^2} e_\mu e_\nu x_\mu x_\nu \tag{94.31}$$

and Einstein's equations become

$$\frac{12A}{S^5 H} e_\mu e_\nu x_\mu x_\nu = \frac{8\pi\gamma}{c^2} \rho^* u_\mu u_\nu \tag{94.32}$$

We form the invariants on both sides of the equation, getting

$$\frac{8\pi\gamma}{c^2} \rho^* = \frac{12A}{S^3 H^3} \tag{94.33}$$

These invariants are equal to R; therefore we could have used equation (94.10) directly with the value of H from (94.30) inserted for calculating the right-hand side of (94.33). Since the density ρ^* is positive the constant A must also be positive.

With the use of (94.33) equation (94.32) gives

$$u_\mu = H \frac{e_\mu x_\mu}{S} \tag{94.34}$$

and, on going over to contravariant components we get

$$u^\mu = \frac{x_\mu}{HS} \qquad (94.35)$$

We have obtained a solution of Einstein's equations corresponding to a non-vanishing mass density ρ^* uniformly distributed over all space. (In Newtonian theory such a solution does not exist.) This result was first obtained by A. A. Friedmann in the 1922 paper mentioned above [24].

We write the solution obtained in explicit form. We have

$$ds^2 = \left(1 - \frac{A}{S}\right)^4 (dx_0^2 - dx_1^2 - dx_2^2 - dx_3^2) \qquad (94.36)$$

where

$$S = \sqrt{(x_0^2 - x_1^2 - x_2^2 - x_3^2)} \qquad (94.02)$$

It is interesting to note that this expression is invariant not only under the group of homogeneous Lorentz transformations, but also under inversions

$$x'_\mu = \frac{A^2}{S^2} x_\mu \qquad (94.37)$$

The latter, however, have no direct physical significance because they transform the region $S > A$ into the region $S' < A$, and only the case $S > A$ has physical significance. It is also easy to find the equations relating the coordinates x_μ to harmonic coordinates x_μ^*, namely

$$x_\mu^* = \left(1 + \frac{4}{3}\frac{A}{S} + \frac{A^2}{S^2}\right)x_\mu \qquad (94.38)$$

The harmonic coordinates do not change under the inversion (94.37). In the problem of isolated masses the preferred role of the harmonic coordinates was based on the boundary conditions discussed in Section 93, including the condition of Euclidean behaviour at infinity. In Friedmann-Lobachevsky space, however, the conditions are quite different and the " conformally-Galilean " coordinates, in which ds^2 is of the form (94.36), are more appropriate to the character of the problem.

We discuss the motion of matter that corresponds to the solution obtained. In the equation of continuity

$$\frac{\partial[\sqrt{(-g)}\cdot\rho^* u^\mu]}{\partial x_\mu} = 0 \qquad (94.39)$$

we must put

$$\sqrt{(-g)}\cdot\rho^* u^\mu = \frac{3Ac^2}{2\pi\gamma}\frac{x_\mu}{S^4} \qquad (94.40)$$

whence it is evident that it is satisfied by virtue of the identity

$$\frac{\partial}{\partial x_\mu}\left(\frac{x_\mu}{S^4}\right) = 0 \qquad (94.41)$$

The velocity field is characterized by the quantities (94.35). We have

$$\frac{dx_\mu}{dx_0} = \frac{u^\mu}{u^0} = \frac{x_\mu}{x_0} \qquad (94.42)$$

For directness of interpretation we put $x_0 = ct$ and can then write

$$\frac{dx_i}{dt} = \frac{x_i}{t} \tag{94.43}$$

whence for each mass

$$x_i = v_i t \tag{94.44}$$

where v_i is constant. Since $S^2 > 0$ we must have

$$v_1^2 + v_2^2 + v_3^2 < c^2 \tag{94.45}$$

In the auxiliary Galilean space each mass moves with a constant velocity proportional to its coordinates and therefore in this space all distances increase proportionately with time. This is, properly speaking, only true for the auxiliary Galilean space, but qualitatively the conclusion that relative distances increase with time remains valid in the physical space also. Such an expanding space is thus the background which here replaces Euclidean space. The observable physical consequences of this at first sight paradoxical result will be examined in the following section.

The quantities v_i introduced by equation (94.44) may be considered as the coordinates of a given mass measured with a scale increasing with " time " t. With this scale the coordinates of each mass point are constant. Therefore, from the point of view of the equations of motion the v_i are a type of Lagrangian coordinates (as distinct from the Eulerian coordinates x_i.) We introduce into ds^2 as spatial variables the three quantities v_i and as a time variable the quantity τ which is proportional to S and given by

$$\tau = \sqrt{\left[t^2 - \frac{1}{c^2}(x_1^2 + x_2^2 + x_3^2)\right]} \tag{94.46}$$

Our transformation is then

$$x_i = \frac{v_i \tau}{\sqrt{(1 - v^2/c^2)}}; \qquad t = \frac{\tau}{\sqrt{(1 - v^2/c^2)}} \tag{94.47}$$

Evidently relation (94.36) is identically satisfied. We have

$$dx_i = \frac{v_i}{\sqrt{(1 - v^2/c^2)}} d\tau + \frac{\tau}{\sqrt{(1 - v^2/c^2)}}\left(\delta_{ik} + \frac{v_i v_k}{c^2 - v^2}\right)dv_k \tag{94.48}$$

and

$$dt = \frac{1}{\sqrt{(1 - v^2/c^2)}} d\tau + \frac{\tau}{\sqrt{(1 - v^2/c^2)}} \frac{v_i \, dv_i}{c^2 - v^2} \tag{94.49}$$

whence

$$c^2 \, dt^2 - (dx_1^2 + dx_2^2 + dx_3^2) = c^2 \, d\tau^2 - \tau^2 \, d\sigma^2 \tag{94.50}$$

where

$$d\sigma^2 = \frac{(d\mathbf{v})^2 - [\mathbf{v} \times d\mathbf{v}]^2/c^2}{(1 - v^2/c^2)^2} \tag{94.51}$$

This is the square of the element of arc length already known to us from the Lobachevsky-Einstein velocity space of Section 17. In place of (94.51) we can also write

$$d\sigma^2 = \frac{1}{1 - v^2/c^2}\left(\delta_{ik} + \frac{v_i v_k}{c^2 - v^2}\right)dv_i \, dv_k \qquad (94.52)$$

If instead of A we introduce a constant α such that

$$S = c\tau ; \qquad A = c\alpha \qquad (94.53)$$

we obtain for ds^2

$$ds^2 = \left(1 - \frac{\alpha}{\tau}\right)^4 (c^2 \, d\tau^2 - \tau^2 \, d\sigma^2) \qquad (94.54)$$

The quantity τ may be called the proper time in the auxiliary Galilean space. The physical proper time on the other hand is the quantity T determined by the equation

$$T = \int_\alpha^\tau \left(1 - \frac{\alpha}{\tau}\right)^2 d\tau = \tau - \frac{\alpha^2}{\tau} - 2\alpha \log \frac{\tau}{\alpha} \qquad (94.55)$$

Here the convention is to count time from that very distant epoch (some thousands of millions of years ago) when the galaxies observed to-day were much closer together than they are now. There is no sense in applying the above equation to yet earlier epochs because it ignores the direct gravitational interaction of the galaxies which could have been considerable at that time.

The spatial part of ds^2 ,which corresponds to a fixed value of the universal time T (and therefore also to fixed τ) is equal to

$$dl^2 = \tau^2\left(1 - \frac{\alpha}{\tau}\right)^4 d\sigma^2 \qquad (94.56)$$

This describes a Lobachevsky space of constant negative curvature. Its volume is infinite.

We consider the mass of those galaxies whose velocities in the auxiliary Galilean space are within given limits. If ρ^* is the invariant density this mass is

$$dM = \rho^* \, dV \qquad (94.57)$$

where dV is the volume element in the Lobachevsky space with the metric (94.56). As is easy to calculate from (94.52) the volume element in the velocity space is

$$dV_\sigma = \frac{dv_1 \, dv_2 \, dv_3}{(1 - v^2/c^2)^2} \qquad (94.58)$$

Therefore the volume element in the Lobachevsky space is

$$dV = \tau^3\left(1 - \frac{\alpha}{\tau}\right)^6 dV_\sigma \qquad (94.59)$$

and the mass dM is

$$dM = \rho^*\tau^3\left(1 - \frac{\alpha}{\tau}\right)^6 dV_\sigma \qquad (94.60)$$

The equation (94.33) for the invariant density may be written in the form

$$\rho^* = \frac{3c^2}{2\pi\gamma} \cdot \frac{A}{S^3(1 - A/S)^6} \qquad (94.61)$$

whence, using (94.53) we get

$$\rho^{*}\tau^{3}\left(1 - \frac{\alpha}{\tau}\right)^{6} = \frac{3\alpha}{2\pi\gamma} \qquad (94.62)$$

Inserting this expression into (94.60) we get

$$dM = \frac{3\alpha}{2\pi\gamma} \, dV_{\sigma} \qquad (94.63)$$

which can also be written as

$$\gamma \, dM = \frac{3\alpha}{2\pi} \frac{dv_{1} \, dv_{2} \, dv_{3}}{(1 - v^{2}/c^{2})^{2}} \qquad (94.64)$$

In the study of the red shift in the spectra of distant galaxies it is customary to characterize the shift by the speed v^{*} which would produce it if it could be ascribed entirely to Doppler effect in ordinary Galilean space. From the theory of the red shift which will be developed in the following section it follows that, *as long as it is small compared to the speed of light*, this effective speed is related to the speed discussed here by the equation :

$$v^{*} = \frac{\tau + \alpha}{\tau - \alpha} v \qquad (94.65)$$

With the aid of this relation the previous equations may be more easily interpreted. If we put

$$\alpha^{*} = \alpha \left(\frac{\tau - \alpha}{\tau + \alpha}\right)^{3} \qquad (94.66)$$

equation (94.64) can be written approximately as

$$\gamma \, dM = \frac{3\alpha^{*}}{2\pi} \, dv_{1}^{*} \, dv_{2}^{*} \, dv_{3}^{*} \qquad (94.67)$$

Integrating over solid angle and over the absolute magnitude of the effective speed, we obtain the relation

$$\gamma(M - M_{0}) = 2\alpha^{*}(v^{*3} - v_{0}^{*3}) \qquad (94.68)$$

Hence we can get an estimate of α^{*} from an estimate of the mass $M - M_{0}$ of those galaxies which have effective Doppler speeds in the range between v_{0}^{*} and v^{*}.

95. Theory of the Red Shift

The hypothesis that the structure of very large regions of space containing many galaxies is of the nature of the structure of Friedmann-Lobachevsky space found unexpected confirmation in the phenomenon of the red shift in the spectra of galaxies discovered by the astronomer Hubble [25]. It was shown that all the lines of the galactic spectra are shifted towards the red end of the spectrum and that this shift is the greater the more distant the galaxy.

In this section we shall give a theory of the red shift based on the hypothesis mentioned.

We first write the expression for ds^{2} in the form

$$ds^2 = \left(1 - \frac{\alpha}{\tau}\right)^4 (c^2\, dt^2 - dx^2 - dy^2 - dz^2) \tag{95.01}$$

Here α is a positive constant and τ is given by

$$\tau = \sqrt{\left(t^2 - \frac{r^2}{c^2}\right)}; \qquad r^2 = x^2 + y^2 + z^2 \tag{95.02}$$

Expression (95.01) actually contains not one constant but two because the origin of time reckoning or, equivalently, the value of τ for the present epoch remains unknown. In principle, the theory of the red shift makes it possible to determine these two constants by observation. Also, the theory permits of verification if the mean density ρ^* of matter in space is known.

The change of the frequency of light arriving from a distant star arises as a result of two effects : the Einstein effect (Section 51) which is operative when light passes from a region with one value of the gravitational potential g_{00} to a region with another value, and the Doppler effect (Section 13) which is operative when the radiating system is in motion.

The fact that Friedmann-Lobachevsky space is conformally-Galilean considerably simplifies the discussion of the law of light propagation. For in a space having the squared line element (95.01) the law for the propagation of a wave front has the form

$$\frac{1}{c^2}\left(\frac{\partial \omega}{\partial t}\right)^2 - \left[\left(\frac{\partial \omega}{\partial x}\right)^2 + \left(\frac{\partial \omega}{\partial y}\right)^2 + \left(\frac{\partial \omega}{\partial z}\right)^2\right] = 0 \tag{95.03}$$

which is exactly the same as the corresponding law in Galilean space-time. The equations of the characteristics will therefore be the same as in the Galilean case ; in particular the surfaces

$$t - \frac{r}{c} = \text{const}; \qquad t + \frac{r}{c} = \text{const} \tag{95.04}$$

are characteristics. The entire discussion related to the law of wave front propagation and the form of the characteristics can be taken over without change from the Galilean case to that of conformally-Galilean space-time. In particular the whole theory of the Doppler effect remains unchanged.

After these preliminary remarks we go on to derive the equations for the change of the frequency of light.

We shall use a coordinate system with its origin in the Sun or on the Earth (it is immaterial which we choose because of the smallness of the relative distance of Sun and Earth compared with the distance from other galaxies). Assume that at $t = t_0$ light is emitted by a distant star which then is located at the distance $r = r_0$. The value of τ_0 corresponding to time t_0 and distance r_0 is

$$\tau_0 = \sqrt{\left(t_0^2 - \frac{r_0^2}{c^2}\right)} \tag{95.05}$$

according to (95.02). By the equation of the characteristic,

$$t_0 + \frac{r_0}{c} = t + \frac{r}{c} \tag{95.06}$$

this light reaches the Earth ($r = 0$) at the instant $t = t_0 + r_0/c$ which corresponds to a value of τ given by

$$\tau = t_0 + \frac{r_0}{c} \tag{95.07}$$

From this equation and (95.05) we get

$$\frac{\tau_0}{\tau} = \sqrt{\left(\frac{t_0 - (r_0/c)}{t_0 + (r_0/c)} \right)} \tag{95.08}$$

On the other hand, if the emitting star moves with the velocity corresponding to the mean velocity of matter in Friedmann-Lobachevsky space, then, according to (94.34)

$$\frac{r_0}{t_0} = v ; \qquad (v > 0) \tag{95.09}$$

where v is the constant speed of the star in the auxiliary Galilean space. From (95.08) and (95.09) we obtain

$$\frac{\tau_0}{\tau} = \sqrt{\left(\frac{c - v}{c + v} \right)} \tag{95.10}$$

We now consider the frequency change. Let ω_0 be the proper frequency of the emitter and ω_0^* the frequency in the auxiliary Galilean space in the frame of reference of the emitter. The two quantities are connected by the relation

$$\frac{1}{\omega_0} = \frac{1}{\omega_0^*} \left(1 - \frac{\alpha}{\tau_0} \right)^2 \tag{95.11}$$

The conversion factor is the value derived from (95.01) of the quantity $\sqrt{(g_{00})}/c$ at the time and place of emission. In the auxiliary Galilean space an emitter of frequency ω_0^* is moving with speed v away from the Earth. The frequency ω^* received on the Earth is then obtained by the usual theory of the Doppler effect and is

$$\omega^* = \omega_0^* \sqrt{\left(\frac{c - v}{c + v} \right)} \tag{95.12}$$

According to (95.10) this relation may be written in the form

$$\tau \omega^* = \tau_0 \omega_0^* \tag{95.13}$$

It now remains to pass from the frequency ω^* in the auxiliary Galilean space to the frequency ω in physical space. The transition is effected by an equation analogous to (95.11); but the value of the quantity $\sqrt{(g_{00})}/c$ has to be taken for the place and instant of observation. The relevant equation is

$$\frac{1}{\omega} = \frac{1}{\omega^*} \left(1 - \frac{\alpha}{\tau} \right)^2 \tag{95.14}$$

From (95.11), (95.13) and (95.14) we get finally

$$\tau\left(1 - \frac{\alpha}{\tau}\right)^2 \omega = \tau_0\left(1 - \frac{\alpha}{\tau_0}\right)^2 \omega_0 \tag{95.15}$$

Here, ω_0 is the proper frequency of the emitter, e.g. of a hydrogen atom, and ω the frequency of the light reaching the Earth from an identical emitter on a distant star. Since $\tau > \tau_0$ and the factor of ω in (95.15) is an increasing function of τ, we have $\omega < \omega_0$; thus the frequency *decreases* and the displacement of a visible spectral line is therefore towards the red end of the spectrum.

In our proof the inclusion of the change of $\sqrt{g_{00}}$ in passing from the star to the Earth corresponds to taking the Einstein effect into account whereas the transformation according to equation (95.12) takes account of the Doppler effect.

Let us now investigate the change in the amplitude of a light wave travelling from the star to the Earth. The distance of a star can be judged from the energy current density which is proportional to the square of the amplitude, if stars of the same radiative power are compared. (Novae at their period of maximum brightness may be assumed to have such equal power.)

In a space which has (94.01) for its squared line element the wave equation has the form

$$\frac{\partial}{\partial x_\mu}\left(H^2 e_\mu \frac{\partial \psi}{\partial x_\mu}\right) = 0 \tag{95.16}$$

and if we put

$$\psi = \frac{\psi^*}{H} \tag{95.17}$$

where ψ^* is a new function, the wave equation may be written as

$$H \Box \psi^* - \psi^* \Box H = 0 \tag{95.18}$$

Here $\Box$ is the Galilean d'Alembert operator, so that

$$\Box \psi^* = e_\mu \frac{\partial^2 \psi^*}{\partial x_\mu^2} \tag{95.19}$$

The function H varies incomparably more slowly than ψ^*, therefore the second term in (95.18) may be discarded and the wave equation may be written as

$$\Box \psi^* = 0 \tag{95.20}$$

(this approximation has no effect at all on the expression for the energy current in the wave zone, which alone interests us).

We now take the origin of coordinates to be on the star and consider a spherical wave radiating from there. The quantity ψ^* will then have the form

$$\psi^* = \frac{1}{r} f\left(t - \frac{r}{c}\right) \tag{95.21}$$

and therefore

$$\psi = \frac{1}{rH} f\left(t - \frac{r}{c}\right) = \frac{1}{r(1 - \alpha/\tau)^2} f\left(t - \frac{r}{c}\right) \tag{95.22}$$

The square of the amplitude of ψ will be a quantity proportional to the energy current density I. Therefore we may put

$$I = \frac{B}{r^2(1 - \alpha/\tau)^4} \tag{95.23}$$

where B is a positive constant equal to the energy flux into unit solid angle. Indeed, it follows from the expression for ds^2 which appears in spherical polar coordinates as

$$ds^2 = \left(1 - \frac{\alpha}{\tau}\right)^4 \{c^2 \, dt^2 - dr^2 - r^2(d\vartheta^2 + \sin^2 \vartheta \, d\varphi^2)\} \qquad (95.24)$$

that the surface element on a sphere about the source is†

$$dS = r^2\left(1 - \frac{\alpha}{\tau}\right)^4 \sin \vartheta \, d\vartheta \, d\varphi \qquad (95.25)$$

Hence the flux of energy through an element of the surface S is

$$I \, dS = B \sin \vartheta \, d\vartheta \, d\varphi \qquad (95.26)$$

which shows that B is the flux through unit solid angle.

The quantity B is constant in the frame of reference in which the wave equation and its solution (95.22) have been stated. But it must be remembered that B is a dimensioned quantity whose value depends on the choice of units and of the standards used for its measurement; in the general case the passage to a new frame of reference has an effect on the standards. The dimensions of an energy flux are energy divided by time, or in other words, action times frequency squared. Action is an invariant and the scale of action does not change in the passage from one frame of reference to another. Therefore the energy current changes in such a transition in the same way as the square of a frequency. If the frequency of a quantum emitted on the star and reaching some given region of space is taken as the standard of frequency, the energy current will be numerically constant. But if one takes in every region of space a "local" standard of frequency (for instance the frequency of a quantum corresponding to the same spectral transition but emitted in the region in question and not on the star) the numerical value of the energy flux will change in the ratio $\omega^2 : \omega_0^2$. Naturally measurements made on the Earth employ "terrestrial" and not "stellar" standards, and this corresponds to the second point of view. Therefore, expressing the energy flux and its density in "terrestrial" units we must put‡

$$B = B_0 \frac{\omega^2}{\omega_0^2} \qquad (95.27)$$

and

$$I = \frac{B_0 \omega^2}{\omega_0^2 r^2 (1 - \alpha/\tau)^4} \qquad (95.28)$$

where B_0 is the value of the energy flux into unit solid angle near the star; for stars with equal emissive power (i.e. with equal absolute stellar magnitude) the value of B_0 is the same. Putting

$$I = \frac{B_0}{R^2} \qquad (95.29)$$

where R is the "distance" determined by the apparent stellar magnitude

† Of course, the quantity S in (95.25) has nothing to do with the S of (94.02).

‡ This result agrees with the conclusion of Landau and Lifshitz [23], which they reached from other considerations.

(brightness) we have

$$R = \frac{\omega_0}{\omega} r \left(1 - \frac{\alpha}{\tau}\right)^2 \tag{95.30}$$

In this equation r is the distance, in the auxiliary Galilean space, from the star to the Earth in the frame of reference attached to the star. We express r in terms of τ and τ_0. In the frame of reference mentioned we have

$$\text{for } t = \tau_0; \qquad r = 0 \quad \text{and} \quad \tau = \tau_0;$$

$$\text{for } t = \tau_0 + \frac{r}{c}; \qquad r = r \quad \text{and} \quad \tau = \sqrt{\left\{\tau_0\left(\tau_0 + \frac{2r}{c}\right)\right\}} \tag{95.31}$$

whence

$$\frac{r}{c} = \frac{\tau^2 - \tau_0^2}{2\tau_0} \tag{95.32}$$

Inserting this value of r into (95.30) we get

$$\frac{R}{c} = \frac{\omega_0}{\omega} \cdot \frac{\tau^2 - \tau_0^2}{2\tau_0}\left(1 - \frac{\alpha}{\tau}\right)^2 \tag{95.33}$$

Also, equation (95.15) gives

$$\frac{\omega_0}{\omega} = \frac{\tau}{\tau_0} \frac{(1 - \alpha/\tau)^2}{(1 - \alpha/\tau_0)^2} \tag{95.34}$$

The values of ω_0/ω and of R for different galaxies are connected by the relation which can be obtained from these two equations by eliminating τ_0. To perform this elimination conveniently we introduce another auxiliary quantity[†] y in place of τ_0 to which it is related by

$$y = \frac{(\tau - \tau_0)(\tau + \alpha)}{\tau(\tau_0 - \alpha)} \tag{97.35}$$

and

$$\tau_0 = \frac{\tau(\tau + \alpha + \alpha y)}{\tau + \alpha + \tau y} \tag{95.36}$$

For various galaxies τ_0 may vary within the limits

$$\alpha < \tau_0 \leqslant \tau \tag{95.37}$$

so that the limits of y will be

$$0 \leqslant y < \infty \tag{95.38}$$

Inserting the value of τ_0 into (95.34) we get

$$\frac{\omega_0}{\omega} = \frac{(\tau + \alpha + \tau y)(\tau + \alpha + \alpha y)}{(\tau + \alpha)^2} \tag{95.39}$$

or

$$\frac{\omega_0}{\omega} = 1 + y + \frac{\tau\alpha}{(\tau + \alpha)^2} y^2 \tag{95.40}$$

Also, inserting τ_0 from (95.36) and ω_0/ω from (95.39) into the equation (95.33)

[†] There should be no danger of confusion between this quantity and one of the coordinates in (95.01) and (95.02).

for R/c we get

$$\frac{R}{c} = \frac{(\tau - \alpha)^3}{\tau(\tau + \alpha)}(y + \tfrac{1}{2}y^2) \tag{95.41}$$

We put

$$h = \frac{\tau(\tau + \alpha)}{(\tau - \alpha)^3} \tag{95.42}$$

and recall relation (94.52) for the invariant density ρ^*, by which

$$\rho^* = \frac{3\alpha}{2\pi\gamma}\frac{\tau^3}{(\tau - \alpha)^6} \tag{95.43}$$

Then we have

$$\frac{2}{3}\pi\gamma\frac{\rho^*}{h^2} = \frac{\tau\alpha}{(\tau + \alpha)^2} \tag{95.44}$$

The quantity h has the dimensions of inverse time and the quantity (95.44) is a dimensionless number. Replacing τ and α in (95.41) and (95.39) by these quantities we get

$$\frac{Rh}{c} = y + \frac{1}{2}y^2$$

$$\frac{\omega_0 - \omega}{\omega} = y + \frac{2}{3}\pi\gamma\frac{\rho^*}{h^2}y^2 \tag{95.45}$$

These equations embrace the whole theory of the red shift.

The general trend of the dependence of the shift $(\omega_0 - \omega)/\omega$ on distance is the following.

For small shifts (small y) we can take the right-hand sides of the two equations to be equal. Then we have

$$c\frac{\omega_0 - \omega}{\omega} = Rh \tag{95.46}$$

and the relation between the red shift $(\omega_0 - \omega)/\omega$ and the distance R is linear. The coefficient of proportionality in this linear relation may be determined from observation and this gives a value [25] for the reciprocal of h, of the order

$$\frac{1}{h} \doteqdot 4 \times 10^9 \text{ years} \tag{95.47}$$

(The earlier literature gave a value of $2 \cdot 10^9$ years for $1/h$; the difference is due to an inaccuracy in the earlier estimates of the distance R.) The value (95.47) corresponds to the following value for h

$$h = 8 \times 10^{-18} \text{ sec}^{-1} \tag{95.48}$$

For large shifts, i.e. very large distances, the nonlinear terms in equations (95.45) must have an effect. Their influence must show itself in the fact that the shift increases with distance more slowly than initially; the quantity h determined from (95.46) by observations on the furthest galaxies must prove to be somewhat smaller than if it is determined from observations on nearer galaxies. At the greatest distances, which probably cannot be observed in practice, the relation must again tend towards the linear, but with a smaller factor of proportionality.

In astronomy it is customary to call the left-hand side of (95.46) a speed and to express it in kilometres per second. However, it is necessary to remember that although this quantity has the dimensions of a speed it is not the speed of motion of anything. This is evident, for instance, from the fact that if $\omega < \frac{1}{2}\omega_0$ its magnitude exceeds the speed of light. Also the quantity $c(\omega_0 - \omega)/\omega$ is not a Doppler speed even if the whole shift is interpreted as the result of a Doppler effect in Galilean space. It follows from the ordinary theory of the Doppler effect (see (95.12)) that the effective Doppler speed would be the quantity

$$v_{eff} = c \, \frac{\omega_0^2 - \omega^2}{\omega_0^2 + \omega^2} \tag{95.49}$$

which is close to the quantity on the left-hand side of (95.46) only if the shift is small.

The equations (95.45) are rigorous and give the dependence of the shift on distance for any value of the former. It is possible that in time the accuracy of observations will increase so much that their analysis on the basis of these equations will make it possible to study the coefficient of y^2 in the second equation of (95.45). This will then make it possible to obtain from observations on the red shift not only the constant h (known as Hubble's constant) but also the mean density ρ^*. At present, however, ρ^* can only be determined quite roughly by counting the number of galaxies in sufficiently large volumes of space on the assumption that each galaxy has the same mass as our Galaxy (of the order of 10^{11} solar masses or 2×10^{44}g). Such an estimate gives a density of the order

$$\rho^* \doteqdot 4 \times 10^{-29} \text{ g/cm}^3 \tag{95.50}$$

A more vivid idea of the magnitude of this density can be given as follows : The volume of the terrestrial globe is $1\cdot08332 \times 10^{27}\text{cm}^3$ or, roughly, 10^{27}cm^3. In space a volume of this size contains in the mean $0\cdot04$g of matter.[†]

If ρ^* and h are assumed to be known the value of the dimensionless constant

$$b = \frac{8\pi\gamma\rho^*}{3h^2} \tag{95.51}$$

may also be determined. This constant appears both in the equation (95.45), which may be written as

$$\frac{Rh}{c} = y + \frac{1}{2}y^2$$
$$\frac{\omega_0 - \omega}{\omega} = y + \frac{b}{4}y^2 \tag{95.52}$$

and in the relation (95.44), which gives

$$b = \frac{4\tau\alpha}{(\tau + \alpha)^2} \tag{95.53}$$

If we take as values

$$h = 8 \times 10^{-18}\text{sec}^{-1}$$
$$\rho^* = 4 \times 10^{-29}\text{g/cm}^3 \tag{95.54}$$
$$\gamma = \frac{2}{3} \times 10^{-7} \text{ cm}^3/(\text{g. sec}^2)$$

[†] We stress once again that the quantity ρ^* is known with very small accuracy ; its true value may be many times greater or smaller than the value given.

we get

$$b = \frac{\pi}{9} \fallingdotseq \frac{1}{3} \tag{95.55}$$

It is then possible to use (95.53) to determine the ratio τ/α, namely

$$\frac{\tau}{\alpha} \fallingdotseq 10 \tag{95.56}$$

Hence and from (95.42) we have

$$h\tau = \frac{1 \cdot 1}{(0 \cdot 9)^3} \fallingdotseq 1 \cdot 50; \quad h\alpha \fallingdotseq 0 \cdot 15 \tag{95.57}$$

and, using the value of $1/h$ given by (95.47) we get

$$\begin{aligned} \tau &= 6 \times 10^9 \text{ years} \\ \alpha &= 6 \times 10^8 \text{ years} \end{aligned} \tag{95.58}$$

and from (94.45)

$$T = 3 \cdot 2 \times 10^9 \text{ years} \tag{95.59}$$

The following should be borne in mind. The ratio τ/α given by equation (95.53) is real only if b is less than unity, i.e. if for given h the density ρ^* is sufficiently small, as in fact appears to be the case. There exist also solutions of Einstein's equations corresponding to $b > 1$, but for these the conformally-Galilean coordinates we have used are inapplicable because they become complex. It is true that one can introduce other coordinates that are real, but the expression that one gets for ds^2 when $b > 1$ leads to such strange notions concerning the properties of space and time (a finite volume varying periodically with time, etc.) that one can hardly ascribe physical meaning to this case. Therefore we shall not discuss the solution for the case $b > 1$. (This solution was also found by Friedmann.)

As for the solution we have discussed, which corresponds to $b < 1$ (the Friedmann-Lobachevsky space) the following remarks should be made concerning it.

In the first place it is incorrect to see in it some kind of a model of " the Universe as a whole " : such a point of view is unsatisfactory in a philosophical respect. At most Friedmann-Lobachevsky space can serve as the background for a limited number of galaxies just as Galilean space serves as a background for objects such as the Solar system.

The actual applicability of Einstein's equations in their classical form to such enormous dimensions is not so well established as in the case of phenomena on a more limited scale. It is not out of the question that on a cosmic scale these equations will require modification and generalization.

Among the consequences of the solution that we have discussed the most paradoxical is probably the relative shortness of the time T which has elapsed since the galaxies were close together. This time is comparable to the age of the Earth's crust as determined by the radioactive decay of uranium, while it would have been natural to expect the " cosmic " scale of time to be much greater than the " terrestrial "

The fact of the " dispersal " of the galaxies, in all its unexpectedness, is so well established, however, that one need not have any doubts about it. The number of binary stars which is abnormally large from the point of view of stellar statistics, also indicates that in the past the density not only of galaxies but also of stars was probably much greater.

In judging the theory it is also necessary to bear in mind that it is a successful attempt to resolve the Seeliger paradox referred to in Section 94 which arises when one studies a uniform mass density in Euclidean space.

It is therefore beyond doubt that the theory due to A. A. Friedmann which we have described is an important step in the study of space on a cosmic scale.

96. The Development of the Theory of Gravitation and of the Motion of Masses (A Critical Survey)

Einstein's basic paper that laid the foundations of the theory of Galilean space and time made its appearance in 1905 under the heading " On the Electrodynamics of Moving Bodies ". This paper linked together for the first time the principle of the constancy of the speed of light and the principle of relativity, according to which corresponding physical processes exist, and proceed identically in any two inertial frames. To make these two principles compatible it proved necessary to re-examine the notions of space and of time and this led to a theory of a unified space-time. This theory was given the name of " Theory of Relativity ". It is worth noticing that this name did not yet appear in the title of Einstein's paper.

We know now that the principle of relativity reflects the uniformity of space-time: either the total uniformity of Galilean space, or—in a generalized theory—uniformity at infinity, which under certain conditions allows one to introduce harmonic coordinates. In both cases the principle of relativity is expressed by the existence of the group of Lorentz transformations within a definite class of coordinate systems.

During the period when Einstein created his theory of relativity (before his theory of gravitation) the idea that it is possible for physical processes to influence the space-time metric had not yet arisen; in other words, it was then tacitly assumed that the metric was rigid. But if this assumption is made, the principle of relativity expressed in its most general form (in arbitrary coordinates) leads to uniform space, and if one makes the additional assumption that there is no absolute scale, it leads just to Galilean space (Section 49*).

The basic idea of the theory of relativity consists precisely in establishing the metric of space-time and in pronouncing the requirement that the form of the laws of physics should correspond to this metric; since the metric expresses the uniformity of space-time the form of the laws of physics must take into account this uniformity. This requirement means that the equations expressing physical laws must be covariant with respect to Lorentz transformations. The requirement mentioned has a very great heuristic significance because it severely limits the possible form of physical laws. It is, therefore, not surprising that the applications of the Theory of Relativity affect all branches of physics and are too numerous to list.

In the period between 1905 and 1915 Einstein created his Theory of Gravitation. In 1916 he published his fundamental paper under the heading "The

Principles of the General Theory of Relativity ". This title reflects Einstein's point of view regarding his theory—a point of view which we cannot accept as correct. As we have already shown in the Introduction, the basic idea of Einstein's theory of gravitation is by no means that the principle of relativity is generalized for accelerated motion—such a generalization is not possible. *The basic idea consists in assuming that physical processes can influence the space-time metric and in recognizing the unity of metric and gravitation.* These ideas could be formulated with help of the formalism of Riemannian geometry. As to the relativity principle, one may say that it does not play any essential part in the theory of gravitation. The concept of " relativity of motion " is restricted rather than widened in this theory. This is quite natural since the inclusion of the gravitational field in the metric field destroys the uniformity of space-time, which is only locally restored by the application of the equivalence principle. The local analogue of an inertial frame of reference, the " freely falling " frame, is only an approximate realization of the former. On the other hand, the harmonic coordinates, though not local, are only partly analogous to inertial frames.

The fact that the theory of gravitation, a theory of such amazing depth, beauty and cogency, was not correctly understood by its author, should not surprise us. We should also not be surprised at the gaps in logic, and even errors, which Einstein permitted himself when he derived the basic equations of the theory. In the history of physics we have many examples in which the underlying significance of a fundamentally new physical theory was realized not by its author but by somebody else and in which the derivation of the basic equations proposed by the author proved to be logically inconsistent. It is sufficient to point to Maxwell's theory of the electromagnetic field. This theory actually put an end to the conception of mechanics as the basis of physics, but its author and also Hertz, who did so much in verification of the theory, wholly accepted a mechanical picture. Only Lorentz established with full clarity the physical sense of Maxwell's equations, showing that the electromagnetic field itself is a physical reality (i.e. is itself material), being capable of existence in free space and not requiring a special carrier.†

As for the cogency of the derivation, we can recall that Maxwell [27] prefaces the derivation of his famous equations by the exposition of some chapters in mechanics and bases the derivation itself on Lagrange's equations (of the second kind). We know now that from the point of view of logic, a derivation of Maxwell's equations on the basis of mechanics is not possible. But great, and not only great, discoveries are not made by the rules of logic, but by guesswork, or in other words by creative intuition.

It is interesting to trace the path along which Einstein reached his equations of gravitation. This can be done by using Einstein's fundamental paper of 1916 together with his other scientific work and his autobiography published in 1949 on the occasion of his seventieth birthday [26].

As early as 1908 it became clear to Einstein that any attempt to introduce gravitation within the framework of the theory of relativity in Galilean space could not be successful for the following reason. Such a theory predicts a

† It is interesting that this example of an author not fully understanding the physical meaning of his own theory is given by Einstein himself. (Autobiography [26].)

dependence of the *inertial* mass on the internal (and kinetic) energy of a body, but cannot give a dependence of *gravitational* mass on energy as long as the gravitational equations are taken to be linear. At the same time one has the fundamental fact that inertial and gravitational masses are equal, as is proved by the fact that the acceleration of a freely falling body is independent of its composition. Einstein interpreted this fact in the sense of the local equivalence of fields of acceleration and of gravitation.

Hence Einstein concluded that if " accelerated frames of reference " are accepted gravitation and acceleration become indistinguishable. In his *Auto-biography* Einstein writes : " If therefore gravitational fields of arbitrary extension, not restricted *a priori* by spatial boundary conditions, are regarded as possible the concept of an inertial frame becomes completely empty. The notion of ' acceleration relative to space ' then loses all meaning ; so does the Principle of Inertia† and with it Mach's paradox."‡

Further, Einstein concludes from the equivalence of all reference frames (inertial and non-inertial) that the gravitational equations must be covariant with respect to arbitrary coordinate transformations.

Such were the ideas that represented Einstein's starting point in 1908. Let us analyse them. In the first place there is here an incorrect initial assumption. Einstein speaks of arbitrary gravitational fields extending as far as one pleases and not limited by boundary conditions. Such fields *cannot exist*. Boundary conditions or similar conditions which characterize space as a whole are absolutely essential and thus the notion of " acceleration relative to space " retains its significance in some form or another. As for Mach's paradox, it is based, as is well known, on the consideration of a rotating body which has ellipsoidal form and a non-rotating body which is spherical. A paradox arises here only if one denies a meaning to the notion of " rotation relative to space " ; both bodies, that which rotates and that which does not, then appear to be equivalent and it cannot be understood why one of them is spherical and not the other. But the paradox vanishes as soon as one accepts the legitimacy of the notion of " acceleration relative to space ".

The essence of the error committed in the initial assumption consists in *forgetting that the nature of the equivalence of fields of acceleration and of gravitation is strictly local*. Related to this is the fact that *a non-local physical definition of an accelerated frame of reference is impossible*, because a box, rigid scaffolding, etc., of the kind used by Einstein represents an idealization which is only applicable in inertial frames of reference, and not in accelerated frames. But physically the "general principle of relativity ", in the sense that corresponding processes exist in arbitrary reference frames, does not hold at all. Therefore Einstein's conclusion that all reference frames are physically equivalent, is without foundation. But this is the assumption on which Einstein bases his further arguments, in particular his derivation of the covariance of the required equations of gravitation. Naturally it does not follow from the incorrectness of his assumptions that the conclusions drawn are incorrect: the equations of gravitation are indeed covariant, but their covariance is not their distinctive

† Newton's First Law (V.A.F.).

‡ The above quotation is a direct translation from the German text by N.K.

property; it could be achieved with any theory. Thus in Chapter IV of this book we formulated the ordinary theory of relativity in a covariant manner; it is interesting that Einstein himself points out the possibility of such formulation [26], a fact to which we shall return shortly.

Thus at the first stage of constructing a theory of gravitation Einstein accepted as an initial assumption the equality of inertial and gravitational mass, the principle of the equivalence of acceleration and gravity and the requirement of covariance for the equations. The idea of Riemannian geometry and the idea of the unity of metric and gravitation were as yet absent.

The requirement that the equations be covariant played a very large part in the construction of the theory. The circumstance that Einstein " derived " it from the principle of equivalence and ultimately from the equality of inertial and gravitational mass shows that at the time he was creating his theory Einstein considered the general covariance of the equations to be a specific peculiarity of the theory of gravitation. This is said explicitly in the introductory part of the fundamental paper of 1916. Subsequently it was pointed out to Einstein that general covariance by itself does not express any physical law and, apparently, he agreed with this. But his agreement was rather formal, because in fact to the end of his days Einstein connected the requirement of general covariance with the idea of some kind of " general relativity " and with the equivalence of all frames of reference. He never realized the difference between physical equivalence (or physical relativity) in the sense of the existence of corresponding processes in different frames of reference and that formal equivalence which consists in the possibility of using arbitrary coordinate systems independently of whether corresponding physical processes do or do not exist in the systems concerned. In the theory of Galilean space-time physical relativity is directly connected with the uniformity of the space. In the theory of gravitation, where space-time is non-uniform and its metric depends on the processes occurring in it, things are somewhat more complicated. But here also the existence of a kind of relativity within a class of harmonic coordinate systems is a result of the uniformity of the space at infinity (see Sections 49* and 93). Thus in all cases where there is physical relativity, it is connected with uniformity, i.e. with objective properties of space-time and not at all with the use of this or that coordinate system. (The choice of coordinate system has an effect only on the simplicity of the way physical relativity can be expressed: it is expressible most simply in such coordinates in which physically equivalent systems are related by linear transformations.) The mathematical expression for physical relativity does not reduce to the covariance of differential equations: the latter is a necessary but not a sufficient condition for the existence of the former. But Einstein identified physical relativity with the covariance of differential equations, actually believing that general covariance is an extension of the concepts of the physical relativity that formed the basis of his 1905 theory. This is the origin of Einstein's conviction that there exists a " General Principle of Relativity ". This conviction evidenced itself in the fact that he called his theory of gravitation " The General Theory of Relativity " and that in later years he stubbornly adhered to this term. He then named his previous theory, which operated in Galilean space, the " Special " Theory of Relativity contrasting it with his " General " Theory. The confusion of the concepts of physical relativity and formal covariance is particularly clearly shown at one point in Einstein's autobiography where he himself formulates the " special " theory of relativity (i.e. a theory in which, according to Einstein there is no " general relativity ") in the general covariant form, which, according to Einstein, expresses the idea of " general relativity ".

Thus in the period immediately preceding the creation of the theory of gravitation the idea of general covariance appeared to Einstein as a physical idea and it guided him in his researches.

The next important step in the creation of the theory was made when Einstein introduced the generalized expression for the square of the interval, i.e. when he, in fact, introduced the hypothesis of Riemannian geometry for space and time. Einstein approached the idea of Riemannian geometry from the direction of requiring the general covariance of the equations. He made use of the fact that in the " absolute differential calculus " (tensor analysis) which by that time had been fully developed by Ricci, Levi-Civita and others, equations appear from the start in generally covariant form. Thus the requirement of general covariance played an important heuristic role, in spite of the fact that the essence of the matter lay not there, but *in the new hypothesis concerning the character of space-time geometry.*†

In solving the problem of the form of the gravitational equations an important step was made by Einstein in assuming that purely " geometrical " quantities namely the coefficients $g_{\mu\nu}$ in the expression for the squared interval should be considered to play the part of the gravitational potentials, and that no other quantities need be introduced. From among the multitude of possible non-linear generally covariant equations this assumption served to single out almost uniquely one set of equations. To achieve full uniqueness some supplementary considerations had to be introduced, such as the requirements that the mass tensor be conservative and that in the absence of masses there should be a solution corresponding to Galilean space.

These two ideas—the idea of generalizing the metric and the idea of the unity of metric and gravitation—were decisive. Operating with them, Einstein was led to his equations of gravitation

$$R_{\mu\nu} - \tfrac{1}{2}g_{\mu\nu}R = -\varkappa T_{\mu\nu} \tag{96.01}$$

which contain the essence of this theory and represent one of the greatest achievements of human genius. These equations are given in Einstein's 1916 paper.

Subsequently Einstein made attempts to alter these equations but the original form remains the only correct one, provided only the meaning of the mass tensor $T_{\mu\nu}$ is interpreted correctly. We have in mind the circumstance that in the cosmological case the mass tensor is determined only apart from a term proportional to the metric tensor: the factor of proportionality in that term characterizes not only the mass tensor itself but also the properties of space as a whole (the factor plays the part of a cosmological constant). Einstein also attempted to find equations not involving a mass tensor for some " universal field " (*Gesamtfeld*) that was to include gravitation: apparently he con-

† Here we use the word "geometry" in the sense of objective properties of space and time, and not in the sense of the science of these properties.

nectea these attempts with his hopes of creating, independently of quantum theory, a theory of elementary particles that were to be the singularities of the field. These attempts ended in failure and we only mention them because the idea of considering singularities of the field in place of the mass tensor was also pursued in the work of Einstein and his school on the derivation of the equations of motion from the gravitational equations.

Chronologically the first of these papers were those of Einstein and Grommer and of Einstein, published in 1927 [28, 29]. In this work the following question was posed and solved in principle. If the masses are considered as singularities of the field, is it possible to prescribe arbitrarily the motion of these singularities, without violating the gravitational equations? This question was answered in the negative : it emerged that the motion of the singularities could not be prescribed, because it is a consequence of the gravitational equations. Hence it follows in particular that the principle of the geodesic is not independent of the gravitational equations but is a consequence thereof. It is of importance to note that this result is conditioned by the non-linear character of the gravitational equations.

In spite of the enormous importance of this result the two papers of Einstein just mentioned aroused little interest and more than ten years passed before they were followed up.

The development of the ideas laid down in the paper by Einstein and Grommer in 1927 began in the years 1938–39 quite independently in two directions. The work of Einstein, Infeld and their collaborators is concerned with the one development, the work of Fock and his collaborators with the other ; the papers of Papapetrou, which appeared after 1950, can also be counted as going in the second direction.

We examine first the work of the Einstein school.

In a series of papers by Einstein, Infeld and Hoffman (1938) [30] and by Einstein and Infeld (1940) [31], (1949) [32], a method was elaborated which made it possible to derive from the gravitational equations and to write in explicit form an approximation to the equations of motion for pointlike singularities of the field, which represent spherically symmetric bodies of infinitesimal size. The equations were obtained both in the first (Newtonian), and in the following approximation. The authors were guided by Einstein's idea of the undesirability of introducing a mass tensor and therefore started with the gravitational equations with a vanishing right-hand side. (Incidentally, Infeld showed in 1954 that the mathematical work becomes incomparably simpler if, from the start, one introduces a mass tensor involving Dirac delta-functions, corresponding to spherically symmetric singularities.) In attempting to find an exact solution of the mechanical problem of the motion of the field singularities the authors also introduced infinite series in powers of a parameter inversely proportional to the speed of light.

The interpretation of the results of the work of Einstein's school is made difficult by the fact that the coordinate system is not specified from the start (in the way we specified the harmonic coordinate system), but instead is determined from approximation to approximation by means of various supplementary conditions which are sometimes introduced explicitly and sometimes implicitly. In general, however, one can say that the coordinates that are in fact employed in this work differ so little from harmonic coordinates, that the differences have no effect on the equations of motion in second order. If one denotes the harmonic coordinates by (t, x_i) and the coordinates used by Einstein and Infeld by (t', x_i') then in orders of magnitude we have

$$x_i' = x_i + 0 \left(\frac{Lq^4}{c^4}\right), \qquad t' = t + 0 \left(\frac{Lq^5}{c^6}\right) \tag{96.02}$$

where L and q are the parameters we have used repeatedly to characterize the orders of magnitude of length and velocity. This question is discussed in more detail in the author's paper [45].

In those cases when approximations higher than the second are discussed another question arises, in addition to that of the indeterminateness of the coordinate system. It becomes unclear whether the formal solution obtained has physical sense. This doubt is due to the fact that the authors of these papers do not impose the condition of outward radiation and, in fact, make the contrary assertion that there exist certain (unknown) coordinate transformations which reduce the exact equations of motion to Newtonian form, corresponding to a strictly conservative non-radiating system. Both parts of the latter assertion, namely the possibility of reducing more general equations of motion to Newtonian form and the possibility of reducing a non-conservative (radiating) system to a conservative one, seem doubtful.

The 1927 paper by Einstein and Grommer is also the starting point of a series of papers in the other direction.

In our paper [34] published in 1939 we studied the problem of the motion of spherically symmetric non-rotating bodies of finite size and derived equations of motion for them, starting from the gravitational equations. (See also [36].) The particular characteristics of the method used by us are on the one hand the study of the mass tensor, which is determined in parallel with the gravitational potentials, and on the other hand the use of harmonic coordinates : our calculations were so conducted that the equations of motion were obtained from the harmonic conditions. In addition we obtained the gravitational potentials in explicit form (see Sections 82 and 83 of this book).

The fact that harmonic coordinates are important in principle was already noted in our paper of 1939 and it was discussed more fully in the 1947 paper [35], where we pointed out the connection between the question of the uniqueness of the coordinate system and that of the preferred status of the Copernican heliocentric system.

In our 1939 paper the equations of motion were obtained only in Newtonian approximation, but it was mentioned that the work of Petrova would be devoted to the second approximation. That work was indeed completed in 1940 but published only in 1949 [37]. The equations of motion for a system of finite masses in second approximation obtained by Petrova were used by us in our 1941 paper [38] on the integrals of motion of the mass centre.

In 1954 Kashkarov [39] used the same method to derive from the gravitational equations the equations of motion of rotating masses in Newtonian approximation.

In 1950 Fichtenholz [40] reduced the equations of motion in second approximation to Lagrangian form and hence derived their integrals.

In his 1951 paper [41] Papapetrou, independently of Petrova, continued our 1939 work and derived from it the equations of motion for spherically symmetric non-rotating masses in second approximation. However, in Papapetrou's derivation there is an inconsistency of approach in that he chooses *a priori* a weighting function when averaging the equations of motion of a continuous medium over the region of each mass. The choice that Papapetrou implicitly makes is justified only at the end of the calculation by a direct verification of the harmonic conditions. The same remark applies to a more recent paper by Meister [42].

In the domain of the theory of masses in motion a number of new results are derived in this book. We shall not speak here of these or of our results in other domains of the theory of gravitation, referring the reader to the main text. We merely note that for the case of rotating masses of finite size we obtain not only the equations of motion themselves but also their integrals.

In all work on the theory of the motion of masses—both the work of Einstein and his school and our own—the case of an " insular " distribution of masses is discussed, i.e. just the case relevant to our general conclusions on the possibility of introducing a harmonic coordinate system. Therefore the comparison of the two sets of papers gives a vivid illustration of the difference between Einstein's point of view and ours on the question of coordinates and on the fundamental principles of the theory. Apart from these general matters the treatment of some concrete questions connected with the statement of the general problem is also different; while in Einstein's work the masses are thought of as points, we consider extended masses with a definite internal structure. Einstein's interest in point masses appears to be connected with his aforementioned attempts to construct a theory of matter with particles as singular points of the field. Einstein's view of the mass tensor as an " undesirable element " in the theory is connected with these same ideas. In contrast to this view, we consider the mass tensor as a necessary element of the theory and attach special significance to its unique definition and to the examination of the conditions in which such a definition is possible.

Finally, on the question of the radiation of gravitational waves, we consider that although in ordinary astronomical conditions these waves do not play any noticeable part, they do nevertheless exist in principle. Therefore in a rigorous statement of the problem of the motion of masses we would have to include the wave part of the gravitational field; the problem is then no longer a problem of mechanics in the proper sense.

CONCLUSION

We shall attempt a brief exposition of our point of view concerning the theory of space, time and gravitation.

In most ways our standpoint coincides with Einstein's as usually expounded, but on some essential points it is different.

Space and time must be considered in conjunction. They combine into a four-dimensional manifold which is uniform in the absence of gravitation and then constitutes Galilean space. Galilean space possesses a pseudo-Euclidean metric. Its uniformity finds expression in the existence for it of the group of Lorentz transformations, which describe the transition from one inertial frame of reference to another. The property of uniformity is related to the physical principle of relativity, which asserts the existence of corresponding processes in any two inertial frames of reference. Therefore the theory of Galilean space based on the Lorentz transformations is called the Theory of Relativity.

Both the property of uniformity and the whole theory of Galilean space may also be formulated in arbitrary coordinates. However, the privileged character of Galilean coordinates manifests itself in the particular simplicity (linearity) of the transformations that relate inertial coordinate systems, that class of systems within which the physical principle of relativity holds.

The physical basis of the theory of gravitation is the law of the equality of inertial and gravitational mass and its mathematical basis is the hypothesis that space and time possess a Riemannian metric, which is not given in advance and may itself depend on the physical processes occurring in the space (on the position and motion of masses). Owing to the fact that the description of the gravitational field does not involve the introduction of any quantities other than the metric tensor, Einstein's gravitational theory is a realization of the idea of the unity of metric and gravitation. The Riemannian geometry used in the theory of gravitation studies the local properties of space and, in the general case, tells us nothing of the properties of space as a whole. However, in the theory of gravitation local treatment is insufficient, since the field equations are partial differential equations, the solution of which depends decisively on the boundary conditions. In gravitational theory, therefore, one has inevitably to introduce some kind of hypothesis concerning the properties of space as a whole. The simplest and at the same time most important of these hypotheses is the assumption that, at infinity, space is Galilean. Subject to this assumption one can impose on the gravitational potentials such supplementary conditions that the coordinate system is determined uniquely apart from a Lorentz transformation. This coordinate system, which we call harmonic, stands in strong analogy with the ordinary inertial coordinate system.

The physical principle of relativity, understood as the statement that there exist corresponding processes in frames of reference of a certain class, does not hold in the general case of Einstein space, let alone the " General Principle of Relativity " within the class of arbitrary coordinate systems. However, within the class of harmonic coordinate systems a principle of relativity is valid which is fully analogous to the principle that holds in Galilean space. In this case the notion of " corresponding processes " must include the distribution and motion of the masses that determine the metric.

The physical principle of relativity is connected, directly or indirectly, with the uniformity of space: either with full uniformity (Galilean space), or with uniformity at infinity (space permitting the introduction of harmonic coordinates), or else finally with local uniformity; in the last case the principle holds only in the infinitely small. One can achieve local uniformity, i.e. uniformity in the neighbourhood of a single point of space, in a geodesic coordinate system (the principle of local equivalence between acceleration and gravitation). The principle of equivalence thus follows from the Reimannian nature of the metric, but it is already contained in Newtonian mechanics and is closely related to the law of equality of inertial and gravitational mass.

From the point of view of the theory of gravitation the law of the equality of inertial and gravitational mass is valid with all the accuracy with which it is possible to define independently the inertial and gravitational properties of mass. This law is not of local character and is therefore more useful as a basis for deriving Einstein's gravitational equations than the principle of equivalence, which requires the use of a frame of reference in accelerated motion—a concept for which there is no satisfactory physical definition.

Owing to the local nature of the principle of equivalence, it is not a sufficient basis for the statement that fields of acceleration and gravitation are indistinguishable in finite regions of space, and even less for the statement that there exists a " General Principle of Relativity ". Such a conclusion from the local to the general is as inadmissable as would be, for instance, the conclusion that all analytic functions are indistinguishable because they all behave as if they were linear, in the infinitely small.

Since the physical principle of relativity is related to uniformity and since in the theory of gravitation the uniformity is confined either to the infinitesimal or to infinitely remote regions of space, but does not hold in finite regions and at finite distances from masses, the theory of gravitation can evidently not be looked upon as a generalization of the concept of relativity. On the contrary, the theory limits that concept strongly: one can even say that the principle of relativity does not play any essential rôle at all in the theory of gravitation. It is therefore incorrect to call Einstein's theory of gravitation a " General Theory of Relativity " all the more since " The General Principle of Relativity " is impossible under any physical conditions.

The general covariance of equations has quite a different meaning from the physical principle of relativity; it is merely a formal property of the equations which allows one to write them down without prejudging the question of what coordinate system to use. The solution of equations written in generally covariant form involves four arbitrary functions; but the indeterminacy arising from this has no fundamental importance and does not express any kind of " general relativity ". From a practical point of view such an indeterminacy even represents something of a disadvantage. It seems to us that it is preferable to have a mathematical statement of the problem in which uniqueness of the solution may be achieved (naturally to the same extent as the essence of the problem permits).

In our statement of the problem of an isolated system of masses the uniqueness of the solution is achieved by introducing four supplementary equations, the harmonic conditions, and also of boundary conditions, and by passing from a local description to a description of space as a whole. In this way the uniqueness of the solution is achieved in all the problems considered : in the problems of the equations of motion, of radiation, of the form of the rigorous, the approximate and the asymptotic solution of the gravitational equations and so forth.

In the case of an isolated system of bodies the question of the coordinate system is answered in the same way as in the absence of gravitation : there exists a preferred system of coordinates (Galilean or harmonic) but it is also possible to use any other coordinate system. As in the Galilean case, the privileged character of harmonic coordinates shows itself in the linearity of the transformations which connect the coordinate systems within the class in which the physical principle of relativity holds. This property of harmonic coordinates distinguishes them physically from other coordinate sytems; in particular it is this property which allows one, as in the Galilean case, to give preference to the heliocentric theory of the Solar System over the geocentric theory.

The existence of a privileged coordinate system is in the first place important as a matter of principle, in that it reflects objective properties of space. In addition, since this coordinate system is of a standard character, it allows one to establish the geometrical meaning of other coordinates and to make comparisons between solutions found in other coordinates. Finally, harmonic coordinates have great practical significance, because calculations can be simplified enormously by their use.

When discussing regions of space that include many galaxies the notion of an isolated system of masses becomes inapplicable and the properties of space as a whole must be formulated differently (*Friedmann-Lobachevsky space*).

ON THE DERIVATION OF THE
LORENTZ TRANSFORMATIONS

In Section 8 the equations were derived which must be satisfied by the transformation function

$$x'_i = f_i(x_0, x_1, x_2, x_3) \qquad (i = 0, 1, 2, 3) \tag{A.01}$$

in order to ensure that the following two conditions are fulfilled :—

(a) To a uniform rectilinear motion in the coordinates (x_i) there must correspond a motion of the same nature in the coordinates (x'_i) ;

(b) To a uniform rectilinear motion *with light-velocity* in the coordinates (x_i) there must correspond a motion of the same nature in the coordinates (x'_i).

Condition (b) is equivalent to the condition :

(b') To the wave front equation

$$\left(\frac{\partial\omega}{\partial x_0}\right)^2 - \left[\left(\frac{\partial\omega}{\partial x_1}\right)^2 + \left(\frac{\partial\omega}{\partial x_2}\right)^2 + \left(\frac{\partial\omega}{\partial x_3}\right)^2\right] = 0 \tag{A.02}$$

in the coordinates (x_i), there must correspond just such an equation in the coordinates (x'_i).

It was shown in Section 8 that functions satisfying condition (a) must be solutions of the system of equations

$$\frac{\partial^2 f_i}{\partial x_k \, \partial x_l} = \psi_k \frac{\partial f_i}{\partial x_l} + \psi_l \frac{\partial f_i}{\partial x_k}, \tag{A.03}$$

whereas functions satisfying (b) or (b') must be solutions of the system

$$\sum_{i=0}^{3} e_i \frac{\partial f_i}{\partial x_k} \frac{\partial f_i}{\partial x_l} = \lambda e_k \delta_{kl} \tag{A.04}$$

From (A.04) we shall derive another equation similar in form to (A.03). Differentiating (A.04) with respect to x_m and putting

$$\frac{\partial\lambda}{\partial x_m} = 2\lambda\varphi_m \tag{A.05}$$

we obtain

$$\sum_{i=0}^{3} e_i \left(\frac{\partial^2 f_i}{\partial x_k \, \partial x_m} \frac{\partial f_i}{\partial x_l} + \frac{\partial^2 f_i}{\partial x_l \, \partial x_m} \frac{\partial f_i}{\partial x_k}\right) = 2\lambda\varphi_m e_k \delta_{kl} \tag{A.06}$$

We now introduce the quantities Γ^s_{km} defined by the relation

$$\sum_{i=0}^{3} e_i \frac{\partial^2 f_i}{\partial x_k \partial x_m} \frac{\partial f_i}{\partial x_s} = \lambda e_s \Gamma^s_{km} \tag{A.07}$$

Equation (A.06) may then be written as

$$e_l \Gamma^l_{km} + e_k \Gamma^k_{lm} = 2\varphi_m e_k \delta_{kl} \tag{A.08}$$

To find the quantities Γ^s_{km} in terms of the φ_m, we write down two equations obtained from (A.08) by cyclic permutation of the indices k, l, m :

$$e_m \Gamma^m_{lk} + e_l \Gamma^l_{mk} = 2\varphi_k e_l \delta_{lm} \tag{A.09}$$

$$e_k \Gamma^k_{ml} + e_m \Gamma^m_{kl} = 2\varphi_l e_m \delta_{mk} \tag{A.10}$$

Taking their sum, subtracting the original equation (A.08) and using the symmetry of Γ^l_{km} with respect to the lower indices we obtain, after multiplication with e_m

$$\Gamma^m_{kl} = \varphi_k \delta_{lm} + \varphi_l \delta_{km} - e_m \varphi_m e_k \delta_{kl} \tag{A.11}$$

Now, equations (A.07) may be solved with respect to the second derivatives of f_i. Using (A.04) we get

$$\frac{\partial^2 f_i}{\partial x_k \partial x_l} = \sum_{m=0}^{3} \Gamma^m_{kl} \frac{\partial f_i}{\partial x_m} \tag{A.12}$$

Inserting the value of Γ^m_{kl} from (A.11) we obtain finally

$$\frac{\partial^2 f_i}{\partial x_k \partial x_l} - \varphi_k \frac{\partial f_i}{\partial x_l} + \varphi_l \frac{\partial f_i}{\partial x_k} - e_k \delta_{kl} \sum_{m=0}^{3} e_m \varphi_m \frac{\partial f_i}{\partial x_m} \tag{A.13}$$

Such equations for the transformation functions (A.01) follow from condition (b) or (b') that is concerned with motion with the speed of light. On the other hand, condition (a) concerning the uniformity of motion leads to equations (A.03), and these can also be written in the form (A.12) if we put

$$\Gamma^m_{kl} = \psi_k \delta_{lm} + \psi_l \delta_{km} \tag{A.14}$$

We have seen in Section 8 that if both conditions (a) and (b) (or both (a) and (b')) are imposed simultaneously, all second derivatives of the functions f_i are zero, the quantity λ is constant (and can be put equal to unity), and the transformation in question reduces to a Lorentz transformation.

We must now investigate the consequences of condition (a) taken separately and of condition (b) or (b') taken separately.

Equations of the form of (A.12) have been investigated in detail in Section 42, where a necessary and sufficient condition for their complete integrability was given. This condition has the form

$$\frac{\partial \Gamma^m_{kl}}{\partial x_n} - \frac{\partial \Gamma^m_{kn}}{\partial x_l} + \sum_{r=0}^{3} (\Gamma^r_{kl} \Gamma^m_{rn} - \Gamma^r_{kn} \Gamma^m_{rl}) = 0 \tag{A.15}$$

It is deducible from the requirement that the various expressions for third derivatives of the f_i obtainable by differentiation of (A.12) should all agree.

Inserting the expression (A.14) into (A.15) we get

$$\left(\frac{\partial \psi_l}{\partial x_n} - \frac{\partial \psi_n}{\partial x_l}\right)\delta_{mk} + \left(\frac{\partial \psi_k}{\partial x_n} - \psi_k\psi_n\right)\delta_{ml} - \left(\frac{\partial \psi_k}{\partial x_l} - \psi_k\psi_l\right)\delta_{mn} = 0 \quad (A.16)$$

Here we put $k \neq m$; $l \neq m$; but $n = m$ and get

$$\frac{\partial \psi_k}{\partial x_l} - \psi_k\psi_l = 0 \qquad (A.17)$$

Since the value of the index m in (A.16) is arbitrary the restriction to $k \neq m$ and $l \neq m$ is inessential and equation (A.17) must hold for all values of k and l. Evidently this equation is also sufficient for (A.16) to be satisfied, for it follows from it that

$$\frac{\partial \psi_k}{\partial x_l} = \frac{\partial \psi_l}{\partial x_k} \qquad (A.18)$$

and the first term in (A.16) also becomes zero.

We now insert the expression (A.11) into (A.15). In consequence of (A.05) we may put

$$\varphi_{kl} = \frac{\partial \varphi_k}{\partial x_l} = \frac{\partial \varphi_l}{\partial x_k} = \varphi_{lk} \qquad (A.19)$$

Evaluating the left-hand side of (A.15) we obtain after multiplication by e_m

$$(\varphi_{kn} - \varphi_k\varphi_n)e_m\delta_{lm} - (\varphi_{kl} - \varphi_k\varphi_l)e_m\delta_{nm} + (\varphi_{lm} - \varphi_l\varphi_m)e_k\delta_{kn}$$
$$- (\varphi_{mn} - \varphi_m\varphi_n)e_k\delta_{kl} + e_k e_m(\delta_{kn}\delta_{lm} - \delta_{kl}\delta_{nm})\sum_{r=0}^{3} e_r\varphi_r^2 = 0 \qquad (A.20)$$

Putting
$$\Phi_{kl} = \varphi_{kl} - \varphi_k\varphi_l + \tfrac{1}{2}e_k\delta_{kl}\sum_{r=0}^{3} e_r\varphi_r^2 \qquad (A.21)$$

$$\Phi_{kn}e_m\delta_{lm} - \Phi_{kl}e_m\delta_{nm} + \Phi_{lm}e_k\delta_{kn} - \Phi_{mn}e_k\delta_{kl} = 0 \qquad (A.22)$$

Hence it is easy to deduce that necessarily

$$\Phi_{kl} = 0 \qquad (A.23)$$

For, if we multiply the left-hand side of (A.22) by $-e_m$, put $m = n$ and sum over m we get

$$2\Phi_{kl} + e_k\delta_{kl}\sum_{m=0}^{3} e_m\Phi_{mm} = 0 \qquad (A.24)$$

Multiplying the left-hand side of (A.24) by e_k, putting $k = l$ and summing over k we get, after division by 6 :

$$\sum_{m=0}^{3} e_m\Phi_{mm} = 0 \qquad (A.25)$$

Thus the condition for the integrability of (A.03) is (A.17) and the condition of integrability of (A.13) is (A.23). As a result of (A.18) and (A.19) we may put

$$\psi_k = \frac{\partial \psi}{\partial x_k}; \qquad \varphi_k = \frac{\partial \varphi}{\partial x_k} \tag{A.26}$$

where ψ and φ are unknown functions (according to (A.05) we can take $\varphi = \log \sqrt{\lambda}$). Then the conditions of integrability become

$$\frac{\partial^2 \psi}{\partial x_k \, \partial x_l} - \frac{\partial \psi}{\partial x_k} \frac{\partial \psi}{\partial x_l} = 0 \tag{A.27}$$

and

$$\frac{\partial^2 \varphi}{\partial x_k \, \partial x_l} - \frac{\partial \varphi}{\partial x_k} \frac{\partial \varphi}{\partial x_l} + \frac{1}{2} e_k \delta_{lk} \sum_{r=0}^{3} e_r \left(\frac{\partial \varphi}{\partial x_r} \right)^2 = 0 \tag{A.28}$$

If here we put

$$e^{-\psi} = w; \qquad \psi = -\log w \tag{A.29}$$

and also

$$e^{-\varphi} = u; \qquad \varphi = -\log u \tag{A.30}$$

the new unknown functions are seen to satisfy the equations

$$\frac{\partial^2 w}{\partial x_k \, \partial x_l} = 0 \tag{A.31}$$

and

$$\frac{\partial^2 u}{\partial x_k \, \partial x_l} = \frac{1}{2} e_k \delta_{kl} \frac{1}{u} \sum_{r=0}^{3} e_r \left(\frac{\partial u}{\partial x_r} \right)^2 \tag{A.32}$$

Equation (A.31) shows that w is a linear function of the coordinates

$$w = w(0) + w_0 x_0 + w_1 x_1 + w_2 x_2 + w_3 x_3 \tag{A.33}$$

and that therefore

$$\psi_k = -\frac{w_k}{w} \tag{A.34}$$

where the w_k are constants. Inserting these values of the ψ_k into the equation (A.03) for f_i we can write the latter as

$$\frac{\partial^2 (w f_i)}{\partial x_k \, \partial x_l} = 0 \tag{A.35}$$

whence it follows that the quantities $w f_i$ are linear functions. This means that the four functions f_0, f_1, f_2 and f_3 are ratios of linear functions, all with the same denominator w.

We thus arrive at the following conclusion. The most general form of the transformation (A.01) which satisfies condition (a) is a transformation involving linear fractions, all with the same denominator. In the particular case when the denominator reduces to a constant the linear fractions become linear functions.

We now turn to the discussion of equation (A.32) which follows from condition (b) or (b'). In the first place we note that for $k \neq l$ its right-hand side is zero. Therefore the second derivatives of u with respect to two different variables vanish and the function u is additively composed of single variable functions. On the other hand, it follows from (A.32) that the double derivatives of u with respect to a single variable are all equal, apart from a sign

$$e_0 \frac{\partial^2 u}{\partial x_0^2} = e_1 \frac{\partial^2 u}{\partial x_1^2} = e_2 \frac{\partial^2 u}{\partial x_2^2} = e_3 \frac{\partial^2 u}{\partial x_3^2} \qquad (A.36)$$

But each of the quantities of (A.36) can either be a constant or depend on one variable only (that with respect to which the differentiation is performed), they are therefore all equal to the same constant. We call this constant $2C$ and then have

$$\frac{\partial^2 u}{\partial x_k^2} = 2Ce_k; \qquad \frac{\partial^2 u}{\partial x_k \, \partial x_l} = 0 \qquad (k \neq l) \qquad (A.37)$$

and also

$$\sum_{r=0}^{3} e_r \left(\frac{\partial u}{\partial x_r} \right)^2 = 4Cu \qquad (A.38)$$

It follows from (A.37) that u is of the form

$$u = C \sum_{k=0}^{3} e_k x_k^2 - 2 \sum_{k=0}^{3} e_k \alpha_k x_k + B \qquad (A.39)$$

where the α_k and B are constants. Equation (A.38) only gives a relation between the constants namely

$$BC = \sum_{r=0}^{3} e_r \alpha_r^2 \qquad (A.40)$$

According to (A.05) and (A.30) the factor λ in (A.04) is inversely proportional to u^2. We can put

$$\sum_i e_i \frac{\partial f_i}{\partial x_k} \frac{\partial f_i}{\partial x_l} = \frac{1}{u^2} e_k \delta_{kl} \qquad (A.41)$$

Without restriction of generality we can assume that at the origin, i.e. for $x_0 = x_1 = x_2 = x_3 = 0$, we have $u = 1$. This can always be achieved by changing the scale of the f_i or the x_k. With this condition we get

$$B = 1; \qquad C = \sum_{r=0}^{3} e_r \alpha_r^2 \qquad (A.42)$$

and therefore

$$u = 1 - 2 \sum_{k=0}^{3} e_k \alpha_k x_k + \sum_{k=0}^{3} e_k \alpha_k^2 \sum_{l=0}^{3} e_l x_l^2 \qquad (A.43)$$

We replace the quantities φ_k in (A.13) by their values

$$\varphi_k = -\frac{u_k}{u}; \qquad u_k = \frac{\partial u}{\partial x_k} \tag{A.44}$$

and then get

$$u\frac{\partial^2 f_i}{\partial x_k \, \partial x_l} + u_k \frac{\partial f_i}{\partial x_l} + u_l \frac{\partial f_i}{\partial x_k} = e_k \delta_{kl} \sum_{m=0}^{3} e_m u_m \frac{\partial f_i}{\partial x_m} \tag{A.45}$$

If u is of the form (A.43) the conditions of integrability of the system (A.45) are satisfied, and the functions are completely determined by the values at the origin of the functions themselves and their first derivatives. Let these values be

$$(f_i)_0 = a_i; \qquad \left(\frac{\partial f_i}{\partial x_k}\right)_0 = e_k a_{ik} \tag{A.46}$$

Since at the origin $u = 1$, the equation (A.41) gives

$$\sum_{i=0}^{3} e_i a_{ik} a_{il} = e_k \delta_{kl} \tag{A.47}$$

We now put

$$f_i = a_i + \sum_{r=0}^{3} e_r a_{ir} f_r^* \tag{A.48}$$

By virtue of (A.47) these equations can be solved for the f_r^* which are then expressed as linear functions of the f_i. Evidently the f_r^* satisfy the same system of differential equations as the f_i; for the system (A.45) it follows from the linearity of the equations, for the system (A.41) it follows from (A.47). But the initial conditions for the f_r^* are of the form

$$(f_r^*)_0 = 0; \qquad \left(\frac{\partial f_r^*}{\partial x_k}\right)_0 = \delta_{rk} \tag{A.49}$$

Thus if we find a solution of the system (A.43) with initial conditions of the particular form (A.49) equation (A.48) gives us the most general solution of the system.

The system (A.45) may be written in the form

$$\frac{\partial^2(u f_i^*)}{\partial x_k \, \partial x_l} = f_i^* \frac{\partial^2 u}{\partial x_k \, \partial x_l} + e_k \delta_{kl} \sum_{m=0}^{3} e_m u_m \frac{\partial f_i^*}{\partial x_m} \tag{A.50}$$

and, using (A.37) we get

$$\frac{\partial^2(u f_i^*)}{\partial x_k \, \partial x_l} = e_k \delta_{kl} \left(2C f_i^* + \sum_{m=0}^{3} e_m u_m \frac{\partial f_i^*}{\partial x_m} \right) \tag{A.51}$$

Here we put

$$f_i^* = \frac{F_i}{u} \tag{A.52}$$

By use of (A.38) we obtain

$$\frac{\partial^2 F_i}{\partial x_k \, \partial x_l} = e_k \delta_{kl} \frac{1}{u} \left(-2C F_i + \sum_{m=0}^{3} e_m u_m \frac{\partial F_i}{\partial x_m} \right) \tag{A.53}$$

Arguing in the same way as in the discussion of (A.32) we get

$$\frac{\partial^2 F_i}{\partial x_k \, \partial x_l} = 2C_i e_k \delta_{kl} \tag{A.54}$$

with

$$-2CF_i + \sum_{m=0}^{3} e_m u_m \frac{\partial F_i}{\partial x_m} = 2C_i u \tag{A.55}$$

It is easy to see from (A.52) that the initial conditions (A.49) for the f_i lead to conditions of the same form for the F_i. Equation (A.54) together with the initial conditions gives

$$F_i = C_i \sum_{k=0}^{3} e_k x_k^2 + x_i \tag{A.56}$$

Insertion of (A.56) into (A.55) allows us to determine the values of the constants C_i, namely

$$C_i = -\alpha_i \tag{A.57}$$

With these values for the constants equation (A.55) becomes an identity. Therefore we have

$$F_i = x_i - \alpha_i \sum_{k=0}^{3} e_k x_k^2 \tag{A.58}$$

and

$$f_i^* = \frac{x_i - \alpha_i \sum\limits_{k=0}^{3} e_k x_k^2}{1 - 2 \sum\limits_{k=0}^{3} e_k \alpha_k x_k + \sum\limits_{k=0}^{3} e_k \alpha_k^2 \sum\limits_{l=0}^{3} e_l x_l^2} \tag{A.59}$$

We arrive at the following final conclusion:

The form of the most general transformation (A.01) satisfying condition (b) or (b′) is obtained from the transformation

$$x_i^* = \frac{x_i - \alpha_i \sum\limits_{k=0}^{3} e_k x_k^2}{1 - 2 \sum\limits_{k=0}^{3} e_k \alpha_k x_k + \sum\limits_{k=0}^{3} e_k \alpha_k^2 \sum\limits_{l=0}^{3} e_l x_l^2} \tag{A.60}$$

together with the transformation

$$x_i' = a_i + \sum_{k=0}^{3} e_k a_{ik} x_k^* \tag{A.61}$$

where the coefficients a_{ik} satisfy condition (A.47). In addition, a change of scale is possible.

Transformation (A.61) is the usual Lorentz transformation, and (A.60) bears the name of Möbius transformation. The latter has many remarkable properties which, however, we shall not dwell on.

For us, it is important to note that the requirement that the form of the wave front equations be conserved does not by itself lead to the Lorentz transformations since it also allows Möbius transformations. To remove the latter one can make the additional demand that finite values of the initial coordinates should lead to finite values of the transformed ones. This additional requirement is satisfied only if all the constants α_k in the Möbius transformation are zero, making the transformation the identity. Instead of this additional requirement one can make another, namely, the condition that uniform rectilinear motion be conserved (condition (a)); this is how we proceeded in the text. Either of these additional requirements leads uniquely to the Lorentz transformation, apart from a possible change of scale.

It is also of importance that the requirement that the coordinates remain finite refers to space-time as a whole, whereas the conservation condition for uniform straight line motion is strictly local.†

† The discussion and conclusions of this appendix follow very closely those of Weyl [7].

PROOF OF THE UNIQUENESS OF THE ENERGY MOMENTUM TENSOR OF THE ELECTROMAGNETIC FIELD

For the electromagnetic field in vacuum the state functions are the components of the field

$$E_1, E_2, E_3; \qquad H_1, H_2, H_3 \tag{B.01}$$

and the first order equations of motion satisfied by them (field equations) are Maxwell's equations

$$\operatorname{curl} \mathbf{H} - \frac{1}{c} \frac{\partial \mathbf{E}}{\partial t} = 0, \qquad \operatorname{curl} \mathbf{E} + \frac{1}{c} \frac{\partial \mathbf{H}}{\partial t} = 0 \tag{B.02}$$

together with the supplementary conditions

$$\operatorname{div} \mathbf{E} = 0, \qquad \operatorname{div} \mathbf{H} = 0 \tag{B.03}$$

As in Section 23 we shall characterize an infinitesimal Lorentz transformation by the quantities

$$\left. \begin{aligned} \omega_{10} &= \frac{V_x}{c}; & \omega_{20} &= \frac{V_y}{c}; & \omega_{30} &= \frac{V_z}{c}; \\[2mm] \omega_{23} &= \omega_x; & \omega_{31} &= \omega_y; & \omega_{12} &= \omega_z \end{aligned} \right\} \tag{B.04}$$

Using three-dimensional notation we can write down the change in a field component in an infinitesimal Lorentz transformation as

$$\delta \mathbf{E} = \frac{1}{c} [\mathbf{V} \times \mathbf{H}] + [\boldsymbol{\omega} \times \mathbf{E}]$$

$$\delta \mathbf{H} = -\frac{1}{c} [\mathbf{V} \times \mathbf{E}] + [\boldsymbol{\omega} \times \mathbf{H}] \tag{B.05}$$

Comparison of these equations with the general equation (31*.04) gives us the coefficients (31*.09) and at the same time the operators X^{lm}. We get

$$X^{10} = -X^{01} = H_2 \frac{\partial}{\partial E_3} - H_3 \frac{\partial}{\partial E_2} - E_2 \frac{\partial}{\partial H_3} + E_3 \frac{\partial}{\partial H_2} \tag{B.06}$$

and two similar equations obtained from (B.06) by cyclic interchange of the indices 1, 2 and 3. Introducing the antisymmetric set of quantities

$$\left. \begin{aligned} \varepsilon_{ikl} &= +1, \text{ if } (i, k, l) \text{ are an even permutation of } (1, 2, 3), \\ \varepsilon_{ikl} &= -1, \text{ if } (i, k, l) \text{ are an odd permutation of } (1, 2, 3), \\ \varepsilon_{ikl} &= 0, \text{ if there are equal suffixes among the } (i, k, l) \end{aligned} \right\} \tag{B.07}$$

411

we can write down three expressions of the form of (B.06) as follows:

$$X^{i0} = -X^{0i} = \sum_{k,\,l=1}^{3} \varepsilon_{ikl}\left(H_k \frac{\partial}{\partial E_l} - E_k \frac{\partial}{\partial H_l}\right) \cdot \tag{B.08}$$

If one looks upon the set of three quantities X^{10}, X^{20} and X^{30} as a three-dimensional vector, one can replace (B.08) by

$$\mathbf{X} = \left[\mathbf{H} \times \frac{\partial}{\partial \mathbf{E}}\right] - \left[\mathbf{E} \times \frac{\partial}{\partial \mathbf{H}}\right] \tag{B.09}$$

The "spatial" operators X^{ik} with $i,\, k = 1,\, 2,\, 3$ can be written as

$$X^{ik} = -X^{ki} = E_i \frac{\partial}{\partial E_k} - E_k \frac{\partial}{\partial E_i} + H_i \frac{\partial}{\partial H_k} - H_k \frac{\partial}{\partial H_i} \tag{B.10}$$

In Section 31* we introduced the following equation for the change of a field function in an infinitesimal Lorentz transformation

$$\delta f = \frac{1}{2} \sum_{l,\,m=0}^{3} \omega_{lm} X^{lm}(f) \tag{B.11}$$

Inserting for f in turn $f = E_i$ and $f = H_i$ ($i = 1,\, 2,\, 3$) we again return to equations (B.05).

Let us now form the equations that express the vanishing of the divergence of T^μ (they correspond to (31.*16)). We get

$$\sum_{k=1}^{3}\left(\frac{\partial T^{\alpha 0}}{\partial E_k}\frac{\partial E_k}{\partial t} + \frac{\partial T^{\alpha 0}}{\partial H_k}\frac{\partial H_k}{\partial t}\right) + \sum_{i,\,k=1}^{3}\left(\frac{\partial T^{\alpha i}}{\partial E_k}\frac{\partial E_k}{\partial x_i} + \frac{\partial T^{\alpha i}}{\partial H_k}\frac{\partial H_k}{\partial x_i}\right) = 0 \tag{B.12}$$

where $\alpha = 0,\, 1,\, 2,\, 3$. These equations must be algebraic consequences of Maxwell's equations. Let us first write equations (B.02) in the form

$$\left.\begin{array}{l} \dfrac{\partial E_k}{\partial t} = c \sum_{i,\,l} \varepsilon_{kil} \dfrac{\partial H_l}{\partial x_i} \\[3mm] \dfrac{\partial H_k}{\partial t} = -c \sum_{i,\,l} \varepsilon_{kil} \dfrac{\partial E_l}{\partial x_i} \end{array}\right\} \tag{B.13}$$

Eliminating time derivatives from (B.12) with the aid of (B.13) we get

$$\sum_{i,\,k=1}^{3}\left(\frac{\partial T^{\alpha i}}{\partial E_k} - c\varepsilon_{lik}\frac{\partial T^{\alpha 0}}{\partial H_l}\right)\frac{\partial E_k}{\partial x_i} + \sum_{i,\,k=1}^{3}\left(\frac{\partial T^{\alpha i}}{\partial H_k} + c\varepsilon_{lik}\frac{\partial T^{\alpha 0}}{\partial E_l}\right)\frac{\partial H_k}{\partial x_i} = 0 \tag{B.14}$$

These equations must be algebraic consequences of (B.03). Therefore the left-hand sides must be of the form

$$A^\alpha \sum_{i=1}^{3} \frac{\partial E_i}{\partial x_i} + B^\alpha \sum_{i=1}^{3} \frac{\partial H_i}{\partial x_i} = 0 \tag{B.15}$$

Comparing (B.14) with (B.15) we are led to the following relations. In the first place the coefficients of $\partial E_i/\partial x_i$ for $i = 1, 2, 3$ must be equal. This gives

$$\frac{\partial T^{\alpha 1}}{\partial E_1} = \frac{\partial T^{\alpha 2}}{\partial E_2} = \frac{\partial T^{\alpha 3}}{\partial E_3} \tag{B.16}$$

Similarly the coefficients of $\partial H_i/\partial x_i$ must be equal for $i = 1, 2, 3$. Hence

$$\frac{\partial T^{\alpha 1}}{\partial H_1} = \frac{\partial T^{\alpha 2}}{\partial H_2} = \frac{\partial T^{\alpha 3}}{\partial H_3} \tag{B.17}$$

Secondly, for $i \neq k$ the coefficients of $\partial E_k/\partial x_i$ and $\partial H_k/\partial x_i$ in (B.14) must become zero, since such terms do not appear in (B.15). This gives us the relations

$$\frac{\partial T^{\alpha i}}{\partial E_k} - c\varepsilon_{lik}\frac{\partial T^{\alpha 0}}{\partial H_l} = 0 \tag{B.18}$$

$$\frac{\partial T^{\alpha i}}{\partial H_k} + c\varepsilon_{lik}\frac{\partial T^{\alpha 0}}{\partial E_l} = 0 \tag{B.19}$$

Hence if $i \neq k$

$$\frac{\partial T^{\alpha i}}{\partial E_k} + \frac{\partial T^{\alpha k}}{\partial E_i} = 0 \tag{B.20}$$

$$\frac{\partial T^{\alpha i}}{\partial H_k} + \frac{\partial T^{\alpha k}}{\partial H_i} = 0 \tag{B.21}$$

If (i, k, l) is some permutation of $(1, 2, 3)$ we easily see from (B.20) that

$$\frac{\partial^2 T^{\alpha i}}{\partial E_k \partial E_l} = 0 \tag{B.22}$$

and from (B.21) that

$$\frac{\partial^2 T^{\alpha i}}{\partial H_k \partial H_l} = 0 \tag{B.23}$$

Differentiating (B.18) with respect to E_l and using (B.22) we get

$$\frac{\partial^2 T^{\alpha 0}}{\partial E_l \partial H_l} = 0 \qquad (l = 1, 2, 3) \tag{B.24}$$

The same equation can be obtained by differentiating (B.19) with respect to H_l and using (B.23).

Let us now form a system of equations for T^{00}. According to (B.24) we have

$$\frac{\partial^2 T^{00}}{\partial E_l \partial H_l} = 0 \qquad (l = 1, 2, 3) \tag{B.25}$$

Putting $\alpha = 0$ in (B.18) we get

$$\frac{\partial T^{0i}}{\partial E_k} = c\varepsilon_{ikl}\frac{\partial T^{00}}{\partial H_l} \tag{B.26}$$

On the other hand, equation (B.24) for $\alpha = i$ gives

$$\frac{\partial^2 T^{0i}}{\partial E_k \partial H_k} = 0 \qquad \text{(B.27)}$$

Hence

$$\frac{\partial^2 T^{00}}{\partial H_k \partial H_l} = 0 \qquad (k \neq l) \qquad \text{(B.28)}$$

Similarly we obtain

$$\frac{\partial^2 T^{00}}{\partial E_k \partial E_l} = 0 \qquad (k \neq l) \qquad \text{(B.29)}$$

Putting $\alpha = 0$ in (B.19) and replacing k by l we get

$$\frac{\partial T^{0i}}{\partial H_l} = c\varepsilon_{ikl} \frac{\partial T^{00}}{\partial E_k} \qquad \text{(B.30)}$$

Differentiating (B.26) with respect to H_l, (B.30) with respect to E_k and equating the results we obtain

$$\frac{\partial^2 T^{00}}{\partial E_k^2} = \frac{\partial^2 T^{00}}{\partial H_l^2} \qquad (k \neq l) \qquad \text{(B.31)}$$

The system of equations we have obtained for T^{00} is easy to solve. Since T^{00} is a three-dimensional scalar, it can depend on the field components only through the quantities

$$\xi = \tfrac{1}{2}\mathbf{E}^2, \qquad \eta = (\mathbf{E \cdot H}), \qquad \zeta = \tfrac{1}{2}\mathbf{H}^2 \qquad \text{(B.32)}$$

so that

$$T^{00} = f(\xi, \eta, \zeta) \qquad \text{(B.33)}$$

Indeed, this expression is a solution of the equation $X^{ik}(T_{00}) = 0$, where X^{ik} is given by (B.10). Let us now use equation (B.25).

We have

$$\frac{\partial T^{00}}{\partial E_k} = E_k \frac{\partial f}{\partial \xi} + H_k \frac{\partial f}{\partial \eta} \qquad \text{(B.34)}$$

and further

$$\frac{\partial^2 T^{00}}{\partial E_k \partial H_k} = \frac{\partial f}{\partial \eta} + E_k H_k \left(\frac{\partial^2 f}{\partial \xi \partial \zeta} + \frac{\partial^2 f}{\partial \eta^2} \right) + E_k^2 \frac{\partial^2 f}{\partial \xi \partial \eta} + H_k^2 \frac{\partial^2 f}{\partial \eta \partial \zeta} \qquad \text{(B.35)}$$

As a consequence of (B.25) this expression must vanish for $k = 1, 2, 3$.

Evidently one can always make a rotation of axes in such a way that, say for $k = 1$ the quantities E_1 and H_1 vanish simultaneously. Then equations (B.25) and (B.35) with $k = 1$ give

$$\frac{\partial f}{\partial \eta} = 0 \qquad \text{(B.36)}$$

and all second derivatives involving differentiation with respect to η also vanish. If one takes this into account, the same equations for $k \neq 1$ give

$$\frac{\partial^2 f}{\partial \xi \partial \zeta} = 0 \qquad \text{(B.37)}$$

By virtue of (B.36) the equations (B.28) and (B.29) lead to

$$\frac{\partial^2 f}{\partial \xi^2} = 0, \qquad \frac{\partial^2 f}{\partial \zeta^2} = 0 \tag{B.38}$$

Thus the quantity f in (B.33) is a linear function of ξ and ζ. Taking this into account, we get

$$\frac{\partial^2 T^{00}}{\partial E_k^2} = \frac{\partial f}{\partial \xi}, \qquad \frac{\partial^2 T^{00}}{\partial H_i^2} = \frac{\partial f}{\partial \zeta} \tag{B.39}$$

and then equation (B.31) gives

$$\frac{\partial f}{\partial \xi} = \frac{\partial f}{\partial \zeta} \tag{B.40}$$

Since f is a linear function, we get

$$f = \alpha(\xi + \zeta) + \lambda \tag{B.41}$$

where α and λ are constants and therefore

$$T^{00} = \frac{\alpha}{2}(\mathbf{E}^2 + \mathbf{H}^2) + \lambda \tag{B.42}$$

Knowing T^{00} we can find the remaining components of $T^{\mu\nu}$ from equations previously derived. Thus, insertion of the values

$$\frac{\partial T^{00}}{\partial \mathbf{E}} = \alpha \mathbf{E}, \qquad \frac{\partial T^{00}}{\partial \mathbf{H}} = \alpha \mathbf{H} \tag{B.43}$$

into the formula

$$T^{i0} = \tfrac{1}{2} X^{0i}(T^{00}) \tag{B.44}$$

(see (31*.18)) gives the energy flux

$$T^{i0} = \alpha[\mathbf{E} \times \mathbf{H}]_i \tag{B.45}$$

(the Umov–Poynting vector). This quantity may be written in the form

$$T^{i0} = \alpha \sum_{p,q=1}^{3} \varepsilon_{ipq} E_p H_q \tag{B.46}$$

Inserting this expression into the formula

$$T^{ik} = (\tfrac{1}{2} X^{0k} X^{0i} - \delta_{ik}) T^{00} \qquad (i, k = 1, 2, 3) \tag{B.47}$$

we obtain, after some manipulation

$$T^{ik} = \alpha[\tfrac{1}{2}\delta_{ik}(\mathbf{E}^2 + \mathbf{H}^2) - E_i E_k - H_i H_k] - \lambda\delta_{ik} \qquad (i, k = 1, 2, 3) \tag{B.48}$$

Here we have used the relation

$$\sum_{s=1}^{3} \varepsilon_{ips}\varepsilon_{kqs} = \delta_{ik}\delta_{pq} - \delta_{iq}\delta_{kp} \tag{B.49}$$

It is not difficult to verify that the expressions found for the energy tensor also satisfy all the other equations (B.16)–(B.19) and not only those which were used in their derivation.

If one assumes that for $\mathbf{E} = 0$ and $\mathbf{H} = 0$ one should have $T^{\mu\nu} = 0$ one gets $\lambda = 0$. If one interprets $T^{\mu\nu}$ as the energy-momentum tensor (and not the mass tensor), then, with the customary choice of units, one has $\alpha = 1/4\pi$. Thus the tensor $T^{\mu\nu}$ is determined uniquely and the result agrees with the generally accepted formulae (33.23)–(33.25).

PROOF OF THE UNIQUENESS OF THE HYDRODYNAMIC MASS TENSOR

In Section 32, when we were deriving the relativistic generalization of the hydrodynamic equations of an ideal fluid we started from a definite form of the mass tensor. We shall show here that the argument can be conducted in the reverse order: taking the equations of motion as one's starting point one can derive the mass tensor from them.

As functions of state one can take the pressure p and the invariant density ρ^* (two scalars) and the four components u^i of the four-dimensional velocity vector.

The quantities p and ρ^* will be related by the equation of state and the u^i will be connected by the identity

$$\sum_{s=0}^{3} e_s(u^s)^2 = c^2 \tag{C.01}$$

In place of the pressure p it is convenient to take the dynamic pressure P, which is related to p and ρ^* by the equation

$$P = \int_0^p \frac{dp}{\rho^*} \tag{C.02}$$

As a consequence of (32.27) we have

$$P = \Pi + \frac{p}{\rho^*} \tag{C.03}$$

where Π is the potential energy of unit mass. If f is any function of P, ρ^* and the u^i its variation in an infinitesimal Lorentz transformation will be

$$\delta f = \sum_{i=0}^{3} \omega_{ik} e_i u^k \frac{\partial f}{\partial u^i} \tag{C.04}$$

Equating (C.04) to the general expression

$$\delta f = \frac{1}{2} \sum_{i,\,k=0}^{3} \omega_{ik} X^{ik}(f) \tag{C.05}$$

we get the following expression for the operators X^{ik}:

$$X^{ik} = e_i u^k \frac{\partial}{\partial u^i} - e_k u^i \frac{\partial}{\partial u^k} \tag{C.06}$$

417

Evidently the scalars are not involved in the formula for δf and therefore also not in the expression for the operators X^{ik}. As for the partial derivatives with respect to the u^i, it is immaterial in forming the operators X^{ik} whether one assumes all four quantities u^i to be independent or whether one takes into account their relationship (C.01).

We introduce the symmetrical system of quantities

$$a^{ik} = e_i \delta_{ik} - \frac{1}{c^2} u^i u^k \tag{C.07}$$

which possess the properties

$$\sum_{s=0}^{3} e_s a^{is} u^s = 0 \tag{C.08}$$

and we denote by w^i the four-dimensional acceleration vector

$$w^i = \sum_{k=0}^{3} u^k \frac{\partial u^i}{\partial x_k} \tag{C.09}$$

Then the hydrodynamic equations may be written in the form

$$\left(1 + \frac{P}{c^2}\right) w^i - \sum_{k=0}^{3} a^{ik} \frac{\partial P}{\partial x_k} = 0 \tag{C.10}$$

$$\sum_{k=0}^{3} \frac{\partial}{\partial x_k}(\rho^* u^k) = 0 \tag{C.11}$$

In addition, it is necessary to take into account the relation

$$\sum_{s=0}^{3} e_s u^s \frac{\partial u^s}{\partial x_k} = 0 \tag{C.12}$$

which follows from (C.01).

As a consequence of (C.12) we have the equation

$$\sum_{s=0}^{3} e_s u^s w^s = 0 \tag{C.13}$$

and the relations (C.08) show that this equation is consistent with the equations of motion (C.10).

We now write down the equations that express the fact that the divergence of the mass tensor is zero by virtue of the field equations. We have

$$\sum_{s,\,k=0}^{3} \frac{\partial T^{ik}}{\partial u^s} \frac{\partial u^s}{\partial x_k} + \sum_{k=0}^{3} \frac{\partial T^{ik}}{\partial P} \frac{\partial P}{\partial x_k} = \sum_{s,\,k=0}^{3} \lambda_s^i \left\{\left(1 + \frac{P}{c^2}\right) u^k \frac{\partial u^s}{\partial x_k} - a^{sk} \frac{\partial P}{\partial x_k}\right\}$$

$$+ \lambda^i \sum_{k=0}^{3} \left(u^k \frac{d\rho^*}{dP} \frac{\partial P}{\partial x_k} + \sum_{s=0}^{3} \rho^* \delta_{sk} \frac{\partial u^s}{\partial x_k}\right) + \sum_{s,\,k=0}^{3} \mu^{ik} e_s u^s \frac{\partial u^s}{\partial x_k} \tag{C.14}$$

Here the right-hand side represents the sum of the expressions (C.10), (C.11) and (C.12) multiplied by the Lagrangian multipliers λ_s^i, λ^i and μ^{ik} respectively. After introduction of the Lagrangian multipliers equation (C.14) can be looked upon as an identity in the derivatives with respect to the coordinates. Equating first the coefficients of $\partial u^s/\partial x_k$ and then those of $\partial P/\partial x_k$ we obtain

$$\frac{\partial T^{ik}}{\partial u^s} = \lambda_s^i \left(1 + \frac{P}{c^2}\right) u^k + \lambda^i \rho^* \delta_{sk} + \mu^{ik} e_s u^s \tag{C.15}$$

$$\frac{\partial T^{ik}}{\partial P} = -\sum_{s=0}^{3} \lambda_s^i a^{sk} + \lambda^i \frac{d\rho^*}{dP} u^k \tag{C.16}$$

The Lagrange multipliers must be eliminated from these equations. Applying the relation (C.08) to the second equation, we get

$$\lambda^i = \frac{1}{c^2} \sum_{s=0}^{3} e_s u^s \frac{\partial T^{is}}{\partial \rho^*} \tag{C.17}$$

Inserting this value into (C.16) we can write that equation (replacing k by j) in the form

$$\sum_{s=0}^{3} \lambda_s^i a^{sj} = -\sum_{s=0}^{3} e_s a^{sj} \frac{\partial T^{is}}{\partial P} \tag{C.18}$$

We now multiply both sides of (C.15) by a^{sj} and sum over s. On the right-hand side the factor multiplying μ^{ik} becomes zero as a result of (C.08), so that the quantities μ^{ik} are eliminated. The λ_s^i on the other hand enter only through the sum (C.18), which is known. Finally, for the λ^i one can insert their values from (C.17). As a result we obtain a relation which may be written as

$$\sum_{s=0}^{3} a^{js} \left\{ \frac{\partial T^{ik}}{\partial u^s} + \left(1 + \frac{P}{c^2}\right) u^k e_s \frac{\partial T^{is}}{\partial P} - \delta_{ks} \frac{\rho^*}{c^2} \sum_{r=0}^{3} e_r u^r \frac{\partial T^{ir}}{\partial \rho^*} \right\} = 0 \tag{C.19}$$

This is the required system of equations for the tensor T^{ik}, which follows from the condition that its divergence vanishes by virtue of the field equations.

Now we must take into account that the set of quantities T^{ik} form a tensor. This we can do by one of two methods. We can adjoin to (C.19) another system of differential equations, namely

$$X^{rs}(T^{ik}) = e_i \delta_{ir} T^{sk} - e_i \delta_{is} T^{rk} + e_k \delta_{kr} T^{is} - e_k \delta_{ks} T^{ir} \tag{C.20}$$

where the operator X^{rs} has the value given by (C.06). Alternatively, we can write down directly the most general expression for a tensor which is a function of the vector u^s and of certain scalars. This expression has the form

$$T^{ik} = Au^i u^k + Be_i \delta_{ik} \tag{C.21}$$

where the quantities A and B depend only on the scalar ρ^* (or equivalently only on P.) A dependence on the invariant of the vector u^s need not be taken into account, because according to (C.01) that invariant is a constant.

It is easy to verify that the expression (C.21) satisfies the system of equations (C.20). It is a general solution of that system.

We can now insert the expressions (C.21) for T^{ik} into (C.19). We first calculate the internal sum in (C.19), using the relation (C.01). We get

$$\frac{1}{c^2}\sum_{r=0}^{3} e_r u^r \frac{\partial T^{ir}}{\partial \rho^*} = \left(\frac{dA}{d\rho^*} + \frac{1}{c^2}\frac{dB}{d\rho^*}\right)u^i \tag{C.22}$$

Inserting (C.21) and (C.22) into (C.19) and using (C.08) we obtain an equation of the form

$$\sum_{s=0}^{3} a^{js}(Mu^i\delta_{sk} + Nu^k\delta_{si}) = 0 \tag{C.23}$$

or

$$Ma^{jk}u^i + Na^{ji}u^k = 0 \tag{C.24}$$

where we have put for brevity

$$M = A - \rho^*\frac{dA}{d\rho^*} - \frac{\rho^*}{c^2}\frac{dB}{d\rho^*} \tag{C.25}$$

$$N = A + \left(1 + \frac{P}{c^2}\right)\frac{dB}{dP} \tag{C.26}$$

It is evident that the equation (C.24) can hold for all values of i, j and k only if $M = 0$ and $N = 0$. Thus the scalars A and B in the expression for the tensor T^{ik} must satisfy the equations

$$A - \rho^*\frac{dA}{d\rho^*} - \frac{\rho^*}{c^2}\frac{dB}{d\rho^*} = 0 \tag{C.27}$$

$$A + \left(1 + \frac{P}{c^2}\right)\frac{dB}{dP} = 0 \tag{C.28}$$

Differentiating the second equation with respect to ρ^* we obtain

$$\frac{dA}{d\rho^*} + \frac{1}{c^2}\frac{dB}{d\rho^*} + \left(1 + \frac{P}{c^2}\right)\frac{d}{d\rho^*}\left(\frac{dB}{dP}\right) = 0 \tag{C.29}$$

and then the first equation gives

$$A + \left(1 + \frac{P}{c^2}\right)\rho^*\frac{d}{d\rho^*}\left(\frac{dB}{dP}\right) = 0 \tag{C.30}$$

Eliminating A from (C.28) and (C.30) we get

$$\left(\rho^*\frac{d}{d\rho^*} - 1\right)\frac{dB}{dP} = 0 \tag{C.31}$$

Hence

$$\frac{dB}{dP} = -a\rho^* \tag{C.32}$$

where a is a constant. But owing to the relation (C.02) between the dynamical pressure P and the ordinary pressure p we have

$$\rho^*dP = dp \tag{C.33}$$

Therefore equation (C.32) can be written as

$$dB + a\, dp = 0 \qquad (C.34)$$

and its solution gives us

$$B = -ap + \lambda \qquad (C.35)$$

where λ is a new constant. The quantity A may be determined from (C.28) and (C.32); we get

$$A = a\rho^* \left(1 + \frac{P}{c^2}\right) \qquad (C.36)$$

and the expression for the mass tensor takes on the form

$$T^{ik} = a \left[\rho^* \left(1 + \frac{P}{c^2}\right) u^i u^k - p e_i \delta_{ik}\right] + \lambda e_i \delta_{ik} \qquad (C.37)$$

If we assume that at infinity, where $\rho^* = 0$ and $p = 0$, we have $T^{ik} = 0$, then $\lambda = 0$. With the usual choice of units one has to put $a = 1$ in the energy tensor and $a = 1/c^2$ in the mass tensor. This determines both constants and the formula for the mass tensor assumes the following final form:

$$c^2 T^{ik} = \rho^* \left(1 + \frac{P}{c^2}\right) u^i u^k - p e_i \delta_{ik} \qquad (C.38)$$

As a consequence of (C.03) this formula agrees with (32.28).

THE TRANSFORMATION OF THE EINSTEIN TENSOR

(a) The Transformation of the Second Rank Curvature Tensor†

We begin with the transformation of the covariant second rank curvature tensor $R_{\mu\nu}$ and show that in the expression for this tensor, it is possible to separate off terms containing the d'Alembert operator applied to that component $g_{\mu\nu}$ of the metric tensor which has the same suffixes.

By definition we have

$$R_{\mu\nu} = g^{\alpha\beta}R_{\mu\alpha,\,\beta\nu} \tag{D.01}$$

where, by (44.08), the fourth rank curvature tensor is

$$R_{\mu\alpha,\,\beta\nu} = \frac{1}{2}\left(\frac{\partial^2 g_{\mu\nu}}{\partial x_\alpha\,\partial x_\beta} + \frac{\partial^2 g_{\alpha\beta}}{\partial x_\mu\,\partial x_\nu} - \frac{\partial^2 g_{\nu\alpha}}{\partial x_\mu\,\partial x_\beta} - \frac{\partial^2 g_{\mu\beta}}{\partial x_\nu\,\partial x_\alpha}\right) - g_{\rho\sigma}\Gamma^\rho_{\mu\beta}\Gamma^\sigma_{\nu\alpha} + g_{\rho\sigma}\Gamma^\rho_{\mu\nu}\Gamma^\sigma_{\alpha\beta} \tag{D.02}$$

(this equation differs from (44.08) only by the naming of the indices). Therefore

$$R_{\mu\nu} = \frac{1}{2}g^{\alpha\beta}\frac{\partial^2 g_{\mu\nu}}{\partial x_\alpha\,\partial x_\beta} + \frac{1}{2}g^{\alpha\beta}\frac{\partial^2 g_{\alpha\beta}}{\partial x_\mu\,\partial x_\nu} - \frac{1}{2}g^{\alpha\beta}\frac{\partial^2 g_{\nu\alpha}}{\partial x_\mu\,\partial x_\beta}$$
$$- \frac{1}{2}g^{\alpha\beta}\frac{\partial^2 g_{\mu\beta}}{\partial x_\nu\,\partial x_\alpha} - g^{\alpha\beta}g_{\rho\sigma}\Gamma^\rho_{\mu\beta}\Gamma^\sigma_{\nu\alpha} + \Gamma^\rho_{\mu\nu}\Gamma_\rho \tag{D.03}$$

For brevity we put

$$\Gamma_\rho = g_{\rho\sigma}\Gamma^\sigma \tag{D.04}$$

where in agreement with the definition (41.15)

$$\Gamma^\sigma = g^{\alpha\beta}\Gamma^\sigma_{\alpha\beta} \tag{D.05}$$

In (D.03) the first term is already in the form of the d'Alembert operator applied to $g_{\mu\nu}$. The remaining terms may be so transformed that the second derivatives of components of the metric tensor only appear through the first derivatives of the Γ_ρ. To perform this transformation we need the relations

$$\frac{\partial}{\partial x_\mu}\log(-g) = g^{\alpha\beta}\frac{\partial g_{\alpha\beta}}{\partial x_\mu} \tag{D.06}$$

$$g^{\alpha\beta}\frac{\partial g_{\alpha\nu}}{\partial x_\mu} = -g_{\alpha\nu}\frac{\partial g^{\alpha\beta}}{\partial x_\mu} \tag{D.07}$$

and

$$\Gamma^\alpha = -\frac{1}{\sqrt{(-g)}}\frac{\partial}{\partial x_\beta}[\sqrt{(-g)}\cdot g^{\alpha\beta}] \tag{D.08}$$

† See also the papers by de Donder [16] and by Lanczos [17].

which were derived in Section 41. From these relations it follows that

$$\Gamma_\nu = g^{\alpha\beta} \frac{\partial g_{\alpha\nu}}{\partial x_\beta} - \frac{1}{2} \frac{\partial \log(-g)}{\partial x_\nu} \tag{D.09}$$

Differentiating (D.06) with respect to x_ν, we get

$$g^{\alpha\beta} \frac{\partial^2 g_{\alpha\beta}}{\partial x_\mu \partial x_\nu} = \frac{\partial^2 \log(-g)}{\partial x_\mu \partial x_\nu} - \frac{\partial g^{\alpha\beta}}{\partial x_\nu} \frac{\partial g_{\alpha\beta}}{\partial x_\mu} \tag{D.10}$$

We note that owing to the symmetry of (D.10) in μ and ν we have

$$\frac{\partial g^{\alpha\beta}}{\partial x_\nu} \frac{\partial g_{\alpha\beta}}{\partial x_\mu} = \frac{\partial g^{\alpha\beta}}{\partial x_\mu} \frac{\partial g_{\alpha\beta}}{\partial x_\nu} \tag{D.11}$$

Differentiating (D.09) with respect to x_μ we get

$$-g^{\alpha\beta} \frac{\partial^2 g_{\nu\alpha}}{\partial x_\mu \partial x_\beta} = -\frac{1}{2} \frac{\partial^2 \log(-g)}{\partial x_\mu \partial x_\nu} - \frac{\partial \Gamma_\nu}{\partial x_\mu} + \frac{\partial g^{\alpha\beta}}{\partial x_\mu} \frac{\partial g_{\nu\alpha}}{\partial x_\beta} \tag{D.12}$$

In the last term on the right we may replace $\partial g_{\nu\alpha}/\partial x_\beta$ by

$$\frac{1}{2} \left(\frac{\partial g_{\nu\alpha}}{\partial x_\beta} + \frac{\partial g_{\nu\beta}}{\partial x_\alpha} \right) = \Gamma_{\nu,\,\alpha\beta} + \frac{1}{2} \frac{\partial g_{\alpha\beta}}{\partial x_\nu} \tag{D.13}$$

where $\Gamma_{\nu,\,\alpha\beta}$, is the usual Christoffel symbol of the first kind (38.30). Equation (D.12) then appears as

$$-g^{\alpha\beta} \frac{\partial^2 g_{\nu\alpha}}{\partial x_\mu \partial x_\beta} = -\frac{1}{2} \frac{\partial^2 \log(-g)}{\partial x_\mu \partial x_\nu} - \frac{\partial \Gamma_\nu}{\partial x_\mu} + \frac{1}{2} \frac{\partial g^{\alpha\beta}}{\partial x_\mu} \frac{\partial g_{\alpha\beta}}{\partial x_\nu} + \Gamma_{\nu,\,\alpha\beta} \frac{\partial g^{\alpha\beta}}{\partial x_\mu} \tag{D.14}$$

We interchange the indices μ and ν and also the summation indices α and β on the left. Then we can write

$$-g^{\alpha\beta} \frac{\partial^2 g_{\mu\beta}}{\partial x_\nu \partial x_\alpha} = -\frac{1}{2} \frac{\partial^2 \log(-g)}{\partial x_\mu \partial x_\nu} - \frac{\partial \Gamma_\mu}{\partial x_\nu} + \frac{1}{2} \frac{\partial g^{\alpha\beta}}{\partial x_\nu} \frac{\partial g_{\alpha\beta}}{\partial x_\mu} + \Gamma_{\mu,\,\alpha\beta} \frac{\partial g^{\alpha\beta}}{\partial x_\nu} \tag{D.15}$$

Thus the sum of the expressions (D.10), (D.14) and (D.15), half of which enters (D.03), is equal to

$$g^{\alpha\beta} \left(\frac{\partial^2 g_{\alpha\beta}}{\partial x_\mu \partial x_\nu} - \frac{\partial^2 g_{\nu\alpha}}{\partial x_\mu \partial x_\beta} - \frac{\partial^2 g_{\mu\beta}}{\partial x_\nu \partial x_\alpha} \right)$$

$$= -\left(\frac{\partial \Gamma_\nu}{\partial x_\mu} + \frac{\partial \Gamma_\mu}{\partial x_\nu} \right) + \Gamma_{\nu,\,\alpha\beta} \frac{\partial g^{\alpha\beta}}{\partial x_\mu} + \Gamma_{\mu,\,\alpha\beta} \frac{\partial g^{\alpha\beta}}{\partial x_\nu} \tag{D.16}$$

(as a result of (D.11) the remaining terms cancel).

We introduce the notation

$$\Gamma_{\mu\nu} = \frac{1}{2} \left(\frac{\partial \Gamma_\mu}{\partial x_\nu} + \frac{\partial \Gamma_\nu}{\partial x_\mu} \right) - \Gamma^\rho_{\mu\nu} \Gamma_\rho \tag{D.17}$$

The quantities $\Gamma_{\mu\nu}$ are formed in the same way as the symmetrized covariant derivatives of a vector, although Γ_ν is not a vector. As a result of (D.16) the expression (D.03) for $R_{\mu\nu}$ then becomes

$$R_{\mu\nu} = \frac{1}{2} g^{\alpha\beta} \frac{\partial^2 g_{\mu\nu}}{\partial x_\alpha \partial x_\beta} - \Gamma_{\mu\nu} + \frac{1}{2} \Gamma_{\nu,\,\alpha\beta} \frac{\partial g^{\alpha\beta}}{\partial x_\mu} + \frac{1}{2} \Gamma_{\mu,\,\alpha\beta} \frac{\partial g^{\alpha\beta}}{\partial x_\nu} - g^{\alpha\beta} \Gamma_{\sigma,\,\mu\beta} \Gamma^\sigma_{\nu\alpha} \tag{D.18}$$

To simplify the calculations to be performed on the terms involving first derivatives we shall use not only the notation $\Gamma_{\nu,\alpha\beta}$ and $\Gamma^{\nu}_{\alpha\beta}$ for the usual Christoffel symbols but also the notation

$$\Gamma^{\alpha\beta}_{\mu} = g^{\alpha\rho}g^{\beta\sigma}\Gamma_{\mu,\rho\sigma} \tag{D.19}$$

and

$$\Gamma^{\mu,\alpha\beta} = g^{\alpha\rho}g^{\beta\sigma}\Gamma^{\mu}_{\rho\sigma} = g^{\alpha\rho}g^{\beta\sigma}g^{\mu\nu}\Gamma_{\nu,\rho\sigma} \tag{D.20}$$

for the corresponding quantities with raised indices. We note that $\Gamma^{\mu,\alpha\beta}$ is given by

$$\Gamma^{\mu,\alpha\beta} = \frac{1}{2}\left(g^{\mu\rho}\frac{\partial g^{\alpha\beta}}{\partial x_{\rho}} - g^{\alpha\rho}\frac{\partial g^{\beta\mu}}{\partial x_{\rho}} - g^{\beta\rho}\frac{\partial g^{\alpha\mu}}{\partial x_{\rho}}\right) \tag{D.21}$$

We consider the expression

$$A_{\mu\nu} = g^{\alpha\beta}g^{\rho\sigma}\frac{\partial g_{\mu\sigma}}{\partial x_{\beta}}\frac{\partial g_{\rho\nu}}{\partial x_{\alpha}} - g^{\alpha\beta}\Gamma_{\sigma,\mu\beta}\Gamma^{\sigma}_{\nu\alpha} \tag{D.22}$$

whose last term coincides with the last term in (D.18). We write this expression in the form

$$A_{\mu\nu} = g^{\alpha\beta}g^{\rho\sigma}\left(\frac{\partial g_{\mu\sigma}}{\partial x_{\beta}}\frac{\partial g_{\rho\nu}}{\partial x_{\alpha}} - \Gamma_{\sigma,\mu\beta}\Gamma_{\rho,\nu\alpha}\right) \tag{D.23}$$

We insert

$$\frac{\partial g_{\mu\sigma}}{\partial x_{\beta}} = \Gamma_{\sigma,\mu\beta} + \Gamma_{\mu,\sigma\beta} \tag{D.24}$$

and then use the equation

$$\frac{\partial g_{\rho\nu}}{\partial x_{\alpha}} - \Gamma_{\rho,\nu\alpha} = \Gamma_{\nu,\rho\alpha} \tag{D.25}$$

Then we get

$$A_{\mu\nu} = g^{\alpha\beta}g^{\rho\sigma}\left(\Gamma_{\sigma,\mu\beta}\Gamma_{\nu,\rho\alpha} + \Gamma_{\mu,\sigma\beta}\frac{\partial g_{\rho\nu}}{\partial x_{\alpha}}\right) \tag{D.26}$$

Using the notation of (D.19) and relabelling, we may put

$$A_{\mu\nu} = \Gamma^{\alpha\beta}_{\nu}\Gamma_{\alpha,\mu\beta} + \Gamma^{\alpha\beta}_{\mu}\frac{\partial g_{\beta\nu}}{\partial x_{\alpha}} \tag{D.27}$$

Since the coefficient $\Gamma^{\alpha\beta}_{\mu}$ is symmetric in α and β we can replace the factor multiplying it by its symmetric part, which is equal to $\frac{1}{2}\partial g_{\alpha\beta}/\partial x_{\mu}$. For the same reason we can replace $\partial g_{\beta\nu}/\partial x_{\alpha}$ by (D.13). Doing this we get

$$A_{\mu\nu} = \frac{1}{2}\Gamma^{\alpha\beta}_{\nu}\frac{\partial g_{\alpha\beta}}{\partial x_{\mu}} + \frac{1}{2}\Gamma^{\alpha\beta}_{\mu}\frac{\partial g_{\alpha\beta}}{\partial x_{\nu}} + \Gamma^{\alpha\beta}_{\mu}\Gamma_{\nu,\alpha\beta} \tag{D.28}$$

But, as is easy to verify,

$$\Gamma^{\alpha\beta}_{\nu}\frac{\partial g_{\alpha\beta}}{\partial x_{\mu}} = -\Gamma_{\nu,\alpha\beta}\frac{\partial g^{\alpha\beta}}{\partial x_{\mu}} \tag{D.29}$$

Therefore

$$A_{\mu\nu} = -\frac{1}{2}\Gamma_{\nu,\alpha\beta}\frac{\partial g^{\alpha\beta}}{\partial x_{\mu}} - \frac{1}{2}\Gamma_{\mu,\alpha\beta}\frac{\partial g^{\alpha\beta}}{\partial x_{\nu}} + \Gamma^{\alpha\beta}_{\mu}\Gamma_{\nu,\alpha\beta} \tag{D.30}$$

Equating the expressions (D.22) and (D.30) for the $A_{\mu\nu}$ we obtain the relation

$$\frac{1}{2}\Gamma_{\nu,\alpha\beta}\frac{\partial g^{\alpha\beta}}{\partial x_{\mu}} + \frac{1}{2}\Gamma_{\mu,\alpha\beta}\frac{\partial g^{\alpha\beta}}{\partial x_{\nu}} - g^{\alpha\beta}\Gamma_{\sigma,\mu\beta}\Gamma^{\sigma}_{\nu\alpha} = \Gamma^{\alpha\beta}_{\mu}\Gamma_{\nu,\alpha\beta} - g^{\alpha\beta}g^{\rho\sigma}\frac{\partial g_{\mu\sigma}}{\partial x_{\beta}}\frac{\partial g_{\rho\nu}}{\partial x_{\alpha}} \tag{D.31}$$

which enables us to write the expression for $R_{\mu\nu}$ in the following final form

$$R_{\mu\nu} = \tfrac{1}{2} g^{\alpha\beta} \frac{\partial^2 g_{\mu\nu}}{\partial x_\alpha \, \partial x_\beta} - \Gamma_{\mu\nu} - g^{\alpha\beta} g^{\rho\sigma} \frac{\partial g_{\mu\sigma}}{\partial x_\beta} \frac{\partial g_{\rho\nu}}{\partial x_\alpha} + \Gamma^{\alpha\beta}_\mu \Gamma_{\nu,\alpha\beta} \tag{D.32}$$

From this it is easy to obtain an equation for the contravariant components of the second order curvature tensor.

By differentiating relations of the form (D.07) it is simple to derive the equation

$$g_{\mu\sigma} g_{\nu\rho} \frac{\partial^2 g^{\rho\sigma}}{\partial x_\alpha \, \partial x_\beta} = - \frac{\partial^2 g_{\mu\nu}}{\partial x_\alpha \, \partial x_\beta} + g^{\rho\sigma} \left(\frac{\partial g_{\mu\sigma}}{\partial x_\alpha} \frac{\partial g_{\nu\rho}}{\partial x_\beta} + \frac{\partial g_{\mu\sigma}}{\partial x_\beta} \frac{\partial g_{\nu\rho}}{\partial x_\alpha} \right) \tag{D.33}$$

Using this we can write $R_{\mu\nu}$ as

$$R_{\mu\nu} = - \tfrac{1}{2} g_{\mu\sigma} g_{\nu\rho} g^{\alpha\beta} \frac{\partial^2 g^{\rho\sigma}}{\partial x_\alpha \, \partial x_\beta} - \Gamma_{\mu\nu} + \Gamma^{\alpha\beta}_\mu \Gamma_{\nu,\alpha\beta} \tag{D.34}$$

If we then raise the indices μ and ν we get the following simple expression for $R^{\mu\nu}$:

$$R^{\mu\nu} = - \tfrac{1}{2} g^{\alpha\beta} \frac{\partial^2 g^{\mu\nu}}{\partial x_\alpha \, \partial x_\beta} - \Gamma^{\mu\nu} + \Gamma^{\mu,\alpha\beta} \Gamma^\nu_{\alpha\beta} \tag{D.35}$$

The quantity $\Gamma^{\mu\nu}$ is obtained from $\Gamma_{\mu\nu}$ by raising the indices according to

$$\Gamma^{\mu\nu} = g^{\mu\rho} g^{\nu\sigma} \Gamma_{\rho\sigma} \tag{D.36}$$

and may be expressed directly in terms of the Γ^α defined by (D.08) as follows:

$$\Gamma^{\mu\nu} = \frac{1}{2} \left(g^{\mu\alpha} \frac{\partial \Gamma^\nu}{\partial x_\alpha} + g^{\nu\alpha} \frac{\partial \Gamma^\mu}{\partial x_\alpha} - \frac{\partial g^{\mu\nu}}{\partial x_\alpha} \Gamma^\alpha \right) \tag{D.37}$$

(b) Transformation of the Invariant

We now form the invariant of the curvature tensor :

$$R = g_{\mu\nu} R^{\mu\nu} \tag{D.38}$$

We have

$$R = - \tfrac{1}{2} g^{\alpha\beta} g_{\mu\nu} \frac{\partial^2 g^{\mu\nu}}{\partial x_\alpha \, \partial x_\beta} - \Gamma + \Gamma^{\alpha\beta}_\nu \Gamma^\nu_{\alpha\beta} \tag{D.39}$$

where Γ denotes the quantity

$$\Gamma = g_{\mu\nu} \Gamma^{\mu\nu} \tag{D.40}$$

Using the relation

$$\frac{\partial \log (-g)}{\partial x_\alpha} = - g_{\mu\nu} \frac{\partial g^{\mu\nu}}{\partial x_\alpha} \tag{D.41}$$

we obtain from (D.37)

$$\Gamma = \frac{\partial \Gamma^\alpha}{\partial x_\alpha} + \frac{1}{2} \frac{\partial \log (-g)}{\partial x_\alpha} \Gamma^\alpha \tag{D.42}$$

and by virtue of (41.16)

$$\Gamma = - \frac{1}{\sqrt{(-g)}} \frac{\partial^2 \{\sqrt{(-g)} \cdot g^{\alpha\beta}\}}{\partial x_\alpha \, \partial x_\beta} \tag{D.43}$$

Differentiating equation (D.41) with respect to x_β we obtain, in analogy with (D.10)

$$g_{\mu\nu}\frac{\partial^2 g^{\mu\nu}}{\partial x_\alpha \, \partial x_\beta} = -\frac{\partial^2 \log(-g)}{\partial x_\alpha \, \partial x_\beta} - \frac{\partial g^{\mu\nu}}{\partial x_\alpha}\frac{\partial g_{\mu\nu}}{\partial x_\beta} \tag{D.44}$$

Inserting (D.44) into (D.39) we get

$$R = \frac{1}{2}g^{\alpha\beta}\frac{\partial^2 \log(-g)}{\partial x_\alpha \, \partial x_\beta} - \Gamma + \Gamma^{\alpha\beta}_\nu\Gamma^\nu_{\alpha\beta} + \frac{1}{2}g^{\alpha\beta}\frac{\partial g^{\mu\nu}}{\partial x_\alpha}\frac{\partial g_{\mu\nu}}{\partial x_\beta} \tag{D.45}$$

We see that the second derivatives of the metric tensor enter the expression for R only through the second derivatives of $\log(-g)$ and through Γ. The terms involving first derivatives can be transformed with the aid of the relation

$$\Gamma^{\alpha\beta}_\nu\Gamma^\nu_{\alpha\beta} + \frac{1}{2}g^{\alpha\beta}\frac{\partial g^{\mu\nu}}{\partial x_\alpha}\frac{\partial g_{\mu\nu}}{\partial x_\beta} = \frac{1}{2}\Gamma^\nu_{\alpha\beta}\frac{\partial g^{\alpha\beta}}{\partial x_\nu} \tag{D.46}$$

which is easily deducible from the equation

$$\Gamma^{\alpha\beta}_\nu = \frac{1}{2}\frac{\partial g^{\alpha\beta}}{\partial x_\nu} - \frac{1}{2}g_{\rho\nu}\left(g^{\rho\beta}\frac{\partial g^{\rho\alpha}}{\partial x_\sigma} + g^{\sigma\alpha}\frac{\partial g^{\rho\beta}}{\partial x_\sigma}\right) \tag{D.47}$$

We now get the result

$$R = \frac{1}{2}g^{\alpha\beta}\frac{\partial^2 \log(-g)}{\partial x_\alpha \, \partial x_\beta} - \Gamma + \frac{1}{2}\Gamma^\nu_{\alpha\beta}\frac{\partial g^{\alpha\beta}}{\partial x_\nu} \tag{D.48}$$

This expression can be written in the form

$$R = g^{\alpha\beta}\frac{\partial^2 \log\sqrt{(-g)}}{\partial x_\alpha \, \partial x_\beta} - \Gamma^\alpha\frac{\partial \log\sqrt{(-g)}}{\partial x_\alpha} - \Gamma - L \tag{D.49}$$

where

$$L = -\frac{1}{2}\Gamma^\nu_{\alpha\beta}\frac{\partial g^{\alpha\beta}}{\partial x_\nu} - \Gamma^\alpha\frac{\partial \log\sqrt{(-g)}}{\partial x_\alpha} \tag{D.50}$$

Remembering the equation

$$\Box y = g^{\alpha\beta}\frac{\partial^2 y}{\partial x_\alpha \, \partial x_\beta} - \Gamma^\alpha\frac{\partial y}{\partial x_\alpha} \tag{D.51}$$

which gives the d'Alembertian of any function y, we may write

$$R = \Box \log\sqrt{(-g)} - \Gamma - L \tag{D.52}$$

Of course the quantity $y = \log\sqrt{(-g)}$ is not a scalar, but formally the operator of (D.51) may be applied to it. We note that both the first and the second term in (D.52) represent a sum of derivatives of some quantities with respect to coordinates, divided by $\sqrt{(-g)}$. This fact is of importance in the formulation of a variational principle for Einstein's equations, when the quantity L defined by (D.50) plays the part of the Lagrangian (Section 60).

Apart from (D.50) there are several other ways of writing the Lagrangian L. We quote the following

$$L = \frac{1}{2}\Gamma^{\nu,\,\alpha\beta}\frac{\partial g_{\alpha\beta}}{\partial x_\nu} - \Gamma^\alpha\frac{\partial \log\sqrt{(-g)}}{\partial x_\alpha}. \tag{D.53}$$

and also

$$L = g^{\mu\nu}(\Gamma^\beta_{\mu\alpha}\Gamma^\alpha_{\nu\beta} - \Gamma^\alpha_{\mu\nu}\Gamma^\beta_{\alpha\beta}) \tag{D.54}$$

the last form is most commonly encountered in the literature.

(c) Transformation of the Einstein Tensor

The foregoing equations enable us to write down an expression for the divergence-free Einstein tensor

$$G^{\mu\nu} = R^{\mu\nu} - \tfrac{1}{2}g^{\mu\nu}R \tag{D.55}$$

We shall see that the second derivatives of the metric tensor enter $G^{\mu\nu}$ only through second derivatives of the quantity $\sqrt{(-g)}\cdot g^{\mu\nu}$ and through first derivatives of Γ^ν. It is, therefore, convenient to introduce a special symbol for $\sqrt{(-g)}$ times the contravariant components of the metric tensor.

We put

$$\mathfrak{g}^{\mu\nu} = \sqrt{(-g)}\cdot g^{\mu\nu} \tag{D.56}$$

Then equation (41.16) may be written as

$$\Gamma^\nu = -\frac{1}{\sqrt{(-g)}}\frac{\partial \mathfrak{g}^{\mu\nu}}{\partial x_\mu} \tag{D.57}$$

For the following it is convenient to transform all equations in such a way that they involve only derivatives of the $\mathfrak{g}^{\mu\nu}$. In performing the transformation we shall encounter derivatives of the quantity

$$y = \log \sqrt{(-g)} \tag{D.58}$$

which we shall write as follows :

$$y_\alpha = \frac{\partial \log \sqrt{(-g)}}{\partial x_\alpha} \tag{D.59}$$

According to (41.07) we have

$$y_\alpha = \Gamma^\nu_{\alpha\nu} \tag{D.60}$$

For the quantities obtained from the y_α by raising indices we introduce the notation

$$y^\alpha = g^{\alpha\beta}y_\beta \tag{D.61}$$

just as for a tensor (although of course the y^α are not a vector). We have also

$$y^\alpha = \Gamma^{\alpha\beta}_\beta \tag{D.62}$$

where $\Gamma^{\alpha\beta}_\mu$ has the meaning defined by (D.19). We shall denote the second derivatives of y by $y_{\alpha\beta}$:

$$y_{\alpha\beta} = \frac{\partial^2 \log \sqrt{(-g)}}{\partial x_\alpha \partial x_\beta} \tag{D.63}$$

According to (D.21) the $\Gamma^{\mu,\alpha\beta}$ are bilinear functions of the components $\mathfrak{g}^{\mu\nu}$ and of their first derivatives. Inserting the expression for $g^{\mu\nu}$ in terms of $\mathfrak{g}^{\mu\nu}$ into that relation, we obtain

$$\Gamma^{\mu,\,\alpha\beta} = \Pi^{\mu,\,\alpha\beta} + \Lambda^{\mu,\,\alpha\beta} \tag{D.64}$$

where

$$\Pi^{\mu,\,\alpha\beta} = \frac{1}{2g}\left(\mathfrak{g}^{\alpha\rho}\frac{\partial \mathfrak{g}^{\mu\beta}}{\partial x_\rho} + \mathfrak{g}^{\beta\rho}\frac{\partial \mathfrak{g}^{\mu\alpha}}{\partial x_\rho} - \mathfrak{g}^{\mu\rho}\frac{\partial \mathfrak{g}^{\alpha\beta}}{\partial x_\rho}\right) \tag{D.65}$$

and

$$\Lambda^{\mu,\,\alpha\beta} = \tfrac{1}{2}\left(y^\alpha g^{\mu\beta} + y^\beta g^{\mu\alpha} - y^\mu g^{\alpha\beta}\right) \tag{D.66}$$

We shall denote the corresponding quantities with lower indices by $\Pi^\mu_{\alpha\beta}$ and $\Lambda^\mu_{\alpha\beta}$.

We evaluate the determinant of the $\mathfrak{g}^{\mu\nu}$:

$$\text{Det } \mathfrak{g}^{\mu\nu} = \{\sqrt{(-g)}\}^4 \text{ Det } g^{\mu\nu} = g^2 \frac{1}{g} = g \qquad (D.67)$$

Thus the determinant of the $\mathfrak{g}^{\mu\nu}$ is equal to the determinant of the $g_{\mu\nu}$:

$$\text{Det } \mathfrak{g}^{\mu\nu} = \text{Det } g_{\mu\nu} = g \qquad (D.68)$$

From equation (D.66) we obtain

$$g_{\alpha\beta}\Lambda^{\mu,\ \alpha\beta} = -y^\mu \qquad (D.69)$$

and since

$$g_{\alpha\beta}\Gamma^{\mu,\ \alpha\beta} = \Gamma^\mu \qquad (D.70)$$

it follows that

$$g_{\alpha\beta}\Pi^{\mu,\ \alpha\beta} = \Gamma^\mu + y^\mu \qquad (D.71)$$

The last expression is also equal to

$$\Gamma^\mu + y^\mu = -\frac{\partial \mathfrak{g}^{\mu\nu}}{\partial x_\nu} \qquad (D.72)$$

We go on to the transformation of the Einstein tensor

$$G^{\mu\nu} = R^{\mu\nu} - \tfrac{1}{2}g^{\mu\nu}R \qquad (D.55)$$

Our starting point is from the equations

$$R^{\mu\nu} = -\tfrac{1}{2}g^{\alpha\beta}\frac{\partial^2 g^{\mu\nu}}{\partial x_\alpha\ \partial x_\beta} - \Gamma^{\mu\nu} + \Gamma^{\mu,\ \alpha\beta}\Gamma^\nu_{\alpha\beta} \qquad (D.35)$$

and also equation (D.49) for R, which we write in the form

$$R = g^{\alpha\beta}y_{\alpha\beta} - \Gamma^\alpha y_\alpha - \Gamma - L \qquad (D.73)$$

The second derivative of $\mathfrak{g}^{\mu\nu}$ is

$$\frac{\partial^2 \mathfrak{g}^{\mu\nu}}{\partial x_\alpha\ \partial x_\beta} = \sqrt{(-g)}\cdot\left(\frac{\partial^2 g^{\mu\nu}}{\partial x_\alpha\ \partial x_\beta} + y_\beta\frac{\partial g^{\mu\nu}}{\partial x_\alpha} + y_\alpha\frac{\partial g^{\mu\nu}}{\partial x_\beta} + y_{\alpha\beta}g^{\mu\nu} + y_\alpha y_\beta g^{\mu\nu}\right)$$

$$(D.74)$$

and therefore

$$g^{\alpha\beta}\frac{\partial^2 \mathfrak{g}^{\mu\nu}}{\partial x_\alpha\ \partial x_\beta} = \sqrt{(-g)}\cdot\left(g^{\alpha\beta}\frac{\partial^2 g^{\mu\nu}}{\partial x_\alpha\ \partial x_\beta} + 2y^\alpha\frac{\partial g^{\mu\nu}}{\partial x_\alpha} + g^{\mu\nu}g^{\alpha\beta}y_{\alpha\beta} + g^{\mu\nu}y_\alpha y^\alpha\right)$$

$$(D.75)$$

On the other hand we have

$$R^{\mu\nu} - \tfrac{1}{2}g^{\mu\nu}R = -\tfrac{1}{2}\left(g^{\alpha\beta}\frac{\partial^2 g^{\mu\nu}}{\partial x_\alpha\ \partial x_\beta} + g^{\mu\nu}g^{\alpha\beta}y_{\alpha\beta}\right)$$
$$+ \tfrac{1}{2}g^{\mu\nu}(\Gamma^\alpha y_\alpha + \Gamma + L) - \Gamma^{\mu\nu} + \Gamma^{\mu,\ \alpha\beta}\Gamma^\nu_{\alpha\beta} \qquad (D.76)$$

By comparing the last two equations we see that apart from the terms in Γ and $\Gamma^{\mu\nu}$ the same combinations of second derivatives occur in both. The calculation gives

$$R^{\mu\nu} - \tfrac{1}{2}g^{\mu\nu}R = -\frac{1}{2\sqrt{(-g)}}\,g^{\alpha\beta}\frac{\partial^2 g^{\mu\nu}}{\partial x_\alpha\,\partial x_\beta} + \tfrac{1}{2}g^{\mu\nu}(y_\alpha y^\alpha + \Gamma^\alpha y_\alpha + \Gamma + L)$$

$$- \Gamma^{\mu\nu} + y^\alpha\frac{\partial g^{\mu\nu}}{\partial x_\alpha} + \Gamma^{\mu,\,\alpha\beta}\Gamma^\nu_{\alpha\beta} \qquad (D.77)$$

As always, the transformation of the terms involving first derivatives is the most complicated. We have

$$\Gamma^{\mu,\,\alpha\beta}\Gamma^\nu_{\alpha\beta} = \Pi^{\mu,\,\alpha\beta}\Pi^\nu_{\alpha\beta} + \Lambda^{\mu,\,\alpha\beta}\Pi^\nu_{\alpha\beta} + \Lambda^{\nu,\,\alpha\beta}\Pi^\mu_{\alpha\beta} + \Lambda^{\mu,\,\alpha\beta}\Lambda^\nu_{\alpha\beta} \qquad (D.78)$$

Using (D.71) we get

$$\Lambda^{\mu,\,\alpha\beta}\Pi^\nu_{\alpha\beta} + \Lambda^{\nu,\,\alpha\beta}\Pi^\mu_{\alpha\beta} = y_\rho(\Pi^{\nu,\,\mu\rho} + \Pi^{\mu,\,\nu\rho}) - \tfrac{1}{2}(y^\mu\Gamma^\nu + y^\nu\Gamma^\mu) - y^\mu y^\nu$$

$$(D.79)$$

and as a result of

$$\Pi^{\nu,\,\mu\rho} + \Pi^{\mu,\,\nu\rho} = \frac{1}{g}\,g^{\alpha\rho}\frac{\partial g^{\mu\nu}}{\partial x_\alpha} = -g^{\alpha\rho}\frac{\partial g^{\mu\nu}}{\partial x_\alpha} - g^{\mu\nu}y^\rho \qquad (D.80)$$

we have

$$\Lambda^{\mu,\,\alpha\beta}\Pi^\nu_{\alpha\beta} + \Lambda^{\nu,\,\alpha\beta}\Pi^\mu_{\alpha\beta} = -y^\alpha\frac{\partial g^{\mu\nu}}{\partial x_\alpha} - g^{\mu\nu}y_\alpha y^\alpha - \tfrac{1}{2}(y^\mu\Gamma^\nu + y^\nu\Gamma^\mu) - y^\mu y^\nu$$

$$(D.81)$$

Further

$$\Lambda^{\mu,\,\alpha\beta}\Lambda^\nu_{\alpha\beta} = \tfrac{1}{2}y^\mu y^\nu + \tfrac{1}{2}g^{\mu\nu}y_\alpha y^\alpha \qquad (D.82)$$

Hence

$$\Gamma^{\mu,\,\alpha\beta}\Gamma^\nu_{\alpha\beta} = \Pi^{\mu,\,\alpha\beta}\Pi^\nu_{\alpha\beta} - y^\alpha\frac{\partial g^{\mu\nu}}{\partial x_\alpha} - \tfrac{1}{2}g^{\mu\nu}y_\alpha y^\alpha - \tfrac{1}{2}y^\mu y^\nu - \tfrac{1}{2}(y^\mu\Gamma^\nu + y^\nu\Gamma^\mu)$$

$$(D.83)$$

These relations allow us to rewrite (D.77) as

$$R^{\mu\nu} - \tfrac{1}{2}g^{\mu\nu}R = -\frac{1}{2\sqrt{(-g)}}\,g^{\alpha\beta}\frac{\partial^2 g^{\mu\nu}}{\partial x_\alpha\,\partial x_\beta} + \Pi^{\mu,\,\alpha\beta}\Pi^\nu_{\alpha\beta} - \tfrac{1}{2}y^\mu y^\nu$$

$$+ \tfrac{1}{2}g^{\mu\nu}L + \tfrac{1}{2}g^{\mu\nu}(\Gamma^\alpha y_\alpha + \Gamma) - \Gamma^{\mu\nu} - \tfrac{1}{2}(y^\mu\Gamma^\nu + y^\nu\Gamma^\mu) \qquad (D.84)$$

Here we put

$$B^{\mu\nu} = \Gamma^{\mu\nu} + \tfrac{1}{2}(y^\mu\Gamma^\nu + y^\nu\Gamma^\mu) \qquad (D.85)$$

and

$$B = g_{\mu\nu}B^{\mu\nu} = \Gamma + \Gamma^\alpha y_\alpha \qquad (D.86)$$

and we express the $g^{\alpha\beta}$ in terms of the $g^{\alpha\beta}$ in the term involving the d'Alembertian. Then the expression for the Einstein tensor becomes

$$R^{\mu\nu} - \tfrac{1}{2}g^{\mu\nu}R = \frac{1}{2g}\,g^{\alpha\beta}\frac{\partial^2 g^{\mu\nu}}{\partial x_\alpha\,\partial x_\beta} + \Pi^{\mu,\,\alpha\beta}\Pi^\nu_{\alpha\beta} - \tfrac{1}{2}y^\mu y^\nu + \tfrac{1}{2}g^{\mu\nu}L + \tfrac{1}{2}g^{\mu\nu}B - B^{\mu\nu}$$

$$(D.87)$$

Since, according to (D.68), the determinant g can be expressed directly in terms of the $\mathfrak{g}^{\mu\nu}$ we can take it that in (D.87) all terms except L are expressed in terms of the $\mathfrak{g}^{\alpha\beta}$ and their derivatives. It remains for us to express the Lagrangian L also in terms of the same quantities.

By the definition (D.50) we have

$$L = -\tfrac{1}{2}\Gamma^\nu_{\alpha\beta}\frac{\partial g^{\alpha\beta}}{\partial x_\nu} - \Gamma^\alpha y_\alpha \tag{D.88}$$

Here we insert

$$\Gamma^\nu_{\alpha\beta} = \Pi^\nu_{\alpha\beta} + \Lambda^\nu_{\alpha\beta} \tag{D.89}$$

where, by (D.66)

$$\Lambda^\nu_{\alpha\beta} = \tfrac{1}{2}(y_\alpha \delta^\nu_\beta + y_\beta \beta^\nu_\alpha - y^\nu g_{\alpha\beta}) \tag{D.90}$$

Using the relation

$$\Lambda^\nu_{\alpha\beta}\frac{\partial g^{\alpha\beta}}{\partial x_\nu} = -\Gamma^\alpha y_\alpha \tag{D.91}$$

which is easy to deduce from (D.90), we get

$$L = -\tfrac{1}{2}\Pi^\nu_{\alpha\beta}\frac{\partial g^{\alpha\beta}}{\partial x_\nu} - \tfrac{1}{2}\Gamma^\alpha y_\alpha \tag{D.92}$$

Here we express $\partial g^{\alpha\beta}/\partial x_\nu$ in terms of

$$\frac{\partial g^{\alpha\beta}}{\partial x_\nu} = \sqrt{(-g)} \cdot \left(\frac{\partial g^{\alpha\beta}}{\partial x_\nu} + g^{\alpha\beta} y_\nu\right) \tag{D.93}$$

and use equation (D.71), which may be written in the form

$$g^{\alpha\beta}\Pi^\nu_{\alpha\beta} = \Gamma^\nu + y^\nu \tag{D.94}$$

This gives, finally

$$L = -\frac{1}{2\sqrt{(-g)}}\Pi^\nu_{\alpha\beta}\frac{\partial g^{\alpha\beta}}{\partial x_\nu} + \tfrac{1}{2} y_\nu y^\nu \tag{D.95}$$

Now only the $\mathfrak{g}^{\alpha\beta}$ remain under the sign of differentiation.

THE CHARACTERISTICS OF THE GENERALIZED D'ALEMBERT EQUATION

The generalized wave equation, or d'Alembert equation, has the form

$$\Box\psi = 0 \tag{E.01}$$

where $\Box\psi$ is the expression

$$\Box\psi = \frac{1}{\sqrt{(-g)}} \frac{\partial}{\partial x_\alpha}\left(\sqrt{(-g)} \cdot g^{\alpha\beta} \frac{\partial\psi}{\partial x_\beta}\right) \tag{E.02}$$

in which the quantities $g^{\alpha\beta}$ and g have their usual significance.

Cauchy's problem for the equation (E.01) consists in determining the function ψ, if on some hypersurface

$$\omega(x_0, x_1, x_2, x_3) = \text{const.} \tag{E.03}$$

the values of ψ and $\partial\psi/\partial x_0$ are given. We assume that the equation of the hypersurface (E.03) can be solved for x_0 and that therefore

$$\frac{\partial\omega}{\partial x_0} \neq 0 \tag{E.04}$$

We are interested in the possibility of solving Cauchy's problem in some region sufficiently near to the hypersurface (E.03). To evaluate the function ψ in this region one has to be able to calculate the derivatives of ψ at any point of the hypersurface. It is easy to see that the first derivatives can be calculated directly from the initial conditions. For the calculation of second derivatives, however, one necessarily has to use the wave equation. The possibility of determining the second derivatives will then depend on the form of the hypersurface to which the initial conditions refer. If the hypersurface is such that initial conditions relative to it do not determine the values of the second derivatives it is called a characteristic. A characteristic hypersurface has the property that on it discontinuities of the second derivatives are possible. Therefore the moving surface of a wave front must be a characteristic.

Let us consider first the simplest case, when the initial conditions refer to the hypersurface $x_0 = \text{const.}$, i.e. to an initial instant of time. From given values of ψ and $\partial\psi/\partial x_0$ all first derivatives are obtainable by direct differentiation, and also the second derivatives of the form

$$\frac{\partial^2\psi}{\partial x_0\, \partial x_i}, \qquad \frac{\partial^2\psi}{\partial x_i\, \partial x_k} \qquad (i, k = 1, 2, 3) \tag{E.05}$$

(or rather the values of these quantities for fixed x_0). As for the second derivative with respect to x_0, it must be calculated from the wave equation. Explicitly the wave equation has the form

$$g^{00}\frac{\partial^2\psi}{\partial x_0^2} + \ldots = 0 \tag{E.06}$$

431

whére the dots denote terms containing the remaining second derivatives (E.05) and also the known first derivatives. Since by the nature of the metric tensor the quantity g^{00} never vanishes, being always positive, equation (E.06) can always be solved for the remaining second derivative $\partial^2\psi/\partial x_0^2$. This means that if the variable x_0 has the character of a time, the hypersurfaces $x_0 = \text{const.}$ are not charactéristics.

Let us now consider the general case of a hypersurface (E.03). We introduce the variables

$$x_0' = \omega(x_0, x_1, x_2, x_3); \qquad x_1' = x_1; \qquad x_2' = x_2; \qquad x_3' = x_3 \qquad \text{(E.07)}$$

We denote by ψ' the quantity ψ considered as a function of the variables x_0', x_1', x_2' and x_3'. Then we have

$$\psi = \psi'; \qquad \frac{\partial\psi}{\partial x_0} = \frac{\partial\psi'}{\partial x_0'}\frac{\partial\omega}{\partial x_0} \qquad \text{(E.08)}$$

and since (E.04) holds, giving ψ and $\partial\psi/\partial x_0$ for $\omega = \text{const.}$ is equivalent to giving ψ' and $\partial\psi'/\partial x_0'$ for $x_0' = \text{const.}$ As before, these last quantities allow one to calculate all first derivatives and also the second derivatives of the form

$$\frac{\partial^2\psi'}{\partial x_0'\,\partial x_i'}; \qquad \frac{\partial^2\psi'}{\partial x_i'\,\partial x_k'} \qquad (i, k = 1, 2, 3) \qquad \text{(E.09)}$$

whereas the second derivative with respect to x_0' must be determined from the wave equation. The d'Alembertian transformed to the new coordinates has the form

$$\Box\psi = \frac{1}{\sqrt{(-g')}} \frac{\partial}{\partial x_\alpha'}\left(\sqrt{(-g')}\cdot g'^{\alpha\beta}\frac{\partial\psi}{\partial x_\beta'}\right) \qquad \text{(E.10)}$$

where the $g'^{\alpha\beta}$ are obtained from the $g^{\alpha\beta}$ according to the usual tensor transformation rule ; in particular

$$g'^{00} = g^{\mu\nu}\frac{\partial x_0'}{\partial x_\mu}\frac{\partial x_0'}{\partial x_\nu} = g^{\mu\nu}\frac{\partial\omega}{\partial x_\mu}\frac{\partial\omega}{\partial x_\nu} \qquad \text{(E.11)}$$

It is, however, to be remembered that since the new variable x_0 does not necessarily have the character of a time the inequality $g'^{00} > 0$ need not hold.

The transformed wave equation takes on the form

$$\left(g^{\mu\nu}\frac{\partial\omega}{\partial x_\mu}\frac{\partial\omega}{\partial x_\nu}\right)\frac{\partial^2\psi'}{\partial x_0'^2} + \ldots = 0 \qquad \text{(E.12)}$$

where the terms omitted do not involve the second derivative with respect to x_0', but only second derivatives of the form (E.09) and also first derivatives. The values of all the omitted terms on the hypersurface $\omega = \text{const.}$ may be taken to be known from the initial data relating to this hypersurface.

The second derivative with respect to x_0' remains indeterminate if and only if its coefficient in the wave equation (E.12) becomes zero, i.e. if the function ω satisfies the equation

$$g^{\mu\nu}\frac{\partial\omega}{\partial x_\mu}\frac{\partial\omega}{\partial x_\nu} = 0 \qquad \text{(E.13)}$$

This is the equation of the characteristics for the wave equation (E.01).

The characteristics of the generalized wave equation are the same as the characteristics of the generally covariant Maxwell equations discussed in Section 46. Briefly, though not quite rigorously, this result may be justified by the following consideration. Under the condition $\nabla_\nu A^\nu = 0$ Maxwell's equations give rise to equations for the potentials A_ν in which the highest (second) derivatives are grouped in the form of the d'Alembertian. Hence it can be concluded that the characteristics of the generally covariant Maxwell equations have the form (E.13). The lack of rigour in this derivation consists in passing from the characteristics for the potentials to the characteristics for the field. It is not difficult to give a rigorous derivation in which one deals directly with the field components, similar to the procedure of Section 3 for cartesian coordinates in the Euclidean case.

INTEGRATION OF THE WAVE FRONT EQUATION

If
$$\omega(x_0, x_1, x_2, x_3) = 0 \tag{F.01}$$

is the equation of a moving front then, as we know, the function ω satisfies the partial differential equation

$$g^{\alpha\beta}\omega_\alpha\omega_\beta = 0 \tag{F.02}$$

where we have put, for brevity

$$\omega_\alpha = \frac{\partial\omega}{\partial x_\alpha} \tag{F.03}$$

We consider the following problem : determine the form of the wave surface at an instant $x_0 > 0$ when its form is given at the initial instant $x_0 = 0$. We solved a corresponding problem in Section 4 for the case of a Euclidean metric and Galilean coordinates ; we now consider it for the general case.

Let the form of the wave surface at the initial instant be given by the equations

$$\left.\begin{array}{l} x_1 = f_1(u, v) \\ x_2 = f_2(u, v) \\ x_3 = f_3(u, v) \end{array}\right\} \quad \text{for} \quad x_0 = 0 \tag{F.04}$$

These equations may be written in the more symmetric form

$$x_\alpha = f_\alpha(u, v) ; \qquad (\alpha = 0, 1, 2, 3) \tag{F.05}$$

where

$$f_0 \equiv 0 \tag{F.06}$$

Instead of initial data referring to the instant of time $x_0 = 0$ one can consider Cauchy data referring to some hypersurface; then the function f_0 will no longer be identically zero.

If we insert the expressions (F.05) into the equation (F.01) we obtain an identity in u and v. Differentiating this identity with respect to u and to v we get the relations

$$\omega_\alpha \frac{\partial f_\alpha}{\partial u} = 0 ; \qquad \omega_\alpha \frac{\partial f_\alpha}{\partial v} = 0 \tag{F.07}$$

If we adjoin to these the wave front equation (F.02) we can determine from these three homogeneous equations the initial values of the four quantities ω_0, ω_1, ω_2 and ω_3 apart from a common multiplier. Denoting these initial values by the superfix zero we have

$$\omega_\alpha^0 = \lambda\varphi_\alpha(u, v) ; \qquad \lambda = \lambda(u, v) \tag{F.08}$$

where the φ_α are known functions and λ is an arbitrary function of u and v. It should be noted that the ratios of the ω_α^0 are not ᵤ ᵉ uniquely given ; they may have two values, because of the fact that the wave front equation

(F.02) is quadratic in the ω_α. For a unique determination of these ratios one must also indicate in which of the two possible directions the wave is travelling.

To indicate that the left-hand sides of the equations (F.05) represent the initial values of the coordinates we attach the superfix zero to them, writing them as

$$x_\alpha^0 = f_\alpha(u, v) \tag{F.09}$$

We take a point on the initial wave surface (to each such point there corresponds a definite pair of values of u and v) and consider the ray passing through this point. As we saw in Section 38 the differential equations of the ray are the Hamiltonian equations corresponding to the Hamilton-Jacobi equation (F.02). Thus, according to (38.41), the equations have the form

$$\frac{dx_\alpha}{dp} = g^{\alpha\beta}\omega_\beta\,; \qquad \frac{d\omega_\alpha}{dp} = -\frac{1}{2}\frac{\partial g^{\mu\nu}}{\partial x_\alpha}\omega_\mu\omega_\nu \tag{F.10}$$

In Section 38 it was shown that these equations are equivalent to the equations of a null geodesic.

For the ray passing through the point (u, v) the initial values of the variables x_α and ω_α are equal respectively to (F.09) and (F.08). Integrating equation (F.10) with the initial values x_α^0 and ω_α^0 we get

$$\begin{aligned} x_\alpha &= x_\alpha(p\,;\ x_0^0, x_1^0, x_2^0, x_3^0\,;\ \omega_0^0, \omega_1^0, \omega_2^0, \omega_3^0) \\ \omega_\alpha &= \omega_\alpha(p\,;\ x_0^0, x_1^0, x_2^0, x_3^0\,;\ \omega_0^0, \omega_1^0, \omega_2^0, \omega_3^0) \end{aligned} \tag{F.11}$$

Here we insert the initial values (F.09) and (F.08) and so obtain expressions of the form

$$\begin{aligned} x_\alpha &= F_\alpha(\lambda p, u, v) \\ \omega_\alpha &= \lambda\Phi_\alpha(\lambda p, u, v) \end{aligned} \tag{F.12}$$

Since the equations (F.10) do not change under the substitution

$$\omega_\alpha = \lambda\omega_\alpha'\,; \qquad p' = \lambda p \tag{F.13}$$

where λ is constant along the ray, the functions F_α and Φ_α do not depend on λ and p separately but only on their product λp.

The expressions

$$x_\alpha = F_\alpha(p', u, v) \tag{F.14}$$

give the equation of a moving wave surface in parametric form. By eliminating the variables p', u and v one can obtain a relation between the four coordinates (x_0, x_1, x_2, x_3) which is just the equation of a wave surface in the form (F.01).

The proof of the relations and formulae mentioned here may be found in treatises on first order partial differential equations (e.g. see [8]).

As the simplest example let us consider the equation

$$\frac{1}{c^2}\omega_0^2 - (\omega_1^2 + \omega_2^2 + \omega_3^2) = 0 \tag{F.15}$$

with the initial form of the wave surface given by

$$z = f(x, y) \quad \text{for} \quad t = 0 \tag{F.16}$$

Here the cartesian coordinates x and y play the part of the parameters u and v. The equations (F.07) appear as

$$\omega_1 + \omega_3 f_x = 0\,; \qquad \omega_2 + \omega_3 f_y = 0 \tag{F.17}$$

where f_x and f_y are the partial derivatives of f with respect to x and y. From (F.15) and (F.17) we find as one of the possible solutions

$$\omega_0 = \lambda c$$

$$\omega_1 = -\frac{\lambda f_x}{\sqrt{(1 + f_x^2 + f_y^2)}}$$

$$\omega_2 = -\frac{\lambda f_y}{\sqrt{(1 + f_x^2 + f_y^2)}} \qquad \text{(F.18)}$$

$$\omega_3 = \frac{\lambda}{\sqrt{(1 + f_x^2 + f_y^2)}}$$

The other solution is obtained from (F.18) by changing the sign of the square root. In equations (F.17) and (F.18) we should, strictly speaking, write ω_α^0 instead of ω_α, but we omit the superfix zero because in this example the ω_α are constant anyhow. Solving the equations

$$\frac{dx_0}{dp} = \frac{1}{c^2}\omega_0; \qquad \frac{dx_i}{dp} = -\omega_i; \qquad (i = 1, 2, 3) \qquad \text{(F.19)}$$

and assuming that at $t = 0$ we have also $p = 0$, we get

$$x_0 = t = \frac{\omega_0}{c^2}p; \qquad x_i = x_i^0 - \omega_i p \qquad (i = 1, 2, 3) \qquad \text{(F.20)}$$

Here we insert the ω_α from (F.18) and express the parameter p in terms of t. We then have for the first solution

$$x_1 = x + \frac{ctf_x}{\sqrt{(1 + f_x^2 + f_y^2)}}$$

$$x_2 = y + \frac{ctf_y}{\sqrt{(1 + f_x^2 + f_y^2)}} \qquad \text{(F.21)}$$

$$x_3 = f(x, y) - \frac{ct}{\sqrt{(1 + f_x^2 + f_y^2)}}$$

For the second solution (with the opposite direction of propagation) we get

$$x_1 = x - \frac{ctf_x}{\sqrt{(1 + f_x^2 + f_y^2)}}$$

$$x_2 = y - \frac{ctf_y}{\sqrt{(1 + f_x^2 + f_y^2)}} \qquad \text{(F.22)}$$

$$x_3 = f(x, y) + \frac{ct}{\sqrt{(1 + f_x^2 + f_y^2)}}$$

In particular, if we take for the initial wave surface the surface of a sphere of radius a and put

$$f(x, y) = \sqrt{(a^2 - x^2 - y^2)} \tag{F.23}$$

we get from (F.22)

$$x_1 = x\left(1 + \frac{ct}{a}\right)$$

$$x_2 = y\left(1 + \frac{ct}{a}\right) \tag{F.24}$$

$$x_3 = \sqrt{(a^2 - x^2 - y^2)} \cdot \left(1 + \frac{ct}{a}\right)$$

and, after eliminating x and y

$$x_1^2 + x_2^2 + x_3^2 = (a + ct)^2 \tag{F.25}$$

i.e. the surface of a sphere of radius $R = a + ct$, as was to be expected.

NECESSARY AND SUFFICIENT CONDITIONS FOR THE EUCLIDEAN CHARACTER OF THREE-DIMENSIONAL SPACE

In three-dimensional space the second rank curvature tensor R_{ik} has the same number of components, namely six, as the fourth rank curvature tensor $R_{il,mk}$. Therefore one should expect that not only is R_{ik} expressible in terms of $R_{il,mk}$ by the general rule

$$R_{ik} = a^{lm} R_{il,\ mk} \tag{G.01}$$

but that also, conversely, $R_{il,mk}$ can be expressed in terms of R_{ik} (we here omit the label a for components of a three-dimensional tensor).

To find these expressions we introduce a system of antisymmetric quantities ε_{ijh} with $\varepsilon_{123} = 1$, similarly to our procedure in Section 22 and 37 and we construct an antisymmetric pseudo-tensor with the covariant components

$$E_{ijh} = \sqrt{a} \cdot \varepsilon_{ijh} \tag{G.02}$$

and the contravariant components

$$E^{ijh} = \frac{1}{\sqrt{a}} \varepsilon_{ijh} \tag{G.03}$$

For transformations of the coordinates x_1, x_2 and x_3 that have a positive Jacobian

$$D\binom{x'}{x} = \frac{D(x_1', x_2', x_3')}{D(x_1, x_2, x_3)} > 0 \tag{G.04}$$

we have

$$\sqrt{a'} \cdot D\binom{x'}{x} = \sqrt{a} \tag{G.05}$$

and therefore

$$E_{ijh}' \frac{\partial x_i'}{\partial x_p} \frac{\partial x_j'}{\partial x_q} \frac{\partial x_h'}{\partial x_r} = E_{pqr} \tag{G.06}$$

by the rule for forming a determinant. This proves that in such transformations the quantities E_{ijh} behave like a covariant tensor. By the rule for forming a determinant we can also write

$$E_{ikl} a^{ip} a^{kq} a^{lr} = E^{pqr} \tag{G.07}$$

where E^{pqr} has the value (G.03). This proves that E^{pqr} is the contravariant pseudo-tensor corresponding to E_{ikl}. Hence it is simple to obtain the relations

$$E_{ikl}a^{kq}a^{lr} = E^{pqr}a_{ip} \tag{G.08}$$

$$E_{ikl}a^{lr} = E^{pqr}a_{ip}a_{kq} \tag{G.09}$$

and

$$E_{ikl} = E^{pqr}a_{ip}a_{kq}a_{lr} \tag{G.10}$$

We note also the relation

$$E^{pqj}E_{rsj} = \delta_r^p\delta_s^q - \delta_s^p\delta_r^q \tag{G.11}$$

which will be important for the subsequent discussion. It can be proved by the following reasoning. Both sides are different from zero only if $p \neq q$ and $r \neq s$, and apart from their order the pair of numbers (p, q) must coincide with the pair (r, s). If $p = r$ and $q = s$, both sides are equal to $+1$ and if $p = s$ and $q = r$ both are equal to -1. Therefore both sides coincide for all possible values of the indices, so that equation (G.11) is proved.

To find the expression for $R_{il,mk}$ in terms of R_{ik} we introduce the contravariant symmetric second rank tensor A^{pq} by the equations

$$A^{pq}E_{pil}E_{qmk} = R_{il,\,mk} \tag{G.12}$$

and then establish the relation between A^{pq} and R^{pq}. The equations (G.12) may be written in the form

$$\begin{aligned} aA^{11} = R_{23,\,23}; && aA^{22} = R_{31,\,31}; && aA^{33} = R_{12,\,12} \\ aA^{23} = R_{31,\,12}; && aA^{31} = R_{12,\,23}; && aA^{12} = R_{23,\,31} \end{aligned} \tag{G.13}$$

with

$$A^{pq} = A^{qp} \tag{G.14}$$

These equations express the A_{pq} directly in terms of the $R_{il,mk}$.

Inserting (G.12) into (G.01) and using (G.09) and (G.11) we get

$$R_{ik} = A^{pq}(a_{pk}a_{iq} - a_{pq}a_{ik}) \tag{G.15}$$

and if we put

$$A = a_{pq}A^{pq} \tag{G.16}$$

we have

$$R_{ik} = A_{ik} - a_{ik}A \tag{G.17}$$

whence

$$R = a^{ik}R_{ik} = -2A \tag{G.18}$$

and therefore

$$A_{ik} = R_{ik} - \tfrac{1}{2}a_{ik}R \tag{G.19}$$

Thus A_{ik} is simply the three-dimensional conservative tensor.

Inserting the corresponding contravariant tensor into (G.12) we obtain the required expression of the fourth rank tensor in terms of the second rank tensor :

$$R_{il,\,mk} = (R^{pq} - \tfrac{1}{2}a^{pq}R)E_{pil}E_{qmk} \tag{G.20}$$

From the equations just obtained we can deduce the following important consequence. We know (Section 42) that the necessary and sufficient condition for the possibility of reducing a given quadratic form ds^2 to a form with constant coefficients is the vanishing for the fourth rank curvature tensor. This result obviously also applies to the purely spatial three-dimensional quadratic form

$$dl^2 = a_{ik} \, dx_i \, dx_k \tag{G.21}$$

for the reduction of which to the Euclidean form

$$dl^2 = dx_1'^2 + dx_2'^2 + dx_3'^2 \tag{G.22}$$

the necessary and sufficient condition is the equation

$$R_{il, \, mk} = 0 \tag{G.23}$$

where the quantity on the left-hand side is the three-dimensional tensor. But by (G.20) the fourth rank curvature tensor is, in three-dimensional space, expressible in terms of the second rank curvature tensor. Therefore the necessary and sufficient condition for the Euclidean character of a three-dimensional space is the vanishing of the second rank curvature tensor.

REFERENCES

CLASSICAL PAPERS

[1] EINSTEIN, A., Zur Elektrodynamik bewegter Körper, *Ann. Phys. Lpz.*, **17**, 891, 1905.
[2] EINSTEIN, A., Die Grundlage der allgemeinen Relativitätstheorie, *Ann. Phys. Lpz.*, **49**, 760, 1916.
[3] LORENTZ, H. A., Electromagnetic phenomena in a system moving with any velocity smaller than that of light, *Proc. Acad. Sci. Amsterdam*, **6**, 809, 1904
[4] POINCARÉ, H., Sur la dynamique de l'électron, *R.C. Circ. Mat. Palermo*, **21**, 129, 1906.
[5] EINSTEIN, A., *The Meaning of Relativity*, Princeton, 1955, 4th ed.
[6] LORENTZ, H. A., EINSTEIN, A. and MINKOWSKI, H., *Relativitätsthorie*, Berlin, 1923.

SPECIALIST LITERATURE

[1] CARTAN, E., La théorie des groupes et la géométrie, *L'enseignement math.*, **26**, 200–225, 1927.
      Reprinted in *Œuvres Complètes*, Part 1, Vol. II, p. 841, Paris, Gauthier-Villars, 1952.
[1a] FOKKER, A. D., Albert Einstein, Inventor of Chronogeometry, *Synthèse*, **9**, 442–444, 1955.
[2] ALEXANDROV, A. D., On the meaning of the theory of relativity, *Zh. Leningr. Univ.*, **8**, 103, 1953.
[3] ALEXANDROV, A. D. and OVCHINNIKOV, V. V., Some remarks on the foundation of the theory of relativity, *Zh. Leningr. Univ.*, **11**, 95, 1953.
[4] UMOV, N. A., *Collected Works*, Gostekhizdat, 1950.
[4a] UMOV, N. A., Ableitung der Transformationen, die mit dem Relativitätsprinzip verträglich sind, *Phys. Z.*, **11**, 908, 1910.
[5] ·UMOV, N. A., *The Equation of Motion for the Energy of a Body*, Odessa, 1874.
[6] MANDELSTAM, L. L., *Complete Collected Works*, Vol. V, Lectures on the Physical Basis of the Theory of Relativity, published by the Academy of Sciences of the U.S.S.R., 1950.
[7] WEYL, H., *Mathematische Analyse des Raumproblems*, Berlin, Springer, 1923.
[8] SMIRNOV, V. I., *A Course of Higher Mathematics*, Vol. IV.
[9] KAGAN, V. F., *Foundations of Geometry*, Part 1, Moscow–Leningrad, 1949.
[10] KRUTKOV, YU. A., *The Stress Tensor and the Solution of General Problems in the Static Theory of Elasticity*, Akad. Nauk, U.S.S.R., 1949.
[11] SHEKHTER, V. M., *Zh. Leningr. Univ.*, No. 11, 1956.
[12] PLANCK, M., *Vorlesungen über die Theorie der Wärmestrahlung*, Leipzig, 1923.
[13] LEBEDEV, P. N., Untersuchungen über die Druckkraft des Lichtes, *Ann. Phys. Lpz.*, **6**, 433, 1901.
[14] LEVI-CIVITA, T., *The Absolute Differential Calculus*, London, 1927.
[15] WEYL, H., *Space, Time, Matter*, London, Methuen, 1922.
[16] DE DONDER, T., *La gravifique einsteinienne*, Paris, 1921.
[17] LANCZOS, C., *Phys. Z.*, **23**, 537, 1923.
[18] SCHWARZSCHILD, K., *S.B. Preuss. Akad. Wiss.* p. 189, 1916.
[19] KRYLOV, A. N., *Lectures on Approximate Calculation*, Academy of Sciences of U.S.S.R., 1944.
[20] MØLLER, C., On homogeneous gravitational fields in the general theory of relativity and the clock paradox, København, 1943. *Matt.-fys. Medd.*, **2** (No. 19).
[21] LIAPOUNOFF, A., *Sur certaines séries de figures d'équilibre d'un liquide heterogène en rotation*, Leningrad, 1925 and 1927.
[22] LIAPOUNOFF, A., Recherches dans la théorie de la figure des corps célestes, *Notes of the Imperial Academy of Sciences*, Sér. VIII, **14**, No. 7, 1903.

[23] LANDAU, L. and LIFSHITZ, E., *Classical Theory of Fields*, Cambridge, Mass., 1951.

[23a] FOCK, V. A., Three lectures on relativity theory, *Rev. Mod. Phys.*, **29**, 325, 1957.

[24] FRIEDMANN, A., Über die Krümmung des Raumes, *Z. Phys.*, **10**, 377, 1922.

[25] HUBBLE, E., *Mon. Not. R. Astron. Soc.*, **133**, 658, 1953.

[26] EINSTEIN, A., *Albert Einstein, Philosopher-Scientist*, Library of Living Philosophers, 1949, Illinois, U.S.A.

[27] MAXWELL, J. C., *Treatise on Electricity*, Oxford, 1873.

[28] EINSTEIN, A. and GROMMER, J., *Sitzb. Berl. Akad.*, p. 2, 1927.

[29] EINSTEIN, A., *Sitzb. Berl. Akad.*, p. 235, 1927.

[30] EINSTEIN, A., INFELD, L. and HOFFMANN, B., The gravitational equations and the problem of motion, *Ann. Math.*, **39**, No. 1, 65, 1938.

[31] EINSTEIN, A. and INFELD, L., *Ann. Math.*, **41**, 455, 1940.

[32] EINSTEIN, A. and INFELD, L., On the motion of particles in general relativity theory, *Canad. J. Math.*, **1**, 209, 1949.

[33] INFELD, L., On the motion of bodies in general relativity theory, *Acta Phys. Polonica*, **13**, 187, 1954.

[34] FOCK, V. A., On the motion of finite masses in the general theory of relativity, *Zh. Eksp. i. Teor. Fiz.*, **9**, 375, 1939.

[34a] FOCK, V. A., Sur le mouvement des masses finies d'après la théorie de gravitation Einsteinienne, *J. Phys. U.S.S.R.*, **1**, 81, 1939.

[35] FOCK, V. A., The systems of Copernicus and Ptolemy in the light of the general theory of relativity. Symposium, *Nicolas Copernicus*, published by the Academy of Sciences of the U.S.S.R., 1947.

[36] FOCK, V. A., Some applications of the ideas of Lobachevsky's non-Euclidean geometry to physics. Symposium, by A. T. KOTELNIKOV and V. A. FOCK, *Some Applications of Lobachevsky's Ideas to Mechanics and Physics*, Gostekhizdat, 1950.

[37] PETROVA, N., On the equations of motion and the matter tensor for a system of finite masses in the general theory of relativity (Dissertation, Leningrad University, 1940), *Zh. Eksp. i. Teor. Fiz.*, **19**, 989, 1949.

[38] FOCK, V. A., On the integrals of mass centre motion for two finite masses in the general theory of relativity, *Dokl. Akad. Nauk U.S.S.R.*, **32**, 28, 1941.
      Also *C.R. Acad. Sci. URSS*, **32**, 25, 1941 (in French).

[39] KASHKAROV, V. P., On the equations of motion of a system of finite masses in Einstein's gravitational theory, *Zh. Eksp. i Teor. Fiz.*, **27**, 563, 1954.

[40] FICHTENHOLZ, I. G., The Lagrangian form of the equations of motion in second approximation, *Zh. Eksp. i Teor. Fiz.*, **20**, 233, 1950.

[41] PAPAPETROU, A., Equations of motion in general relativity, *Proc. Phys. Soc.*, **A64**, 57, 1951.

[42] MEISTER, H. J., Die Bewegungsgleichungen in der allgemeinen Relativitätstheorie, *Ann. Phys. Lpz.*, 6th Series, **19**, 268, 1957.

[43] TODOROV, I. T., On a uniqueness theorem for the wave equation (in Russian), *Uspekhi Mat. Nauk (N.S.)*, **13**, 211, 1958.

[44] FOCK, V. A., Einstein statics in conformal space, *Zh. Eksp. i Teor. Fiz.*, **38**, 1476, 1960.

[45] FOCK, V. A., Comparison of different coordinate conditions in Einstein's theory of gravitation, *Zh. Eksp. i Teor. Fiz.*, **38**, 108, 1960.

[46] MÖSSBAUER, R. L., *Z. Phys.*, **151**, 124, 1958; *Uspekhi Fiz. Nauk*, **72**, 658, 1960, transl. *Soviet Phys. (Uspekhi)*, **3**, 866, 1961.

[47] JANKIEWICZ, C. *Bull. int. Acad. Cracovie (Acad. pol. Sci.) Série des Sci. Math., Astr. et Phys.*, **X**, 299 & 403, 1962.

INDEX

443